MODERN PHYSICS FOR THE ENGINEER

MODERN PHYSICS FOR THE ENGINEER

ROYAL WELLER

H. P. ROBERTSON

LEONARD I. SCHIFF

FREDERICK SEITZ

CHARLES KITTEL

W. D. HERSHBERGER

WILLIAM A. FOWLER

R. V. LANGMUIR

GLENN T. SEABORG

W. K. H. PANOFSKY

JESSE GREENSTEIN

DAVID T. GRIGGS

ROGER REVELLE

LEONARD B. LOEB

WALKER BLEAKNEY

SIMON RAMO

JOHN BARDEEN

J. B. WIESNER

LOUIS N. RIDENOUR

Edited by
LOUIS N. RIDENOUR
Vice President, International
Telemeter Corporation;
Visiting Professor of Engineering,
University of California,
Los Angeles

1954

McGraw-Hill Book Company, Inc.

NEW YORK   TORONTO   LONDON

The Authors

Royal Weller, Ph.D., Chief Scientist, Naval Air Missile Test Center, Point Mugu, California

H. P. Robertson, Ph.D., Professor of Mathematical Physics, California Institute of Technology

Leonard I. Schiff, Ph.D., Professor of Physics and Executive Head of the Department, Stanford University

Frederick Seitz, Ph.D., Professor of Physics, University of Illinois

Charles Kittel, Ph.D., Professor of Physics, University of California, Berkeley

W. D. Hershberger, Ph.D., Professor of Engineering, University of California, Los Angeles

William A. Fowler, Ph.D., Professor of Physics, California Institute of Technology

R. V. Langmuir, Ph.D., Associate Professor of Electrical Engineering, California Institute of Technology

Glenn T. Seaborg, Ph.D., Professor of Chemistry, University of California, Berkeley

W. K. H. Panofsky, Ph.D., Professor of Physics, Stanford University

Jesse Greenstein, Ph.D., Professor of Astrophysics, California Institute of Technology; Mount Wilson and Palomar Observatories

David T. Griggs, Professor of Geophysics, University of California, Los Angeles

Roger Revelle, Ph.D., Professor of Oceanography and Director, Scripps Institution of Oceanography

Leonard B. Loeb, Ph.D., Professor of Physics, University of California, Berkeley

Walker Bleakney, Ph.D., Professor of Physics, Princeton University

Simon Ramo, Ph.D., Vice President and Executive Director, the Ramo-Wooldridge Corporation and Research Associate, California Institute of Technology

John Bardeen, Ph.D., Professor of Physics and of Electrical Engineering, University of Illinois

J. B. Wiesner, Professor of Electrical Engineering and Director, Research Laboratory of Electronics, Massachusetts Institute of Technology

Louis N. Ridenour, Ph.D., Vice President, International Telemeter Corporation and Visiting Professor of Engineering, University of California, Los Angeles

Foreword

Modern engineering rests on a base of experimental and theoretical work in the sciences as well as on the works of centuries of our engineering predecessors. The time lag between scientific discovery and engineering application has in recent years been drastically shortened, so that it is more than ever necessary for the engineer to be aware of the significant developments in the fields of the physical sciences.

To this end, the departments of engineering at the University of California, in cooperation with the subject departments, arranged a series of lecture courses in modern physics, mathematics, and chemistry for their staffs, students, and graduates in order to make them aware of the advances in the sciences. Each course consists of a series of invitation lectures, presented by teaching scientists prominent in their fields, from the University of California and other western and eastern universities, and is offered under the sponsorship of University Extension.

We are pleased to share the stimulating experience of the *Modern Physics for the Engineer* lecture series with you, the reader, through the pages of this book.

BALDWIN M. WOODS
Professor of Mechanical Engineering
Vice President, University Extension
University of California
Los Angeles

L. M. K. BOELTER
Professor of Engineering
Dean, College of Engineering
University of California
Los Angeles

MORROUGH P. O'BRIEN
Professor of Engineering
Dean, College of Engineering
University of California
Berkeley

Preface

An extension course having the same title as this book was given in the academic year 1947–1948 at the University of California, Los Angeles. It was intended to familiarize engineers with some of the current advances in physics, on the theory that, in our technological society, the physics of today is the engineering of tomorrow. This course was so well attended and generally so successful that it was decided to offer a similar series of lectures in the academic year 1952–1953. With the encouragement of Dean L. M. K. Boelter of the College of Engineering, University of California, Los Angeles, and under his general supervision, a committee was organized to plan for the newer version of the course. This committee, which included both members of the University of California, Los Angeles, faculty and interested people from industry and from a nearby government laboratory, consisted of Joseph Kaplan, Chairman, L. M. K. Boelter, William Bollay, J. C. Dillon, John Miles, R. R. O'Neill, L. E. Root, Ernest Sporleder, and Royal S. Weller.

The McGraw-Hill Book Company, Inc., learning of the plans for the course, suggested that a collection of the lectures making up the course might be useful, both as collateral reading in connection with similar courses which might be given in other institutions, and as a volume of general interest for the technical man in any scientific or engineering field. Preliminary arrangements were made looking toward the publication of the present volume.

In the early summer of 1952, the committee planning the course decided it would be useful to appoint an individual as general coordinator of the project, responsible for executing the committee's plans. Dean Boelter offered me this responsibility, which I accepted with great pleasure.

The many detailed arrangements concerned with the giving of the course were ably handled by J. C. Dillon of Engineering Extension at the University of California, Los Angeles, and his staff, notably Mrs. Bernice Park. The course itself enjoyed an unprecedented attendance; there were 606 paid registrations and a substantial additional attendance

ix

by interested members of the University of California, Los Angeles, faculty. Most of the lectures given at the University of California, Los Angeles, were repeated before sizable groups organized at the Naval Electronics Laboratory, San Diego, and the Naval Ordnance Test Station, China Lake. A similar course, with many of the same lecturers, was organized and given at the University of California, Berkeley, under the able direction of Prof. W. A. Nierenberg of the Department of Physics.

Little in the way of logical organization of the sequence of topics covered in the lectures could be achieved in the course itself. The dates of specific lectures were sometimes determined by an attempt at organization, but more often by the lecturer's convenience. In any case, the course really consisted of a series of lectures on special topics whose nature was determined by the professional interests of the various lecturers.

In retrospect it appears that a reasonably logical arrangement of the subjects covered in the course is possible. The one I prefer is represented by the arrangement of chapters in this book. There are three main categories, into one or another of which each of the chapters can be classified. Only the first of these, which I have labeled "The Laws of Nature," represents physics under the narrow definition of its scope. The chapters in this part of the book are concerned with what we know of matter, radiation, and the laws of their interaction.

I have called the second part of the book "Man's Physical Environment." The chapters which make up this part deal with the application of physical laws and techniques of investigation to the study of the universe, of the earth, and of the air. This, if you will, is applied physics, although the level at which it is applied and the aims of the investigators concerned still qualify under the general definition of basic science as opposed to engineering.

In the third part of the book the chapters deal with the application of physics to an important field of engineering. The field concerned is rather new, very broad in scope, and of vast practical significance. It is the field of modern electronics and the communication and information-processing techniques which modern electronics is making possible. This field is still developing so rapidly that it is making extraordinary demands on basic science.

Since the lectures which form the basis for this book were given in a special-topics course, the treatment of any subject offered here must be fragmentary and incomplete. Some readers may feel that the organization of the book is *ad hoc* and artificial. Perhaps it is, but the chapters had to appear in a serial order, and the present order is the one that appeals to me. At all events, each chapter is written by a man who is a recognized authority in the field that he treats. What is said is therefore authoritative; I hope it will be as interesting to the reader as it has been to me.

Uniformity of style and of level of treatment manifestly cannot be attained in a book with as many authors as this one has. Some editorial attention has been paid to achieving enough uniformity to avoid confusing the reader, but plenty of discrepancies remain. The reader's indulgence is asked.

I am grateful to Dean Boelter for giving me the opportunity of helping to organize this very interesting project, to the lecturers in the course and the authors of chapters in this book for their part in the program, to Mr. Dillon and Mrs. Park for their work in making the course a success, and to my secretary Doris Read for her considerable assistance in preparing the manuscript for publication.

LOUIS N. RIDENOUR

Contents

PART 2. MAN'S PHYSICAL ENVIRONMENT

10   Astrophysics
235

11   High-pressure Phenomena with Applications to Geophysics
272

Introduction*

ROYAL WELLER
CHIEF SCIENTIST, U.S. NAVAL AIR MISSILE TEST CENTER
POINT MUGU, CALIFORNIA

Human activity is motivated by many conflicting desires. Prominent among these are the desire for security and continuity, the desire for prestige and power, the desire for recognition, and, in some persons, a strong urge for new experiences. Others possess a tendency to escape from reality, frequently as a result of inability or unwillingness to cope with it.

On these desires is founded the occupational structure of the real world. The provision of food, shelter, clothing, and medicine satisfies the need for security as do police and fire departments and, in a larger sense, armies and navies, although these latter may become instruments of power. The entertainment world and what may be called aesthetic activity serve largely to satisfy the desire to substitute fantasy for reality. Transportation and communication assist and amplify all the foregoing. The desire for power and prestige, either by individuals or by groups, frequently determines the extent to which they do all these things. If this is a "materialistic" catalogue of functions, let us hasten to add that it is not at all complete but is intended merely to delineate the areas in which engineers work.

It is the function of the engineer to devise, construct, and operate the technological systems by which the material demands of society are satisfied. To do this he draws on the laws of nature as defined by the scientist, on the material and manpower resources about him, and on a vast store of recorded empirical knowledge known as engineering art, tradition, good commercial practice, and so on. The extent to which the engineer draws on material and manpower resources depends on the extent of the approval with which society views his accomplishments.

---

* The views expressed herein are those of the author and do not necessarily represent official opinions of the U.S. Navy or the Naval Service in general.

The extent to which he draws on the laws of nature depends on the rate at which the scientist uncovers new facts and devises new theories. The extent to which he draws on engineering tradition depends on his point of view and education.

At the present writing the engineer enjoys a degree of social approval unprecedented in history. The lay public has recently witnessed the creation of such bizarre and complex machines that no radical proposal is viewed with much skepticism. Material and manpower resources are being expended on engineering projects at a tremendous rate, and the empirical lore which these groups are recording is so voluminous as to defy cataloguing and adequate dissemination. Hand in hand with this effort in technological development goes a corresponding endeavor in basic science.

When technology was young, the engineer and scientist were less readily separable and one who investigated and applied the laws of nature was known as a "natural philosopher." His interest encompassed all these laws and their available applications. As complexity appeared, largely through the use of natural power sources to replace animate labor, engineering became separated from pure science and gradually compartmentalized. Thus we had civil, electrical, mechanical, and chemical engineers for a time, and only those laws of nature bearing on these specialized activities were studied in such compartments. A mechanical engineer was not expected to be familiar with Maxwell's equations of electromagnetic-energy propagation.

In the past few years we have further compartmentalized. Metallurgical, aeronautical, illumination, electronic, acoustic, and many other subclasses of engineering have appeared, each with its own small field of basic science to exploit.

From time to time there appear phenomena which cast some doubt on the wisdom of this compartmentalizing. A few years ago the suspension bridge from Tacoma, Washington, to Gig Harbor experienced catastrophic structural failure. The reasons for this failure were aerodynamic in nature and were not in the civil engineers' compartment. The subject of aerodynamic stability was quickly inserted into this compartment, and it developed that the Tacoma bridge was not the sole example of a structure for which resonance existed within the frequency range of wind-vortex generation. An interesting example of compartmentalization occurred during an earthquake in Los Angeles in the summer of 1952. In a large construction project the fluorescent lighting fixtures are reported to have fallen from their mountings. Apparently the structural requirements for resisting earthquakes were not in the illumination engineers' compartment. Many other such examples can be cited.

In general one can say that compartmentalizing directs the attention of the compartmentees to the continued refinement of *things as they are.* It results in efficient designs. It causes things to be done reproducibly on a large scale. It yields mass production. Some of these things are good. The technology of the United States is based on machine manufacture of interchangeable parts. Our national security is similarly founded. On the other hand, new ideas seldom occur to thoroughly compartmented people. In the past, at least, we have looked abroad for many of the ideas in technology which we have exploited, and this has been explained by some in terms of the broader fundamental training which is common in Europe.

Engineering courses of instruction have, by convention, been divided into two parts. In one of these the basic rules of science are delineated, and the student is expected to solve a number of problems exemplifying these rules in order to fix them in his mind. Subjects in this category are physics, chemistry, and mathematics. Most of the problems solved are numerical in nature and, if one does not inquire too closely into their reality, admit of exact answers. This is the way in which Ohm's law, Avogadro's law, Hooke's law, and others are presented.

In the second category of instruction the student is expected to become familiar with "good engineering practice" by imitating the work of other engineers. Here the subject matter is frequently called "design." The material aspects of an electric power transformer, say, are studied, and the neophyte attempts to design a simple one to a conventional set of specifications. His departures from "good engineering practice" are pointed out to him, and he begins the worship of his professional ancestors. Where it is convenient, the relationships between his "design" and the basic rules of science are also pointed out to him, and, to this extent, his design courses are utilized as further case material for the first category of learning. But, in general, the fundamental reasons for designing a circuit or a structure in a certain way are concealed in a systematic adherence to traditional procedures.

There are a number of reasons for teaching design from an arbitrary, or handbook, basis. Not the least of these is the limited mathematical capacity of both the average student and his teacher. A close examination of the problems solved in undergraduate physics courses will disclose that they are concerned with situations having "lumped constants" in the circuit engineer's language. Such problems can be solved in many cases by simple arithmetic and in most cases without the calculus. On the other hand, a problem with nonuniformly distributed constants requires one to be familiar with such things as higher-order differential equations. A similar example may be cited in courses concerned with stress analysis. In order to make stress-distribution problems amenable to easy solution, they are classified into such categories as beams, shafting, columns, and the like. These are problems involving separable coordinate systems and, again, can generally be solved by a moderate use of arithmetic. Where the coordinates are not easily separable, as in the case of a loaded cam, differential equations of a complex nature are involved, and such problems are seldom attempted.

In a general way one can say that "good practice" and "handbook engineering" result from inadequate mathematical capability plus the happy discovery that arbitrary correction factors found in the literature will usually suffice for cases encountered in engineering offices. This sort of training encourages the compartmentalizing process. It tends to make the average engineer one who is strongly dependent on compendiums of technical data. He seldom thinks of the fundamental rules governing materials and processes and may even become suspicious of those who do deal in such commodities. It is generally necessary for some curious outsider to create genuinely new ideas for exploitation.

When a student graduates from an engineering college, he generally finds that his skill in design is of primary importance to his employer. He soon becomes steeped in the traditions of his company. The basic reasons for the physical judgments which he produces continue to recede farther and farther into the background. There are but few engineers who attempt to place a basic physical interpretation on such things as automobiles, buildings, television sets, and curling irons.

Success in engineering generally lies along one of the following lines:

a. Inventing a new device or process which replaces another on an economic or user-demand basis
b. Making an existing device or process "better" on the same basis
c. Reproducing existing equipment or services economically

We may, if we like, divide engineering into research, development, testing, production, and sales. In a country which contains about a half million engineers, most are engaged in production and sales. However, the significant advances in engineering science and art are nearly always the product of those members of the profession who do, in fact, keep basic principles in mind and draw on them whenever possible, whether they are employed in research or production.

During the war of 1939–1945 there took place a very marked acceleration in technological development, the reasons for which have not always received their fair share of thoughtful attention. In this country, at the outset of the war, there developed a critical shortage of engineers to design and build the weapons and accessory equipment needed and to provide the essential domestic goods required to prevent a severe drop in our standard of living. It is true that we permitted a disastrous drop in the production of engineers themselves, and in civilian automobiles, for example, we stopped production. But as far as the ordinary necessities of life are concerned, we superimposed the war on our peacetime economy and carried the double burden with success. It is instructive to see, in part, how this was accomplished.

The war led to the development of many new military devices. Besides atomic bombs we produced radars, proximity fuses, rockets, new aircraft types, and many other things besides. It appeared that the shortage of engineers did not much hamper this effort.

As a matter of fact there were many people working in basic science before the war who had come to believe that a professorship was the ultimate goal of a professional career in physics, chemistry, mathematics, and similar scientific fields. These people suddenly found themselves confronted with offers of employment to apply their knowledge to engineering. Astronomers became ballisticians, spectroscopists became metallurgists, and mathematicians became circuit analysts. The admixture of these people with practicing engineers produced results far in excess of a simple augmentation of engineering manpower. While previously such individuals had often been considered too "theoretical" and "impractical" for engineering projects, it speedily became evident that they brought to bear a broader and more fruitful point of view. Before the war the delay experienced between scientific discovery in the physics laboratory and common application in engineering was, in many cases, nearly a generation. The mixture of basic scientists with engineers reduced this delay to a very few years. Indeed, it proved beyond any doubt that the channels of communication between physics and engineering were very poor indeed and that engineering education had not bridged the gap with any marked success.

In many developmental organizations, both governmental and industrial, the impact of physics was such as to cause many physicists to rise to the top of such groups as directors of technical programs. This situation has persisted, and it is still quite common for students graduating in physics to receive rather lucrative industrial employment without any great exertion. We have experienced a breaking down of barriers on a wide scale. But it is too much to attribute the success of our wartime developmental effort to either group alone. They were coexistent before the war, but they had not had an adequate opportunity to react on each other.

We have said, in discussing the teaching of engineering, that one class of studies is intended mainly to fix in the student's mind some of the rules of science. It may be useful to examine some of these rules. Many engineers imagine Ohm's law and the like to be immutable. If this book has no permanent effect other than to throw doubt on such a belief, it will have been worth the effort. There is perhaps no better definition of a "basic" science as distinguished from an "applied" science than that the former's "laws" are viewed with suspicion and are subject to change when required. The laws of conservation of energy and conservation of matter are now meaningless when taken separately. The law of the conservation of momentum still persists, but we must invent strange particles in order to preserve it. As to engineering laws, we know that Hooke's law, for example, is merely a loose statistical description. In a typical steel structure it is a first approximation which permits an initial idealized calculation of stresses.

Where engineers are concerned with routine repetitive processes, it is probable that a close examination of the laws of physics is not required. However, whenever an engineer desires to improve designs or processes, he should be sure that his familiarity with the basic rules is sufficient to keep him from making mistakes.

The basic rules of science are generalizations which are obtained by considering a wide variety of physical situations. They will change as we obtain more experimental evidence. They will become broader as more and more correlation is discovered between events previously thought to have no connection with each other. It is permissible to conceive of physical phenomena which violate presently accepted rules. It is simply unlikely that one can produce such phenomena, the degree of unlikelihood being more or less proportional to the weight of evidence in favor of the rule. For example, a few years ago it seemed to engineers that the existence of materials exhibiting dielectric constants of several thousand was quite unlikely. Today we have strontium-barium titanates which show this property. There was, however, no basic rule which seemed to prohibit such properties. The unlikelihood was based simply on the fact that no such material had been observed. On the other hand, it seems unlikely that a material will be found available to engineers with a specific heat of 100 or better. What we know about the structure of matter seems to deny the possibility of such materials. It therefore does not seem profitable to try to produce one. A careful study of the rules of science and an understanding of their reasons for existence will frequently save the engineering profession a great deal of time and energy.

In the long run we desire, as I believe Bridgman has said, to understand the past and to predict the future. To understand the past, we need more than just a description of the phenomena which have occurred. We need to have classifications and correlations of these phenomena so that we can perceive general rules of behavior for the physical world. A huge collection of uncorrelated data is of little use. Its entropy is too great and its potential too low. The same data properly correlated have a high potential. If we look into the past of engineering, we find that some data are correlated and some are not. When the correlated data are subjected to analyses, and the possible generalities drawn from them, we shall find that we have the rules of physics, chemistry, mathematics, and the other sciences involved.   To understand the *past* of engineering, we first must understand the basic sciences which contributed to it. Nearly all the nonchemical engineering we know today is based on the so-called *classical* physics: mechanics, heat, light, sound, electricity, magnetism, and wave motion.   One partial exception is the field of electronics and radio, which has grown so rapidly since the turn of the century.   The other major exception is nuclear engineering.

If we desire to predict the future in engineering, we may do so in a limited way since, fortunately, we may still be sure that physics will point the way.   The new engineering of the next few years will be in part the application of the physics described in the chapters which follow. Those of us who wish to participate in this progress will require two things: an understanding of the basic rules governing the behavior of matter and energy as they are discovered and a familiarity with the various kinds of arithmetic which will be necessary to apply these rules quantitatively.

PART 1
The Laws of Nature

1

Relativity and the Foundations
of Mechanics

H. P. ROBERTSON

PROFESSOR OF MATHEMATICAL PHYSICS
CALIFORNIA INSTITUTE OF TECHNOLOGY

"That part of Physics, which is the oldest and simplest, and is therefore to be considered as the foundation for the understanding of many other parts of Physics, concerns itself with the investigation of motion and the equilibrium of bodies. It is called Mechanics."—Ernst Mach, *Die Mechanik in ihrer Entwickelung*, 1883.

1.1 Introduction

With these stark words Mach began his treatment of mechanics, destined to be the culminating achievement of the classical phase of that discipline which had its origins in the investigations of Galileo and Newton. For even as these words were being written, there was brewing a conflict between the venerable classical mechanics and the burgeoning electromagnetic theory of Maxwell and Hertz, a conflict which was within the decade to have its *experimentum crucis* in the observations of the American physicists Michelson and Morley. The final resolution of the conflict was achieved twenty years later through the insight of Einstein, who found it possible to restore harmony between the two domains only by a radical revision of the fundamental concepts of space and time. The new theory of mechanics, the special theory of relativity, was at once one to which Mach's words, suitably modified, could be applied— even though the special theory was soon to be incorporated by Einstein into a generalization which enabled him to reduce gravitation to a kinematical phenomenon.

It is my intention in the present chapter to trace for you the development of mechanics from its geometrical background in ancient Greece to the present time. It will be my contention that theoretical mechanics

11

first measured up to the observed facts when, in the seventeenth century, it was formulated in a way which brought out the relativity of motion— the classical principle of relativity. The concept of the independence of space and time that was held in this classical theory brought it into con- flict with the relativity of motion implied by electromagnetic theory, and was replaced in the special principle of relativity by a unified space- time framework, whose metrical structure was, however, independent of its physical content. The observed equality of inertial and gravitational mass suggested to Einstein the possibility of reducing gravitational forces to kinematical ones, analogous to the well-known centrifugal and Coriolis forces of classical mechanics. This could only be done, as was indeed done in the general theory of relativity, by surrendering the rigid a priori metrical structure of space-time, allowing its structure to be determined— or at least influenced—by its specific physical content.

I shall, on the other hand, not attempt to deal with the even more revolutionary modifications forced upon mechanics by quantum phe- nomena. These are discussed in other chapters, and in any case the program I have laid down for myself is presumptuous enough without poking into these fields! It will suffice for my purposes to remark that there does exist at present a precarious harmony between the special theory of relativity and quantum mechanics, as exemplified by Dirac's theory of the electron and the more recent developments in quantum electrodynamics. In contrast with this fruitful and relatively peaceful interaction between the special theory of relativity and quantum theory, the outlook for a theory which will encompass and truly unify the gravita- tional and elementary-particle fields is at present far from bright—not because of conflict between the two, but rather because of their apparent complete indifference to each other.

1.2 The Classical Principle of Relativity

One can trace in the classical mechanics of motion three separate stages —geometry, kinematics, and dynamics. These three stages are to this extent independent, that although each of the latter two is influenced by its predecessors in the series, it is not determined by them. And since one or another of them is modified in each of the theories under review, it will be well to trace them down in order.

1.2.1 *Geometry*. For our purposes we must consider geometry as primarily an inductive, rather than a deductive, science. For in the final analysis we are concerned with the measurement, by physical means, of the distances between physical objects. We lay down certain definite prescriptions as to how distances, and through them angles, are to be measured, and it is an empirical matter what the observed metrical struc- ture will turn out to be—whether or not, for example, the measures so obtained will conform to the Pythagorean theorem of Euclidean geometry within the errors of measurement. Certain of the salient features of Euclidean geometry—measurement of areas, cylindrical volumes, and the proportions of pyramids—were in fact arrived at by the Egyptians as the result of induction from homely observation. These crude beginnings were extended by the Greeks and developed into a logical discipline, in which the empirical results could be obtained deductively from a few relatively simple definitions and postulates.

The system of Euclidean geometry thus obtained will repay a closer examination, in order critically to appraise its position in the science of mechanics. The three-dimensional extended manifold with which it deals, the mathematical representation of our physical space, admits the extremely important notion of *congruence;* thus two triangles are said to be congruent if two sides and the included angle of one are equal, respectively, to two sides and the included angle of the other, irrespective of their positions and orientations in space.   The relation of this geometrical notion of congruence to the mechanical notion of *rigid body* is immediately obvious on recalling the method employed by Euclid in proving the over-all equality of two such triangles: one of the triangles is applied to the other in such a way as to bring corresponding elements into coincidence. Thus Euclidean geometry is one in which the notion of a rigid body is possible, in the sense that such a body on being moved from one position and orientation into any other position and orientation remains congruent to itself during the motion.   The metrical structure of Euclidean space is thus homogeneous and isotropic.   In a more precise mathematical language, borrowed in part from mechanics, we may say that Euclidean space admits a six-parameter group of motions under which its structure is preserved and which is such that any of the ∞^6 configurations $\Gamma(P, d, \phi)$ consisting of a point P, a direction d through P, and a fan ϕ of directions through P containing d can, by an appropriate motion of the group, be brought into coincidence with any other such configuration $\Gamma'(P', d', \phi')$.

Euclidean geometry admits also the notion of *similitude*, developed and used extensively in Book VI of the "Elements." This concept, in contrast with that of *congruence*, depends on the existence of a unique parallel to a given straight line from an arbitrary point outside the line—a notion which would seem to have no compelling physical source, such as that supplied by rigid bodies for the notion of congruence.

Now I think you will agree that, if the metrical structure of space is to be independent of its physical content, or if it is to admit the possibility of rigid bodies, then it must indeed exhibit the degree of symmetry implied by the notion of congruence.   But I now invert the question and ask whether such a space must necessarily be Euclidean—and if not, what further forms might it assume? The first satisfactory answer to this question was given early in the last century by the Hungarian mathematician Bolyai and the Russian mathematician Lobachewski, who independently shewed that a consistent system of geometry (the so-called hyperbolic geometry) could be developed in which space is infinitely extended in all directions, but in which there exists an infinity of parallels to a given line from a point outside it. The German mathematician Riemann followed this work some years later with a system of congruence geometry in which space is finite but unbounded, in which there exist no parallel lines; the simplest two-dimensional example is the geometry of the surface of a sphere, the great circles of which play the role of straight lines, any two of which do in fact intersect. In each of these non-Euclidean geometries there exists a magnitude R having the physical dimensions $[L]$ of a length which provides a natural unit of measurement and which in the two-dimensional example of Riemann's geometry may be taken as the radius of the sphere; hence it is not surprising that in them the notion of similitude has no place. It is customary, however, to characterize these geometries instead by a quantity K having the physical dimensions $[L]^{-2}$, which for the sphere is just $1/R^2$. This "curvature" K is zero for Euclidean space, negative for the hyperbolic types, and positive for those proposed by Riemann. This development was subsequently elegantly rounded out by the German physiologist and physicist Helmholtz and the Norwegian mathematician Lie, who showed that any geometry possessing the degree of symmetry required for the existence of rigid bodies is necessarily one of the above types.

We return after this brief excursion into non-Euclidean geometry to the subject at hand, the classical theory of mechanics. At the time this theory was formulated, the only geometry available was that of Euclid, which had certainly not come into conflict with experience and which was quite universally accepted as the basic framework for physics and astronomy. The position of Euclidean geometry was subsequently entrenched by the authority of the philosopher Kant, who regarded space as a form of intuition whose structure was given a priori. This preeminence of Euclidean geometry in physical science was not seriously to be challenged until the advent of the general theory of relativity forty years ago.

1.2.2 *Kinematics.* The problem of describing the motion of bodies, such as particles and rigid bodies, in space is that of kinematics. This description requires a notion of *time* and a means of measuring *duration*. Newton postulated the existence of an "absolute, true and mathematical" time, which "of itself flows equably without regard to anything external," and was again reinforced by Kant, who considered time a necessary a priori form of intuition. As a measure of the flow of time in his immediate neighborhood, an observer may adopt some cyclical phenomenon, such as the swing of a pendulum, and consider that its successive cycles have equal duration. The refinement of this procedure, by the accepted methodology of inductive science, to eliminate extraneous effects on the standard adopted is a long and tedious process which we must here pass over lightly. It suffices to note that for most scientific purposes the rotation of the earth about its axis may be taken as a measure of the uniform flow of time; the standard unit, the second, is then defined as 1/86,400 of the mean solar day. However, even this standard may upon occasion be challenged, as when we are concerned with the dynamical effects of tidal friction on the rotation of the earth. Experience has shown that, within the limits of observational error, the various kinds of clocks which have suggested themselves to man all keep the same time, when corrected for identifiable extraneous influences. It is of course conceivable that there are categories of cyclical processes, *e.g.*, atomic or nuclear processes, whose rates diverge from the mechanical standard sufficiently over the ages to be of considerable cosmogonic significance. Such a proposal has indeed been advanced by the late English astrophysicist E. A. Milne, in an attempt to reconcile the uncomfortably short time scale of the expanding universe with the at least comparable age of the earth, as determined from the evidence of radioactivity in the rocks.

But after adopting a local standard of time, such as a pendulum clock for terrestrial experiments or the rotation of the earth for astronomical observations, we are still faced with the task of extending this time to other possible observers, *i.e.*, of synchronizing our clock with those of others. This can be accomplished in practice by either of two principal methods—that of transporting the clock bodily from its original position A to a new position B, and that of sending time signals from A to B. For most purposes requiring accuracy, including marine and aerial navigation, the latter method has at least augmented, if not entirely supplanted, the former; the method of signals alone will be considered here. A possible theoretical solution of the problem of extending the local time of an observer at A to one at B is for him to send out a signal, say, at time t_A, to B, where it is immediately reflected back to A and received there at time t'_A; the time t_B at which the radarlike reflection takes place at B may then be taken as the arithmetic mean $t_B = (t_A + t'_A)/2$ of the times of emission and reception at A. I say only that this procedure may possibly solve the problem, for it is clear that the consistency of the time thus extended will depend on the physical laws governing the type of signal employed; thus the definition implies that the average speed of the signal from A to B is the same as that for the return trip, and this may be affected, for example, by the states of motion of the observer at A and the mirror at B.

But in talking about speeds and states of motion in defining time we are getting ahead of ourselves; for it is one of our prime purposes in extending time to enable ourselves to define speeds and states of motion. And while we must eventually face up to the problem, it can be avoided for the time being; for in the classical theory clocks could in principle be synchronized by the employment of signals for which $t_A = t'_A$ and therefore $= t_B$, that is, by signals having infinite speed. This proposal is not so preposterous as it appears at first sight, because for most mundane purposes the speed of light is practically infinite; this is, in fact, just the procedure we use in checking our pocket watches by glancing at the face of the town clock some blocks away.

We assume then, with Newton, that we have an absolute space, whose geometry is Euclidean and can be explored by rigid rods, and an absolute time, whose uniform flow can be measured at any point in space by suitably chosen clocks. Because the metrical structure of space is everywhere and in every direction the same, there is a complete relativity of position and orientation. An observer A may, by the erection of a suitable coordinate system, say rectangular cartesian coordinates, assign to each point P of space a triad $x^a = (x, y, z)$, where $a = 1, 2, 3$, of real numbers which uniquely specify its position relative to the origin O. The distance Δs between two points P_1 and P_2, whose coordinates are, respectively, $x_1{}^a$ and $x_2{}^a$, is then given by the Pythagorean theorem

$$(\Delta s)^2 = \sum_a (x_2{}^a - x_1{}^a)^2 \tag{1.1}$$

or by the equivalent differential formula

$$ds^2 = \sum_a (dx^a)^2 \tag{1.2}$$

for two neighboring points x^a, $x^a + dx^a$.

The motion of a particle, such as a physically identifiable element of a gas or rigid body, may be described by giving the coordinates x^a of the geometrical point at which it is located at time t, that is, by specifying its coordinates x^a as definite functions $x^a(t)$ of the time. The velocity of the particle relative to the origin at time t is then the temporal derivative $v^a = dx^a/dt$ of its coordinate triad, and its relative acceleration $a^a = dv^a/dt$.

It will be found profitable to conceive of the world of space and time as a four-dimensional extension, a typical point $x^i = (t; x, y, z)$, where $i = 0, 1, 2, 3$, of which is the *event* E which takes place at the position $x^a = (x, y, z)$ of space at time t. We will further find it desirable to construct a pictorial representation of this four-dimensional world of events on suppressing one of the spatial coordinates, say by considering the situation only in the "plane" $x^3 = z = 0$, as in Fig. 1.1. The "space" $t = 0$ is taken as a horizontal plane, and the subsequent spaces $t = $ const.

are taken as planes parallel thereto and at distances t above it. The "world line" of the origin O of A's coordinate system, *i.e.,* the locus of the events $x^a = 0$, t arbitrary, is here represented by the straight line OA, but this is here quite arbitrary, for it could at the present kinematic stage of our development equally well be represented by any curve which winds steadily upward through the planes $t = $ const. The world line of the particle whose position at time t is $x^a(t)$ is represented by such a

curve DE and its velocity v^a by the projection along the direction AO of the tangent four-vector $v^i = (1,\ v^a)$ onto the space $t = $ const.

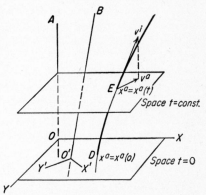

As implied above, the situation could equally well be viewed from the standpoint of any other observer B in quite arbitrary motion with respect to A. The world line of B's origin of cartesian coordinates $x'^a = 0$ is some curve $x^a = b^a(t)$, and the directions of B's coordinate axes at time t are obtainable from those of A by some Euclidean rota-

Fig. 1.1 The classical world picture.

tion, whose parameters depend on t. The equations expressing this Euclidean motion of translation plus rotation may be taken in the form

$$x^a = \sum_b A_b{}^a(t)x'^b + b^a(t) \tag{1.3}$$

from which the coordinates x^a to be assigned the event $E(t,\ x^a)$ by A can be computed from the coordinates x'^a assigned E at time t by B, and vice versa. The three functions $b^a(t)$ defining the translation are quite arbitrary, but the nine coefficients $A_b{}^a(t)$ defining the rotation are in essence reduced to three by the imposition of the six quadratic conditions

$$\sum_a A_b{}^a A_c{}^a = \delta_{bc} = \begin{cases} 1 \text{ if } b = c \\ 0 \text{ otherwise} \end{cases} \tag{1.4}$$

required to ensure that the distance in the new coordinate system is obtained from the coordinate differences with the aid of the Pythagorean theorem.

Two special cases of this general transformation (1.3) will be of special concern in the sequel. The first of these is that in which B is moving uniformly relatively to A along a straight line with constant speed v. B's origin may then be chosen to coincide with A's at time $t = 0$, and the common direction of the x and x' axes taken in the direction of motion. On taking the directions of the transverse axes the same in the two systems, the relations between the coordinates, velocities, and accelerations in the two systems are given by

$$x = x' + vt \qquad y = y' \qquad z = z' \qquad (1.5a)$$
$$v^1 = v'^1 + v \qquad v^2 = v'^2 \qquad v^3 = v'^3 \qquad (1.5b)$$
$$a^1 = a'^1 \qquad a^2 = a'^2 \qquad a^3 = a'^3 \qquad (1.5c)$$

The other case of special interest is that in which B's axes are rotating with constant angular speed ω with respect to A's about some constant direction. On taking this constant direction as that of the x and x' axes, and the y and y' axes as coinciding at time $t = 0$, the required transformation is

$$x = x' \qquad y = y' \cos \omega t - z' \sin \omega t \qquad z = y' \sin \omega t + z' \cos \omega t \qquad (1.6a)$$

By differentiating once with respect to t we may find v^a as a function of the v'^b, x'^b, and t and by a second differentiation, the acceleration a^a as a function of the a'^b, v'^b, x'^b, and t. It suffices, however, to consider these relations only at the time $t = 0$ when the two sets of axes coincide; then

$$v^1 = v'^1 \qquad v^2 = v'^2 - \omega z' \qquad\qquad v^3 = v'^3 + \omega y' \qquad (1.6b)$$
$$a^1 = a'^1 \qquad a^2 = a'^2 - 2\omega v'^3 - \omega^2 y' \qquad a^3 = a'^3 + 2\omega v'^2 - \omega^2 z' \qquad (1.6c)$$

We can now survey kinematics, in terms of the world picture given in Fig. 1.1, as follows. The four-dimensional world of space and time is striated into spaces $t = \text{const.}$ of sets of simultaneous events, and this resolution into space and time is *absolute*, in the sense that it is common to all possible observers. The rudimentary metrical structure of this four-dimensional world is such that the only absolute measure of distance or duration, common to all observers, between two events $E_1(t_1; x_1{}^a)$ and $E_2(t_2; x_2{}^a)$ is

   a. The distance interval Δs, Eq. (1.1), if the two events E_1 and E_2 are simultaneous, *i.e.*, if $t_2 = t_1$
   b. The time interval $\Delta t = t_2 - t_1$

Note that any attempt to define the "distance" between two non-simultaneous events by means of the relation (1.1) cannot have any absolute significance; the interval so defined is, for example, zero for an observer whose world line passes through the two events.

   We have employed only rectangular cartesian coordinates in our discussion of kinematics, but we could equally well use any other coordinate system, *e.g.*, spherical polar coordinates whose origin, polar axis, and meridian plane are moving arbitrarily with respect to the original observer A. The invariant distance between two simultaneous events in such a system is, however, no longer of the simple form (1.1).

1.2.3 *Dynamics.* The task of dynamics is that of describing, or predicting, how a physical body moves, or will move, under given physical circumstances, *e.g.*, a planet forming part of a solar system or an electron in an atom or molecule. Naturally, it is also necessary to consider the reaction of the body under examination on its surroundings; for it is itself part of the surroundings of these latter. The task can sometimes be simplified if the observed effect of the body on its surroundings is so small as to be negligible for the purposes in mind; in the ideal limit, where its reactions are completely neglected, we speak of such a body as a *test body*. And in any case when we are concerned, as here, only with principles, we do in the classical and relativity mechanics assume that any system may be considered as an assemblage of bodies whose geometrical extensions are so small that they may be neglected; such a body has then only the geometrical attributes of a point, and is called a *particle*. We do not here go into the question of whether or to what extent such an extreme idealization is justifiable for actual physical bodies, such as an electron or other "elementary" particles.

The problem of dynamics immediately raises the question of what the natural state of motion of a body removed from all interaction with its surroundings would be. Here again the solution proposed must be justified in accordance with the accepted methodology of inductive science, by demonstrating that the deviations from the contemplated natural state of motion do in fact decrease when the suspected agent is appropriately modified or if possible removed—as done, for example, by Galileo in observing the motion of bodies on smooth planes inclined at various angles to the horizontal. The establishment of such a natural state of motion, even if only an unrealizable ideal, is an enormous stride forward in solving the problem of dynamics, as the sources of the observed deviations may then be sought out and their influence codified in physical law.

It is clear from our discussion of geometry that we cannot expect to find such a natural state of motion to consist in a tendency of bodies to aggregate in one or more preferred positions in space. In spite of the ever-present tendency of terrestrial bodies to fall toward the center of the earth, the familiarity of even the most primitive with the celestial bodies precludes the serious maintenance of such a doctrine in an awakening scientific society. Our tradition was, with the adoption of the Euclidean congruence geometry, wedded to the principle of the relativity of position and orientation.

The next most obvious possibility is that it may be possible to choose a frame of reference for space in such a way that the natural state of motion for any body is a state of rest relative to this preeminent frame. This view cannot be rejected a priori; it was in fact held by the Aristotelian school in ancient Greece, on formalistic a priori grounds, and constituted part of the heritage passed down through the centuries to a reawakening West.   The motion of a body, starting from rest under the influence of a constant impelling force, is discussed at length in Aristotle's "Physics"; from this it is possible to deduce the underlying law of motion, which may be taken in modern terminology in the form

$$\text{Mass} \times \text{velocity} = \text{force}$$

Naturally, adherence to such a law incurred great difficulties in rationalizing the behavior of stubborn Nature—as even Aristotle admits in raising the question

If everything that is in motion, with the exception of things that move themselves, is moved by something else, how is it that some things, *e.g.*, things thrown, continue to be in motion when their [source of] movement is no longer in contact with them?

But it is hardly profitable to follow Aristotle's gyrations in trying to wriggle out of the corner he has thus painted himself into; I find myself quite willing to agree with William Whewell's estimate

Now it may truly be said, that in scarcely any one instance are the answers, which Aristotle gives to his questions, of any value.

Thus the Aristotelian physics cannot be considered as otherwise than a complete failure.   It collected no general laws from facts; and consequently, when it tried to explain facts, it had no principles which were of any avail.

Velocity can accordingly no more be taken as absolute than could position, and we are naturally forced on to consider acceleration as a possible candidate—a step which was not taken until the awakening of science from the long intellectual sleep of the Middle Ages.   Through the genius of Galileo it was established that there were indeed preferred reference systems, in which deviations of a body from a state of rest or of uniform motion in a straight line could be attributed to the specific influence of other bodies.   This class of preferred reference systems, each of which is accordingly at rest or moving with a constant velocity relative to each of the others, we shall call *inertial* or *Galilean;* the transformation from one Galilean frame to another can, on appropriate choice of coordinate origin and axes, be taken in the simple form given by Eqs. (1.5). This tendency of a body to preserve its uniform motion (including rest) relative to a Galilean frame is called *inertia*, the measure of which is the *mass* of the body.

Since now the linear acceleration $a^a = d^2x^a/dt^2$ of a particle is common to all observers of the privileged Galilean class, in the sense that its components are those of a fixed vector, it qualifies for the designation *absolute* as I have used the term above—and since the rotation of a collection of particles, as in a rigid body, involves acceleration of the individual parts, rotation also qualifies as an absolute.   We must be careful, however, not to be paralyzed into intellectual stagnation by our own mellifluous words; it would perhaps be more prudent to say "acceleration relative to the Galilean class" rather than "absolute acceleration."   This is not a mere verbal quibble, for it has been maintained by Mach that the inertia of a body has its source in the existence of other bodies in the universe, such as the great nebulae which are found in ever-increasing numbers as our telescopes reach farther out into space.   It may not be worthwhile to speculate on whether the property of inertia would disappear if there were no other bodies in the universe, for we can by no conceivable means rid ourselves of them.   But if the current interpretation of the red shift observed in the spectra of light from extragalactic nebulae—that it is caused by a velocity of recession—is correct, it may be that Nature is preparing to give our remote descendants an opportunity to learn whether inertia decreases when other bodies escape from causal relations with them.   It is well to remember then that, like Alice's potions, our word "absolute" is to be taken with a goodly dose of caution.

Our world picture given in Fig. 1.1 has, with the admission of acceleration as a somewhat qualified absolute, obtained considerably more of an inner structure, even though this addition does not affect its metrical relations.   The planes t = const., representing physical space at various times t, may be slid over themselves so that the world lines of all Galilean observers appear as straight lines; the rate of deviation of the world line of a particle from its tangent at an event E upon it can then be taken as a measure of the influences exerted on the particle by external circumstances.

With this as a background, we are prepared to review rapidly the foundations of classical mechanics, as expressed in Newton's laws of motion.   The first law states:

I. Every body perseveres in its state of rest or of uniform motion in a straight line, except insofar as it is compelled to change that state by impressed forces.

This we have already exploited in setting up the Galilean privileged reference systems.

I follow Mach in passing next to the third law of motion:

III. Reaction is always equal and opposite to action; that is to say, the actions of two bodies upon each other are always equal and directly opposite.

This law we employ to get a measure of the inertia of bodies.   From it it follows that, regardless of the exact mechanism of interaction (but excluding for the nonce electromagnetic interactions) between two particles P and Q, their oppositely directed accelerations a_P and a_Q along the line joining them are always in a fixed numerical ratio $a_P/a_Q = m_{QP}$; this fixed ratio, depending only on the two bodies and not on the particular mode of interaction, is taken as the *mass* of Q relative to that of P.   It is a further implication of this law and the evidence behind it that the mass m_{RQ} assigned to a third particle R by allowing the pair QR to interact is consistent with the mass m_{RP} obtained by interaction of the pair RP, that is, $m_{RP} = m_{RQ}m_{QP}$.   From this it follows that we can assign a numerical mass m_R to a particle R which is a measure of its inertia under all possible circumstances; we need no longer qualify the mass as relative to the particular body with which R is at the moment interacting.   It is of course still necessary to choose some mass, say P, as the arbitrary unit of mass; because of the indifference of the ratio m_{RP}/m_{QP} to the unit chosen, we may suppress the subscript P in the notation and write $m_{RQ} = m_R/m_Q$.   The third law then assumes the familiar form

$$m_Q a_Q = m_R a_R$$

Within the limits of the classical theory, the mass m of an identifiable body is the sum of the masses of all its constituents, however resolved, and is independent of all external circumstances, including motion relative to an observer and the flow of time.   It is an inherent constant property of the body, which is conserved under all circumstances; this result will, as we shall see, no longer hold in the Einstein theories.

Finally I consider the second law of motion:

II. Change of motion is proportional to the moving force impressed, and takes place in the direction of the straight line in which such force is impressed.

Here "motion" is then interpreted as *momentum*

$$p^a = mv^a \tag{1.7}$$

the product of mass and velocity, and "change of motion" as rate of change of momentum.   The second law then states that

$$F^a = ma^a \tag{1.8}$$

This I take, again following Mach, as the definition of *force;* the primary value of this concept is that it enables us to reduce great categories of observations to a few relatively simple physical laws.

As an example of the value of the force concept, I remind you of Newton's law of universal gravitation—the basis for the classical theory of celestial mechanics which seemed capable, almost without exception, of accounting quantitatively for the motions of celestial bodies.   This law states that a particle of mass m at a distance r from a particle of mass M is acted upon by a force

$$F^a = - \frac{GMm}{r^2} \frac{x^a}{r} \tag{1.9}$$

where $G = 6.67 \times 10^{-8}$ cm^3/g sec^2 is Newton's constant of gravitation. Note that this force is proportional to the inertial mass m of the particle of interest, and hence that the acceleration of the particle is independent of its mass; this remarkable equivalence of gravitational and inertial mass was to find its first theoretical explanation in Einstein's general theory of relativity.

The problem of determining the gravitational force acting on a given particle due to any finite distribution of matter can be reduced to that of finding the *gravitational potential* $V(t, x^a)$ throughout space, defined as the work done on a unit particle against the gravitation of the distribution in bringing the test particle from infinity to the position occupied by the particle of interest. The potential is that solution of Poisson's equation

$$\nabla^2 V \equiv \sum_a \frac{\partial^2 V}{\partial x^{a2}} = 4\pi G\rho \tag{1.10}$$

which vanishes at infinity; here $\rho(t, x^a)$ is the mass density of the distribution at $P(x^a)$ at time t. The gravitational force acting on the particle, of mass m, is then

$$F^a = -m \frac{\partial V}{\partial x^a} \tag{1.11}$$

The rapid increase in knowledge of electricity and magnetism during the first half of the nineteenth century uncovered new influences which were hopefully attacked with the conviction that they could be brought fully within the scope of classical mechanics. But, while electrostatic and magnetostatic phenomena could indeed be so treated, it became apparent that truly electromagnetic phenomena could be fitted into the scheme only by attributing *mechanical* properties to the electromagnetic field. Thus, while it was possible to describe the motion of particle of charge e and velocity v^a with the aid of the expression

$$F^a = e \left[E^a + \frac{(v \times H)^a}{c} \right] \tag{1.12}$$

for the ponderomotive force, in a field whose electric and magnetic field strengths were E^a and H^a, it was clear that fully to preserve the law of interaction it would be necessary to endow the field with such properties as energy and momentum.

During the second half of the century this mechanization of the electromagnetic field was in fact achieved to a striking degree. As an example of particular interest to us later, the phenomenon of radiation pressure effects an interchange between the energy of the field and that of the matter upon which the radiation falls which implies that with each amount E of radiant energy there is associated an inertia equivalent to that possessed by a mass

$$m = \frac{E}{c^2} \tag{1.13}$$

where $c = 2.998 \times 10^{10}$ cm/sec is the velocity of light *in vacuo*. This is by no means to say that mass and radiant energy can be converted one into the other, but it does form a conceptual background within which such an interchangeability may be entertained without inconsistency. We shall return to this, and to the role played in it by the velocity of light c which has perforce already insinuated itself into our extension of mechanics, in the succeeding sections.

But first we return for a moment to the problem of the description of motion from the standpoint of a non-Galilean observer. We have in our discussion of kinematics allowed for this possibility; how will the non-Galilean character of his motion affect, and thus be recognizable in, his dynamics? As an example of this situation, consider an observer B whose y' and z' axes are rotating with a constant angular speed ω with respect to a Galilean observer A; the kinematic relations between the two are given by Eqs. (1.6). If now B defines the force F'^a acting on a particle of mass m, at position x'^a at time t, in accordance with the second law of motion, he will find that $F'^1 = F^1$ but that

$$F'^2 = F^2 + m \cdot 2\omega v'^3 + m \cdot \omega^2 y'$$
$$F'^3 = F^3 - m \cdot 2\omega v'^2 + m \cdot \omega^2 z'$$

where F^a is the force defined by the Galilean observer A at the event in question. Thus B observes, in addition to the force F^a adduced by A, two "kinematical" forces acting in his $y'z'$ plane—the Coriolis force perpendicular to the projection (v'^2, v'^3) of the velocity on the $y'z'$ plane and of magnitude $2m\omega$ times the magnitude of this projected velocity, and the centrifugal force of magnitude $m\omega^2 r'$ directed away from the x' axis. Linear or angular acceleration of B's coordinate system would give rise to further kinematic forces, the d'Alembert forces so useful in reducing problems in kinetics to problems in statics. These forces, which impart to any particle an acceleration dependent only on its position and velocity and not on its mass, can be identified and eliminated by transformation to a Galilean frame of reference. Not so the gravitational force (1.9), however; for, although it imparts the same acceleration to any particle placed at a given point in the field, the dependence of this acceleration on position over extended regions of space is not of the kind which can be obtained by going over to a non-Galilean frame. The elimination of gravitation as a dynamical force requires a far more radical change in the geometrical-kinematical framework, such as that offered by the general theory of relativity.

We may summarize the implications of our considerations for the subject at hand as follows. The classical principle of relativity asserts the complete relativity of position and velocity, in the sense that it is impossible by any mechanical experiment to determine an absolute position or an absolute velocity. There exists a set of privileged reference frames, the Galilean, between which the transformations may be reduced to the form

$$t' = t \qquad x' = x - vt \qquad y' = y \qquad z' = z \qquad (1.14)$$

where the constant velocity v can be any number. Any acceleration, including rotation, relative to such a frame is absolute, in the sense that it has a common measure for all Galilean observers.

1.3   The Conflict between the Classical Principle of Relativity and Electromagnetic Theory

While classical mechanics closed the door to the possibility of discovering, by mechanical means, a unique frame of reference for velocity, the nineteenth century saw hope of establishing just such a frame by optical or other electromagnetic means. The wave theory of light, which had been supported by a long series of investigators from Hooke to Fresnel, was put on a firm basis by the studies of Faraday, Maxwell, and Hertz on the electromagnetic field. It was argued, in analogy with waves in gases and elastic solids, that the electromagnetic disturbance must be waves in some medium, the mechanical properties of which should determine the velocity of propagation. And although all attempts to bring this "luminiferous ether" within the ken of the mechanical conception of the physical world ultimately failed, it nevertheless appeared that it should be possible for us to determine our velocity with respect to it by appropriate optical experiments.

That the ether cannot be swept along bodily by the earth's atmosphere is proved by the existence of annual aberration in the light from stars, which checks within the limits of observational accuracy the kinematical result of compounding the velocity of light *in vacuo* with the velocity of the earth in its orbit—some 30 km/sec. From this it would appear that at least some time during the year there should be an ether wind at the surface of the earth of at least 30 km/sec, or about one-ten-thousandth the velocity c of light. Many optical experiments theoretically capable of detecting a velocity of this magnitude have been carried out; all of them have failed to detect such a motion, but not without yielding suggestive by-products

At first sight the most promising possibility for detecting the ether drift through the laboratory is by exploiting the difference in the velocity c/n of light in ponderable mediums of different indices of refraction n. If we assume that the ether is not entrained by such a medium, we should expect on classical kinematics that the velocity of light, relative to the medium, in the direction of motion should be simply the difference $c/n - v$, where v is the forward velocity of the medium with respect to the ether. It is readily shown that this would, in certain of the experiments, lead to effects depending on the first power of the ratio v/c, but

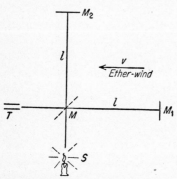

Fig. 1.2 The Michelson-Morley experiment.

although these first-order effects should easily be observable, the experiments failed to detect them. To mention but one such experiment, it was shown by Airy in 1871 that the constant $v/c = 20''.5$ of annual aberration is unchanged when the telescope is filled with water (!) instead of air. Here the quasi-mechanical theories of the ether had a certain temporary success, for as early as 1818 Fresnel had predicted that a body moving through the ether should partially drag the ether along with it, not with the full velocity v of the body but with the fraction κv, where $\kappa = 1 - 1/n^2$ depends on the index of refraction of the body. Under this hypothesis the absolute velocity of the beam in the direction of motion should be $c/n + \kappa v$, whence its velocity relative to the body should be $c/n - v/n^2$, instead of the quantity $c/n - v$ used in the predictions. This change just cancels out the first-order effects predicted. We shall return to this point later, when it will be shown that the expression $c/n + \kappa v$ for the absolute velocity is in fact, to terms of first order in v, just the sum of the velocities c/n and v when compounded in accordance with the kinematics implied by the special principle of relativity.

The experiment which finally pointed the way to the breakthrough into a new and more satisfactory theory was the celebrated one performed by Michelson and Morley in 1887. Whereas the previous experiments, involving ponderable mediums and explicable in terms of the Fresnel drag coefficient κ, were of first order in v/c, the Michelson-Morley experiment is of second order in this ratio—a very much more exacting requirement on experimental technique. The experimental arrangement, highly schematized, is illustrated in Fig. 1.2. The principle of the experiment, without going into the refinements necessary in practice, is as follows. A beam of light from a source S falls on a half-silvered mirror M, set at an angle of 45° to the beam, which breaks up the beam into two parts.   The reflected part travels down one arm of the interferometer to a mirror M_1, which reflects it back through M into a telescope T.   The transmitted portion on the other hand travels down the perpendicular arm to the mirror M_2, which reflects it back to M and thence by reflection into the telescope.   On being thus reunited, the two coherent partial beams give rise to interference fringes in the telescope.   Now any change Δt in the difference of the travel times of the two beams will give rise to a phase shift $\nu \Delta t$, where ν is the frequency of the light used, and this phase shift will be observed as a displacement of the fringes of the same amount.

In order to compute the expected fringe shift, assume for the moment that the horizontal component v of the ether wind is in the direction $M_1 M$ as indicated; then the velocity of the first beam on the trip up to M_1 is $c - v$ and on the return trip $c + v$ (for the index of refraction of air is sensibly unity).   Hence the time it takes this beam to travel up and down the arm $M M_1$, of length l, is

$$t_1 = \frac{l}{c + v} + \frac{l}{c - v} = \frac{2lc}{c^2 - v^2} = \frac{2l}{c} \left[1 + \left(\frac{v}{c} \right)^2 + \cdots \right] \quad (1.15)$$

The second beam, transmitted through M, must head slightly up the ether stream in order to reach the mirror M_2, for it is being carried downstream with velocity v; the square of the component of its velocity along the arm $M M_2$ is therefore, by the Pythagorean theorem of classical kinematics, equal to $c^2 - v^2$.   Since this also gives its velocity for the return trip $M_2 M$, the time required for the total lateral journey is

$$t_2 = \frac{2l}{(c^2 - v^2)^{1/2}} = \frac{2l}{c} \left[1 + \frac{1}{2} \left(\frac{v}{c} \right)^2 + \cdots \right] \quad (1.16)$$

which differs from t_1 in second order by the quantity lv^2/c^3.   Although we do not know which way the ether wind is blowing, it is clear that if we now rotate the whole apparatus about a vertical axis there will occur during the rotation a change Δt in the travel times of the two beams which is just equal to twice the difference $t_1 - t_2$ found above.   Hence there should appear in the telescope a fringe shift of amount

$$\Delta f = 2\nu(t_1 - t_2) \sim 2 \frac{l}{\lambda} \frac{v^2}{c^2} \quad (1.17)$$

where λ is the wavelength of the light.   Even if v were as little as 30 km/ sec, the predicted shift in this first experiment would be about 0.4 fringe; the apparatus was capable of resolving 0.01 fringe, but the largest shift observed was only 0.02.   Since the experiment was repeated at different times of the year and was completely redone later by Michelson and others without detecting shifts of anything like the magnitude expected, it is safe to conclude that the predicted effect does not exist.

To account for this failure to detect our motion through the ether, the Irish physicist FitzGerald suggested in 1892 the possibility that the longitudinal dimensions of bodies moving through the ether suffer a contraction, relative to the transverse dimensions, of magnitude

$$\frac{1}{\gamma} = \left[1 - \left(\frac{v}{c}\right)^2 \right]^{\frac{1}{2}} \tag{1.18}$$

This hypothesis was later adopted by the Dutch physicist Lorentz, who gave it a partially satisfactory justification on the basis of the electromagnetic theory of the structure of matter. Lorentz recognized that in order to carry through this explanation it was necessary to extend time in a way different from that of classical kinematics. However, Lorentz was unwilling to take the radical step of subjecting the classical principle of relativity to the alteration which a thoroughgoing acceptance of his results would entail. For him there still existed a stationary ether, but Nature had somehow frustrated our every attempt to determine our motion with respect to it—it was as though she had taken a lesson from Lewis Carroll's aged man:

> But I was thinking of a plan
> To dye one's whiskers green,
> And always use so large a fan
> That they could not be seen.

1.4   The Special Principle of Relativity

It was left to Einstein to cut the Gordian knot that tied the electromagnetic wagon to the ethereal hitching post. If it is impossible by electromagnetic means to determine one's velocity with respect to the supposed seat of electromagnetic phenomena, we again have a relativity of motion—but one which is admittedly, in view of the null result of the Michelson-Morley experiment, inconsistent with the classical principle of relativity which served so well in mechanics. Since electromagnetic theory will not yield to the classical principle, we must search out the relativity principle which it itself implies and then attempt to alter the structure of classical mechanics to conform to the new principle. In carrying out this program I choose a way which differs in detail from that taken by Einstein, but the results and their position in the scientific structure are the same.

1.4.1   *Optics.*   Let us therefore admit that there exists a relativity of motion for electromagnetic phenomena, such that it is impossible for two observers A, B in uniform motion with respect to each other to arrive by optical or other electromagnetic means at an intrinsic distinction between them. We shall again assume that their geometry is Euclidean; let their coordinates be so chosen that their origins coincide at an event from which they both reckon time and that the direction of motion of B with respect to A is along the common x and x' axis, Fig. 1.3. We adopt the FitzGerald contraction hypothesis, according to which the distance x' measured by B along the direction of relative velocity v must be corrected by multiplication by a factor k/γ before being compared with the corresponding distance $x - vt$ measured by A, whereas the transverse distances y', z' measured by B need be multiplied only by k in order to equate them with the corresponding distances y, z measured by A. The factor k can at most depend on the magnitude of the

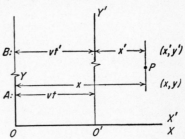

Fig. 1.3 Relations between moving observers.

velocity v and must reduce to unity for $v = 0$, for then the measurements of A and B must coincide. Altogether, then, we have

$$kx' = \gamma(x - vt) \qquad ky' = y \qquad kz' = z \qquad (1.19)$$

In accordance with the relativity principle here adopted, B must correct the measurements made by A in an exactly similar manner before comparing them with his own; the only formal difference is that A is moving in the negative direction along B's x' axis, i.e., the velocity of A with respect to B must be taken as $-v$. This makes no difference in k or γ, but the v in the first of Eqs. (1.19) must be changed in sign; the new relations are

$$kx = \gamma(x' + vt') \qquad ky = y' \qquad kz = z' \qquad (1.20)$$

We have had to allow for the possibility that the extended time t' employed by B differs from that set up by A.

It follows immediately from the transverse equations that $k^2 = 1$, and since k must be $+1$ for $v = 0$, it follows that $k = +1$ for all values of v. We also see that we have, in adopting the FitzGerald contraction hypothesis, automatically limited our kinematics to observers whose relative speed v does not exceed the speed c of light. We can now solve the first equations of the two sets for t' as a function of t and x, whence we obtain the Lorentz transformation

$$t' = \gamma\left(t - \frac{vx}{c^2}\right) \qquad x' = \gamma(x - vt) \qquad y' = y \qquad z' = z \qquad (1.21)$$

for the relation between the coordinates $x^i = (t; x, y, z)$ assigned an event E by the observer A and the coordinates $x'^i = (t'; x', y', z')$ assigned the same event by B. The inverse transformation is obtained by interchanging the two sets of coordinates and replacing v by $-v$:

$$t = \gamma\left(t' + \frac{vx'}{c^2}\right) \qquad x = \gamma(x' + vt') \qquad y = y' \qquad z = z' \quad (1.22)$$

Let us now examine the effect of this new kinematics on the world picture introduced in connection with the classical theory. There is no longer a hard-and-fast striation of the world into space and time; the time coordinate, as well as the spatial ones, change from observer to observer. The situation is depicted in Fig. 1.4. But although we have lost absolute time, we have gained a metrical structure over the whole of space-time, for there is now an absolute measure of the interval between *any* two events which is richer than the mere absolute time difference we had before. Because of the uniformity of space-time, it suffices to establish this for the interval between the (arbitrarily chosen) origin O and the event E; it follows from the Lorentz transformation (1.21) that the quantity σ defined by

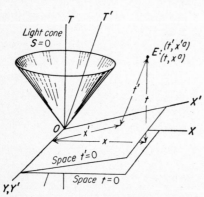

Fig. 1.4 The special relativistic world picture.

$$\sigma^2 = x^2 + y^2 + z^2 - c^2t^2 = x'^2 + y'^2 + z'^2 - c^2t'^2 \qquad (1.23)$$

is an absolute invariant, *i.e.*, it has the same numerical value computed in either set of coordinates. This quantity σ, the *space-time interval* between the events O and E, is seen to coincide with the ordinary spatial distance s between them as measured by an observer—if such exists—for which the two events are simultaneous; a little reflection shows that this is possible if and only if the event E lies outside the light cone $\sigma = 0$ of all light rays passing through the origin O.

It follows from the equation $\sigma = 0$ of the light cone with vertex at 0, whose generators are the light rays passing through 0, that the velocity of light has the same magnitude c for all observers connected by Lorentz transformations. This constancy of the velocity of light can be utilized by each observer A to extend his local time, as measured along his straight world line by means of a local clock, to any event by the method of time signals discussed in our introductory remarks; the extended time thus obtained is in fact just the time t involved in the present considerations.

It may be noted that, if the event E lies within the light cone $\sigma = 0$, the quantity σ^2 defined by Eq. (1.23) is negative; it will therefore be found convenient for such timelike intervals OE to use instead of σ the real quantity τ defined by

$$\tau^2 = t^2 - \frac{(x^2 + y^2 + z^2)}{c^2} \tag{1.24}$$

It can be shown that this τ is in fact just the *time* which a Lorentzian observer whose world line passes through O and E would measure as the duration of the timelike interval OE.

The structure of space-time thus established means that the *kinematics* employed by the Lorentzian observers in the special theory of relativity is in fact the *geometry* of the four-dimensional manifold whose metrical relations are defined by the quantity σ, or alternatively τ. We have in our treatment arrived at the space-time structure by postulating a principle of relativity between members of a privileged class of observers, the Lorentzian, whose spatial measurements are subject to the FitzGerald contraction. The same result could be obtained by following Einstein in postulating an optical relativity, expressed by linear transformations, and requiring that the velocity of light must be the same for all observers of the set. In either case the existence of a relativity principle is postulated, as the Michelson-Morley null result is not alone strong enough to lead us inductively to the Lorentz transformations and thence to the metrical structure. But since the formulation of the special theory of relativity in 1905, two further second-order optical experiments have been made, which together with the Michelson-Morley experiment just suffice to lead us to these results by pure induction. These are the experiment of Kennedy and Thorndike (1932), which is similar to the Michelson-Morley but uses an interferometer with the two arms of different lengths, and that of Ives and Stilwell (1938), which measures second-order Doppler displacements in light emitted by fast-moving particles. The first of these, together with the Michelson-Morley experiment, establishes the validity of the Lorentz equations in second order to within the factor $k(v)$, and the latter shows that $k(v) = 1$ up to and including terms of second order in v/c.

But we cannot in the time at our disposal go further into these important optical experiments, nor can we begin adequately to develop the space-time geometry to which they lead—a four-dimensional geometry which was first recognized in 1908, by the German mathematician Hermann Minkowski, as the appropriate vehicle for the special theory of relativity. I confine myself to indicating briefly those consequences of it which account for the partial success of the FitzGerald contraction and the Fresnel drag coefficient in explaining away the null results of the older optical experiments.

How, then, are we to understand the apparent contraction of a rod in motion with respect to an observer if the space-time interval between two events is the same for all Lorentzian observers? The situation is illustrated in the Minkowski diagram in Fig. 1.5, in which we have represented only time and the relevant spatial dimensions x, x'. One end of

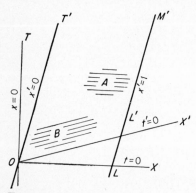

Fig. 1.5 The FitzGerald contraction.

B's measuring rod is held at his spatial origin $x' = 0$, the world line of which is therefore the t' axis OT'; the other end of the unit rod is held at $x' = 1$, and its world line is $L'M'$. The physical measuring rod, with its spatial extension and temporal duration, is here represented by the two-dimensional strip $OL'T'M'$ generated by the world lines of all its particles along $0 \leq x' \leq 1$. The spatial section OL' of this strip with B's x' axis is the rod as contemplated by B at time $t' = 0$, and its invariant interval σ as defined in Eq. (1.23) is of course unity. But the observer A striates the physical space-time rod into spatial sections parallel to his x axis; for him the rod at time $t = 0$ is represented by the intersection OL of the strip with his spatial axis OX, and it is this interval OL which he finds to have suffered the "contraction" with respect to OL'. To prove this we have only to compute the x coordinate of L, the intersection of the lines $t = 0$ and $x' = 1$; the result $x = 1/\gamma$ follows immediately from the second of the Eqs. (1.21). The two observers are simply measuring different space-time intervals.

To interpret from our present standpoint the Fresnel drag coefficient, we must examine the law of composition of velocities implied by the new kinematics. The observer B measures the velocity of a moving point $x'^a = x'^a(t')$ at the event E on it as $v'^a = dx'^a/dt'$; what velocity v^a will A assign to the point at the same event? The equation $x^a = x^a(t)$ of the world line, as seen by A, is given implicitly by Eqs. (1.22), where the x'^a are considered as functions of the parameter t'. From these we obtain

$$v^a = \frac{dx^a}{dt} = \frac{dx^a/dt'}{dt/dt'} \tag{1.25}$$

or

$$v^1 = \frac{v'^1 + v}{1 + vv'^1/c^2} \qquad v^2 = \frac{v'^2}{\gamma(1 + vv'^1/c^2)} \qquad (1.26)$$

and a similar expression for v^3. Now suppose that there is a ponderable medium, of index of refraction n, at rest in B's reference frame. Then a beam of light traveling along the x' axis will be measured by B to have a velocity $v'^1 = c/n$; by the result (1.26) obtained above, its velocity with respect to A will then be

$$v^1 = \frac{c/n + v}{1 + v/cn} = \frac{c}{n} + \left(1 - \frac{1}{n^2}\right)v + \cdots \qquad (1.27)$$

to terms of first order in v. But this is just the result obtained by Fresnel with the aid of the "drag coefficient" $\kappa = 1 - 1/n^2$. Note also that if $n = 1$ we obtain the previous result that the velocity c of light *in vacuo* is the same for the two observers.

One further effect, the apparent slowing down of clocks in motion, deserves mention, as it has been quite directly confirmed in recent years by observations on cosmic rays. It follows from Eq. (1.24) that the t duration, as measured by A, of an interval along B's world line of t' duration τ is given by $t = \gamma\tau$. This may be interpreted as meaning that, as viewed by A, B's clock is running slow, at the rate $1/\gamma$. This gives rise to the celebrated paradox of the traveling twin: if one of two identical twins Paul travels to a distant star and returns at speed v, he should find that during the trip he has aged but t/γ years to his twin Peter's t years. (Note that stay-at-home Peter cannot make the same claim to relative youth on the basis of the special theory of relativity, as has sometimes incorrectly been maintained, for Peter's world line represents a natural state of motion, whereas Paul's does not because of the absolute acceleration to which he has been subjected.) A direct confirmation of this effect is now to be found in the fact that laboratory experiments on μ mesons show them to have a proper half-life τ of about 2 μsec, whereas measurements on the penetrating component of cosmic rays indicate that such μ mesons travel some 4000 to 13,000 m after their formation. But these fast-moving particles could not on the average travel more than $c\tau \sim 600$ m in a t time of 2 μsec; the factor γ must in fact be greater than 10, which is consistent with the particle speeds v inferred from the energy of the particles.

1.4.2 *Mechanics.* We now begin to see a possibility for the reconciliation of classical mechanics with the new relativity principle required by optical, and other electromagnetic, phenomena. The Galilean transformation (1.14) expressing the classical principle of relativity is the limiting case of the Lorentzian transformation (1.21) of the new relativity when we allow the velocity of light c to go to infinity. Since the classical mechanics was exclusively concerned with terrestrial or celestial situations in which the relative velocities were very small compared with that of light, the velocity of light might well there be taken as infinite. Scrutiny of the new equations, especially those for the composition of velocities (1.26), brings out in strong support of this contention the fact that the discrepancy is only of the second order $(v/c)^2$, which for the earth relative to the sun is of order 10^{-8}. Clearly no great violence will be done to the achievements of classical mechanics by forcing it to conform to the new kinematics; we may then search for an *experimentum crucis*, presumably in the realm of high-speed particles, to test the revision.

We first note that in classical mechanics the independent variable is the universal time t, the only absolute measure associated with an event on the world line of a particle. But in the new mechanics, time is relative; the extension of an observer's time to the events on the world line of the particle is dependent on the state of motion of the observer. It would therefore seem appropriate to seek to replace the time t by some measure which is common to all Lorentzian observers and which coincides with the Newtonian time on allowing $c \to \infty$. The quantity τ, defined for a finite timelike interval OE by Eq. (1.24), offers such an invariant measure; in order to apply it to curvilinear world lines, we must, however, break it up into the differential elements

$$d\tau^2 = dt^2 - \frac{(dx^2 + dy^2 + dz^2)}{c^2} \qquad (1.28)$$

associated with pairs x^i, $x^i + dx^i$ of neighboring events along the world line. We may then define the *proper time* τ of an event on the world line as the integral of this $d\tau$ along the world line from some arbitrary origin on it. The velocity $v^a = dx^a/dt$ of the classical theory may then be replaced by the rate of change $u^a = dx^a/d\tau$; but since in the new theory the time $t = x^0$ appears as a noninvariant coordinate in parallel with the spatial coordinates x^a, it would seem appropriate to supplement the spatial components u^a, where $a = 1, 2, 3$, with the time component u^0. This vector velocity u^i, where $i = 0, 1, 2, 3$, is the four-dimensional analogue of direction cosines in ordinary space and, like them, is subject to a quadratic identity which expresses the fact that it is of unit length:

$$(u^0)^2 - \sum_a \frac{(u^a)^2}{c^2} = 1 \qquad (1.29)$$

On subjecting the coordinates x^i to a Lorentzian transformation, the components of this "four-vector" u^i undergo exactly the same linear transformation as the coordinates—in contradistinction to the linear fractional transformation (1.26) suffered by the v^a.

The velocity enters into the Newtonian measure of motion of a particle, the linear momentum, on multiplication by the inertial mass of the particles. Because our new mechanics is to correspond for $c = \infty$ to the old, we are justified in here taking the mass of the particle as the ideal limit of the classical measure in situations where the relative velocities become negligible with respect to c; the mass so determined will be called the *proper mass* and be denoted by m_0. The momentum p^i is then defined as the four-vector

$$p^i = m_0 u^i = m v^i \tag{1.30}$$

where the second form is obtained from the first on defining

$$m = p^0 = m_0 \frac{dt}{d\tau} = \frac{m_0}{[1 - (v/c)^2]^{1/2}} \tag{1.31}$$

The last expression on the right is obtained from the one before it with the aid of Eq. (1.28). The fourth component p^0 of the momentum has indeed some claims to be called the mass m of the particle relative to an observer with respect to whom it is moving with velocity v; it is, however, not an intrinsic property of the particle, as m_0 is, as it depends as well on its relation to an accidental observer.

We are finally prepared to write down the analogue of Newton's second law of motion, defining force as proper rate of change of momentum:

$$F^i = \frac{d}{d\tau} (m_0 u^i) = u^0 \frac{d}{dt} (m v^i) \tag{1.32}$$

The spatial components $i = a = 1, 2, 3$ of these equations differ from the classical equations of motion, as expected, only in terms of second order in v/c. But something new has been added—the equation defining F^0. In order to interpret it, it will be convenient first to consider these equations as written down for a Lorentzian observer B who is moving instantaneously with the particle at an event E on its path. B finds that, at this event E, $u'^0 = 1$, $u'^a = 0$, and, by differentiating the quadratic condition (1.29) and substituting these values for the u'^i, that $du'^0/d\tau = 0$ at E. Hence in this proper reference system, the new component F'^0 of the force turns out to be the proper rate of change of the proper mass m_0; if, as in classical mechanics, the inertia of the particle is to remain constant, we must have $F'^0 = 0$. It can be shown, with the aid of the Lorentz transformation, that in an arbitrary inertial system this condition becomes

$$u^0 F^0 = \sum_a \frac{u^a F^a}{c^2} \tag{1.33}$$

To illustrate the meaning of the fourth of the new equations in an arbitrary reference system, we consider the case of a charged particle moving in an electromagnetic field. The classical expression (1.12) for the ponderomotive force is now to be replaced by its special relativistic generalization

$$F^a = e\left[u^0 E^a + \frac{(u \times H)^a}{c} \right] \tag{1.34}$$

The time component of the equations of motion may now, on imposing the condition (1.33) for the constancy of mass, be written in the form

$$\frac{d}{dt} mc^2 = \sum_a ev^a E^a \tag{1.35}$$

The expression on the right is the t rate at which the field is doing work on the particle, and since $mc^2 \sim m_0 c^2 + \frac{1}{2} m_0 v^2 + \cdots$, this result includes as the classical approximation the theorem that the rate of change of the kinetic energy of the particle is equal to the rate at which work is done on it. But more than that, the appearance here of $m_0 c^2$ further prepares the formal background for the possibility hinted in Eq. (1.13) that mass and energy may be interchangeable and that it is only the sum of the two, when expressed in appropriate units, that is conserved. That this is indeed the case has in the succeeding decades been only too strikingly realized by the release of nuclear binding energy in atomic bombs and, even more radically from the physical if not from the sociological point of view, in the complete conversion of matter into energy in the annihilation radiation accompanying the disappearance of an electron and a positron on collision.

The validity of the new equations of motion of matter in interaction with electromagnetic fields, including the predicted dependence of relative mass on velocity, was established within a few years of their appearance. But in these days of high-speed particle accelerators, with energies extending up into billions of electron volts, their validity is no longer a challenge to the physicist, but rather an engineering principle upon which to base sound design. The special principle of relativity has thus successfully been extended from the electromagnetic environment, in which it perforce made its appearance, to encompass the mechanical aspects as well. We may summarize it by saying that there exists a set of intrinsically indistinguishable inertial reference frames, between which the Lorentzian transformations obtain, which define the natural state of motion for the description of both electromagnetic and mechanical phenomena.

1.4.3 *Gravitation*. Throughout all this development we have had nothing to say about the theory of gravitation, which was the cornerstone of the classical mechanistic view of the world. The revolution with which we have in this chapter been concerned has in fact thrown no light on gravitational phenomena, but it behooves us for the sake of logical completeness to indicate briefly how they may be brought within the formal scheme of special relativity.

I first note that an obvious generalization of Poisson's equation (1.10), satisfying the special principle of relativity, is given by the equation

$$\nabla^2 V - \frac{1}{c^2}\frac{\partial^2 V}{\partial t^2} = 4\pi G\rho \tag{1.36}$$

for the potential $V(t, x^a)$ due to a mass distribution of density $\rho(t, x^a)$. This implies, in passing, that gravitation is propagated *in vacuo* with the velocity of light—but vouchsafes no more intimate connection between the two.

If now we require that the proper mass m_0 of a particle in this potential field remain constant, we must consider it as moving at an event E of its world line under the influence of only that component of the gradient $-\partial V/\partial x^i$ which lies in the proper space of the particle at E. On carrying out this vector resolution, in accordance with the Minkowski spacetime geometry, the spatial components of the moving force are found to be

$$F^a = -m_0\left(\frac{\partial V}{\partial x^a} + \frac{u^a}{c^2}\frac{dV}{d\tau}\right) \tag{1.37}$$

the time component F^0 is given in terms of the F^a by Eq. (1.33). The resulting equations of motion are then

$$\begin{aligned}
\frac{d^2t}{d\tau^2} &= \frac{1}{c^2}\frac{\partial V}{\partial t} - \frac{u^0}{c^2}\frac{dV}{d\tau} \\
\frac{d^2x^a}{d\tau^2} &= -\frac{\partial V}{\partial x^a} - \frac{u^a}{c^2}\frac{dV}{d\tau}
\end{aligned} \tag{1.38}$$

These rather strange-looking equations agree with the Newtonian equations of motion on neglecting terms of order $(v/c)^2$; they are just as successful in accounting for the motions of the heavenly bodies, except that the one outstanding anomaly of the classical theory—the anomalous advance of about 40 seconds of arc per century in the perihelion of Mercury—is increased by one-third.

While we have with this short excursion brought gravitation formally within the structure of special relativity, we have not thereby contributed anything to the description of the phenomena nor to an understanding of the amazing equivalence of gravitational and inertial mass. For these we must pass on to an even more radical revision of notions of space and time—that put forward by Einstein in his general theory of relativity.

1.5 The General Theory of Relativity

We remarked, in discussing classical mechanics, that the force of gravity resembles such forces as those of d'Alembert or Coriolis, in that the acceleration it imparts to a particle is independent of the mass of the particle. But only within a very restricted region of space-time can the gravitational field be approximated by one of these fictional force fields— as, for example, in an accelerated elevator. The logical position of gravitation within the special theory of relativity is not different in principle from its position in the classical mechanics; nevertheless we shall find it convenient to start with the special-theory formulation to give some indication of the kind of modification of our concepts of space and time which enabled Einstein to reduce gravitation to a kinematical force and to establish the equivalence of gravitational and inertial mass.

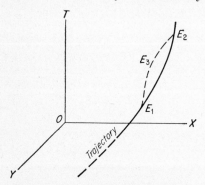

Fig. 1.6 The dynamical trajectory.

The rather revolting differential equations of motion (1.38) proposed above can be replaced by an elegant variation principle, the generalization of Hamilton's principle in classical mechanics, to which they are completely equivalent. Let us agree to call any timelike world line which satisfies these equations of motion a *trajectory*, to distinguish it from other world lines which may be drawn in our world picture, Fig. 1.6. Then it is quite easy to show that the integral

$$T = \int e^{V/c^2} \, d\tau \tag{1.39}$$

computed along a trajectory between any two events E_1, E_2 on it has a larger value than when computed along any neighboring world line $E_1E_3E_2$ between the same two events.

This geometrical principle has two consequences which are worthy of note. In the first place, if we set $V = 0$, the world lines along which T is maximal are just the straight world lines of all possible Lorentzian observers; this is a more sober reflection of the famous Peter-Paul paradox of special relativity, according to which the straight time path between two events is the longest. Secondly, if we go over to t as the integration variable in T and expand the new integrand in powers of

$1/c^2$, our principle goes over in the limit $c \to \infty$ into the Hamiltonian principle of classical mechanics, which asserts that the integral

$$-H = \int (V - \tfrac{1}{2}v^2)\, dt \qquad (1.40)$$

of the difference between the potential and kinetic energies of a particle (of unit mass) is maximal when taken over a dynamical trajectory.

Now while the Hamiltonian principle was quite useful, as well as ornamental, it did not lead to any very illuminating purely geometrical interpretation of the dynamical trajectories. The situation with respect to the new action principle (1.39) is much more encouraging; if we magnify the linear elements $d\tau$ at each event $E(x^i)$ of our world picture in the ratio e^{V/c^2}, where V is the gravitational potential of the field at E, we obtain a new space-time metric

$$dT^2 = e^{2V/c^2} \left[dt^2 - \frac{(dx^2 + dy^2 + dz^2)}{c^2} \right] \qquad (1.41)$$

whose maximal world lines are the dynamical trajectories of the gravitational field. The comparison with the Hamiltonian principle shows that the Newtonian approximation depends only on the term of first order in V in the coefficient of dt^2; the somewhat simpler metric

$$dT^2 = \left(1 + \frac{2V}{c^2} \right) dt^2 - \frac{(dx^2 + dy^2 + dz^2)}{c^2} \qquad (1.42)$$

would therefore give the same classical approximation—and would reduce the anomalous perihelion advance to some 14 seconds of arc per century.

But this is enough to show that it *is* possible to reduce the gravitational forces to kinematic ones by a change in the four-dimensional geometry of space-time and to indicate that the one outstanding anomaly of the Newtonian system may perhaps be brought into order by an appropriate choice of the second-order terms in the metric. There remain, however, the problem of the adaptation of Poisson's equation to the new geometry and the problem of the equivalence of gravitational and inertial mass.

These are the problems which are solved most elegantly by Einstein's general theory of relativity. Poisson's equation is replaced by a set of nonlinear field equations which express certain of the curvatures of the four-dimensional world in terms of the mass-energy, momentum, and stresses of its material and energetic content; thus it is the *inertial* mass which determines the metric field which replaces gravitation as an explicit force. The dynamical trajectories of an isolated particle in the field are then, as in the examples above, a maximal world line—a consequence, in fact, of the nonlinear field equations themselves, without further postulation of equations of motion. The anomaly in the motion of the perihelion of Mercury is accounted for; two other minute second-order effects, the red shift in the spectrum of light from stars and the deflection of light passing the sun, were predicted in advance of their actual observation. These three second-order effects are all obtained from Schwarzschild's solution for the field of a single massive body; the metric may in this case be taken, in the analogue of spherical polar coordinates, as

$$dT^2 = \left(1 + \frac{2V}{c^2}\right) dt^2 - \frac{(1 + 2V/c^2)^{-1}dr^2 + r^2(d\vartheta^2 + \sin^2 \vartheta \, d\phi^2)}{c^2} \quad (1.43)$$

where $V = -GM/r$ is the Newtonian potential due to a spherical mass M.

We cannot, of course, enter into the details of this theory of gravitation here, but we can indicate how it fits into the trend of thought traced in this chapter. In the first place, the metrical properties of space-time are no longer a priori or absolute; they are conditioned by its metrical content. Mach's hypothesis concerning the origin of inertia is not borne out by the theory, although it appears in modified form in the highly technical assumption that the metrical properties of the world are uniquely determined by the distribution of matter within it. The natural states of motion are the maximal curves, which are, as in all theories here dealt with except Aristotle's, determined by second-order differential equations. This means that there passes through a given event in a given direction (*i.e.*, with a given velocity) a unique natural trajectory; a particle passing through this event in this direction, but whose world line tends to depart from the natural path, suffers an absolute acceleration which, when multiplied by the inertial mass of the particle, is a measure of the external force acting on it. By a similar but more technical consideration of the relation of the world lines, described by the points of an extended body, to the natural trajectories to which they are instantaneously tangent, it is possible to determine the absolute rotation of the body. In both cases it is clear that the word *absolute* must be qualified as meaning relative to the actual world structure, with its welter of natural trajectories, which is in turn conditioned by the material content. To repeat, the gravitational influence is completely absorbed by the structure; a particle subject to no other influence has absolute acceleration zero—there is no "gravitational force."

By allowing the structure to be contingent upon the material content, we have surrendered the relativity of position and velocity which characterized all the previous theories except Aristotle's, in which velocity was absolute. The geometry in general no longer possesses a group of motions—a lack considered by the philosopher Whitehead so serious as to cause him to reject the theory. Only in special circumstances—as in the cosmological speculations to which we shall return at the end—is there any remnant of the kind of uniformity which characterized the older world pictures. There is then, in the sense in which the term was used in the classical and special theories, *no* general principle of relativity; two observers can, in general, distinguish one from the other by intrinsic observations, such as the measurement of space-time curvatures in their neighborhoods. Each observer A is free to assign space-time coordinates x^i to events E at will and express his physical observations and laws in terms of them—as, for example, his determination $g_{ij}(x)$ of the coefficients of the metric form which determines the world structure. He can from his own formulation arrive at the formulation of any other observer B, such as the coefficients $g'_{ij}(x')$ of the metric form as measured by B, once he knows the relation $x'^i = x'^i(x)$ between the coordinates assigned each event E. There is behind this possibility of translation a general principle of covariance, but it is a self-imposed methodological principle, rather than one embodying a uniformity in the data of experience. Only if it were possible, for example, for the observer B so to choose his coordinates x' that his metric coefficients $g'(x')$ were exactly the same functions of the x' as A's coefficients $g(x)$ were of his coordinates x, that is, if $g'(x') = g(x')$, would we have the possibility of a principle of relativity between them. The principle of covariance is, however, not specific to the general theory of relativity; it has only there come fully into its own as a sound methodological principle because of the absence of a special class of privileged observers, between the members of which a principle of relativity obtains and whose descriptions of the physical world are characterized by an innate simplicity. We need only point to the Lagrangian theory in classical mechanics to establish this point.

1.6 Relativistic Cosmology

As a tailpiece to our long excursion through the development of principles of relativity, we glance briefly at a development which restores some uniformity to our world picture and thus readmits some measure of relativity in the strict sense. It is remarkable that our primitive experience of Nature has been restricted to motions which are exceedingly slow in comparison with the velocity of light. Only within the past few decades have we been able to find, at great distances from us, macroscopic bodies—the extragalactic nebulae millions or hundreds of millions of light-years away—whose speeds begin to exhaust the possible range from zero to c, the velocity of light. And even here there is a significant restriction, for it appears that the bodies within any given neighborhood—such as within the great clusters of nebulae—exhibit a remarkably small dispersion of velocities. To this we may add the observation that, by and large, there is a sensible uniformity to the density of matter, provided we take our element of volume of sufficient size—perhaps a cube of a few million light-years on a side. All this suggests that, in considering the astronomically observable universe as a whole, it may be worthwhile to take as a zeroth approximation a world picture in which

> a. There is in each space-time neighborhood a preferred state of motion, which so varies from neighborhood to neighborhood that it is possible to combine the corresponding proper spaces into a smooth hypersurface
> b. The density of matter is, in the large, uniform over this common hypersurface

The first of these assumptions smacks of Aristotle's preferred states of rest, but here we have at least some justification for it in the empirical motions. The distinguished mathematician Hermann Weyl has based it on a quasi-metaphysical postulate that all matter now within our observable universe has always in the past constituted a causally related whole. The second postulate guarantees the degree and kind of spatial uniformity which implies a congruence geometry, and hence a structure of one of the classical non-Euclidean types (including Euclidean) characterized by a curvature K which is constant over the whole of space. But this curvature must, in view of the observed recession of the distant nebulae, be decreasing with time—unless, perchance, it is zero. Equivalently, the corresponding "radius of curvature" $R = K^{-\frac{1}{2}}$ must be increasing.

This world picture, which was first proposed in 1889 by the French philosopher Calinon (but without its present *raison d'être*), can readily be fitted into the general theory of relativity, as has been done by a number of investigators, beginning with the Russian mathematician Friedmann and the Belgian Lemaître. But it need not be so tied down; such a model has been set up on a priori grounds by Milne, whose "cosmological principle" is a statement of the assumption, implicit above, that the universe presents, except for local irregularities, the same aspect to all the privileged observers when viewed from corresponding events on their own world lines. Within the past few years this principle has been extended by Milne's compatriots, Bondi, Gold, and Hoyle, to assert an equivalence when viewed from any event, not merely corresponding ones; since they admit the reality of the expansion, their stationary model must allow the actual creation of matter.

The riddles presented by the expanding universe—the short time scale and the high density of matter required by the general relativistic models and the as yet unobserved elements, such as different time scales and the creation of matter, required by the alternatives—will, it is hoped, be straightened out in time by the patient method of inductive science. When this occurs, we shall have established, as the crudest of all approximations to the real world, a cosmological principle of relativity.

2
Atomic Structure

L. I. SCHIFF

PROFESSOR OF PHYSICS, STANFORD UNIVERSITY

2.1 Development of the Concept of the Atom

Our detailed knowledge of atomic structure is quite new, but the concept of the atom is very old. The Greeks Anaxagoras (500–428 B.C.) and Democritus (460–370 B.C.) and the Roman poet Lucretius (94–55 B.C.) speculated that matter consists of very small indivisible atoms that were assumed to be indestructible and uncreatable. Philosophical reasoning, which played a decisive role in the development of ancient ideas concerning natural phenomena, is now mainly of interest in improving our understanding of principles that are established in the first place by careful analysis of experimental observations. This makes all the more interesting a curious parallel between views expressed by Lucretius and by the contemporary theoretical physicist Dirac, who had a leading part in the development of modern quantum mechanics.

In arguing the need for the existence of atoms—those things which are of the least nature—Lucretius writes:[1]

Moreover, if there be not a least thing, all the tiniest bodies will be composed of infinite parts, since indeed the half of a half will always have a half, nor will anything set a limit. What difference then will there be between the sum of things and the least of things? There will be no difference; for however completely the whole sum be infinite, yet things that are tiniest will be composed of infinite parts just the same. And since true reasoning cries out against this, and denies that the mind can believe it, you must . . . confess that there are those things that consist of no parts at all and are of the least nature.

Dirac gives a similar argument for the need for a description of atoms that is different from the classical description of bulk matter:[2]

The necessity to depart from classical ideas when one wishes to account for the ultimate structure of matter may be seen, not only from experimentally estab-

[1] Corresponding numbered bibliographic references appear at the end of the chapter.

lished facts, but also from general philosophical grounds.   In a classical explanation of the constitution of matter, one would assume it to be made up of a large number of small constituent parts and one would postulate laws for the behaviour of these parts, from which the laws of the matter in bulk could be deduced.   This would not complete the explanation, however, since the question of the structure and stability of the constituent parts is left untouched.   To go into this question, it becomes necessary to postulate that each constituent part is itself made up of smaller parts, in terms of which its behaviour is to be explained.   There is clearly no end to this procedure, so that one can never arrive at the ultimate structure of matter on these lines.   So long as *big* and *small* are merely relative concepts, it is no help to explain the big in terms of the small.   It is therefore necessary to modify classical ideas in such a way as to give an absolute meaning to size.

When these two quotations are compared, it must of course be remembered that Lucretius had nothing but philosophical reasoning with which to work, whereas Dirac uses it only to supplement inferences drawn from experiment.

The first experimental evidence for the existence of atoms came from the field of chemistry.   Dalton's law of combining weights (1811) stated that elements and compounds combine to form other compounds only in definite proportions.   The simplest explanation for this observation was that there are basic units, atoms in the case of elements and molecules in the case of compounds, of which bulk matter is composed and which combine in particular ways.   The electrical nature of atoms was established about forty years later with Faraday's discovery of the laws of electrolysis.   This work showed that a definite quantity of electricity is required to electroplate out of solution an atomic weight of a monovalent element.   In other cases a small integer multiple of this amount suffices, and this multiple is usually equal to the chemical valence.

In the latter half of the nineteenth century, the development of the kinetic theory of gases, mainly by Maxwell, Clausius, and Boltzmann led to the first direct measurements of atomic dimensions—sizes and weights.   By the turn of the century, the reality of atoms was well established, and a firm basis had been laid for the experimental and theoretical researches of the last fifty years which have provided us with our present detailed knowledge of atomic structure.

2.2   Electrons

Toward the end of the nineteenth century, a number of investigations were made of the discharge of electricity through rarefied gases.   It was found that rays proceed from the negative electrode or cathode, which travel along fairly straight paths and can produce phosphorescence when they strike the glass walls of the enclosure.   These cathode rays were shown to be negatively charged particles—now called electrons—by

J. J. Thomson in 1897. Thomson's method consisted in passing the particles through an electric and a magnetic field and measuring the deflection of the paths. He was able in this way to measure the ratio of charge to mass of electrons, and he found that this ratio had the same value regardless of the material of the cathode from which they arose.

The first direct precision measurement of the charge of an electron was made by Millikan in 1909. He found that droplets of oil small enough to fall very slowly through air under the influence of gravity could be made to gain positive or negative electric charge and then be moved by an electrostatic field. Comparison of the rate of fall with and without the applied field, and knowledge of the viscosity of air, makes possible a determination of the charge on a droplet. This charge was always found to be an integer multiple of a smallest value, which is identified with the electronic charge. Negatively charged droplets have an excess and positively charged droplets a deficiency of electrons.

Just as Thomson found that all cathode rays, regardless of the source, had the same charge-to-mass ratio, so Millikan found that, regardless of the composition of the droplets or the method of charging them, the measured unit charge was always the same. Thus electrons were shown to be a universal constituent of matter. At the same time, it was realized that, because of their very small mass, the negative charge of the electrons in a neutral atom is balanced by a positive component that must contain substantially all the mass of the atom. It was then reasonable to suppose that this positive component accounted for the chemical and weight differences between various elements.

2.3   The Rutherford-Bohr Nuclear Atom Model

Thomson made an unsuccessful attempt to account for the structure of atoms by assuming that the positive charge was distributed more or less uniformly over a region of the known size of the atom (about 10^{-8} cm) and that the electrons were embedded throughout this positive charge at particular points of equilibrium. Disturbance by some external agency would then result in oscillation of the negative electrons about their equilibrium positions, with consequent radiation of electromagnetic waves. This model was, however, unable to account for some of the most obvious features of atomic spectra.

About the same time, Rutherford was investigating the behavior of α particles in their passage through matter. These particles, given off by several of the naturally radioactive elements, were identified as helium atoms that had lost two electrons and were traveling at speeds of the order of 10^9 cm/sec. In 1909 and 1910, Geiger and Marsden found that α particles incident on very thin foils of gold and platinum were occasionally deflected through angles of more than 90°, even though they would almost always pass through the foil with small deviations of the order of 1°.   In 1911, Rutherford showed that the occasional large deflections implied the existence of very large electrostatic forces between gold atoms and incident α particles, so large as to be incompatible with the Thomson model of the atom.   This led him to propose the nuclear atom model, according to which all the positive charge and nearly all the mass of the atom are concentrated in a small region at the center—the nucleus —with the surrounding electrons filling out the volume of the atom.

It is worth going through some simple numerical calculations to see how the experimental information on α-particle scattering leads directly to an upper limit on the size of the nucleus.   Suppose first that an α particle of mass M, speed v, and charge $2e$, where e is the electronic charge, is to be scattered by a Thomson atom of diameter 10^{-8} cm.   It was already known that the number of electrons Z in a neutral atom, according to which the magnitude of the atomic positive charge is equal to Ze, is of the order of, and somewhat smaller than, the atomic weight. Since these electrons are distributed throughout the atom, their average distance apart is roughly $10^{-8}/Z^{1/3}$ cm.   Now the large deflections of the α particles must be due to the positive charge, since the electrons have too small mass.   The largest volume of unneutralized positive charge has magnitude about e and linear dimensions R approximately equal to $10^{-8}/Z^{1/3}$ cm.   This can exert a force $2e^2/R^2$ on the α particle, for a time of the order of $10^{-8}/v$ sec, and so transfer an amount of momentum to the α particle roughly equal to the product of this force and time.   The angle of scattering in radians is then approximately equal to the ratio of this momentum transfer to the original momentum Mv of the α particle. We thus conclude that the angle of scattering on collision with a single Thomson atom has the order of magnitude

$$\vartheta_1 \cong \frac{2e^2 Z^{2/3}}{10^{-16}} \frac{10^{-8}/v}{Mv} \qquad \text{radians}$$

If we insert the values $e = 4.8 \times 10^{-10}$ esu, $Z = 79$ for gold (a slightly higher value might have been assumed at that time), $v = 10^9$ cm/sec, and $M = 6.6 \times 10^{-24}$ g, we find that $\vartheta_1 \cong 1.3 \times 10^{-4}$ radian or 0.007°. Now in a gold foil 5×10^{-5} cm thick such as was used in the Geiger and Marsden experiments, there are about 3×10^{18} atoms per cm² of foil.   These atoms have a diameter of 10^{-8} cm, so that on the average an α particle will collide with 230 gold atoms as it traverses the foil. Each collision produces a deflection of order ϑ_1, and since these deflections are random as to orientation about the original direction of motion of the α particle, elementary probability theory shows that the result of n collisions is to produce an average deflection $\vartheta_1 n^{1/2}$.   Thus the average deflection, according to the Thomson model, should be about 0.01°. A more complete calculation shows that the probability of a deflection greater than 90° is many orders of magnitude smaller than observed.

If on the other hand we assume with Rutherford that there is a very small, massive, positively charged nucleus, then the strength of the electrostatic field available to deflect the α particle is limited only by its closeness of approach to the nucleus. The α particle is then a helium nucleus, and hence also very small. A deflection of the order of 90° requires a momentum transfer to the α particle of order Mv and therefore a distance of closest approach R such that the product of the force

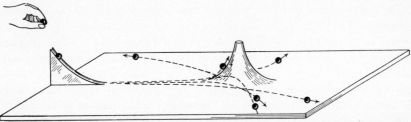

Fig. 2.1 Mechanical model of an atomic nucleus, for demonstrating Rutherford scattering. The balls represent α particles, whose kinetic energy is proportional to the height from which they are released on the incline. The rise represents the repulsive potential energy of the nucleus, which turns the balls away and causes them to be scattered through large angles for nearly direct hits. (*Reprinted from "Classical and Modern Physics" by H. E. White, copyright* 1940, *D. Van Nostrand Company, Inc.*)

$2Ze^2/R^2$ and the time R/v is equal to Mv. This gives for R the expression $R \cong 2Ze^2/Mv^2$, which with the above numerical values is equal to 5.5×10^{-12} cm. This means that the nucleus cannot be much larger than 10^{-12} cm in radius. The probability of such a large deflection can now be estimated by multiplying the area of a circle of radius R by the number of gold atoms per cm^2 of foil; the result is 0.0003. Thus about one α particle in 3000 would be expected to be deflected through an angle greater than about 90°; this crude estimate is in excellent qualitative agreement with the experimental observations.

The mathematical development of Rutherford's theory of α-particle scattering not only gave results in quantitative agreement with the experiments of Geiger and Marsden, but enabled the latter to determine the magnitude of the nuclear charge. In all cases where a comparison was possible, this number Z, now called the atomic number, was equal to the number of electrons in the neutral atom, which was measured by Barkla from the absorption of X rays. While this agreement added greatly to the plausibility of the nuclear atom model, there were still difficulties with the arrangement of the electrons around the nucleus. It is easily seen that there is no stable equilibrium if the electrons are at rest.   This is obvious in hydrogen (one electron); in helium (two electrons) the only arrangement with any symmetry is that in which the electrons are equidistant from the nucleus and on opposite sides, and in this case the repulsive force between electrons is only one-eighth of the attractive force between the nucleus and each electron.   In the general case, the proof is the same as that of Earnshaw's theorem in electrostatics. On the other hand, if the electrons move in stable orbits around the nucleus, so that the electrostatic force of attraction to the nucleus is balanced by the centrifugal force, the electrons are continually accelerated. Now it is well known that accelerated charges radiate electromagnetic waves; the continuous loss of energy by radiation would then cause the electrons to spiral into the nucleus and destroy the atom as originally constituted.

Before going further with the nuclear-atom model, we go back a decade to 1900, when Planck postulated the existence of discrete units of radiant energy—light quanta—in order to explain the experimental observations on the spectral energy distribution of radiation from a hot black body. It had been known from classical thermodynamics how to show that the total energy emitted per unit area must be proportional to the fourth power of the absolute temperature (Stefan-Boltzmann law), in agreement with experiment.   And classical theory had also shown that the emitted energy in the wavelength interval $d\lambda$ must be of the form $E\lambda \, d\lambda = \lambda^{-5} f(\lambda T) \, d\lambda$, where T is the absolute temperature and f is a definite function that depends only on the product of λ and T.   This relation (a consequence of Wien's displacement law) was also in agreement with experiment, but all attempts to calculate the form of the function f—which was known from experiment—failed.   Planck assumed that electromagnetic energy of frequency ν or wavelength $\lambda = c/\nu$, where c is the speed of light, could be emitted or absorbed only in amounts that were integer multiples of $h\nu$, where h is a constant that has the same value for all frequencies.   He was then able to calculate the function f and its dependence on h, now called Planck's constant, and show that this function agrees both in shape and magnitude with the experimental results if h is chosen to have a particular value.

This quantum hypothesis was soon put to work by Einstein to help explain, first, the photoelectric effect (1905) and, then, the specific heats of solids (1907).   In the photoelectric effect, Einstein assumed that an electromagnetic wave of frequency ν incident on a metal surface could only be absorbed by the electrons of the metal in units of energy $h\nu$; it was found that this explained the dependence of the energy of the emitted photoelectrons on the frequency of the incident light.   In similar fashion, he showed that the dependence of the specific heats of many solids on temperature could be understood to good approximation if it was assumed that an atom of the solid with natural frequency of vibration ν could only have energies of vibration that were integer multiples of $h\nu$. These two successes greatly strengthened the confidence of physicists in Planck's quantum hypothesis.

Quite independently of the development of the quantum idea, a great deal of work had been done on the classification of the spectral lines emitted by atoms. In the last decade of the nineteenth century, Rydberg showed that the values of $1/\lambda$ for many different lines of an atom could be expressed as the differences between pairs of term values. The same term value might be related to several different lines, so that a complicated spectrum of many lines could be specified by a relatively small number of term values. He suggested that lines, as yet unobserved, might be found that would correspond to new combinations of known term values. Such lines were actually discovered later by Ritz (1908) and provide examples of what is now known as the Ritz combination principle.

This, then, was the situation in 1911. On the one hand, Rutherford had demonstrated the existence of the atomic nucleus, but the behavior of the atomic electrons was not understood. On the other hand, Planck and Einstein had shown that light of frequency ν is emitted and absorbed in energy units equal to $h\nu$, and Rydberg and Ritz had discovered the relationship between term values and spectral lines when expressed as reciprocal wavelengths or, what is the same except for the multiplying constant c, when expressed as frequencies. The next, and decisive, steps were taken by Bohr in 1913. First, he redefined the term values to be energy states or levels of the atom, by multiplying by hc the term value expressed as a reciprocal wavelength. The emission of a light quantum is then assumed to correspond to the transition of an atom from a higher to a lower energy level, and the energy lost by the atom is carried off by the quantum. In this way the quantum hypothesis is made consistent with the combination principle. Second, he modified the quantum hypothesis so as to provide a rule for the calculation of the energy levels of the simplest atom, hydrogen.

We now obtain Bohr's rule as a special case of a more general statement of the quantum hypothesis, which was derived later by Wilson (1915) and by Sommerfeld (1916). Suppose that we apply Planck's form of the quantum hypothesis to a particle of mass m that is attracted to a point of equilibrium by a force that is equal to K times its distance from this point. If pulled aside a distance A and released from rest, it will oscillate harmonically along a straight line with amplitude A and frequency $\nu = (1/2\pi)(K/m)^{\frac{1}{2}}$. But the amplitude can only have values such that the energy of oscillation is an integer multiple of $h\nu$. This condition can be rewritten in a different form. Suppose that at any time t the distance x from equilibrium can be written as $x = A \sin 2\pi\nu t$;

the momentum at that time is

$$p = m \frac{dx}{dt} = 2\pi\nu A \cos 2\pi\nu t = 2\pi\nu m (A^2 - x^2)^{1/2}$$

Then the relation between p and x can be expressed as

$$\left(\frac{p}{2\pi\nu m A}\right)^2 + \left(\frac{x}{A}\right)^2 = 1$$

This is the equation of an ellipse in the px plane with semiaxis $2\pi\nu m A$ along the p direction and semiaxis A along the x direction. The area of this ellipse is π times the product of the semiaxes, or $2\pi^2\nu m A^2$. Now the total energy of the oscillating particle is the initial potential energy $\frac{1}{2}KA^2 = 2\pi^2\nu^2 m A^2$, or ν times the area of the ellipse. Thus one way of making the energy an integer multiple of $h\nu$ is to require that the area of the ellipse be an integer multiple of h.

The substitution of the quantum condition on the area of the ellipse for the quantum condition on the energy of the oscillator seems at first to be unnecessarily complicated and devious. However, apart from the fact that the application of the new quantum condition to the hydrogen atom gives the experimentally observed energy levels, as we shall see, it possesses an important formal advantage. The area of the ellipse associated with the harmonic oscillator is equal to the integral of the momentum with respect to the coordinate for a complete cycle of the motion. This is readily generalized to systems with more than one degree of freedom, since the coordinates and their associated momenta are the variables employed in Hamilton's formulation of mechanics, which is widely used. When expressed in this way, the Bohr-Wilson-Sommerfeld quantum condition is applied to each degree of freedom of the system by requiring that the integral of each momentum (in the Hamiltonian sense) with respect to its coordinate over a cycle of the motion is equal to an integer multiple of h.

The application to the hydrogen atom can now be made. We assume that the electron of mass m moves with speed v in a circular orbit of radius a about a very massive nucleus of charge e. Then the electrostatic and centrifugal forces are in equilibrium if $e^2/a^2 = mv^2/a$. The coordinate for this orbit is the angular variable ϕ, which varies from 0 to 2π for a complete cycle of the motion. The Hamiltonian momentum associated with ϕ is the angular momentum $J = mva$. The quantum condition is then that $\int_0^{2\pi} J \, d\phi = nh$, where n is an integer; this yields $2\pi mva = nh$. The total energy of the electron is the sum of its kinetic energy and its (negative) electrostatic potential energy:

$$E = \frac{1}{2} mv^2 - \frac{e^2}{a}$$

Elimination of v between these three equations enables us to solve for E and a; the result is

$$E = -\frac{2\pi^2me^4}{n^2h^2} \qquad a = \frac{n^2h^2}{4\pi^2me^2}$$

The values of E given by this formula agree very well with the term values obtained from the observed spectrum of hydrogen. Moreover, the atomic size given by the formula for a with small values of n (about 10^{-8} cm) is also in agreement with experiment.

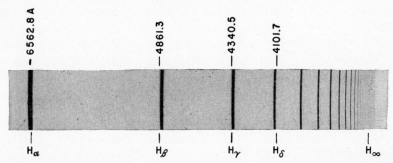

Fig. 2.2 The Balmer series of hydrogen. The frequencies of these spectral lines are proportional to the differences between the energy level with $n = 2$ and the energy levels with larger values of n. (*Reprinted from "Atomic Spectra and Atomic Structure" by Gerhard Herzberg, published by Dover Publications, Inc.*)

The difficulty arising from the continuous loss of energy of electrons moving in stable orbits, due to radiation, still remains in the background of the foregoing discussion. Bohr resolved this by simply assuming that the electrons do not radiate when they are in such energy levels (often called stationary states). The classical laws of radiation are assumed to be inapplicable to an electron in a stationary state. On the other hand, the transition from one such state to another is accompanied by the emission of a quantum of radiation that has an energy equal to the difference between the two energy levels and a frequency equal to this energy divided by h. It was generally realized that this was an unsatisfactory state in which to leave the theory, but substantial improvement did not come until the late 1920's, after the development of quantum mechanics. The quantum theory of radiation is now in a reasonably satisfactory state but is sufficiently recondite so that no attempt will be made to discuss it in this book.

2.4 Atomic Number and Atomic Weight; Isotopes

Shortly after Dalton proposed his law of combining weights, Prout suggested in 1815 that all atoms are made up of hydrogen atoms as an elementary substance. This hypothesis was based on the nearly integral values of the atomic weights then known.   Later work showed, however, that there are substances that do not have integer atomic weights, notably chlorine with atomic weight 35.5; this led to the abandonment of Prout's hypothesis.

In the 1890's, when cathode rays were being investigated, Goldstein and Wien discovered a new kind of ray which traveled in straight lines down the discharge tube in the opposite direction to the cathode rays. If a hole or canal was made in the cathode, these new rays could be made to pass through and appear by themselves on the far side.   They were first called canal rays, and later positive rays when it was found that they had a positive charge.   Thomson started investigating these rays in 1911, using methods similar to those he had used earlier with electrons. He was able to show that the positive rays are partially ionized atoms— atoms that have lost one or more of their electrons—and to measure their weight.   In 1912, he found that there are two kinds of neon atoms, of atomic weights 20 and 22, comprising 90 per cent and 10 per cent, respectively, of normal neon.   This makes the average atomic weight of neon about 20.2, in good agreement with the chemically measured value.

This discovery not only led to a revival of Prout's hypothesis, but showed that it is not the mass of an atom that determines its chemical properties, since the two kinds of neon are chemically identical.   In 1871, Mendelyeev had arranged the elements then known into a periodic table in accordance with their chemical properties.   It was now suggested on the basis of Rutherford's and Barkla's work that the ordinal number of an element in the periodic table should be identified with the number of electrons in the neutral atom, which is equal to the nuclear charge; this is now called the atomic number.   The validity of this suggestion was definitely established by Moseley in 1914 from a study of the frequencies of X-ray lines.   We would expect Bohr's formula for the energy levels of hydrogen to apply to the energies of the innermost electrons in a heavier element if the nuclear charge is made Ze instead of e, that is, if the Bohr formula is multiplied by Z^2.   Then the quantum energy, or frequency, of a particular kind of X-ray line arising from the transition of an inner electron should be proportional to Z^2 as one element is compared with another.   Moseley showed that this is almost always the case if Z is identified with the ordinal number in the periodic table.   The few exceptional cases were ultimately shown to agree with what is now called Moseley's law.

This work completed the present-day picture of atoms as consisting of nuclei of integer mass number A and integer charge number or atomic number Z surrounded by Z electrons (if the atoms are not ionized).   The chemical properties are determined by Z, and atoms with the same Z and different A are called *isotopes* of each other.   The actual mass of an isotope is not exactly equal to the integer A (when the units are chosen so that oxygen has mass 16) but is very close to it. The chemical atomic weight, which may be far from an integer, is the average value of the isotopic weights of that atom, weighted in accordance with their relative abundances.

While the atomic number is far more important in determining the chemical properties of an element than the atomic weight, the two numbers are of comparable importance in determining the nuclear properties. It is now known, for example, that radioactive isotopes of nearly all elements can be produced; they have the same Z as the stable isotopes of these elements that are found in nature but different A.

2.5 Protons and Neutrons

The lightest nucleus is that of the abundant isotope of hydrogen, with Z and A both equal to unity. It is believed to be an elementary particle in the same sense that the electron is and is called the proton. So long as these were the only two elementary particles known, it was natural to attempt a theory of nuclear structure in which protons and electrons were the basic constituents. While there was some evidence to support this view, notably the emission of β particles (fast electrons) from certain radioactive nuclei, there were also serious difficulties. Since these will be described in Chap. 6, there will be no further discussion here except for the remark that the difficulties were mainly related to the existence of electrons within nuclei.

The discovery of the neutron by Chadwick in 1932 made available another basic constituent for a theory of nuclear structure. The neutron has no electric charge and a mass only slightly greater than that of the proton. Thus, instead of assuming that a nucleus of charge number Z and mass number A is composed of A protons and $A - Z$ electrons, one could assume that it is composed of Z protons and $A - Z$ neutrons. There are, of course, other possible combinations if all three particles can exist within nuclei. However, the discovery of the neutron made it possible to dispense with electrons within nuclei, and the resulting proton-neutron model of nuclear structure has proved quite satisfactory.

2.6 The Exclusion Principle and the Periodic Table

The periodic table was discovered by Mendelyeev from an empirical study of the chemical properties of the elements. In its present form, the table shows elements of similar chemical properties in the same column and elements with consecutive values of Z in the same row. The periodic return to similar chemical properties as Z increases is well illustrated by the noble gases, the alkali metals, and the halogens. The noble gases have atomic numbers as follows: helium (2), neon (10), argon (18), krypton (36), xenon (54), radon (86). Each of them is immediately followed by an alkali metal and immediately preceded (except for helium) by a halogen. The chemical inertness of the noble gases suggests that 2, 10, 18, 36, 54, and 86 electrons form particularly stable structures, *i.e.*, electrons cannot then be easily shared with other atoms to form molecules. The great chemical activity of the alkali metals and the halogens confirms this picture, since the former have, outside the stable noble-gas structure, an extra electron that can easily be given up, and the latter can advantageously accept an electron in order to form the stable structure. These stable structures or closed shells of electrons lie in successive layers around the nucleus, the first containing 2 electrons, the second $10 - 2 = 8$ electrons, the third $18 - 10 = 8$ electrons, and the others 18, 18, and 32 electrons.

In order to understand this sequence of closed shells—2, 8, 8, 18, 18, 32—and ultimately the finer details of the periodic table, it is necessary to know, concerning the possible orbits for electrons around the nucleus, more than was developed in connection with Bohr's theory of the hydrogen atom. At that point, we quantized the angular motion of the electron in its orbit and introduced the quantum number n, which could take on the values 1, 2, 3, . . ., ∞. A similar quantization can be made for the radial motion, and results in the introduction of an additional quantum number. When both quantizations are made, it is convenient to define a new angular quantum number l, a radial quantum number n', and a total quantum number $n = n' + l + 1$. n' and l must be positive integers or zero (and hence cannot exceed $n - 1$), and as before n must be a positive integer.

For the motion of an electron in the Coulomb field of a bare nucleus, the energy levels are given by Bohr's formula and depend only on the total quantum number n, not on the separate values of n' and l. But if the field is that of an atom, not a bare nucleus, all except the innermost electrons will have other electrons between it and the nucleus, which will partially screen the nuclear field. This has two important effects on the energy levels. First, it makes the effective value of the nuclear charge smaller than the true value, by an amount that depends on how far out from the nucleus the orbit of a particular electron lies. For the innermost electrons the effective nuclear charge is close to Z, and for the outermost electrons it is close to unity. Second, it makes the energy level depend somewhat on l, as well as on n. The orbits with large l have relatively large values of angular momentum, which means that the electron moves roughly perpendicular to its radius vector from the nucleus, or in a nearly circular orbit. The orbits with small l, on the other hand, move more nearly back and forth along a radius, or in a very eccentric elliptical orbit. This means that electrons with small l spend more time

Table 2.1 The Periodic Table of the Elements. The chemical symbol and the atomic number are above the name, and the approximate atomic weight is below. Elements in the same column have similar chemical properties. The rare earths (atomic numbers 58 through 71) and the heaviest elements (atomic numbers greater than 90) do not fit into the sequence defined by the chemical properties and are listed below.

I	II	III	IV	V	VI	VII	VIII	O
H 1 Hydrogen 1.0078								He 2 Helium 4.003
Li 3 Lithium 6.940	Be 4 Beryllium 9.02	B 5 Boron 10.82	C 6 Carbon 12.00	N 7 Nitrogen 14.008	O 8 Oxygen 16.000	F 9 Fluorine 19.00		Ne 10 Neon 20.18
Na 11 Sodium 22.99	Mg 12 Magnesium 24.32	Al 13 Aluminum 26.97	Si 14 Silicon 28.06	P 15 Phosphorus 31.0	S 16 Sulfur 32.06	Cl 17 Chlorine 35.46		A 18 Argon 39.94
K 19 Potassium 39.10	Ca 20 Calcium 40.08	Sc 21 Scandium 45.10	Ti 22 Titanium 47.90	V 23 Vanadium 50.95	Cr 24 Chromium 52.01	Mn 25 Manganese 54.93	Fe 26 Iron 55.85 / Co 27 Cobalt 58.94 / Ni 28 Nickel 58.69	
Cu 29 Copper 63.57	Zn 30 Zinc 65.38	Ga 31 Gallium 69.72	Ge 32 Germanium 72.60	As 33 Arsenic 74.91	Se 34 Selenium 78.96	Br 35 Bromine 79.92		Kr 36 Krypton 83.7
Rb 37 Rubidium 85.48	Sr 38 Strontium 87.63	Y 39 Yttrium 88.92	Zr 40 Zirconium 91.22	Nb 41 Niobium 92.91	Mo 42 Molybdenum 95.95	Tc 43 Technetium	Ru 44 Ruthenium 101.7 / Rh 45 Rhodium 102.9 / Pd 46 Palladium 106.7	
Ag 47 Silver 107.88	Cd 48 Cadmium 112.41	In 49 Indium 114.76	Sn 50 Tin 118.70	Sb 51 Antimony 121.76	Te 52 Tellurium 127.61	I 53 Iodine 126.92		Xe 54 Xenon 131.3
Cs 55 Cesium 132.91	Ba 56 Barium 137.36	La 57 Lanthanum 138.92	Hf 72 Hafnium 178.6	Ta 73 Tantalum 180.88	W 74 Tungsten 183.92	Re 75 Rhenium 186.31	Os 76 Osmium 190.2 / Ir 77 Iridium 193.1 / Pt 78 Platinum 195.2	
Au 79 Gold 197.2	Hg 80 Mercury 200.61	Tl 81 Thallium 204.39	Pb 82 Lead 207.21	Bi 83 Bismuth 209.0	Po 84 Polonium 210	At 85 Astatine		Rn 86 Radon 222
Fr 87 Francium 223	Ra 88 Radium 226.0	Ac 89 Actinium 227.0	Th 90 Thorium 232.12					

Rare earths	Ce 58 Cerium 140.13	Pr 59 Praseodymium 140.92	Nd 60 Neodymium 144.27	Pm 61 Promethium	Sm 62 Samarium 150.43	Eu 63 Europium 152.0	Gd 64 Gadolinium 156.9	Tb 65 Terbium 159.2	Dy 66 Dysprosium 162.46	Ho 67 Holmium 164.94	Er 68 Erbium 167.20	Tm 69 Thulium 169.4	Yb 70 Ytterbium 173.0	Lu 71 Lutecium 175.0
Heaviest elements	Pa 91 Protactinium	U 92 Uranium 238.07	Np 93 Neptunium	Pu 94 Plutonium	Am 95 Americium	Cm 96 Curium	Bk 97 Berkelium	Cf 98 Californium	— 99	— 100				

close to the nucleus than those with large l and hence are screened less by the inner electrons and have larger effective Z values. This increases the magnitude of their negative electrostatic energy and makes their energy levels lower than those of electrons which have the same n and larger l.

We now ask how many orbits are possible that have a given pair of values for n and l. The answer can be obtained from a study of the *Zeeman effect*—the effect of a weak magnetic field on the spectrum of an atom. Two important conclusions emerge from this study. First, an orbit with quantum numbers n and l can be oriented in space in $2l + 1$ different ways. This means that a third quantum number must be introduced to specify the orbit; this is called m_l, and it can take on all integer values (positive, negative, and zero) ranging from $-l$ to $+l$. Just as the quantum number l provides a measure of the orbital angular momentum of an electron, the quantum number m_l provides a measure of the component of this angular momentum vector along some fixed axis in space, which is usually taken to be the direction of the magnetic field if there is one present. It may seem strange at first that the orientation of the orbit should be restricted in this way, but it is no stranger than restricting the magnitude of the orbital angular momentum by the quantum number l.

The second conclusion, discovered by Uhlenbeck and Goudsmit in 1925 from study of the Zeeman effect, is that a fourth quantum number is required. This quantum number m_s is associated with the electron spin angular momentum in the same way that m_l is associated with l. The quantum number l implies an orbital angular momentum equal to $lh/2\pi$ (this is analogous to the result for the circular orbits in hydrogen, obtained earlier, which made the orbital angular momentum mva equal to $nh/2\pi$). The spin angular momentum is found to be $s = \frac{1}{2}$, in units of $h/2\pi$, permitting $2s + 1 = 2$ values for m_s; these values are $+\frac{1}{2}$ and $-\frac{1}{2}$.

An electron state may now be specified uniquely by four quantum numbers: n, l, m_l, m_s. The energy increases as n increases, and for given n it increases as l increases; the energy is independent of m_l and m_s in the absence of a magnetic field. For $n = 1$, l can only be zero; there is then one orientation of the orbit, two orientations of the electron spin, and hence two possible states altogether. For $n = 2$, l can be zero or 1; with $l = 1$ there are three orientations of the orbit, and for each of these there are again two orientations of the spin. Thus with $l = 1$ there are six possible states, and with $l = 0$ there are two possible states as before. In general, l can vary from 0 to $n - 1$, and for each value of l there are $2(2l + 1)$ possible states.

If now we look at the sequence of closed shells 2, 8, 8, 18, 18, 32, we see that the number 2 is the number of possible states for $n = 1$, 8 is

Table 2.2   The Electron Configurations of the Elements.*   An atom contains all the filled shells that occur above and to the left of its position in the table. The rare earths ($Z = 58$ through 71) occur when the $4f$ shell is being filled, and the heaviest elements ($Z > 90$) are believed to occur when the $5f$ shell is being filled; both groups are omitted from the table.

	s	s^2	p	p^2	p^3	p^4	p^5	p^6	d	d^2	d^3	d^4	d^5	d^6	d^7	d^8	d^9	d^{10}
$1s$	H 1	He 2																
$2s$	Li 3	Be 4																
$2p$			B 5	C 6	N 7	O 8	F 9	Ne 10										
$3s$	Na 11	Mg 12																
$3p$			Al 13	Si 14	P 15	S 16	Cl 17	A 18										
$4s, 3d$ — $4s^0$																		
$4s$	K 19	Ca 20											Cr 24					Cu 29
$4s^2$									Sc 21	Ti 22	V 23		Mn 25	Fe 26	Co 27	Ni 28		Zn 30
$4p$			Ga 31	Ge 32	As 33	Se 34	Br 35	Kr 36										
$5s, 4d$ — $5s^0$																		Pd 46
$5s$	Rb 37	Sr 38									Cb 41	Mo 42	Tc 43	Ru 44	Rh 45			Ag 47
$5s^2$									Y 39	Zr 40								Cd 48
$5p$			In 49	Sn 50	Sb 51	Te 52	I 53	Xe 54										
$6s, 4f, 5d$ — $6s^0$																	Ir 77	
$6s$	Cs 55	Ba 56															Pt 78	Au 79
$6s^2$									La 57	Hf 72	Ta 73	W 74	Re 75	Os 76				Hg 80
$6p$			Tl 81	Pb 82	Bi 83	Po 84	At 85	Rn 86										
$7s, 5f, 6d$ — $7s^0$																		
$7s$	Fa 87	Ra 88																
$7s^2$									Ac 89	Th 90								

* E. U. Condon and G. H. Shortley, "The Theory of Atomic Spectra," p. 333, Cambridge University Press, London, 1935.

the number of possible states for $n = 2$, 18 is the number for $n = 3$, and 32 is the number for $n = 4$. This suggests that, when each state of a given n is occupied by an electron, a stable closed shell is formed. To make this plausible, we assume that it is not possible to put more than one electron in a particular state. This is a statement of the exclusion principle, discovered by Pauli in 1925 from a study of atomic spectra at about the same time that the extra quantum number of the electron was identified with its spin.

We can now see why the closed shells appear in the observed order. We adopt current spectroscopic notation and denote an electron shell by a number and a letter, such as $3d$. The number is the value of n, and the letter represents the value of l according to the following code: $0 = s$, $1 = p$, $2 = d$, $3 = f$, $4 = g$. (This code is a relic of the early classification of spectral series, when s, p, and d stood for sharp, principal, and diffuse, respectively, as terms descriptive of the appearance of the lines of a series.) The lowest shell is $1s$, which can accept two electrons, and is filled at helium. The next shells are $2s$ and $2p$, which together can accept eight electrons, and are filled (along with the $1s$ shell) at neon. The next shells are $3s$, $3p$, and $3d$. Here, we must consider the $3d$ shell along with the $4s$ shell; it turns out that the increase in energy due to the increase in n from 3 to 4 is more than compensated by the decrease in energy due to the decrease in l from 2 to 0. Thus the $3d$ shell has a higher energy than the $4s$ shell, and the filling of the $3s$ and $3p$ shells by themselves produces a stable configuration with eight more electrons at argon. The next shells are $4s$, $3d$, and $4p$; $4d$, $5s$, etc., have significantly higher energies. These can accept 18 electrons, which brings us to krypton. This pattern is repeated with the $5s$, $4d$, and $5p$ shells, which add 18 more electrons and bring us to xenon. Finally, the $6s$, $4f$, and $5d$ shells have comparable energies, again because of the competition between increasing n and decreasing l; the filling of these shells along with the $6p$ shell requires 32 additional electrons, which gives radon.

The exclusion principle has other consequences, apart from the periodic table. It is basic to an understanding of the electrical and cohesive properties of solids, to the theory of ferromagnetism, and to the theory of molecular binding. Since it turns out that protons and neutrons, as well as electrons, obey the exclusion principle, it is also of decisive importance in nuclear structure.

2.7 Atomic Spectra; the Vector Model

The characteristics of atomic spectra, like the chemical properties of atoms, can be closely related to the periodic table. The reason is the same: both derive primarily from the states of the outermost or valence electrons, and the same l shells recur more or less periodically as Z increases. It is true that the n value of the valence electrons increases throughout the periodic table, but it has much less effect on the behavior of the valence electrons than does the l value.

To go further, it is necessary to make some simplifying approximation that will make it possible to deal with complex atoms that contain many electrons. We assume that each electron moves in a spherically symmetric electrostatic potential that is the resultant of the nuclear potential and the potentials due to all the other electrons. The repulsion between any pair of electrons is only about $1/Z$ as large as the attraction between an electron and the nucleus, so that the fluctuations in the force on any one electron due to occasional close encounters with the other electrons are relatively small if Z is large. We therefore average over the positions of the other electrons to obtain a spherically symmetric potential and start from what is called the central-field approximation. A state characterized by n, l, m_l, and m_s is defined for each electron, with the exclusion principle requiring that there be no more than one electron in each state.

The electrons that are in closed shells can be ignored for most purposes, since they do not change their states in ordinary optical transitions. Further, since states with given n and l and all possible orientations of the orbital and spin angular momenta are filled, the resultant angular momentum of the closed-shell electrons is zero. The reason this last point is important is that the way in which the angular momenta of the valence electrons (those which lie outside the closed shells) are coupled together determines the structure of the spectrum, and any group of electrons (such as those in closed shells) that has zero resultant angular momentum will not be coupled to the valence electrons and hence need not be considered.

The principal reason that the angular momenta of the valence electrons are coupled to each other is that the central-field approximation does not exactly represent the electrostatic interaction between electrons, since it is averaged over their positions. The residual interaction perturbs the orbits of the electrons and makes the orientation of the angular-momentum vector of one electron dependent on that of the others, of course with limitations imposed by the exclusion principle. It turns out that this effect can be represented to good approximation by assigning a resultant orbital angular-momentum quantum number L and a resultant spin angular-momentum quantum number S to the group of valence electrons. This does not quite complete the picture, since there is a relatively weak interaction between the orbital and spin angular momenta of each electron, which now shows up as a dependence of the energy of the atom on the total angular-momentum quantum number J, which is the resultant of L and S. The term *vector model* is used to describe the orientations of these angular-momentum vectors in various cases. The coupling just described applies to what is called the Russell-Saunders case, discovered in 1925; it is also referred to as the LS coupling scheme. It is very useful in dealing with the valence-electron spectra of complex atoms.

It was recognized shortly after the establishment of the combination principle that not all transitions between atomic energy levels actually occur. Those which occur with high probability (allowed transitions) can be codified by means of what are called *selection rules*. The most important selection rule in the Russell-Saunders case is that all the following occur in a transition: (1) only one electron changes its state, and it changes so that l increases or decreases by one unit; (2) L changes by not more than one unit (*i.e.*, it may remain unchanged or increase or decrease by one unit); (3) S does not change; and (4) J changes by not more than one unit, except that if J is initially zero its final value must be unity. When all these conditions are satisfied, the atom can emit electric dipole radiation; the most intense spectral lines are of this type. The selection rules, which were first derived empirically from a study of observed spectra, can now be fully justified by means of quantum mechanics.

2.8   Failures of the Old Quantum Theory

Most of what has been described thus far is now called the old quantum theory. It began in 1900 with Planck and ended in 1925 with the discovery of quantum mechanics. But it was realized by the early 1920's that, in spite of the successes of the old quantum theory, it was far from satisfactory as a theory of atomic structure. The failures of the old quantum theory can be divided into two classes. On the one hand, it encountered practical difficulties: there were too many phenomena that it either described incorrectly or could not explain at all. On the other hand, it encountered conceptual difficulties: the fundamental ideas could not be clearly and consistently understood in terms of it. It is worth considering some specific situations in which these failures are apparent.

The intensities and breadths of spectral lines could not be calculated by means of the old quantum theory, except with the help of the empirically determined selection rules, and these were often difficult to apply. Bohr introduced the correspondence principle in 1923 in an attempt to make use of the correspondence between classical theory and the limiting form of the quantum theory for large orbits, in order to justify the selection rules and to calculate the intensities of certain transitions. This effort met with some success and was of importance in preparing the way for the advent of quantum mechanics.

The quantization rules were designed to handle periodic systems and were of no value in dealing with aperiodic phenomena, such as collisions. Experiments of Rutherford and collaborators (1919–1921) on the scattering of α particles by hydrogen showed up anomalies which could not be understood in terms of classical collision theory, even when reasonable assumptions were made concerning departures from the Coulomb law of force at short distances. In such cases, the old quantum theory had nothing to add to classical theory.

The conceptual failures of the old quantum theory were even more striking. Why should there be an electrostatic attraction between the electron and the proton in a hydrogen atom when the accelerated electron cannot radiate? Both attraction and radiation arise from the elec-

Fig. 2.3   A diffraction experiment in which light from S passes through the two slits in A to form a diffraction pattern at B.   (*By permission from "Quantum Mechanics" by L. I. Schiff, copyright 1949, McGraw-Hill Book Company, Inc.*)

tronic charge, and both do in fact occur with macroscopic charged bodies. Why should electromagnetic radiation be emitted and absorbed in discrete quanta when it is transmitted from place to place in the form of waves that exhibit diffraction and interference?

This unsatisfactory duality between the particle and wave pictures of electromagnetic radiation can be discussed in terms of a simple diffraction experiment, which is illustrated schematically in Fig. 2.3. A light source S illuminates a diaphragm A in which two slits are cut. A diffraction pattern appears at a photosensitive screen B; the maxima and minima of the intensity of light at B are indicated by the wavy line just to the left of B. The photoelectrons ejected from B are most numerous at the peaks of the diffraction pattern and are absent at the minima. Here we have the radiation behaving as a wave during its passage from source through slits to screen, since it exhibits diffraction, but behaving as a stream of light quanta or photons when it ejects electrons from B. To understand this, we might at first suppose that the diffraction pattern is due to an interference between different photons that pass through the two slits, thus explaining the observations entirely in terms of the particle picture.   That this is not a sufficient explanation may be shown by decreasing the intensity of the light until an average of only one photon at a time is in transit between source and screen.   The diffraction pattern still appears as the statistical distribution of the large number of photons accumulated over a sufficiently long time.   Thus it cannot be produced by any interaction between photons and must be regarded as a statistical property of a single photon.   We may then ask how it is that a stream of independent photons, each of which can presumably pass through only one of the slits, can produce a diffraction pattern of the type illustrated only when both slits are open.   Or to put the question another way, how can the presence of an open slit through which a photon does not go prevent that photon from reaching a part of the screen (diffraction-pattern minimum) it would be likely to reach if that slit were closed?

Quantum mechanics resolves this paradox in much the same way that relativity resolves paradoxes that arise from the assumed simultaneity of events that occur at some distance from each other.   It begins by asking whether the events that comprise the supposed paradox can actually be observed by a realizable experimental arrangement.   As we shall see, it turns out that it is impossible to determine through which slit a photon passes without destroying the diffraction pattern indicated in Fig. 2.3. Then the question above: " . . . how can the presence of an open slit through which a photon does not go prevent that photon . . . " becomes meaningless, because within the framework of the contemplated experimental arrangement it is impossible to tell whether or not the photon does go through a particular slit.   This hard-headed attitude is one of the most characteristic features of modern physics.   We adopt what Bridgman calls the operational point of view and believe only what it is possible to measure with real experiments.   In particular, we do not stretch such mental constructs as photons and waves beyond the point of experimental confirmation: just because a bullet can easily be shown to have passed through a particular one of several holes in a wall, we do not assume that a photon behaves in the same way.   For it is easy to determine through which hole the bullet passes without disturbing it significantly, *e.g.*, by taking a photograph.   But we shall see that the analogous disturbance in the case of a photon is a very serious one: it requires a substantially different experimental arrangement which yields substantially different results.

2.9   The Uncertainty Principle and Complementarity

In 1924, de Broglie suggested that matter, as well as radiation, has both particle and wave properties.   The relation he assumed between particle momentum and wavelength was the same as that already known to exist for light waves and quanta. A photon of frequency ν and energy $E = h\nu$ carries a momentum $p = E/c = h/\lambda$, where λ is the wavelength. In an analogous manner, de Broglie proposed that a particle of momentum p have associated with it a wave of length $\lambda = h/p$. He was then able to account for the Bohr quantization rule for the circular orbits in hydrogen by assuming that only those orbits are possible for which a standing wave can exist around the orbit. This means that the circumference of the orbit must be an integer multiple of the wavelength, or $2\pi a = n\lambda = nh/mv$, which is the same as Bohr's condition. While this did not provide a complete new mechanics, it pointed the way for the formulation of quantum mechanics in terms of waves, by Schrödinger in 1926. In the meantime, Heisenberg had made the initial discovery of quantum mechanics in 1925, in its matrix form, using Bohr's correspondence principle as a starting point. Shortly after, Davisson and Germer (1927) and G. P. Thomson (1928) independently observed the diffraction of electrons by crystals and thus provided direct confirmation of de Broglie's matter-wave hypothesis.

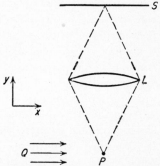

Fig. 2.4 An experiment for the localization of a particle P by means of one of the scattered quanta Q, which is focused by the lens L to form an image on the screen S. (*By permission from "Quantum Mechanics" by L. I. Schiff, copyright 1949, McGraw-Hill Book Company, Inc.*)

Our discussion of quantum mechanics in the next section will deal only with the wave or Schrödinger formulation. However, it was established by Schrödinger and by Eckart in 1926 that this wave theory is completely equivalent to Heisenberg's matrix formulation. The proof of this formal equivalence actually preceded the insight into the physical meaning of quantum mechanics that was provided by Heisenberg's uncertainty principle (1927) and Bohr's complementarity principle (1928). These two principles are best illustrated by some simple idealized experiments.

We consider first an experiment to determine the position of a particle P by scattering a light quantum Q from it (see Fig. 2.4). This photon is to be focused by a lens L to form an image on a screen S from which the position of P can be inferred. The best resolving power of L is known (either experimentally or from the theory of wave optics) to provide an uncertainty Δx in the x coordinate of the position of P,

$$\Delta x \sim \frac{\lambda}{\sin \epsilon}$$

where λ is the wavelength of the radiation, and ϵ is the half angle subtended at P by L. Thus Δx can be made as small as desired by making λ as small as is necessary. However, we shall now show that this introduces an uncertainty Δp_x in the x component of the momentum of P, which gets larger as λ gets smaller. The photon has a momentum h/λ, and since its final direction is uncertain by ϵ because of the finite aperture of the lens, the x component of its momentum after it is scattered into the lens is uncertain by $(h/\lambda) \sin \epsilon$. Since momentum is conserved between photon and particle, we have also that $\Delta p_x \sim (h/\lambda) \sin \epsilon$.

This provides an example of the uncertainty principle: $\Delta x \, \Delta p_x \gtrsim h$. It is impossible to know the position and the momentum of a particle with arbitrarily high accuracy; if one is known very accurately, the other cannot be. The same kind of uncertainty relation applies to all pairs of position-momentum variables that appear in Hamiltonian theory; *e.g.*, it applies to the angle around a plane orbit and the angular-momentum component perpendicular to the plane of the orbit. It also applies to energy and time: if it is desired to know the energy of a system with an uncertainty ΔE, a length of time at least as large as $\Delta t \sim h/\Delta E$ must be allowed for accomplishing the measurement.

The complementarity principle states that atomic phenomena cannot be described with the completeness demanded by classical dynamics; some of the elements that complement each other to make up a complete classical description are actually mutually exclusive, and these complementary elements are all necessary (although not at the same time) for the description of various aspects of the phenomena. From the point of view of the experimenter, the complementarity principle states that the physical apparatus available to him has such properties that measurements more precise than those permitted by the uncertainty principle cannot be made. In the experiment just described, for example, the experimenter can choose a long wavelength for the measurement, thus affecting the particle's momentum only slightly but providing a poor determination of its position. Or he can choose a short wavelength and get a good position determination, but only at the cost of losing knowledge of the particle's momentum. In this case, the two extreme complementary experimental arrangements consist in the use of very long and of very short wavelengths of incident radiation.

We are now in a position to discuss further the diffraction paradox described in the preceding section. Two contrasting experimental arrangements that would complement each other classically may be considered. One of these is illustrated in Fig. 2.3. It is assumed that the distance from A to B is large compared to the distance between the two slits, and this in turn is large compared to the wavelength of the light. Then the distribution of intensity in the diffraction pattern at B determines to good approximation the distribution in angle of the photons as they leave the slits in A, and hence also the distribution of the y components of momentum of the photons beyond A.

The second experimental arrangement, shown in Fig. 2.5, determines through which of the two slits each photon passes and hence it provides information on the y coordinates of the positions of the photons as they leave the slits. This is accomplished by having each photon register itself as it passes through a slit by bouncing off one of a number of indicators C. In doing so, it gives up a portion of its y component of momentum to the indicator, and this amount may be uncertain by the amount Δp_y. If now we do not want the diffraction pattern destroyed,

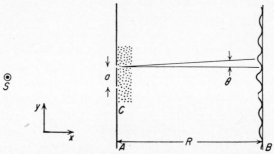

Fig. 2.5 The experimental arrangement of Fig. 2.3, modified by the addition of photon indicators C. (*By permission from "Quantum Mechanics" by L. I. Schiff, copyright 1949, McGraw-Hill Book Company, Inc.*)

we must not permit this uncertainty to be large enough to cause the photon to hit a minimum in the diffraction pattern at B when it was supposed to have hit a maximum. We must require then that $\Delta p_y \ll \vartheta p_x$, where $p_x = h/\lambda$ for photons of wavelength λ. The angle ϑ is known either experimentally or from the theory of wave optics to be equal to $\lambda/2a$. Now if we also want to know which slit the photon passed through, the struck indicator must have a position uncertainty less than half the distance between slits: $\Delta y < \frac{1}{2}a$. We thus arrive at an uncertainty relation that must be valid for the indicator if (1) the diffraction pattern is not to be destroyed, and (2) we are to know through which slit a photon passes. This relation is

$$\Delta y \, \Delta p_y \ll \frac{1}{2}a\vartheta p_x = \frac{1}{4}h$$

We thus see that if we insist on both (1) and (2), which would be contrary to reality since it would then be possible to close the other slit without damaging the diffraction pattern, we find that the uncertainty principle is violated. On the other hand, if we accept the uncertainty principle as a limitation on realizable experiments, we find that there is no contradiction with reality. From the point of view of the complementarity principle, there are two extreme complementary experimental arrangements: that of Fig. 2.3 measures the distribution in p_y for photons leaving the slits (*i.e.*, the diffraction pattern), and that of Fig. 2.5 measures the distribution in y (*i.e.*, the slit through which each photon passes).

2.10   Wave Packets and Quantum Mechanics

Since waves are generally more familiar to engineers and physicists than matrices, it is easier to introduce quantum mechanics by way of the Schrödinger wave equation than by the Heisenberg matrix equations. In doing this, it is convenient to make use of a mathematical procedure that is fundamental to all wave theory: the Fourier transform. We know that, if an oscillatory motion is to consist of but a single frequency, it must be a pure sine wave without beginning or end. At the opposite extreme, we know that a very short pulse can be built up by superposing many pure sine waves that are spread over a broad band of frequencies. In the general case, the Fourier transform provides a simple qualitative relationship between the duration in time of a more or less oscillatory motion and the spread in frequencies of the sine waves from which it can be constructed. If we call the former Δt and the latter $\Delta \nu$, the relation is $\Delta t \, \Delta \nu \gtrsim 1$. The term *wave packet* is generally used to designate a motion of this type that is fairly well localized in time and in frequency.

Wave packets in space are also useful. In this case, a space coordinate x replaces the time, and the reciprocal wavelength $1/\lambda$ replaces the frequency. If Δx is the spatial extent of the packet and $\Delta(1/\lambda)$ is the range of reciprocal wavelengths covered by its Fourier transform, it can be shown that $\Delta x \, \Delta(1/\lambda) \gtrsim 1$. A space wave packet provides a natural model for a particle, such as an electron; it can possess a principal wavelength λ that is associated with the momentum of the particle through the de Broglie relation $\lambda = h/p$, and it can have a small spread in wavelengths about the principal value that gives it a finite extent Δx in space. We then see that the Fourier transform is the mathematical expression of the uncertainty principle, since $\Delta(1/\lambda) = (\Delta p)/h$. In the same way, the Fourier transform for frequency and time is the mathematical expression of the energy-time uncertainty principle, provided that we always define the frequency of a wave as $1/h$ times the energy of the corresponding particle.

The representation of particles by wave packets, and the relations $p = h/\lambda$ and $E = h\nu$, can be put to a further test by computing the velocity with which such a packet will travel. We know that this is the group velocity associated with the wave motion, which is equal to $d\nu/d(1/\lambda)$. When this is expressed in terms of energy and momentum of the particle, it becomes dE/dp. Now for a particle of mass m whose velocity is much less than that of light, there are the well-known relations $E = p^2/2m$ and $p = mv$. We see then that $dE/dp = p/m = v$, so that the group velocity of the packet is just equal to the velocity of the particle, as indeed it must be if the packet is to represent the particle.

So far we have postulated the existence of waves without specifying their precise nature. We have, however, made two tacit assumptions. First, we have assumed that the waves can be superposed and hence interfere with each other and with themselves. And second, we have assumed that the particle is most likely to be found where the wave amplitude is large and will not be found at all where the wave amplitude is zero. The first assumption provides an important clue to the structure of the equation that the wave amplitude must satisfy: it must be a linear equation, in order that solutions of it can be superposed to form new solutions. The second assumption provides an important clue as to the interpretation of the wave amplitude: it must be possible to compute from this amplitude a probability function that shows where the particle is most and least likely to be found. Finally, the correspondence principle tells us that the form of the equation must be such that, in the classical limit, the wave amplitude predicts motions of the particle which are in agreement with those of classical dynamics.

It is then possible to set up a linear partial differential equation—the Schrödinger wave equation—whose solutions are complex functions of the space coordinates and the time. The square of the magnitude of such a wave function for particular values of the independent variables is proportional to the probability of finding the particle at that point in space and that instant of time. Other mathematical operations on the wave function provide additional information concerning the motion of the particle; e.g., the square of the magnitude of the space Fourier transform of the wave function is proportional to the probability of finding the particle with a particular momentum. The wave function is the quantum analogue of the classical trajectory; it contains everything that can be known about the behavior of the particle, and is automatically consistent with the physical principles of uncertainty and of complementarity.

REFERENCES

1. Bailey, C., "Lucretius on the Nature of Things," p. 47 (Book I, *circa* line 615), Oxford University Press, New York, 1910.
2. Dirac, P. A. M., "The Principles of Quantum Mechanics," 3d ed., p. 3, Oxford University Press, New York, 1947.

Suggested reading, arranged approximately in order of increasing difficulty.

Frisch, O. R., "Meet the Atom," A. A. Wyn, Inc., New York, 1947.
Hecht, S., "Explaining the Atom," The Viking Press, Inc., New York, 1947.

Hoffman, B., "The Strange Story of the Quantum," Harper & Brothers, New York, 1947.

Semat, H., "Introduction to Atomic Physics," Rinehart & Company, Inc., New York, 1947.

Richtmyer, F. K., and E. H. Kennard, "Introduction to Modern Physics," 4th ed., McGraw-Hill Book Company, Inc., New York, 1947.

Bohm, D., "Quantum Theory," Prentice-Hall, Inc., New York, 1951.

Schiff, L. I., "Quantum Mechanics," McGraw-Hill Book Company, Inc., New York, 1949.

3
Physics of the Solid State

FREDERICK SEITZ
PROFESSOR OF PHYSICS, UNIVERSITY OF ILLINOIS

3.1 Introduction

The scientific investigation of crystalline solids has a long history and tradition. These materials have had special attention almost since the dawn of science. In spite of this long history, the study of their properties retains a freshness of interest and viewpoint which is somewhat surprising at first sight. The reason, however, is not difficult to find. The crystalline state occurs widely in condensed matter and presents the observer with a combination of both complexity and simplicity which intrigues the scientific imagination. It is always challenging to apply some new aspect of the theory of matter to crystalline solids because they have yielded so well to persistent attack. In addition, of course, crystalline solids have great technical interest because a large fraction of the materials of engineering use are crystalline.

The present chapter will place emphasis on those properties of crystalline solids which can be understood on the basis of present atomic theory. This aspect of the study of solids has had increased attention since 1900 when modern atomic theory became the principal focal point of the interest of the physicist and chemist. In a sense this period of investigation came to its climax in 1927 when the quantum-mechanical laws of motion, which replaced Newton's equations of motion in the atomic domain, first became clearly understood. Although the quantum-mechanical laws were not available in an accurate form before 1927, it does not follow that the work done in the period between 1900 and 1927 on the properties of crystalline solids was unimportant. Many of the most basic ideas concerning crystals which are accepted today were discovered during that time. However, after 1927 one could proceed upon a systematic study of solids with complete confidence that one had an understanding of the laws which governed the constituent atoms. The transition made

69

it possible to possess a far more exact science of solids than had been feasible previously.

We shall consider two aspects of the atomic physics of solids, namely, the properties of the perfect crystal and the influence of imperfections in the volume of the crystal. The perfect crystal, which is a type of conceptual idealization almost never found in nature, is the prototype which can be understood most simply in terms of atomic theory. Fortunately, many of the physical properties of actual crystals, such as the density, refractive index, heat capacity, and elastic constants, are essentially the same as those of the ideal prototype so that the study of the ideal crystal gives valuable information concerning the origin of such properties.

On the other hand, a very large number of the properties of actual crystals, such as their ductility, breaking strength, and electrical conductivity, are strongly dependent on deviations from ideal behavior. Such properties can be understood only with appropriate appreciation of the nature and behavior of imperfections in crystals. So far, the greatest progress has been made in the study of a special family of imperfections which can inhabit the interior of crystals and which are caused either by accidents in growth or by such factors as temperature. We shall devote a portion of this chapter to a discussion of these imperfections, since it now appears that they may yield to systematic study. There are other imperfections, in particular those which are localized near the surface, which are not yet thoroughly understood or correlated. These will undoubtedly furnish the topic for a suitable discussion at some time in the not too distant future.

As stated previously, the development of a theory of the perfect crystal from an atomic standpoint started about 1900 but did not become thoroughly established until the discovery of quantum mechanics. Between 1927 and 1940 this development was in a sense the central topic of the physics of solids, occupying the attention of most of the investigators in the field. By 1940 the most important boundaries of the field had been fairly well defined, although many interesting aspects of the subject still remained for research. Conversely, the study of imperfections in crystals began in a highly tentative way during the period in which the theory of perfect crystals was becoming established and did not undergo acceleration until the investigation of perfect crystals was well advanced. A large part of the most interesting knowledge of imperfect crystals has accumulated since 1945. In fact this topic is in an exciting period of research and development at the present time.

If the author were asked, he would hazard a guess that the next aspect of the physics of solids which will come to the center of the stage is that concerning surface properties. However, the development of this field is still only in its most rudimentary beginnings. It will be necessary to evolve widely applicable and highly reliable experimental techniques for studying the surfaces of crystals before they can become the object of the same systematic investigation that has characterized the study of ideal crystals and of crystals containing internal imperfections.

3.2 Elementary Atomic Principles

As Professor Schiff has pointed out so lucidly in Chap. 2, the techniques of modern physics have demonstrated that all matter is composed of atoms.   The individual atom of a typical element consists of a small positively charged nucleus containing most of the mass of the atom and surrounded by a cloud of electrons.   The number of unit positive charges on the nucleus determines the chemical species of the atom.   When the atom is neutral, the number of electrons in the surrounding cloud equals the number of unit charges on the nucleus.   In general, the volume in which the electron cloud is distributed can, to the first approximation, be regarded as a sphere having a diameter of the order of 10^{-8} cm.   Both the diameter of the nucleus and that of the electron are far smaller than this.   The heavier atoms are some-

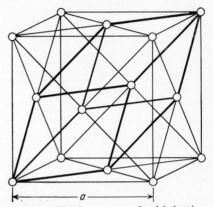

Fig. 3.1 The face-centered cubic lattice, characteristic of copper and a number of other metals. About one-third of all metals crystallize in this structure. The small spheres represent the copper atoms, although not in proportion to their actual size in relation to the interatomic spacing of the lattice.

what larger than the lighter atoms, hydrogen being the smallest of all.   The concept of a spherical atom is not exact, but it is a useful approximation.

In crystalline matter, the constituent atoms are arranged in a very regular lattice array.   More exactly, the entire crystal is constructed from a single geometrical unit called the *unit cell*, which is repeated over and over again as one moves in three directions from a given cell. Figure 3.1 shows the lattice structure of copper, the spheres representing the copper atoms.   In this case the cell contains only one atom.   Figure 3.2 shows the lattice structure of sodium chloride, which has one sodium and one chlorine atom in the unit cell.   Figure 3.3 shows the lattice structure of diamond, one of the crystalline forms of carbon.   In this case there are two carbon atoms in the unit cell of the lattice.

It is customary, in the physics of solids, to equate the diameter of an atom to the spacing between the center of one atom and that of its

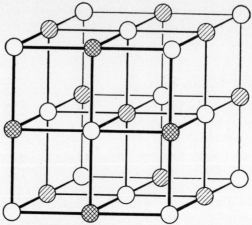

Fig. 3.2 The lattice of sodium chloride. The open spheres represent one kind of ion, such as sodium, and the hatched spheres the opposite, such as chlorine, although the two types of ion are completely interchangeable. Again, as in Fig. 3.1, the ions are not represented in true proportion but are made smaller for visual clarity. It can be seen that each sodium ion is surrounded by six chlorine ions, and vice versa.

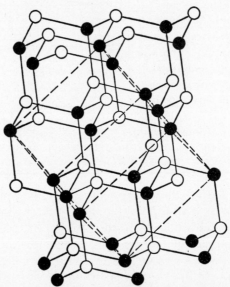

Fig. 3.3 The lattice of diamond. In diamond both the full and empty spheres are carbon atoms. There are two atoms per unit cell in this case. The open spheres form a face-centered cubic lattice, analogous to Fig. 3.1, as do the closed spheres. The unit cube of the lattice is shown by dotted lines. It can be seen that each carbon atom is joined to four others. These four atoms lie at the corners of the tetrahedron centered at the first atom. Zinc sulfide forms a similar lattice in which the open spheres are zinc atoms and the closed spheres sulfur atoms.

nearest neighbor in the most common crystalline form of the pure element, for this distance would be exactly equal to the diameter if the atoms actually were spheres which were in contact in the lattices. Although the diameter derived in this way is an approximate quantity, it is sufficiently well defined to be useful.

3.3   The Ideal Solid Types

There are a number of ways of classifying the ideal types of crystalline solid. One which has a number of virtues employs four classifications, namely, (1) metals and alloys, (2) salts, (3) valence crystals, (4) molecular crystals.

The ideal metals, of which substances such as copper, silver, gold, aluminum, and the alkali metals are prototypes, have a bright metallic luster, are good conductors of electricity with a conductivity that increases as one goes toward the absolute zero of temperature, and have a high ductility which borders on butter-softness when the metals are exceedingly pure.

The ideal alloys are the compounds formed by the ideal metals. Such compounds frequently possess the high electrical conductivity and much of the ductility of the ideal pure metals. This is particularly likely to be the case when the constituent metals lie close to one another in the electromotive series and when the atomic diameters are nearly alike. The most interesting alloys of commerce fall into two broad groups: namely, substitutional and interstitial alloys. Substitutional alloys are compounds in which the constituent atoms may be substituted for one another in the lattice without disrupting the structure. Alpha brass, formed of copper and zinc, or bronze, formed of copper and tin, are ideal examples. In such cases the atomic diameters are the same to within 15 per cent, and the atoms lie close in the electromotive series. In interstitial alloys one of the constituent atoms is sufficiently small compared with the other so that the former may fit into the interstices of the lattice of the latter. In general, interstitial alloys are formed only if the smaller atom has a diameter that is less than 60 per cent that of the larger. Steel formed by carbon and iron is an interesting borderline interstitial alloy, the carbon atom being smaller than the iron atom.

The salts, of which the alkali halides and the simple metal oxides and sulfides are prototypes, are compounds formed of an ideal metal and a strongly electronegative element, according to strict rules of chemical combination. When soluble in water, they are good electrolytes. In fact, at a sufficiently high temperature all exhibit in the crystalline state an internal electrolytic conductivity resulting from the migration of ions. The study of these materials leads to the notion that they are composed of positive and negative ions of the metallic and electronegative constituents which are present in such relative number as to leave the resultant crystal neutral.   The salts are often highly ductile.   For example, pure crystals of sodium chloride and of silver chloride are almost as ductile as ideal metals.

Diamond is the ideal valence crystal.   It is a monatomic solid with a very high heat of sublimation and great hardness.   The term valence crystal originates in the fact that each carbon atom in diamond is surrounded by a number of other carbon atoms equal to its valence, namely, four.   The ideal valence crystal is a good electrical insulator in the pure state.   Elemental boron is probably another ideal valence crystal which resembles diamond in many respects.   Its crystal structure, *i.e.*, the arrangement of atoms in the crystal, shows fivefold coordination, as if the electronegative valence were the determining factor.

Prior to the war, it was not known with certainty whether elements such as silicon and germanium should be classed more nearly as metals or valence crystals.   On the one hand, these materials have the type of valence arrangement found in diamond, and are moderately hard and brittle.   On the other hand, as normally made they are electronic electrical conductors at room temperature.   The extensive studies of the electrical properties of these materials which were made during and after the war, however, have left little doubt that they are more nearly like the ideal valence crystals than like the metals, although there are what might be called strong traces of metallic behavior.

The ideal molecular crystals are substances such as crystalline dry ice (CO_2), solid methane, and the solid rare gases.   These materials are excellent electrical insulators and have a very low heat of sublimation, the evaporated unit being the chemical molecule.   The ideal molecular solids can be best described by regarding them as a crystalline aggregate of molecules which are very strongly bound internally but which are weakly bound with one another so that they sublime at relatively low temperatures.

It must be emphasized that the preceding classification of the ideal types of solids is somewhat arbitrary.   Most solids have properties which are intermediate between two or more of the ideal types.   For example, many insulators, such as quartz, partake of the properties of both ionic and valence types; many pure metals, such as bismuth, have some of the characteristics of valence crystals; and many alloys, such as Mg_3Sb_2, have saltlike properties.

3.4   The Electronic Structure of Solids

The really great advance in our understanding of the properties of ideal solids took place when it became possible to discuss in an understandable way the behavior of the electrons about the atoms in crystalline solids, since the influence of crystalline binding upon these electrons determines the most important properties of the solids.   We shall attempt to emphasize the influence of chemical binding by discussing the changes in energy states of electrons as one passes from a collection of free atoms to the crystal.

Chapter 2 has emphasized the fact that the electrons in the cloud about the nucleus of an atom have discrete energy levels.   Figure 3.4 shows the prototype system of levels for the electrons in atoms.   The spacings between these levels vary greatly as one passes from one end of the periodic chart to the other, increasing in this process, but the qualitative scheme of levels remains unchanged.   In a simple descriptive way, one can say that each of the levels represents a possible group of states of orbital motion of one of the electrons in the cloud.   The discreteness of these levels is a feature characteristic of quantum mechanics, in contrast with Newtonian mechanics which would permit a continuous spectrum of possible orbital states.

A second important law governing the behavior of electrons in the atomic cloud is the Pauli exclusion principle, which states that only a finite number of electrons may be in a given energy level at the same time.   This number, known as the degeneracy of the level, is the number of different states of motion associated with the level; it is given by the integer shown on the far left-hand side of the levels in Fig. 3.4. The Pauli exclusion principle prohibits more than two electrons from being in the ground level (1s), more than two from being in the next to the ground level (2s), more than six from being in the third from the ground level (2p), etc.   As one passes from element to element in the periodic

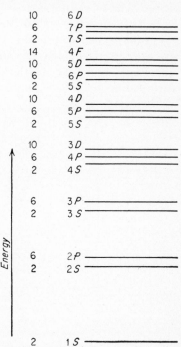

Fig. 3.4   Schematic energy level diagram for the electrons in atoms.   The electronic levels are discrete and tend to cluster into groups termed *shells*. The numbers to the far left give the maximum number of electrons that may occupy each level according to the Pauli exclusion principle.   The symbols immediately to the left of the levels, 1s, 2s, 2p, etc., are level designations which have historical significance.   Atoms corresponding to cases in which well-separated groups of levels are completely occupied have rare-gas properties.   In hydrogen there is one electron in the 1s level; in helium two electrons are in this level; in lithium two electrons are in the 1s level, and one electron is in the 2s level; etc.

chart, increasing the number of electrons in the cloud by one at each step, the system of levels shown in Fig. 3.4 is filled to successively higher stages. The repetition in pattern of levels shown in the figure accounts for the periodic properties of the elements.

Consider a box containing 1 mole (*i.e.*, 6.03×10^{23}) of atoms of a given species so sparsely distributed that the atoms are not in contact with one another. In this large system of atoms the number of levels shown in Fig. 3.4 will be multiplied by the number of atoms in the box,

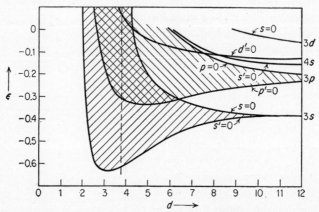

Fig. 3.5 Behavior of the electronic energy levels of sodium as sodium atoms arranged in the typical lattice array are brought together from large distances. The horizontal axis gives the separation in atomic units of distance (0.531×10^{-8} cm). The vertical axis gives the energy in Rydberg units (13.54 ev). The $3s$ level splits into a band when d is decreased to about 10. The $3p$ level splits at larger distance. The two bands begin to overlap when d is about 6.3. The vertical dotted line corresponds to the observed interatomic spacing ($d = 3.9$). At this spacing the electrons behave almost as if they were perfectly free, except for the restrictions of the Pauli exclusion principle. The bands of levels are not completely continuous, but are composed of a closely spaced sequence of discrete levels which cannot be resolved in a diagram of this type.

if we take account of the fact that a given electron may choose an orbit on any one of the N atoms. That is, the degeneracy of possible levels is increased by a factor N because this number of atoms is present. This fact will not be altered if the atoms in the box are arranged in the same geometrical pattern as in the crystal, so long as they do not touch.

We can expect, however, that the system of levels will change if we decrease the spacing of the highly expanded lattice until the atoms can begin to touch one another. Once the atoms begin to touch, the electrons on any one atom will be influenced by the presence of the neighboring atoms.

Figure 3.5 shows what happens in the exceedingly interesting case of sodium when a group of sodium atoms arranged in the characteristic lattice pattern of sodium are brought together. The horizontal axis represents the spacing between the centers of nearest neighbors, whereas the vertical axis represents energy. It will be seen that the highly discrete atomic levels of the valence electrons shown on the right-hand end of the diagram split into bands as overlapping occurs. These bands are not continuous as they might seem from the picture. Actually they contain a distribution of discrete levels which are very finely spaced and cannot be resolved in the diagram. If the atoms are pushed together closely enough, the bands originating from individual atomic levels over-

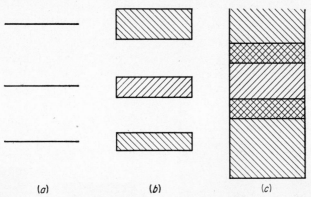

Fig. 3.6   Three characteristic dispositions of the electronic levels in condensed matter. (a) Highly discrete and highly degenerate levels of the separated atoms corresponding to the far right-hand side of Fig. 3.5. (b) Intermediate state of separation corresponding to distances such as $d = 8$ in Fig. 3.5 at which the atomic levels have split into bands but the bands do not yet overlap. (c) Levels for relatively close separation when the bands have overlapped extensively.

lap and one obtains a quasi-continuous system of levels starting from a certain lowest point. The vertical dotted line in the picture designates the behavior of levels at the actual atomic separation in sodium. At this observed distance the levels are quasi-continuous above the bottommost point originating from the 3s band shown.

It will be noted that, at larger spacing, farther to the right in the diagram, the bands originating from individual atomic levels do not overlap, at least toward the bottom of the diagram. Thus at three characteristic distances in the diagram, the disposition of levels is as shown in Fig. 3.6. Figure 3.6a shows the discrete levels of the widely separated atoms, 3.6b shows an intermediate stage where the atomic levels have split into bands but do not overlap, whereas 3.6c shows the completely overlapping system.

It is interesting to note in passing that the electron clouds about the atoms are greatly distorted as one goes from the right-hand end of Fig. 3.5 to the actual spacing. Instead of showing the spherical clustering characteristic of the free atom, the cloud has spread almost uniformly throughout the lattice at the observed spacing of the crystal. This transition is characteristic of that which occurs in the ideal metal and is not true of all types of solid. It may be observed that the higher electronic levels of the atom split into bands sooner than the lower levels as the atoms are brought together. This effect is related to the circumstance that the higher levels are associated with orbits having larger diameters than the lower levels, so that the orbits on different atoms overlap sooner for the higher levels.

We may now consider the manner in which the quasi-continuous levels are occupied by the electrons. In the normal state of the free atom, the

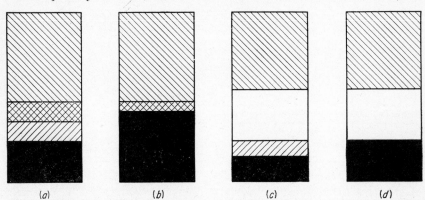

(a)   (b)   (c)   (d)

Fig. 3.7 Several typical systems of energy bands.   (a) A case in which neighboring bands of levels overlap and in which the occupied region of levels, represented by the dark region at the bottom, extends only part way in the lower band.   (b) A case in which the occupied levels extend into the region of overlap of the two bands.   (c) A case in which two neighboring bands do not overlap and in which the occupied system of levels extends only part way in the lowest band.   (d) A case, like that of (c), in which the bands do not overlap and in which the occupied region extends throughout the lowest band.   Cases a, b, and c correspond to metals, whereas case d corresponds to an insulator.

electrons in the atom occupy the lowest levels in the densest possible manner permitted by the exclusion principle. No low-lying level is vacant if there is an electron in a higher level. In other words, the levels are filled in such a way that there are no vacancies below the uppermost occupied level. Exactly the same principle is valid for the levels of the solid. The solid is in its state of lowest energy, *i.e.*, the equilibrium state in the absence of excitation, when all the levels below the uppermost occupied one are filled. The degeneracies of the levels in the quasi-continuous bands and the number of electrons in the solid are such that this usually means that the uppermost occupied band is filled to an appreciable extent as is shown in Fig. 3.7 for some typical cases which will be discussed presently.

In describing the normal chemical properties of an atom, one usually needs to focus attention only on the uppermost occupied levels of the atom, for the lower levels are usually unaffected by chemical binding. For example, in lithium, which has three electrons, two of which are in the lowest atomic level (1s) and one of which is in the next (2s) level, only the 2s level has an appreciable effect upon the chemical properties. The electrons in the lower level are so close to the nucleus relative to those in the upper level that they do no more than screen the nuclear charge. Similarly, if one is discussing the normal electrical, mechanical, or chemical properties of solids, it is sufficient to focus attention upon the uppermost occupied bands. The bands originating from the lower levels are usually broadened negligibly because the electrons moving in the corresponding orbits are too close to the nuclei to be affected by the aggregation of atoms in the solid.

Figure 3.7 shows several typical electron-level bands in solids under different interesting cases of occupation by electrons. Figure 3.7a represents the case similar to that for sodium (Fig. 3.5) at the observed spacing. The bands originating from different atomic levels have overlapped so that one has a completely quasi-continuous spectrum starting from a given lowest point. The darkened region shows such a typical occupied region of the spectrum as might occur if there is one valence electron per atom.

Figure 3.7b shows the manner in which the same system of levels might be filled if there were two valence electrons per atom. In the second case the spectrum is filled considerably higher, although not necessarily twice as high since the levels are not uniformly distributed in the band.

Figure 3.7c shows a case in which the bands originating from different atomic levels have not overlapped but are separated by a gap indicated by the clear area. In such a case, one of the bands may be partly filled with electrons as in c or may be entirely filled as in d.

It may be noted that in case 3.7d the bottom band is completely filled whereas the upper band is completely empty. It might seem, at first sight, as though the case 3.7d is highly accidental; i.e., it might appear accidental that the number of electrons and the number of energy levels are so balanced that the lower band would be completely filled and the upper band completely empty. Actually this situation is very common and, as we shall see below, is typical of the insulating crystal. It is common because there is a simple mathematical relation between the number of electronic levels in a band derived from an atomic level and the number of unit cells in the lattice, the ratio of the two being a simple, even integer such as 2, 4, or 6. Thus case 3.7d can occur whenever the number of valence electrons on the atoms in a unit cell is equal to this integer ratio.

It is relatively easy to see that the cases represented by Fig. 3.7a, b,

and c describe metallic conductors.   The essential reasoning is as follows:
Whereas the electronic energy levels of free atoms describe states in
which the electron is bound to the nucleus of the atom in something
approaching a state of orbital motion, the electronic levels of the solids
which are grouped into the bands described above correspond to states
of motion of the electron in which it passes from one atom to another.
The ease of passage from one atom to another is in a sense determined
by the width of the band.   The wider the band, the greater the ease of
this transition; the narrower the band, the more difficult the transition.
When the band is infinitely narrow, as at the right-hand side of Fig. 3.5
where the separation of atoms is great, the electrons will cease to make
transition from one atom to another.

Thus the neighboring levels in the quasi-continuous band describe
states of motion of an electron in a solid with slightly different velocities
through the crystal.   If the crystal contained only one electron in one
of the possible states of motion and if an electric field were applied to
the crystal, thereby exerting a force upon the charged electron, the electron would be compelled to change its state of motion as a result of this
force, i.e., it would jump from one electron state to another, corresponding to the normal process of acceleration.   In a densely filled region of
the spectrum, such as the dark regions shown in each of the diagrams of
Fig. 3.7, the exclusion principle acts in such a way that occupied states
corresponding to electrons moving in opposite directions with the same
velocity occur pairwise.   Moreover, neighboring states corresponding to
slightly different states of velocity are also occupied.   As a result the
electrons in the main body of the distribution cannot be accelerated—
the Pauli exclusion principle prevents this process.   However, the electrons at the very top of the occupied regions in Fig. 3.7a, b, and c, which
border unoccupied levels, can undergo acceleration with relatively little
inhibition and hence can conduct an electric current.   It is a general rule
that whenever the uppermost occupied levels are very close to unoccupied
levels, as in Fig. 3.7a, b, and c, the solid is a metal.

On the other hand, the situation shown in Fig. 3.7d describes an
insulator.   In this case, the occupied region extends exactly to the top
of the band and the highest occupied level is separated by a gap from
the nearest unoccupied level.   The electrons in the occupied region form
a very tightly interlocking statistical assembly in which all motions
exactly compensate, even in the presence of an electrostatic field that
would be sufficient to induce a current in a good metal.   Thus 3.7d corresponds to an insulator.   If one applies a sufficiently strong electric field to
this material, it is possible to excite an electron from the top of the filled
band to the bottom of the empty band.   In general the field necessary is
very large, comparable to the breakdown strength of good insulators.

We see that the quantum-mechanical description of the electronic energy levels in solids, as represented by the diagrams of Fig. 3.7, gives a very direct explanation of the differences between metals and insulators.

Figure 3.8, which is the analogue of Fig. 3.6, shows the behavior of the electronic energy levels of the carbon atom when the atoms are arranged into the diamond lattice and are brought together to the actual atomic spacing represented by the vertical dashed line. In this some-what unique case, the bands originating from the two atomic levels over-

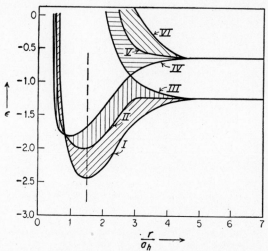

Fig. 3.8 A diagram analogous to Fig. 3.5 for carbon atoms arranged in the lattice of diamond. The vertical dashed line corresponds to the actual atomic spacing. It may be seen that in this case the atomic levels split into bands which become separated on overlapping. There are just enough electrons in the unit cell to fill the lowest band system completely, so that diamond is an insulator.

lap and then split apart to form a low-lying band which is separated from higher bands by energy gaps. There is just the right number of valence electrons in carbon to fill the lower band completely, in agreement with the fact that diamond is an insulator.

A study of the distortion of the initial spherical distribution of electrons about the separated carbon atoms shows that in the crystalline solid the electrons tend to become concentrated in the direction between nearest neighboring atoms. This result is in excellent agreement with the intuitive chemical notion that in valence compounds the valence electrons tend to localize in bonds directed along the lines connecting nearest neighboring atoms.

Theoretical studies of the energy diagrams for the common salts show the following facts. If one starts with separated atoms in the ionic state, i.e., as Na^+ and Cl^- ions in the case of sodium chloride, and then arranges the ions into the typical lattice array and brings the system together, the levels of the ions split into bands but do not overlap. In other words, the electrons in the ionic solid retain a strong memory of the ionic state. Moreover, a study of the electron distribution in the ionic crystals shows that it is closely the same as that which would obtain in the free ions. These results support the well-founded view of the chemists that the salts are essentially composed of aggregates of ions.

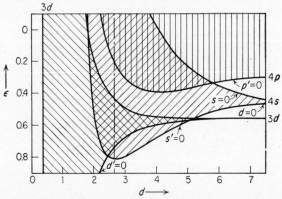

Fig. 3.9 A diagram similar to Figs. 3.5 and 3.8 for the case of metallic copper. In this case the $4s$ and $4p$ levels, which resemble the $3s$ and $3p$ levels of sodium (Fig. 3.5), split into wide overlapping bands. The $3d$ level, however, which is associated with a shielded inner shell, begins to split for much smaller separations and is not very broad at the observed interatomic spacing. The $3d$ electrons in the metals immediately preceding copper, namely iron, cobalt, and nickel, are responsible for the strong magnetic properties. In copper the top of the occupied region lies well above the top of the $3d$ band, so that the $3d$ electrons do not participate in conduction, although they do in metals preceding copper in the periodic chart.

Similarly, if one regards molecular crystals as if they were produced by assembling the constituent molecules, one finds that, at the actual intermolecular spacing observed in the crystal, the molecular energy levels are split into very narrow bands as a result of the aggregation. This supports the view that the valence electrons in molecular solids retain an exceedingly strong memory of the bonds which occur in the free molecules.

Figure 3.9 shows the energy-band diagram, as a function of interatomic spacing, for copper. The $4s$ and $4p$ atomic levels behave very much like corresponding levels in sodium. In fact these levels are closely analogous to those of sodium, even in the free atom. On the other hand, the $3d$ level behaves in a rather different way. This level breaks into a band only when the atomic spacing is much smaller than is the case for the $4s$ and $4p$ levels, so that this band is still quite narrow even at the observed interatomic spacing, designated by the vertical dashed line. The striking behavior of the 3d level is associated with the fact that it corresponds to orbital motions in the free atom involving a much smaller diameter than the orbital motions corresponding to the 4s or 4p electrons.

The 3d band is believed to be completely occupied in metallic copper, since the relative positions of the d band and the band arising from the s and p electrons are probably as shown in Fig. 3.10. In consequence, the conduction properties in copper are determined primarily by the electrons at the top of the band arising from the sp levels, which are much like those in metallic sodium.

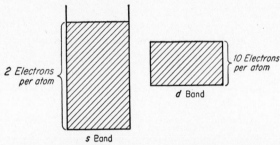

Fig. 3.10   The relative disposition of the s and d bands in copper and metals near copper.   The s band, which is like the band arising from the s and p levels in metallic sodium, is broad and contains, on the average, two electrons per atom.   The d band is narrow and contains all ten d electrons, so that the relative density of levels is far higher in the d band.   In copper the s band is occupied to a point well above the top of the d band, although this is not the case in the ferromagnetic elements preceding copper.

To summarize the results of this section, it may be stated that the two primary effects of solid binding upon the valence electrons in typical solids are to permit the electrons to jump from one atom to another with an ease measured by the breadth of the energy bands and to produce a distortion of a spherical electronic cloud in a way which varies from one of the solid types to another.   The Pauli exclusion principle acts to limit the ease with which the electrons may be accelerated by an electrostatic field in any solid.   This inhibition is exceedingly strong if the uppermost occupied band of levels is completely filled and is separated from the nearest empty band by a gap.   In this case the substance is an insulator rather than a metallic conductor.

MEANS OF ALTERING THE ELECTRON DISTRIBUTION

It was mentioned in the previous section that the distribution of electrons in metals and in insulators can be altered by applying an electrostatic field.   In general, the field must be quite strong in insulators.

There are other common means of altering the electron distribution in solids. A few of these may be listed.

3.5 Influence of Temperature

If the temperature of the crystal is raised above absolute zero, the electrons can participate in the energy of thermal motion. The electrons at the top of the occupied region in a metal are particularly easy to affect, since they can easily make transitions to the unoccupied levels above. Thus, as the temperature is raised, the boundary between the filled and the unfilled regions becomes fuzzy as a result of this excitation. The width of the fuzzy region is proportional to the temperature and, in most solids, is of the order of 1 per cent of the width of the occupied region at room temperature.

The thermal excitation of the conduction electrons has several interesting influences. For example, the ease with which the electrons can be influenced by an electrostatic field is altered. This is one of the factors governing the electrical resistivity of a metal. Similarly, the energy absorbed by the electrons as a result of thermal excitation contributes to the heat capacity of the solid. This is relatively easy to measure at temperatures near that of liquid helium (4°K) where other contributions to the specific heat, particularly that resulting from atomic oscillation, become very small.

The electrons in an ideal insulator can be affected by temperature only if the temperature is sufficiently high to eject electrons from the filled to the empty band. This will be easier, the narrower the gap between the filled and empty levels. This gap is sufficiently small in materials such as gray tin, silicon, germanium, and tellurium so that a measurable number of electrons are excited from the filled to the empty bands and can be detected by the electrical conductivity which they impart to the material. Materials showing this effect at a sufficiently low temperature are termed *intrinsic semiconductors;* they form a very interesting class of useful materials. The gap is sufficiently large in the good insulators such as diamond and sodium chloride so that the corresponding electronic conductivity will appear only at very high temperatures. Many good insulators can be transformed to semiconductors by the addition of suitable impurity agents. Such materials are termed *impurity semiconductors* and will be discussed in Sec. 3.19.

3.6 Influence of Light

One of the discoveries of modern physics has been the fact that a beam of light of a given wavelength, or frequency, behaves like a stream of particles, termed *photons* or *light quanta*, having an energy E which is related to the frequency ν by the equation

$$E = h\nu \qquad\qquad (3.1)$$

where h is a universal constant known as *Planck's constant*. An electron may interact with a particle of light and absorb this energy, thereby being excited. This process can take place only under restrictions involving the energy and the velocity of the electron. For example, if an electron in a given energy state is to absorb a light quantum, there must be a second energy state with an energy $E = h\nu$ above the first. However, other restrictions may occur to prevent the process or make it unlikely.

The energy condition is always satisfied in metals of the kind depicted in Fig. 3.7a and 3.7b, which seem to be the usual cases. Thus metals usually can absorb at least a fraction of the light which is incident upon them. Since the light must pass through the surface of the metal, it is also possible for a fraction to be reflected. One aspect of the theory of solids deals with the determination of the ratio of absorbed and reflected light as a function of wavelength. It has proved possible to understand many of the most interesting phenomena concerning reflectivity, such as the high reflectivity of metallic aluminum and silver, the characteristic colors of metals such as copper and gold, and the transparent behavior of typical insulators.

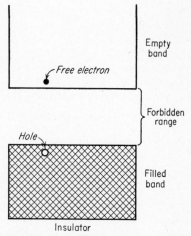

Fig. 3.11 Diagrammatic representation of a free electron and a hole in an insulator. An electron which occupies a normally empty band of an insulator can move about freely, conducting a current. Similarly, a vacant level in the normally filled band permits the electrons in the filled band to conduct a current. The characteristics of this conductivity are such that it is convenient to regard the absent electron as a particle, termed a *hole*, which behaves as if it were positively charged.

When the electrons in the filled band of an insulator absorb light, an electron may be transferred to the empty band. The insulator may then be conducting, both because of the presence of the electron in the empty band and because of the presence of the vacant level in the filled band. The vacant level, or *hole* as it is commonly called, permits the electrons in the filled band to conduct a current in much the same way that a bubble in an otherwise full vessel of water allows the fluid to have a net flow when the vessel is shaken (see Fig. 3.11). It is possible to show that a hole near the top of the filled band behaves very much like a positive charge, so that the holes are sometimes called positive holes. The onset of electrical conductivity under the action of light is commonly called *photoconductivity*.

3.7   Other Means of Exciting Electrons

There are many other ways in which the electrons in solid materials may be excited to higher energy states.   For example, the ionizing radiations produced by radioactive materials or by accelerating machines such as cyclotrons can cause excitation when they pass through the solid. Many such effects have been observed and put to practical use in suitable instruments.

PROPERTIES DETERMINED BY THE
IDEAL SOLID

There are a number of properties of crystalline solids that are essentially the same for ideal solids and for real solids containing a limited degree of imperfection.   These properties can be discussed in terms of the theory of ideal solids and, in a sense, provide a test of the development leading to the unraveling of the properties of ideal solids or of the basic equations of quantum mechanics as applied to ideal solids.   Unfortunately, it is very difficult to obtain accurate solutions for the fundamental equations even when the solid is idealized.   As a result, only a few detailed quantitative comparisons have been made up to the present time, and progress on extending such solutions is very slow because of the overwhelming computational difficulties.

It may be added that exactly the same computational difficulties plague the problem of solving the basic problems of chemistry with the use of the equations of quantum mechanics.   Perhaps the innovations in computational techniques associated with the development of modern high-speed digital computers (Chap. 18) will eventually make it possible to handle a far wider range of problems than is feasible at the present time.

By way of summarizing our understanding of the properties of ideal crystals, we shall discuss a few of the more important areas in which a degree of success has been achieved thus far.

3.8   Cohesion

The cohesion of a solid can be measured in terms of the energy required to decompose it into isolated atoms or molecules.   This energy in turn is determined experimentally by measuring the heat of sublimation of the solid, a subject of wide interest to thermochemists for many years.   The heat of sublimation is little affected by imperfections present in the lattice, so that it is a property which can be correlated with the properties of the ideal solid.

It can be seen from Fig. 3.5 that, when the energy levels of atomic sodium split into bands as the atoms are brought together, some portions of a given band are raised relative to the atomic level from which the band originated, whereas others are depressed. In the case of the lowest band of interest, namely, the one derived from the 3s level, the band contains enough levels to accommodate two electrons per atom. Actually, sodium contains only one electron per atom in the valence shell. Thus the valence electrons are concentrated in the lower half of the band which is, on the average, depressed relative to the atomic level. This means that the electrons in the crystalline solid have a lower energy than the electrons in the free atom, or, expressed in another way, the energy of the system of atoms is decreased in going from the gas to the solid. The difference in the energy of the atoms in the gaseous phase and in the crystalline phase is the cohesive energy or heat of sublimation of the crystal.

It has proved possible to make theoretical estimates of the cohesive energy in the case of a few simple solids. Among the metals, for example, calculations which are accurate to within a few per cent have been carried out in the cases of metallic lithium and sodium. Within this accuracy there is excellent agreement between the observed and calculated values.

Similar accuracy has been achieved in the case of simple ionic crystals, such as sodium chloride, and substances closely related to them. In these substances, a large part of the cohesion can be related to the strong electrostatic attraction between the positive and negative ions of which the lattice is composed.

Comparable calculations have been made for simpler molecular crystals. Only the valence crystals have resisted relatively precise calculations in terms of the fundamental equations of quantum mechanics. These substances are difficult to treat because of the large amount of distortion of the electronic clouds and the fact that the band systems are quite complex.

It should be added that somewhat different approximational techniques must be used in treating each of the solid types. There is room for a great deal of intuition in judging which technique will be most successful.

3.9 Elastic Constants

The forces required to deform a solid homogeneously are proportional to the deformation. The coefficients of proportionality are called the elastic coefficients or Hooke's constants; they can be measured to a high precision. The calculation of these coefficients from first principles is much more difficult than the calculation of the cohesive energies, because the coefficients are related to the second derivatives of the energy versus interatomic-distance function.   It is necessary to be able to apply the basic equations of quantum mechanics to very high precision to obtain good relative accuracy in the determination of the elastic constants. As a result, these coefficients have been computed with relative precision only for one or two of the simplest solids, in particular for the alkali metals lithium and sodium.   Less precise values have been obtained in other cases; there is little doubt at the present time that, if one could handle the basic equations with sufficient accuracy, the equations of quantum mechanics would yield proper values of the elastic constants.

3.10   Atomic Frequencies

The elastic coefficients determine the relation between deformation and force when the deformation is uniform over a distance large compared to atomic spacing.   There is much interest in the relationship between force and deformation when the deformation varies appreciably over a distance comparable to atomic dimensions.   One way of looking upon the problem of determining this relationship is as follows.   Suppose that a sine-like wave of atomic displacement passes through the lattice much as a wave of sound passes through the air.   It is interesting to know the connection between the wavelength of the disturbance and the frequency with which the atoms will oscillate back and forth as a wave passes through.   In the realm of very long waves, the connection is determined by the elastic constants.   However, the relationship varies as the wavelength becomes comparable to atomic dimensions.

Practically no calculations have been made from first principles even in the simplest solids.   Instead it is necessary to describe the relationships in terms of functions containing initially undetermined parameters or constants which are ultimately determined by comparing the consequences of the initial assumptions regarding the functions with experimental quantities.   This practice of relating observation to theory by the introduction of parameters which are determined by comparing theory and experiment is very widespread in the theory of solids and is exceedingly useful at the present stage of development where exact application of the theory presents so much difficulty.

3.11   Specific Heats of Crystalline Solids

When a crystalline solid is heated, it absorbs energy, the relationship between absorbed energy and temperature being described conveniently in terms of the molar heat, which is the energy absorbed per mole of substance when this amount of material is heated 1°C.   Heat is absorbed because certain internal motions in the crystalline solid are stimulated.

The simplest type of stimulation is that of the waves of atomic oscillation described in the previous section. As the temperature of the crystal becomes higher and higher, the amplitude of atomic oscillation becomes greater and greater and more and more waves of vibration pass back and forth within the crystal. The proper understanding of the relationship between the frequency of a given wave and the energy associated with it at a given temperature required the developments of quantum theory. A given wave having a frequency ν becomes excited thermally only when the temperature is such that the relationship $kT \sim h\nu$ is satisfied. At temperatures lower than this, the given mode of oscillation will not be stimulated by temperature to an appreciable extent. In most of the crystalline solids, practically all the energy absorbed when the solid is heated stimulates lattice vibrations.

The conduction electrons of metals may absorb some thermal energy, the electrons near the top of the occupied band being excited as a result (see Sec. 3.5). The corresponding contribution to the specific heat is usually measurable at very low temperatures, i.e., in the so-called helium range near 4°K, but usually is not appreciable near room temperature. On the other hand, some metals which have partly filled d shells, of the type found in the iron-group elements preceding copper, possess a relatively large electronic contribution to the specific heat because there is a high density of electrons at the top of the filled band available to absorb thermal energy. Thus in metals such as iron, cobalt, and nickel, the electronic specific heat is fully comparable to the vibrational specific heat in the vicinity of room temperature.

3.12 Phase Changes

A given crystalline solid need not maintain the same lattice structure over all ranges of temperature and pressure. In fact, many crystalline solids change their lattice structure on being heated. For example, iron will change its lattice from body-centered cubic to face-centered cubic if it is heated above 900°C. This type of phase change is very common.

The underlying principles governing phase changes are correlated in the subject of thermodynamics, and it is possible to relate the transition temperatures and pressures to the way in which a given crystalline solid absorbs energy in the two phases and to other parameters. In brief, the transition temperature is that at which the free energies of the crystal in the two phases are equal. Small progress has been made in relating the phase changes to fundamental quantum-mechanical principles for the same reason that difficulty is encountered in determining the specific heats from first principles; it is too difficult to calculate the energies of atomic oscillation and similar quantities from first principles. In spite of this, the procedure wherewith experimental data are combined with theoretical knowledge to determine arbitrary constants has given considerable breadth of understanding of the origin of phase changes, and there are few profound mysteries in this field at the present time.

3.13   Electrical Conductivity

The electrical properties of crystals constitute a topic of widespread practical interest which has been the object of much thought. As we have seen in Sec. 3.4, the basic issue of whether a given substance is a metal, a semiconductor, or an insulator is determined by the disposition of occupied and unoccupied levels. On the other hand, the extent to which the electrons of a metal may conduct a current is determined by factors much more subtle than the density and distribution of electron levels. This is demonstrated by the fact that the electrical resistivity of most pure metals decreases as one decreases the temperature and becomes exceedingly small at very low temperatures.

Theoretical evidence shows that the electrical resistivity would be essentially zero if the electrons near the top of the filled band could move freely when accelerated by an electric field. What actually occurs is that electrons accelerated in a given direction are deflected from that direction by various obstacles. The most important of these obstacles is related to the vibrational movement of the lattice. The oscillating atoms deflect the electrons and hence constitute a resistance to motion. Since the amplitude of atomic oscillation is closely related to the specific heat, there is a close correlation between the electrical resistivity in the ideal pure metal and the specific heat. This is indicated by the fact that both the electrical resistivity and the specific heat drop to very low values near the absolute zero of temperature.

If the metal is impure, or highly distorted, the electrons may be deflected either by the impurity atoms or by the flaws in the crystal lattice. This contribution to the electrical resistivity appears even at the absolute zero of temperature and gives rise to a component of electrical resistance known as *residual resistivity*. In alloys containing a large percentage of a foreign atom, the residual resistivity may be larger than the component of resistivity arising from lattice vibrations in the vicinity of room temperature.

Some metals such as lead and tin, known as *superconductors*, lose all traces of electrical resistivity at finite temperatures, usually near 4°K. The origin of this interesting effect is not well understood at present, although there is reason to believe that it arises from a close coupling between the lattice vibrational waves and the electrons. For nearly fifty years this topic has remained an outstanding mystery.

3.14   Magnetism

The magnetic properties of crystals are of no less interest than the electrical properties, although many subtle effects remain to be understood.   (See Chap. 4).   The great majority of solids are either attracted or repelled by a magnetic pole with a relatively feeble force.   Materials which are repelled are termed *diamagnetic*.   The universal source of diamagnetism resides in the fact that a charge moving in a fixed, closed orbit will tend to alter its motion in the presence of a magnetic field in such a way as to generate an internal field which repels the solid from the magnet.

Materials which are attracted to a magnet are termed *paramagnetic*. The universal source of paramagnetism resides in the fact that each electron behaves like a small permanent magnet which, given sufficient freedom, will orient itself in such a way as to be attracted by a magnetic pole. This alignment is impossible if electrons are restrained by the Pauli exclusion principle in such a way that their magnetic effects cancel one another and if they are prevented from altering their orientation without a large change of energy.   Cancellation of this type occurs in practically all good insulators; hence they are universally diamagnetic.   On the other hand, the electrons near the top of the filled region in metals can align their spins in such a way as to give a net attractive force because of the presence of vacant levels very near the filled ones.   Hence many metals are paramagnetic.

The strongest paramagnetism is observed in substances which have partly filled d shells.   Such shells occur among insulating salts, such as those of the iron-group elements or the rare earths, as well as among metals.

In ferromagnetic materials, of which metallic iron, cobalt, and nickel are the outstanding prototypes, the spins of a fraction of the electrons in the partly filled d shells are spontaneously aligned parallel to one another so that the solid has a permanent magnetic moment.   All these materials are closely related to the paramagnetic materials, but differ in the important respect that it is not necessary to apply an external magnetic field in order to have an excess of electrons with aligned spins.

IMPERFECTIONS IN THE INTERIOR
OF CRYSTALS

As was mentioned in the introduction, a large number of the properties of crystals are critically determined by imperfections, *i.e.*, by deviations from ideal behavior.   The unraveling of the manner in which imperfections influence the behavior of crystals is still in the process of development, and it is difficult to speak with finality on most phases of this topic at the present time.   However, the general outline seems to be at least qualitatively clear so that some of the major principles and rules can be discussed.

It is convenient to take the viewpoint that the ideal crystal represents the matrix in which the imperfections can act. The manner in which the imperfections behave in any given case is determined both by the properties of the ideal crystal and by the intrinsic properties of the imperfection. Most analysis in this area has focused on a case in which the density of imperfection is small, *i.e.*, in which each imperfection can be regarded as being physically separated by perfect crystal from other imperfections of a similar kind. This is the somewhat idealized limit of "the nearly perfect crystal." There are, quite naturally, many crystals found in nature in which the density of imperfections is so high that the dilute approximation is not good. It is doubtful that any such crystals possess properties which are radically and qualitatively different from those of crystals containing the dilute distribution of imperfections. Or, expressed in another way, there is probably a far smaller difference between the properties of crystals containing a high and a low density of imperfections than there is between the properties of the ideal crystal and the crystal containing a small number of imperfections.

It appears at the present time that there are six outstanding and generally distributed imperfections. Unquestionably, other specialized imperfections can be found in relatively particular materials, but the six primary imperfections occur so widely that we can safely focus attention upon them in the present discussion. The six imperfections are as follows:

    a. Lattice vibrational quanta (phonons)
    b. Free electrons and holes
    c. Excitons
    d. Vacancies and interstitial atoms
    e. Foreign atoms
    f. Dislocations

We shall consider the principal properties of each of these imperfections.

3.15 Phonons

Perhaps the simplest type of crystal imperfection is that which occurs when lattice vibrational waves are stimulated within the interior of the crystal, as may be done by heating the crystal or by placing it in contact with an appropriate sonic oscillator. Such waves may pass back and forth within the crystal specimen and, in the case in which they are relatively randomly distributed, as when associated with heat motion, they may interfere constructively and destructively. In constructive interference, a substantial amount of energy may be concentrated in a very small region of the lattice, such as at a single atom, and cause large local changes.

It is convenient to associate hypothetical particles called *phonons* with each of the possible modes of oscillation of the crystal and to regard the lattice as containing a distribution of such particles, much like the molecules of a gas, when vibrational waves are stimulated. This formalism resembles closely the practice of regarding light waves as consisting of particles called photons. The passage of vibrational waves through the lattice can then be regarded as the passage of a system of particles which can combine with one another through mutual interaction. The generation of phonons requires energy, so that their creation can be associated with the component of specific heat arising from lattice vibrations.

3.16 Free Electrons and Holes

The normal insulator contains a completely filled band and a completely empty band separated by an energy gap. If one introduces electrons into the empty band (Fig. 3.10) or removes electrons from the filled band, the crystal becomes an electronic conductor. The extra electrons in the conduction band or the holes in the empty band can be viewed as imperfections which alter the properties of the insulator radically and, indeed, transform it to an electronic conductor. The free electrons or holes may be injected from outside the lattice, or they may be produced pairwise as in the ideal semiconductor. As we shall see later, they may also be derived from impurity atoms.

The free electrons and holes can be scattered by collision with the phonons, if the lattice is above the absolute zero of temperature. This scattering contributes to the electrical resistivity of the conductor. In fact the temperature-dependent resistivity of metals discussed in Sec. 3.13 originates in this way, although it was described in different language.

3.17 Excitons

We noted previously, in Sec. 3.6, that a hole behaves like a positive charge. As a result, it can attract an electron. This attractive force is much like the attraction between the electron and proton in a hydrogen atom. In fact, the two particles, namely, the electron and the hole, can combine in states of motion which correspond to those associated with the normal orbital levels of the hydrogen atom. These levels are related to states of motion in which the two particles cannot conduct a current because they are intimately combined to yield a neutral product. This product is commonly called an *exciton*.

Since the electron and the hole are more stable in the exciton state than they would be when free, because of the gain in attractive energy, it follows that any insulator possesses a series of exciton states which lie below the conduction levels described so well by the band theory (see

Sec. 3.4).   Thus, if one excites an insulating crystal with light quanta of gradually increasing energy, the first transitions will be to nonconducting exciton states rather than to the conducting states.

An exciton may collide with phonons and, if the latter have enough energy, be decomposed into an electron and a hole, thereby rendering the crystal conducting.   It is believed that this process occurs very rapidly in the simplest intrinsic semiconductors such as germanium and silicon. Similarly the exciton may interact with a free electron or hole and disappear, giving up its excitation energy to the electron or hole.   It has been found in the case of the alkali halides that the energy imparted by excitons to loosely bound electrons is sufficient to eject the latter from the surface of the crystal under appropriate circumstances.

It is clear that a crystal containing an exciton is radically different from one which does not, because the exciton may generate a free electron and a hole or may cause other changes which can be measured.

3.18   Vacancies and Interstitial Atoms

A crystal may contain extra atoms in interstitial positions between the normal atoms of the lattice, or it may contain vacant lattice sites.   In fact, both an interstitial atom and a vacant lattice site may occur spontaneously if a group of phonons combine to impart so much energy to a normal atom of the lattice that it is ejected from its normal position to an interstitial position.   This type of process occurs frequently at elevated temperatures in all solids and is responsible for many of the most interesting properties of crystals at high temperatures.   For example, the spontaneous generation of vacant lattice sites in the alkali halides is responsible for the electrolytic conductivity which can be observed in these crystals just below the melting point.   The presence of vacant lattice sites makes it possible for the normal atoms to jump from one position to another, much as a vacancy in a densely crowded parking field makes it possible to rearrange cars.

Similarly, vacancies in a lattice of metals at elevated temperatures make it possible for the atoms to diffuse about.   Interstitial atoms may play a similar role.   In both these examples, namely, that of electrolytic conductivity in the salts and atomic diffusion in metals, the interaction of the vacancies or interstitial atoms with phonons plays a very important role in promoting migration.   In general, the vacancy or interstitial atom can move only when it is given a large amount of thermal energy through concentration of phonons at a single region of the lattice.

3.19   Foreign Atoms

Foreign atoms can alter the properties of the ideal crystal in a large number of ways.   We have seen that the electrical resistivity of metals can be changed by foreign atoms which scatter the conduction electrons. This also occurs in semiconductors.

Impurity atoms can alter the properties of insulators quite radically by introducing new energy levels in the gap between the filled and the empty band. A large number of crystalline materials are made luminescent by the presence of such extra levels which play a role in absorbing and emitting light quanta. Similarly, appropriately placed impurity atoms may be ionized either by light or by phonons, thereby producing either free electrons or free holes. The great majority of the photoconductors and semiconductors that are used commercially derive their properties from the presence of foreign atoms which are added in carefully controlled amounts.

It may also be mentioned that the electrolytic conductivity of salts can be influenced by the presence of impurities. If a sodium ion is replaced by a divalent ion such as calcium, the crystal would contain an excess positive charge unless a second sodium were to leave the lattice, producing a vacancy. Such vacancies, as we have seen above, influence the electrolytic conductivity of the salt. Thus the electrolytic conductivity may be enhanced by adding suitable impurities.

3.20 Dislocations

The dislocation is the imperfection which produces the most profound changes in crystalline substances. Its properties are presently understood only to a limited extent. It can appear in a variety of forms in a crystalline solid, one of the typical and most interesting being that shown in Fig. 3.12. It will be seen that the section of the crystal above the horizontal line AB contains one extra atomic plane normal to this line. This imperfection, which is called a Taylor-Orowan dislocation, has the following properties:

a. It can move through the lattice under application of a very low stress, thereby causing the lattice to deform plastically. In brief, it is believed that the normal plastic properties of crystalline solids are derived from the presence of dislocations. If the dislocations did not occur, crystals would be highly elastic for a very wide range of stress.

b. The dislocation may act as a catalyst for the production of many other internal transformations. For example, it requires no more energy to produce an interstitial atom or a vacancy at a Taylor dislocation than it does at the surface of a crystal. Thus such dislocations are believed to act as convenient sources and sinks for vacancies and interstitial atoms within crystals. In other words, dislocations play an important role in processes concerning electrolytic conductivity and diffusion.

c. Impurity atoms may congregate at dislocations so that the interaction between the two has an important influence both upon the behavior of the impurity atoms and upon the plastic properties of a crystal. Much of the effect of alloying agents on the plastic properties of metals is believed to be related to interaction between foreign atoms and dislocations.

d. When dislocations are set in motion during plastic flow, they can generate both interstitial atoms and vacancies in excess of the equilibrium number associated with the given temperature. As a result, plastic flow may have a significant effect, at least in a transient manner, upon the electrolytic conductivity and atomic diffusion in a solid.

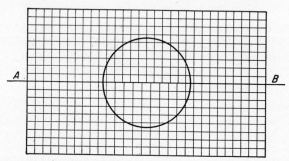

Fig. 3.12 A cross section through one of the principal types of dislocation, called a Taylor-Orowan dislocation. The dislocation line runs normal to the page. The disorder reaches its peak at the center of the circle shown, the circle being drawn only to focus attention on the region of disorder. It may be seen that above the plane *AB* there is one more atom, or lattice cell, than below the plane so the portion of the crystal above the plane *AB* behaves as if it had an extra half plane extending vertically to the plane *AB*. The region of the half circle above *AB* is compressed relative to the normal lattice, whereas that in the lower half circle is under tension.

These few comments probably serve to indicate quite clearly that the topic of imperfections in crystals could easily form the basis for a chapter as long as that devoted here to the entire subject of solids.

REFERENCES

Seitz, F., "The Modern Theory of Solids," McGraw-Hill Book Company, Inc., New York, 1940.

Seitz, F., "The Physics of Metals," McGraw-Hill Book Company, Inc., New York, 1943.

Shockley, W., "Electrons and Holes in Semiconductors," D. Van Nostrand Company, Inc., New York, 1950.

Mott, N. F., and G. W. Gurney, "Electronic Processes in Ionic Crystals," Oxford University Press, New York, 1940.

Mott, N. F., and H. Jones, "The Theory of Metals and Alloys," Oxford University Press, New York, 1936.

Shockley, W., "Imperfections in Nearly Perfect Crystals," John Wiley & Sons, Inc., New York, 1952.

Cottrell, A. H., "Theory of Dislocations," Oxford University Press, New York, 1953.

4

Magnetism

CHARLES KITTEL

PROFESSOR OF PHYSICS

UNIVERSITY OF CALIFORNIA, BERKELEY

4.1 Types of Magnetic Behavior

It is useful to distinguish five types of magnetism:

a. Paramagnetism is principally associated with electron spins in a system with weak mutual interaction among the spins. The magnetic susceptibility χ follows the Curie law (Fig. 4.1a)

$$\chi = \frac{C}{T} \tag{4.1}$$

where C is a constant called the Curie constant and T is the absolute temperature; χ is defined by

$$\chi = \frac{M}{H} \tag{4.2}$$

where M is the magnetization (magnetic moment per unit volume) and H is the magnetic field intensity; the permeability is given by $\mu = 1 + 4\pi\chi$. A typical paramagnetic substance is ferric ammonium sulfate $Fe(NH_4)_2(SO_4)_2 \cdot 12H_2O$; each ferric ion has five parallel electron spins, while the H_2O, NH_4, and SO_4 groups dilute the ferric ions so as to keep their mutual spin interactions weak.

b. Ferromagnetism occurs when the interaction between the spins on paramagnetic ions is strong and directed so as to keep neighboring spins pointing the same way. At a temperature T_c called the *Curie point,* ferromagnetism is destroyed by thermal agitation. Above the Curie point the susceptibility follows the Curie-Weiss law (Fig. 4.1b)

$$\chi = \frac{C}{T - T_c} \qquad (T > T_c) \tag{4.3}$$

and below the Curie point we have the complex behavior characterizing

97

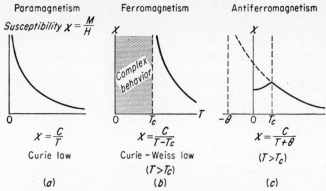

Fig. 4.1 Temperature dependence of the magnetic susceptibility in (a) paramagnetism; (b) ferromagnetism; (c) antiferromagnetism.

the domain processes involved in the technical magnetization curve.   A typical ferromagnetic substance is iron.

  c. Antiferromagnetism occurs when the interaction between neighboring ions tends to make neighboring spins point in opposite directions. The susceptibility has the same positive sign here as in paramagnetism and ferromagnetism but has the temperature dependence shown in Fig. 4.1c; above the Curie point

$$\chi = \frac{C}{T + \vartheta} \qquad (T > T_c) \qquad (4.4)$$

On cooling below the Curie temperature T_c, the spins lock in with antiparallel orientations, as shown in Fig. 4.2.   A typical antiferromagnetic substance is manganese oxide, MnO.

  d. Ferrite-type magnetism has many of the characteristics of ferromagnetism but results from antiferromagnetic interactions when the oppositely directed spins have unequal magnitudes.   The material will have

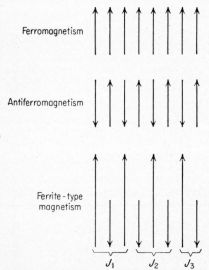

Fig. 4.2 Spin arrangements characterizing ferromagnetism, antiferromagnetism, and ferrite-type magnetism at temperatures well below the Curie temperature.

a resultant magnetization equal to the difference of the magnetizations of the two sets of spins.   The reciprocal susceptibility above the Curie point is not a linear function of temperature, as it was in Eqs. (4.1), (4.3), and (4.4), but is now a more complicated function of the temperature

(Fig. 4.3). In the cases of practical interest the behavior below the Curie point is identical with ferromagnetism. A typical example of ferrite-type magnetism is magnetite or ferrous ferrite, $FeO \cdot Fe_2O_3$; here the spin of one Fe^{3+} ion is oppositely directed to the combined spin of the other Fe^{3+} and the Fe^{2+} ion.

e. Diamagnetism is characterized by negative values of the susceptibility. It occurs in all substances and may be superimposed on other types of magnetism, although diamagnetic susceptibilities are usually

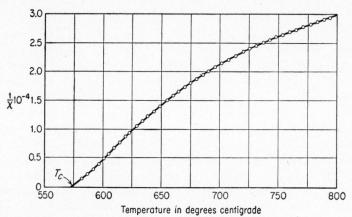

Fig. 4.3. Reciprocal susceptibility of magnetite, $FeO \cdot Fe_2O_3$, above the Curie temperature.

considerably smaller in absolute magnitude than other susceptibilities. Diamagnetism is an effect of electromagnetic induction: the orbital motion of electrons around atoms is modified by the application of a magnetic field in such a sense as to oppose the increase of flux passing through the electronic orbits. The associated susceptibility is usually independent of temperature. A typical diamagnetic substance is benzene. In the remainder of this chapter we shall neglect diamagnetism.

The practical applications of magnetism in industry all involve ferromagnetism or ferrite-type magnetism: these are essentially equivalent as regards the applications. Paramagnetism is important in experimental physics, as the only existing method for attaining temperatures below 1°K involves the adiabatic demagnetization of a paramagnetic salt. Nuclear paramagnetism is used to calibrate and control magnetic field intensity in electromagnets. Antiferromagnetism and diamagnetism do not seem to have found any industrial or experimental application.

This chapter will be devoted chiefly to ferromagnetism, but it is useful first to discuss paramagnetism as an introduction to the general properties of magnetic substances.

4.2 Paramagnetism

It is a fundamental result of the Dirac theory of the electron that an electron should behave as if endowed with a spin angular momentum of $h/4\pi$ about an axis through the center of the electron; here h is Planck's constant. We say that an electron has a spin $S = \frac{1}{2}$ measured in units of $h/2\pi$. The magnetic moment associated with the spin of an electron is a Bohr magneton

$$\mu_B = \frac{eh}{4\pi mc} \tag{4.5}$$

Most magnetic moments are known from gyromagnetic and microwave resonance experiments to be associated with the spin moment of the electron, orbital moments being of secondary importance for the magnetic moment although they are important for other features of the magnetic behavior.

In most chemical compounds, especially in organic compounds, every atom will have a net magnetic moment of zero because the spin moments of the electrons on each atom usually cancel each other out. But besides a number of special situations, there are groups of chemical elements where individual atoms may have a resultant spin. Such groups include the elements in the first transition group of the periodic table (Sc, Ti, V, Cr, Mn, Fe, Co, Ni, and Cu), the rare-earth elements, and the transuranic elements.

The most important relationship in paramagnetism is the Curie law $\chi = C/T$. We derive this for the special case of N atoms per unit volume, each atom bearing one uncompensated electron spin, so that $S = \frac{1}{2}$. There are now two spin orientations possible in a magnetic field, corresponding to the values $\pm\frac{1}{2}$ of the z component of the spin. The difference in energy between the two orientations is $\mu_B H - \mu_B(-H) = 2\mu_B H$. In thermal equilibrium the number of atoms in the two states must follow the Boltzmann distribution law, so that the numbers are in the ratio

$$\frac{N_-}{N_+} = e^{-W/kT} = e^{-2\mu_B H/kT} \tag{4.6}$$

where k is the Boltzmann constant and W is the energy difference between the two states. For usual laboratory fields and not too low temperatures, we have $\mu_B H/kT \ll 1$, so that to a sufficient approximation

$$\frac{N_-}{N_+} \cong 1 - \frac{2\mu_B H}{kT} \tag{4.7}$$

and

$$\frac{N_+ - N_-}{N} \cong \frac{\mu_B H}{kT} \tag{4.8}$$

The net magnetization is, using Eq. (4.8),

$$M = \mu_B(N_+ - N_-) \cong \frac{N\mu_B{}^2 H}{kT} \qquad (4.9)$$

so that

$$\chi = \frac{M}{H} = \frac{N\mu_B{}^2}{kT} \qquad (4.10)$$

which is in the form of the Curie law. For an arbitrary angular-momentum quantum number J and Landé factor g, it may be shown that the Curie constant is given by

$$C = NJ(J + 1)\frac{g^2\mu_B{}^2}{3k} \qquad (4.11)$$

4.3 Ferromagnetism

The central fact of ferromagnetism is the existence of spontaneous magnetization in the absence of applied fields. To make spins line up more or less the same way below the Curie temperature, we need an energy of interaction ΔW between adjacent spins in the lattice of the order of

$$\Delta W \approx kT_c \qquad (4.12)$$

For a Curie temperature $T_c \approx 10^3{}°\mathrm{K}$, we find that ΔW must be of the order of 10^{-13} erg. This is equivalent to an effective magnetic field

$$H_{eff} \approx \frac{\Delta W}{\mu_B} \approx 10^7 \text{ oersteds} \qquad (4.13)$$

This would be a fantastically large field if it were of magnetic origin. Purely magnetic interactions can be shown to produce internal fields only of the order of the saturation magnetization, or $\approx 10^3$ oersteds, and are thus too weak to account for ferromagnetism.

Heisenberg showed that the energy of orientation of adjacent spins in ferromagnetism may be attributed to the quantum-mechanical exchange interaction. This interaction energy is usually written as

$$\Delta W = -2J\vec{S}_1 \cdot \vec{S}_2 \qquad (4.14)$$

where J is the *exchange integral* between atoms 1 and 2; $\vec{S}$ is the spin vector. The exchange energy is a consequence of the Pauli exclusion principle, whereby a change in the spin orientation of an atom must necessarily be accompanied by a change in the distribution of electronic charge around the atom. It is an important truth that *the exchange energy is of electrostatic rather than magnetostatic origin.*

The most convenient approximate method of deriving the Curie-Weiss law, Eq. (4.3), is to treat the exchange energy as equivalent to an effective magnetic field H_{exch} proportional to the magnetization:

$$H_{exch} = \lambda M \tag{4.15}$$

where λ is a constant known as the Weiss constant or the molecular field constant.

It is not practical to calculate λ explicitly from the principles of quantum theory; one has to be content with estimating λ from the observed values of the Curie constant and Curie point, using Eq. (4.18) below.[1]

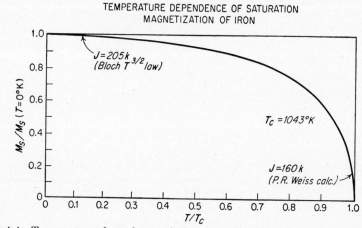

TEMPERATURE DEPENDENCE OF SATURATION MAGNETIZATION OF IRON

Fig. 4.4 Temperature dependence of the saturation magnetization of iron. By fitting the results of advanced theories to the observed curve, it is possible to estimate the value of the exchange integral J, and one finds $J = 205k$ and $J = 160k$ in two different temperature regions.

Above the Curie point we may assume that the Curie law obtains, provided that the total field be taken as the sum of the applied field and the exchange field. Thus, from Eqs. (4.1) and (4.15),

$$MT = C(H + \lambda M) \tag{4.16}$$

so that, on solving for M/H,

$$\chi = \frac{C}{T - T_c} \tag{4.17}$$

which is of the Curie-Weiss form; here

$$T_c = C\lambda \tag{4.18}$$

At and below T_c, spontaneous magnetization occurs. The observed temperature dependence of the saturation magnetization of iron is shown in Fig. 4.4.

Values of the saturation magnetization of representative ferromagnetic substances are given in Table 4.1, together with the Curie points and the effective magnetic moment per magnetic atom. We note that the largest saturation magnetization occurs in gadolinium, for which $4\pi M_S = 25,000$.

The value of the saturation magnetization is an important factor in the engineering applications of ferromagnetic materials. In most applications we would like to have as high a saturation magnetization as possible.

Table 4.1 Saturation Magnetization and Curie Points of Ferromagnetic Substances*

Substance	Saturation magnetization M_s		Magnetic moment n_{eff} (at 0°K) in μ_B per atom	Ferromagnetic Curie temp., °K
	At room temp.	At 0°K		
Fe.................	1707	1752	2.221	1043
Co.................	1400	1446	1.716	1400
Ni.................	485	510	0.606	631
Gd................	1090	1980	7.10	289
Dy................	1830 (88°K)	.....	....	105
MnBi..............	600	675	3.52	630
Cu₂MnAl...........	430	(580)	(4.0)	603
Cu₂MnIn...........	500	(600)	(4.0)	506
MnAs..............	670	870	3.40	318
MnB...............	147	.....	....	533
Mn₄N..............	183	.....	0.24	745
MnSb..............	710	.....	3.53	587
CrTe..............	240	.....	2.39	336
CrO₂..............	...	.....	2.07	
MnOFe₂O₃..........	358	.....	5.0†	783
FeOFe₂O₃..........	485	.....	4.2†	848
CoOFe₂O₃..........	...	.....	3.3†	793
NiOFe₂O₃..........	240	.....	2.3†	863
CuOFe₂O₃..........	290	.....	1.3†	728
MgOFe₂O₃..........	143	.....	1.1†	583

* After C. Kittel, "Introduction to Solid State Physics," John Wiley & Sons, Inc., New York, 1953.

† Calculated per molecule $MOFe_2O_3$, where M is the bivalent cation.

But other physical properties are usually of far greater importance in determining the use to which a given material may be put: whether it will be magnetically hard and suitable for a loudspeaker magnet or magnetically soft and suitable for a power transformer or pulse transformer. Materials of nearly the same saturation moment may have permeabilities which differ by factors of 10^4 to 10^6. The explanation of these differences and the explanation of the characteristic features of the technical magnetization curve (Fig. 4.5) are the province of domain theory. We discuss domain theory in the next section.*

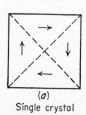

Fig. 4.5 The technical magnetization curve. The *coercive force* H_c is the reverse field necessary to bring the induction B to zero; the *remanence* B_r is the value of B at $H = 0$; the *saturation induction* B_s is defined as the limiting value of $(B - H)$ for large H.

4.4 Ferromagnetic Domains

The central problem of domain theory is to explain how a relatively weak magnetic field (in some substances as low as 0.01 oersted) can alter the observed magnetic induction by an appreciable amount, in view of the 10^7-oersted exchange field, very much stronger than the applied field. Pierre Weiss (1907) showed the way out of the difficulty. He assumed that the actual specimens are composed of a number of small regions called *domains*, within each of which the local magnetization is saturated. A schematic arrangement of domains with zero resultant magnetic moment is shown in Fig. 4.6a for a single crystal. In polycrystalline samples it was imagined by early workers that each

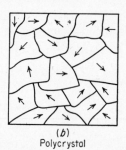

(a)
Single crystal

(b)
Polycrystal

Fig. 4.6 Schematic domain arrangements for zero resultant magnetic moment in a single crystal (a) and in a polycrystalline specimen (b). The domain structure of the polycrystalline specimen has been drawn for simplicity as if each crystallite contained only a single domain; this is not usually the case.

crystallite might contain a single domain and that the resultant magnetic moment could be zero by virtue of a random distribution of grain axes, as

---

* The discussion which follows draws heavily on a review article by the author, *Revs. Mod. Phys.*, **21**: 541–583 (1949); the material is also covered in a 16-mm motion picture, "Action Pictures of Ferromagnetic Domains," available on loan from the Publications Department, Bell Telephone Laboratories, Inc., 463 West St., New York 14, New York.

indicated in Fig. 4.6b. We know now that domains can be larger or smaller than a crystal grain, depending on conditions.

The increase in the value of the resultant magnetic moment of the specimen under the action of an applied magnetic field may be imagined to take place on the domain theory by two independent processes, as was suggested by R. Becker: by an increase in the volume of domains which are favorably oriented with respect to the field, at the expense of unfavorably oriented domains, or by rotation of the directions of magnetization toward the direction of the field. These two methods by which the resultant magnetization may change are shown in Fig. 4.7. In weak fields the magnetization changes usually proceed by means of domain-boundary displacements, so that the domains change in size. In strong fields the magnetization usually changes by means of rotation of the direction of magnetization.

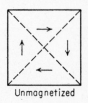

Unmagnetized

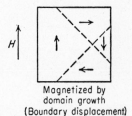

Magnetized by
domain growth
(Boundary displacement)

What causes the formation of domains? This question was first answered in 1935 by Landau and Lifshitz, who showed that domain structure is a natural consequence of the various contributions to the energy—exchange, anisotropy, and magnetic—of a ferromagnetic body. We first consider briefly the experimental evidence for the existence of domains. The most direct evidence of domain structure is furnished by photomicrographs of domain boundaries obtained by the technique of magnetic powder patterns. This method, applied originally by Bitter (1931), has in the hands of Elmore, Williams, and others

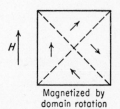

Magnetized by
domain rotation

Fig. 4.7 Fundamental magnetization processes.

provided convincing proof that domains exist in the shapes and sizes expected theoretically and furthermore that they behave under applied mechanical and magnetic forces as predicted by theory.

The powder-pattern method consists in placing a drop of colloidal suspension of finely divided ferromagnetic material, such as magnetite, on the carefully prepared surface of the ferromagnetic crystal under study. It is found on observation through a microscope that the colloid particles in the suspension become strongly concentrated about certain well-defined lines which represent the boundaries between domains magnetized in different directions. The reason why the colloid particles concentrate near these boundaries is that in their vicinity there exist very strong local magnetic fields which attract the magnetic particles.

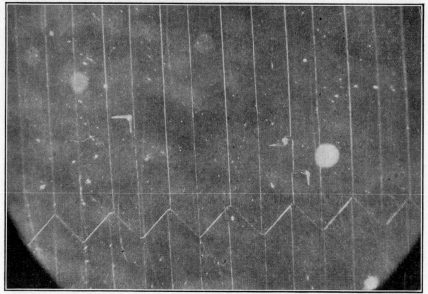

Fig. 4.8   Simple domain structure in iron.   (*H. J. Williams.*)

Fig. 4.9   Complex domain structure in a silicon-iron crystal.   (*After Williams, Bozorth, and Shockley.*)

A photograph of a simple domain structure in iron is shown in Fig. 4.8. A more complex type of domain structure is shown in Fig. 4.9; structures with this general "tree" character arise when the crystal surface is slightly inclined with respect to a cube face.

We may understand the origin of domains by considering the structures shown in Fig. 4.10, each representing a cross section through a ferromagnetic single crystal. In (a) we have a saturated configuration consisting of a single domain; as a consequence of the magnetic "poles"

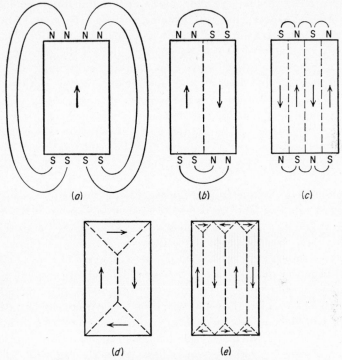

Fig. 4.10   The origin of domains.

formed on the surfaces of the crystal, this configuration will have a high value of the magnetic energy $(1/8\pi)\int H^2\, dV$. The magnetic energy for a square cross section will be of the order of $M_s{}^2 \approx 10^6$ ergs/cm^3.

In (b) the magnetic energy has been reduced by a factor of roughly one-half as a result of dividing the crystal into two domains magnetized in opposite directions. The subdivision process may be carried further as in (c): with N domains it turns out that the magnetic energy is reduced (because of the reduced spatial extension of the field) to approximately $1/N$ of the magnetic energy of the saturated configuration (a).

The subdivision process may be expected to continue until the energy required to establish an additional boundary layer or interface, separating two domains magnetized oppositely, is greater than the reduction in magnetic field energy consequent on the finer subdivision. It may be appreciated that a boundary layer does indeed have a certain amount of energy associated with it: on opposite sides of the boundary the magnetization is directed in antiparallel directions; now since the exchange forces favor parallel and oppose antiparallel orientations of the magnetization, the expenditure of energy to establish a boundary layer will naturally be required. We shall estimate this energy below after an examination of the nature of the boundary layer, and we shall find that the energy is of the order of 1 erg/cm^2 of boundary surface. If then we suppose tentatively that there are $N = 10^3$ domains per cm, the total boundary energy in a crystal cube 1 cm on each edge will be of the order of 10^3 ergs and the magnetic energy will also be of the order of 10^3 ergs. This situation represents approximately the equilibrium number of domains for the *particular geometrical arrangement shown.*

It is possible to devise domain arrangements such as (d) for which the magnetic energy is zero. In (d) the boundaries of the triangular prism domains (termed *domains of closure*) near the end faces of the crystal make equal angles—45°—with the magnetization in the rectangular domains and with the magnetization in the domains of closure; therefore the component of magnetization normal to the boundary is continuous across the boundary, and no poles are formed anywhere in the crystal. As there are no poles, there is no magnetic field associated with the magnetization, and we may speak of the flux circuit being completed within the crystal—thus giving rise to the phrase "domains of closure" for the domains near the surfaces of the crystal which act to complete the flux circuit.

The extent to which the subdivision of the closure configuration (e) proceeds will depend on the energy requirements of the domains of closure. It is not immediately obvious that the optimum closure configuration of type (e) will necessarily have a lower energy than the optimum butt-end configuration of type (c), and in fact approximations to both types of termination are found in different materials. The energy required to form a domain of closure in a uniaxial crystal such as cobalt comes principally from what is called the *crystalline anisotropy energy.* The anisotropy energy tends to make the magnetization of a domain line up along certain crystallographic axes. The axes thus favored are known as preferred axes, or axes of easy magnetization. Such axes are well established experimentally, and it is known that a considerably larger amount of energy may be required to saturate a specimen along an arbitrary axis than along one of the preferred axes. In cobalt the hexagonal axis of the crystal is the only preferred axis, and cobalt is accordingly referred to as uniaxial. In iron, which is cubic, the preferred axes are the cube edges; in nickel, which is also cubic, the preferred axes are the body diagonals. Figure 4.11 shows magnetization curves for cobalt in directions of easy and hard magnetization.

In cobalt, if the basic rectangular domains are magnetized along the easy axis of magnetization, then the domains of closure will by necessity be magnetized in hard directions. In a cubic crystal such as iron, it is possible for both the basic domains and the closure domains to be magnetized along different easy axes. The energy expenditure in this case arises from magnetostriction: since the closure domains are magnetized along different axes from the basic domains, they will tend to be elongated by *magnetostriction* along different axes, and in order to fit the various domains together in the crystal structure we have to do work against elastic forces.

Magnetostriction denotes the dependence of the length of a ferromagnetic crystal in a given direction on the direction of the magnetization relative to the crystal axes. We may think of magnetostriction as arising from the dependence of the crystalline anisotropy energy on the state of strain of the lattice: thus it may be energetically favorable for a cubic crystal such as iron or nickel to

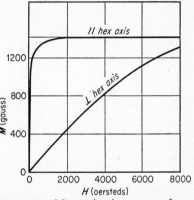

Fig. 4.11 Magnetization curves for a cobalt single crystal, parallel and perpendicular to the hexagonal axis.

deform slightly from the exactly cubic condition if doing so will lower the anisotropy energy by more than it raises the elastic energy.

We may summarize the theory of the origin of domains as follows: *domain structure has its origin in the possibility of lowering the energy of a system by going from a saturated configuration, such as (a), with high magnetic energy to a domain configuration, such as (c) or (e), with a lower energy.*

A particularly simple type of domain structure is shown in Fig. 4.12; this structure has been realized by Williams and Shockley with a single crystal of silicon iron which was cut to the form of a hollow rectangle with legs accurately parallel to easy directions of magnetization. When the crystal is saturated entirely in one sense, the domain boundaries are the 45° lines shown in (a); when part of the crystal is magnetized clockwise and part counterclockwise, then the square-shaped boundary in (b) is formed in addition. Magnetization changes are then found to take place by the movement of the square-shaped boundary; it was noted as shown in Fig. 4.13 that the flux changes correspond quantitatively to the displacements of the domain wall. These experiments have also shown

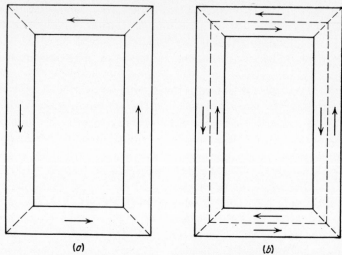

Fig. 4.12 Simple domain structures in single crystal of iron in form of rectangular loop, with legs parallel to easy directions of magnetization.

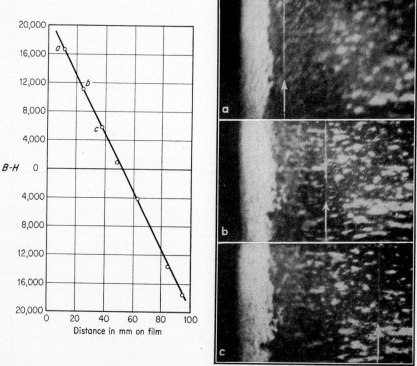

Fig. 4.13 (*Left*) Magnetization vs. displacement of the domain boundary, and (*right*) patterns showing the domain boundary in three different positions.

that there is no connection between the sizes of domains and the Barkhausen noise spectrum. It has been shown that the Barkhausen discontinuities correspond to irregular fluctuations in the motion of a domain boundary, rather than to complete domain reversal. Continued Barkhausen noise has been observed attending the motion of a single domain wall. This discovery frees the subject from the difficulties which had been raised by the earlier interpretation; *e.g.*, the apparent "domain volume" of 10^{-8} to 10^{-9} cc indicated by the Barkhausen effect has no direct connection with actual domain volumes, which may be very much greater.

4.5 Coercive Force

The coercive force is perhaps the most sensitive property of ferromagnetic materials which is subject to our control and is one of the most important criteria in the selection of ferromagnetic materials for practical applications. The essential difference between material for permanent magnets and material for transformer cores lies in the coercive force, which may range from the value of 600 oersteds in a loudspeaker magnet (Alnico V) and 12,000 in a special high-stability magnet (MnBi) to the value of 0.5 in a commercial power transformer (silicon-iron) or 0.004 in a pulse transformer (Supermalloy). Thus the coercive force may be varied over a range of 5×10^6.

When we have understood the coercive force, we will be a long way toward understanding the saturation hysteresis loss at low frequencies, since the area enclosed by the hysteresis loop is approximately given by the product of the saturation induction B_s times the coercive force. That is, the energy dissipated on going once around a hysteresis loop is of the order of $B_s H_c$, to within a factor of 2 to 4. We may, therefore, devote our attention to the single factor H_c.

The coercive force in magnetically soft (low H_c) materials may be understood from the following picture: The total energy of a given specimen may vary depending on the position of domain boundary, as a result of local variations in internal strains, impurities, crystallite dimensions, etc.; the variation is indicated schematically in Fig. 4.14. In the absence of an applied magnetic field the boundary will be situated at some minimum position such as (A) in the figure. In the presence of a field the boundary will be unable to make a large displacement to the extreme right (D) unless the energy is increased by a sufficient amount to enable the boundary to pass over the point B corresponding to the maximum boundary energy.

The increase in energy must be furnished by the reorientation of the local magnetization M_s in the applied field H, and the value of H which suffices to reverse about one-half of the magnetization of the specimen will be the coercive field H_c.

Qualitatively this picture of the coercive process explains the fact that the coercive force diminishes as the (precipitated) impurity content decreases and also as internal strains are removed through annealing; it also explains why it is that alloys containing a precipitated phase are magnetically hard.

The coercive force of one type of magnetically hard material may be understood from a quite different picture; we refer to materials composed of very small grains or fine powders where each particle is always magnetized to saturation as a single domain. The fact that a sufficiently

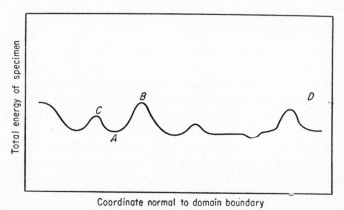

Fig. 4.14   Variation in energy of specimen as a function of the position of the domain boundary.

small particle, with diameter less than 10^{-4} or 10^{-5} cm, is composed of a single domain is a result of domain theory which has been confirmed by experiment. It can be shown that with such very small particles the formation of a domain boundary is energetically unfavorable: this is essentially because too large a proportion of the volume of a small particle would be contained within the wall—the wall thickness being independent of the particle size.

If a small particle is constrained to remain as a single domain, it will not be possible for magnetization changes and reversal to take place by means of the process of boundary displacement which usually requires relatively weak fields; instead the magnetization of the particle must rotate as a whole, a process which may require large fields depending on the anisotropy energy of the material or the shape of the particle: this is because we must rotate the magnetization over the energy hump corresponding to a direction of hard magnetization. The coercive force of fine iron particles is expected theoretically to be about 250 oersteds on the basis of rotation opposed by the crystalline anisotropy energy, and this is of the order of the observed value. The high coercive force of Alnico V is believed to be associated with single-domain particles of a precipitated phase in a state of fine subdivision.

If the small particles possess an elongated shape, we may have a high coercivity because of the anisotropy of the energy of the demagnetizing field, even if the crystalline anisotropy energy is low.   That is, the magnetization tends to line up along the long axis of the specimen, and a strong field may have to be applied to turn the magnetization through the short axis.   This appears to be the explanation of the high coercive force of the alloy FeCo in fine powder form; the alloy is known to have a low anisotropy energy from single crystal measurements, so that the anisotropy energy alone cannot explain the observations, but the shape effect must be invoked.

4.6   Reversible Permeability

The extent of the range of field strength over which the permeability is reversible is determined by the distance through which a domain boundary may move without passing over a peak in the curve of wall energy vs. distance; with reference to Fig. 4.14, one such region of reversible permeability is the region CAB.   When the domain boundary leaves this region, it moves irreversibly to the extreme right or extreme left of the figure.   The reversible permeability is determined by the irregularities of the curve of boundary energy vs. displacement and thus is determined by essentially the same physical conditions as the coercive force.

4.7   The Bloch Wall

The term Bloch wall denotes the transition layer which separates adjacent domains magnetized in different directions.   It is named after F. Bloch (1932), who was the first to study the nature of the transition layer.   The essential idea of the Bloch wall is that the entire change in spin direction between domains magnetized in different directions does not occur in one discontinuous jump across a single atomic plane. Rather, the change of direction will take place in a gradual way over many atomic planes (Fig. 4.15).   The reason for the gradual nature of the change is the fact that for a given total change of spin direction the exchange energy is lower when the change is distributed over many spins than when the change occurs abruptly.

This behavior may be understood from the expression [Eq. (4.14)]

$$w_{exch} = JS^2\phi^2 \tag{4.19}$$

for the exchange energy between two spins making a small angle ϕ with each other; here J is the exchange integral and S is the spin angular momentum measured in units of $h/2\pi$.   Let the total desired change of angle be ϕ_0; if the change occurs in N equal steps, then the angle change between neighboring spins is ϕ_0/N, and the exchange energy between each pair of neighboring atoms is

$$w_{exch} = JS^2 \left(\frac{\phi_0}{N}\right)^2 \tag{4.20}$$

The total exchange energy of the line of $N + 1$ atoms is thus

$$W_{exch} = JS^2 \frac{\phi_0^2}{N} \tag{4.21}$$

If the total change of angle between domains is $\phi_0 = \pi$, corresponding to a reversal of magnetization direction on passing through the wall, then

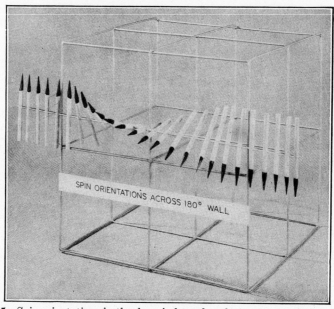

SPIN ORIENTATIONS ACROSS 180° WALL

Fig. 4.15   Spin orientations in the domain boundary between oppositely magnetized domains.

the exchange energy of a line of atoms through a wall 100 atoms in thickness is of the order of $kT_c/100$, as compared with kT_c for a wall only one atom-layer in thickness.

Since the exchange energy of a wall is inversely proportional to the thickness, the wall might spread out until it filled a sizable proportion of the crystal, were it not for the restraining effect of the anisotropy energy, which acts to limit the width of the transition layer. The spins contained within the wall are largely directed away from the axes of easy magnetization, so that there is a certain amount of anisotropy energy associated with the wall. The amount of anisotropy energy will be roughly proportional to the thickness of the wall, since the thickness is a measure of the total volume directed away from the axes of easy magnetization. The actual thickness and energy of the transition layer are the result of a balance between the competing claims of exchange energy and anisotropy energy, the former tending to increase the thickness and the latter tending to decrease the thickness.

The energy per unit surface area may be represented to a good approximation as the sum of contributions from exchange and anisotropy energies:

$$\sigma_w = \sigma_{exch} + \sigma_{\text{anisotropy}} \tag{4.22}$$

The exchange energy is given approximately by Eq. (4.21) for each line of atoms through the wall and normal to the plane of the wall. There are $1/a^2$ such lines per unit area, where a is the lattice constant; whence

$$\sigma_{exch} = \frac{\pi^2 J S^2}{N a^2} \tag{4.23}$$

The anisotropy energy is of the order of the anisotropy constant K, which is a measure of the anisotropy energy per unit volume, times the volume, or

$$\sigma_{\text{anisotropy}} \approx KNa \tag{4.24}$$

so that

$$\sigma_w \approx \frac{\pi^2 J S^2}{N a^2} + KNa \tag{4.25}$$

which is a minimum with respect to N when

$$\frac{\delta \sigma_w}{\delta N} = 0 = -\frac{\pi^2 J S^2}{N^2 a^2} + Ka \tag{4.26}$$

or

$$N = \left(\frac{\pi^2 J S^2}{K a^3}\right)^{1/2} \tag{4.27}$$

We have then the result that the thickness of the wall measured in atomic separations is approximately equal to the square root of the ratio of the exchange integral to the anisotropy energy per unit cell. For order of magnitude, in iron,

$$N \approx \left(\frac{kT_c}{K a^3}\right)^{1/2} \approx \left(\frac{10^{-13}}{10^5 10^{-23}}\right)^{1/2}$$
$$\approx 300 \text{ lattice constants}$$
$$\approx 1000 \text{ A}$$

The total wall energy per unit area is

$$\sigma_w = 2\pi \left(\frac{JKS^2}{a}\right)^{1/2} \tag{4.28}$$

which in iron is of the order of magnitude

$$\sigma_w \approx \left(\frac{kT_cK}{a}\right)^{\frac{1}{2}} \approx \left(\frac{10^{-13}10^5}{10^{-8}}\right)^{\frac{1}{2}}$$
$$\approx 1 \text{ erg/cm}^2$$

4.8 Frequency Dependence of Magnetic Phenomena

The response of ferromagnetic metals to electromagnetic fields of increasing frequency is usually first limited by eddy currents. But in

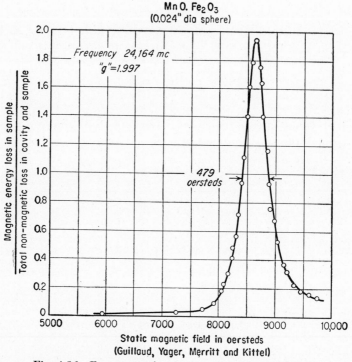

Fig. 4.16 Ferromagnetic resonance in manganese ferrite.

ferrites with electrical resistivities in the semiconductor range, or in finely divided metal powders, the magnetic response at high frequencies may be limited by three other mechanisms:

a. Damping of the domain-boundary motion because of relaxation effects

b. Resonance effects in the boundary motion

c. Rotational ferromagnetic resonance in the anisotropy field of the material

The latter process usually occurs at higher frequencies than the others,

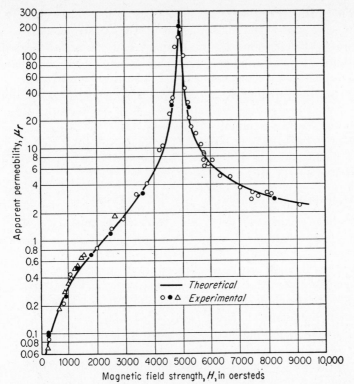

Fig. 4.17 Resonance curve for Supermalloy, according to Yager and Bozorth; the apparent permeability is plotted on a logarithmic scale.

and it determines the maximum usable frequency of a ferromagnetic substance.

Rotational resonance for electron spins in a magnetic field H occurs at a frequency ν_0 given by a relation of the Larmor or Zeeman form:

$$h\nu_0 = 2\mu_B H \tag{4.29}$$

Substituting appropriate numerical values, we find

$$\frac{\nu_0}{H} = 2.80 \text{ Mc/sec per oersted} \tag{4.30}$$

i.e., in a 10,000-oersted field resonance occurs at 28,000 Mc/sec. Experimental results are shown in Figs. 4.16 and 4.17. Now the field H to be substituted in Eq. (4.29) is actually an effective field which may contain contributions from several sources: the static external field, the demagnetizing field, and the anisotropy field

$$H_{\text{anisotropy}} = \frac{2K}{M_s} \tag{4.31}$$

associated with a crystal anisotropy energy K per unit volume. In the absence of a static external applied field the anisotropy field is usually dominant and determines the maximum usable frequency according to Eq. (4.29). In this condition high-anisotropy crystals will have high cutoff (resonance) frequencies, whereas low-anisotropy crystals will be limited to lower frequencies. As materials with high permeability at low frequency usually are characterized by a low anisotropy energy, they will become useless magnetically at relatively low frequencies in comparison with "harder" materials. For an anisotropy field of 1 oersted (as one might find in a material with a permeability of 10,000 or more), the cutoff is near 3 Mc/sec.

4.9 Magnetic Materials

For reference purposes we give in Table 4.2 a summary of the properties of typical high-permeability magnetic materials and permanent-magnet alloys. The range of properties is a striking illustration of the sensitivity of domain processes to the state of stress and subdivision and to the values of the anisotropy and magnetostriction of the ferromagnetic material. In developing a high-permeability material we wish to make the domain boundaries move as freely as possible, free from trapping by strain centers, crystal boundaries, impurities, inclusions, and cavities; we look accordingly for highly purified, oriented, annealed materials of low anisotropy and low magnetostriction (low coupling with internal stresses). In developing a permanent-magnet alloy we wish to suppress completely the existence or motion of domain boundaries, leaving only the domain rotation processes, and these we wish to make as difficult as possible.

4.10 Antiferromagnetism

There has been a great deal of interest in antiferromagnetism since its discovery in 1938 by Bizette, Squire, and Tsai, who worked with manganese oxide, MnO, which has a Curie point of 120°K. The Curie point in an antiferromagnetic is sometimes called the Néel temperature, after the French magnetician L. Néel who first predicted the existence of antiferromagnetism. Data for various substances are given in Table 4.3; here T_c is the actual transition temperature marked by a kink in the curve of susceptibility vs. temperature (Fig. 4.1c) and by a hump in the heat capacity and thermal expansion curves; the constant ϑ is defined by the expression

$$\chi = \frac{C}{T + \vartheta} \tag{4.32}$$

for the susceptibility above the Curie point T_c.

We give here a brief derivation of Eq. (4.32) for a simple situation in

Table 4.2 Data for Magnetic Materials*

High-permeability materials

Material	Form	Approximate per cent composition					Maximum permeability	Saturation flux density B_s, gauss	Coercive force H_c, oersteds
		Fe	Ni	Co	Mo	Other			
Cold-rolled steel	Sheet	98.5					2,000	21,000	1.8
Iron	Sheet	99.91					5,000	21,500	1.0
Purified iron	Sheet	99.95					180,000	21,500	0.05
4% silicon–iron	Sheet	96				4 Si	7,000	19,700	0.5
Grain oriented†	Sheet	97				3 Si	30,000	20,000	0.15
45 Permalloy	Sheet	54.7	45			0.3 Mn	25,000	16,000	0.3
45 Permalloy	Sheet	54.7	45			0.3 Mn	50,000	16,000	0.07
Hipernik	Sheet	50	50				70,000	16,000	0.05
Monimax	Sheet						35,000	15,000	0.1
Sinimax	Sheet						35,000	11,000	
78 Permalloy	Sheet	21.2	78.5			0.3 Mn	100,000	10,700	0.05
4–79 Permalloy	Sheet	16.7	79		4	0.3 Mn	100,000	8,700	0.05
Mu metal	Sheet	18	75		5	2Cr, 5Cu	100,000	6,500	0.05
Supermalloy	Sheet	15.7	79		5	0.3 Mn	800,000	8,000	0.002
Permendur	Sheet	49.7		50		0.3 Mn	5,000	24,500	2.0
2V Permendur	Sheet	49		49		2V	4,500	24,000	2.0
Hiperco	Sheet	64		34		Cr	10,000	24,200	1.0
2–81 Permalloy	Insulated powder	17	81		2		130	8,000	<1.0
Carbonyl iron	Insulated powder	99.9					132		
Ferroxcube III	Sintered powder		$MnFe_2O_4$	$+ ZnFe_2O_4$			1,500	2,500	0.1

* From R. A. Chegwedden, *Metal Progr.*, **54**: 705 (1948).
† Properties in direction of rolling.

Table 4.2 Data for Magnetic Materials (*Continued*)

Permanent-magnet alloys

Material	Per cent composition (remainder Fe)	Coercive force H_c, oersteds	Residual induction B_r, gauss	Energy product BH_{max}, $\times 10^{-6}$ ergs
Carbon steel	1 Mn, 0.9 C	50	10,000	0.20
Tungsten steel	5 W, 0.3 Mn, 0.7 C	70	10,300	0.32
Chromium steel	3.5 Cr, 0.9 C, 0.3 Mn	65	9,700	0.30
17% cobalt steel	17 Co, 0.75 C, 2.5 Cr, 8 W	150	9,500	0.65
36% cobalt steel	36 Co, 0.7 C, 4 Cr, 5 W	240	9,500	0.97
Remalloy or Comol	17 Mo, 12 Co	250	10,500	1.1
Indalloy (sintered)	— Mo, — Co	240	9,000	0.9
Alnico I	12 Al, 20 Ni, 5 Co	440	7,200	1.4
Alnico II	10 Al, 17 Ni, 2.5 Co, 6 Cu	550	7,200	1.6
Alnico II (sintered)	10 Al, 17 Ni, 2.5 Co, 6 Cu	520	6,900	1.4
Alnico IV	12 Al, 28 Ni, 5 Co	700	5,500	1.3
Alnico V	8 Al, 14 Ni, 24 Co, 3 Cu	550	12,500	4.5
Alnico VI	8 Al, 15 Ni, 24 Co, 3 Cu, 1 Ti	750	10,000	3.5
Alnico XII	6 Al, 18 Ni, 35 Co, 8 Ti	950	5,800	1.5
Vicalloy I	52 Co, 10 V	300	8,800	1.0
Vicalloy II (wire)	52 Co, 14 V	510	10,000	3.5
Cunife (wire)	60 Cu, 20 Ni	550	5,400	1.5
Cunico	50 Cu, 21 Ni, 29 Co	660	3,400	0.80
Vectolite	30 Fe_2O_2, 40 Fe_3O_4	1,000	1,600	0.60
Platinum-cobalt	77 Pt, 23 Co	2,600	4,500	3.8
Hyflux	Fine powder	390	6,000	0.97

which the lattice of paramagnetic ions can be divided into two inter-penetrating sublattices A, B such that all nearest neighbors of an ion on sublattice A lie on sublattice B.   This condition is, for example, satisfied by the simple cubic and body-centered cubic lattices but not by the face-centered cubic lattice.   If the only interactions are antiferromagnetic

Table 4.3   Curie Points of Antiferromagnetics

Substance	Transition temperature T_c, °K	Curie-Weiss ϑ, °K	Substance	Transition temperature T_c, °K	Curie-Weiss ϑ, °K
MnO........	122	610	CoO........	291	
MnS........	165	528	NiCl$_2$.......	49.6	68.2
MnSe.......	~150	~435	NiO	523	
MnTe.......	307		α-Mn.......	~100	
MnF$_2$.......	72	113	Cr..........	480	
FeF$_2$........	79	117	CrSb.......	725	~1000
FeCl$_2$........	23.5	48	Cr$_2$O$_3$.......	310	
FeO........	198	570	TiCl$_3$.......	~100	
CoCl$_2$.......	24.9	38.1	FeCO$_3$......	57	

interactions between nearest neighbors, we may write for the magneti-zation above the Curie point, according to the Weiss field theory,

$$TM_A = C'(H - \lambda M_B)$$
$$TM_B = C'(H - \lambda M_A)$$

(4.33)

Here C' is the Curie constant for one sublattice, and the effective field on sublattice A is written as $H - \lambda M_B$, which for positive λ corresponds to antiferromagnetic interactions between A and B.   Adding,

$$TM = T(M_A + M_B) = 2C'H - C'\lambda M$$

(4.34)

so that

$$\chi = \frac{2C'}{T + C'\lambda}$$

(4.35)

or

$$\chi = \frac{C}{T + \vartheta}$$

(4.36)

with

$$C = 2C' \qquad \vartheta = C'\lambda$$

(4.37)

It is not necessary in general that T_c should equal ϑ, although they are equal on the two-sublattice model under nearest-neighbor interactions alone.

The actual spin arrangements in a number of antiferromagnetic sub-stances have been determined recently by a brilliant series of neutron-diffraction experiments performed by Shull and his collaborators. The magnitude of the scattering cross section of a paramagnetic atom depends on the relative orientation of the atomic and neutron magnetic moments; thus neutron diffraction is particularly valuable in looking at spin arrangements in crystals, while X rays are useless for this purpose. The spin structure of MnO as determined by Shull is shown in Fig. 4.18.

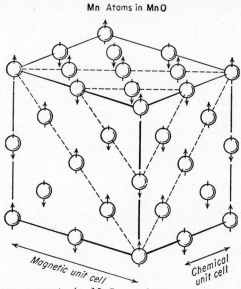

Fig. 4.18 Spin arrangements in MnO, as determined by Shull using neutron diffraction.

4.11 Ferrites

The ferrites of magnetic interest have the composition $MO \cdot Fe_2O_3$, where M is one of, or a mixture of, divalent cations such as Mn, Co, Ni, Cu, Mg, Zn, Cd, or Fe^{2+}. The crystals are cubic and have the spinel structure. We may think of ferrites as derived from magnetite, $FeO \cdot Fe_2O_3$, on replacing the ferrous ions by other divalent ions. The magnetic ions are in two types of interstice: tetrahedral, surrounded by four oxygens, or octahedral, surrounded by six oxygens.

Ferrites are of unusually great interest in modern ferromagnetism. This is for two reasons. First, commercial ferrites (Ferroxcube, Ferramic, etc.) have electrical resistivities in the range 10^2 to 10^6 ohm-cm, as compared with 10^{-5} ohm-cm for iron; the high resistivity (low eddy-current losses) makes them of tremendous value for high-frequency applications in communications and elsewhere. Second, the arrangement of magnetic ions in ferrites is very unusual, with the saturation magnetization arising from an unbalance in an otherwise antiferromagnetic arrangement (Fig. 4.2). This model has been verified in several cases by neutron-diffraction methods.

We mention here several aspects of the Néel theory of the saturation magnetization of ferrites. The value 485 for saturation magnetization

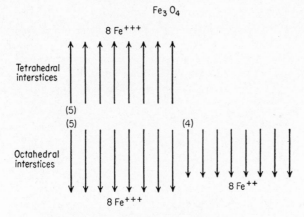

Fig. 4.19 Schematic spin arrangements in magnetite, $FeO \cdot Fe_2O_3$, showing how the moments of the Fe^{3+} ions cancel out, leaving only the moments of the Fe^{2+} ions.

of Fe_3O_4 corresponds to about 4 Bohr magnetons per molecule Fe_3O_4, whereas the value expected if the one Fe^{++} and two Fe^{+++} ions per molecule are lined up parallel to one another is about $14\mu_B$ per molecule. Néel accounts for the discrepancy by supposing that the Fe^{+++} ions are antiparallel to each other, as in Fig. 4.19, so that the resultant moment

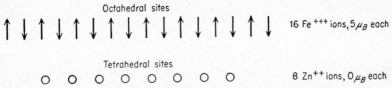

Fig. 4.20 Explanation of zero saturation magnetization in zinc ferrite.

arises only from the Fe^{++} ion. This has a moment of $4\mu_B$ corresponding to a spin of 2; the agreement with the observed moment of magnetite is quite satisfactory. The arrangement of ions in zinc ferrite is shown in Fig. 4.20; this is not ferromagnetic, because the spins cancel out.

REFERENCES

Bates, L. F., "Modern Magnetism," 2d ed., Cambridge University Press, London, 1948.

Becker, R., and W. Doring, "Ferromagnetismus," Springer-Verlag, Berlin, 1939.

Bozorth, R. M., "Ferromagnetism," D. Van Nostrand Company, Inc., New York, 1951.

Stoner, E. C., Ferromagnetism, *Repts. Prog. Phys.*, **11**: 43–112 (1948); **13**: 83–183 (1950).

Stoner, E. C., "Magnetism and Matter," Methuen & Co., Ltd., London, 1934.

Van Vleck, J. H., A Survey of the Theory of Ferromagnetism, *Revs. Mod. Phys.*, **17**: 27–47 (1945).

Van Vleck, J. H., Recent Developments in the Theory of Antiferromagnetism, *J. phys. radium*, **12**: 262–274 (1951).

Van Vleck, J. H., "Theory of Electric and Magnetic Susceptibilities," Oxford University Press, New York, 1932.

5

Microwave Spectroscopy

W. D. HERSHBERGER

PROFESSOR OF ENGINEERING
UNIVERSITY OF CALIFORNIA, LOS ANGELES

5.1 Introduction

In Chap. 2, Professor Schiff traced the atomic concept to Lucretius. Spectroscopy, not to be outdone, may perhaps claim an equally obscure origin in the observations which the patriarch Noah made on the rainbow which followed the great flood (Genesis 9: 14). Noah at that time set up a pattern followed by other spectroscopists ever since, namely observations on a spectrum followed by an appropriate interpretation. However, spectroscopy in the modern sense may be traced back only to 1802 when Wollaston observed seven dark lines crossing the solar spectrum. He was followed closely by Fraunhofer (1814) who reported extensively on the dark lines which cross the solar spectrum and have since been known by his name. Chemical analysis based on spectroscopy owes much of its initial impetus to the joint work of Kirchhoff and Bunsen, published in 1859. They discovered on the sun, by an analysis of the solar spectrum, the two new elements cesium and rubidium, unknown on the earth at that time, as well as that more common metal, gold. In the succeeding years various branches of spectroscopy have grown to maturity; they are distinguished from one another by naming the wavelength region in which observations are taken, *e.g.*, the spectroscopy of the ultraviolet, visible, and infrared regions. Microwave spectroscopy is the newest member of this family. Although most of the work in this new field has been done since World War II, more than 200 papers have already been published,[1] more than 150 gases have been studied, and more than 1800 absorption lines have been reported for gases alone. The present discussion will be limited to two aspects of microwave spectroscopy: (1) the spectra of gases and (2) paramagnetic resonance.

[1] Corresponding numbered bibliographic references appear at the end of the chapter.

Speaking broadly, spectroscopy in the visible and ultraviolet regions yields information on the energies of electrons in atoms and in molecules, while infrared spectroscopy furnishes information on the over-all rotations and the internal vibrations of the molecules themselves. Infrared spectroscopy begins at the long-wavelength limit of the visible spectrum, about 7×10^{-5} cm (also written as 7000 A or 7 μ), and extends through the near infrared (7 μ to 20 μ), where for the most part vibrational molecular spectra are observed, on through the far infrared (20 to 300 μ), where rotational and rotational-vibrational spectra are found. Using this terminology, a K-band klystron or magnetron emits radiation in the microwave range having a wavelength of 1.25 cm, or 1.25×10^8 A, or 125,000 μ. In the language of the radio engineer, it operates at a frequency of 24,000 Mc/sec.

The long-wavelength limit in infrared spectroscopy is set in part by the inadequacy of known sources—hot carbon rods may be used—and in part by the high inherent noise and low sensitivity of known heat detectors. These difficulties are aggravated when one attempts to obtain a monochromatic source and the concomitant high resolution by the use of a narrow slit in a spectroscope. This technique improves wavelength resolution but imposes a corresponding reduction in the useful radiated power. Progress in microwave spectroscopy has been rapid because, among other things, high-intensity monochromatic sources such as klystrons are available; these, used in conjunction with the tools now at hand for manipulating short electromagnetic waves, permit effective spectroscopes to be built. Among the new tools, one may list waveguides, resonant cavities, crystal detectors and mixers, and the other components often grouped together and known as microwave "plumbing." The basic scientific disciplines needed are electromagnetic theory and quantum mechanics. Microwave spectroscopy occupies that part of the spectrum where the techniques are borrowed from the radio engineer but the concepts are borrowed from the spectroscopist, and one is never sure as to whether he is dealing with short radio waves or long heat waves.

Historically, interest in microwave spectroscopy was stimulated by the discovery of the absorption of microwaves in two gases: ammonia and water vapor. In 1934, Cleeton and Williams[2] of the University of Michigan published their observations on the absorption of microwaves in ammonia. They constructed a series of c-w magnetrons operating in the wavelength range from 1.06 to 3.8 cm and focused the radiation from the magnetron into a narrow beam by means of a parabolic mirror. The beam was then transmitted through a 16-in. path of ammonia gas contained in a rubberized cell. Transmitted power was measured by use of a crystal detector. Their measurements disclosed that one-half of the power in a beam of 1.25-cm radiation is absorbed when it traverses a

3-ft path in gaseous ammonia at atmospheric pressure. Their experiments were motivated by earlier infrared observations on the fine structure in the rotational absorption spectrum of ammonia gas in the wavelength region from 70 to 100 μ. These earlier results became intelligible only after a theoretical analysis was made on the harmonic oscillator with two potential minima. The mathematical tool used in such an analysis is, of course, quantum mechanics. The spectrum of the ammonia molecule is of sufficient interest and complexity to serve as an example for tracing some of the main developments in the microwave spectroscopy of gases.

The ammonia molecule, NH_3, is in the form of a tetrahedron with the three hydrogen atoms equidistant from each other and lying in a plane (Fig. 5.1). The nitrogen atom lies outside this plane and is equidistant from the three hydrogens. In one of the normal modes of vibration of the molecule, the nitrogen atom moves in a direction perpendicular to the plane of the three hydrogens. There are two possible positions of minimum potential energy for the nitrogen, one position lying on one side of the plane of the hydrogens and a second position which is the mirror image of the first. The

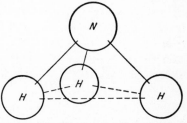

Fig. 5.1   The ammonia molecule.

nitrogen atom can reach the latter only by "tunneling" through the potential barrier arising from the hydrogens, not by an over-all rotation of the molecule. In this "tunneling" process the molecule turns inside out, rather than rotating as a whole. Rotation and inversion are distinguishable processes both in classical and in quantum mechanics. Because this harmonic oscillator has two positions of minimum potential energy, its energy levels occur in closely spaced pairs. The observed microwave absorption arises from transitions between pairs of energy levels corresponding to inversion of the molecule and forms what is called an "inversion" spectrum.

Absorption of microwaves by water vapor made itself evident during World War II[3] when it halted a promising 1.25-cm development. Microwave radar equipment was developed operating first at a wavelength of 10 cm, then at 3.2 cm, and finally at 1.25 cm. The useful range of the 1.25-cm equipment fell woefully short of that anticipated; this effect was presently traced to the absorption of the waves by water vapor in the atmosphere. The absorption arises from a rotational transition in the water molecule. While the water-vapor absorption is much weaker than the ammonia absorption, still it is so large, especially in view of the long ranges desired for search radar, as to render 1.25-cm equipment largely useless except for experimental work.   In fact, one reason for the rapid progress in microwave spectroscopy has been the ready availability of surplus 1.25-cm equipment from the abortive radar program.

5.2 Spectroscopy in Gases

In a typical microwave spectroscope, a klystron generates perhaps 10 milliwatts of power at 24,000 Mc/sec.   This frequency can be varied over a 20 per cent tuning range by mechanical adjustment and over a range of one-tenth of 1 per cent by changes in operating voltages.   Klystrons are available at 10,000 and 24,000 Mc/sec and on an experimental basis up to 50,000 Mc/sec.   For frequencies up to 100,000 Mc/sec—a wavelength of 3 mm—harmonic generation is employed.   The present description will be confined largely to the so-called K band: a frequency near 24,000 Mc/sec.   The power is detected by a crystal detector after it has passed through a gas sample contained in a waveguide—in this case, a hollow metal pipe of rectangular cross section with inside dimensions 0.430 by 0.180 in.   This guide may be 50 ft long; it is filled with the gas at a reduced pressure which may lie in the range from 0.1 to 0.01 mm Hg.   In this pressure range, the absorption lines are narrow and detection techniques are effective.   Frequency is swept cyclically by electronic means, while slow mechanical tuning enables the experimenter to cover the range of the klystron in a search for absorption lines.   The beam deflection in a cathode-ray oscilloscope is synchronized with the electronically swept frequency so as to display the absorption lines of the gas directly on the oscilloscope.   Absorption coefficients of 10^{-8} per cm can be measured; this corresponds to an absorption so feeble that a path length of 10^8 cm or 1000 km would be required to reduce the microwave power to 37 per cent of its initial value.   The human nose will detect ammonia when present in air in the amount of 1 part in 10^6, but a microwave spectroscope can outperform the nose at this task by a factor of about 100.   By reducing gas pressure, line widths as narrow as 250 kc/sec are obtained; in the parlance of the circuit engineer this corresponds to a Q of 100,000.   Line width ultimately is determined by the Doppler effect in the gas, an effect which has its origin in the fact that molecules are moving with thermal velocities with respect to the waveguide system.   Thus the Doppler effect limits the narrowness of lines as ordinarily observed, but the Doppler effect can be circumvented by special technique and line Q's in excess of 2 million are observed, unfortunately with a loss in signal-to-noise ratio as the line is scanned.   Frequencies are measured to 1 part in 10^6; so microwave spectroscopy affords resolution lacking in the conventional infrared or optical range.   This fact, together with the fact that the absorbed quanta have low energy, makes the microwave spectroscope a powerful tool for detecting extremely small differences between energy levels accessible by the method.   Line width, but not line position on a frequency scale, is governed both by pressure and by temperature.   At sufficiently reduced pressures, collision broadening is eliminated.   There remains only Doppler broadening, which varies as the square root of the absolute temperature.   Thus reducing temperature from 300°K or room temperature to 3°K gives an improvement in line sharpness only by a factor of 10.

Most of the spectra observed are rotational in character.   The molecule COS, carbon oxysulfide, which is neither carbon dioxide nor carbon disulfide, is linear and has a moment of inertia of 138×10^{-40} g-cm^2.   The spacing from carbon to oxygen is 1.161 A; that from carbon to sulfur is 1.558 A.   These distances and the moment of inertia are best determined by the present method; before the advent of microwave spectroscopy they were known only to 1 part in 50, while they are now known to 1 part in 500.   Rotational constants are known to 1 part in 10^6.   If sulfur 34 is substituted for sulfur 32 in the COS molecule, the frequency of a given absorption line is shifted about 2 per cent, or 594.62 Mc/sec. Those engineers accustomed to the accuracy with which radio frequencies are measured will note the magnitude of such a change.   COS is a linear molecule, and its microwave spectrum is basically a rotational spectrum. The rotational spectra of symmetrical tops such as CH$_3$Cl or CHCl$_3$ have also been studied as well as those of many unsymmetrical molecules.   In addition, certain molecules such as methyl alcohol, methyl mercaptan, or methylamine display a fine structure which probably arises from hindered internal rotation in the molecule, e.g., the rotation of a methyl group with respect to the rest of the molecule.

The ammonia spectrum observed by Cleeton and Williams consisted of a single line, at the pressure they employed.   However, as pressure is reduced below 1 mm of Hg, a fine structure appears.   There are 30 lines[4] within the tuning range of a K-band klystron.   At a given temperature, ammonia is found in a variety of rotational states, each specified by two quantum numbers.   One quantum number, J, serves to define the total angular momentum $\sqrt{J(J+1)}\, h/2\pi$; a second, K, specifies the angular momentum resolved along the symmetry axis of the molecule $Kh/2\pi$. As K is increased with J fixed, the molecule becomes distorted by centrifugal force, the three hydrogens move increasingly far apart, and the net result is that the potential barrier separating the two stable positions of the nitrogen atom is decreased; the microwave absorption frequency is correspondingly increased.   Thus for each value of J, the frequency of the microwave absorption line is increased as K runs through its permitted range of values: $0, \pm1, \pm2, \ldots, \pm J$.   For fixed K, on the other hand, the three hydrogen atoms approach each other more closely as J increases, the height of the potential barrier is increased, and the microwave absorption frequency goes down.   The positions of the members of the 30-line spectrum for ammonia observable with a K-band klystron are in excellent agreement with the predictions of theory based on the model of the molecule using the two-minimum potential function.

When the gas pressure is further reduced, it is next observed that each line of the ammonia spectrum breaks up into a main central line attended by four smaller satellite lines.[5]   The frequency of the ammonia line corresponding to the $J = 3$, $K = 3$ rotational state is 23,870.11 ± 0.02 Mc/sec.

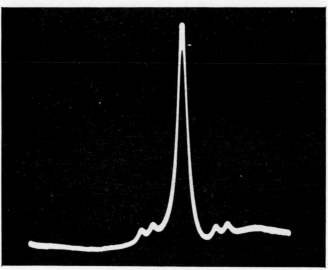

Fig. 5.2   The (3.3) line of ammonia together with the four satellite lines which arise from the quadrupole moment of the nitrogen nucleus.   (*By permission from the RCA Review.*)

The satellites are located symmetrically with respect to line center; the inner pair is offset from line center by ±1.72 Mc/sec, the outer by ±2.34 Mc/sec.   Figure 5.2 shows the (3.3) line of ammonia together with the four satellite lines which arise from the quadrupole moment of the nitrogen nucleus.   The satellite lines have perhaps 2 per cent the intensity of the main line.   They arise because the nitrogen 14 nucleus possesses both angular momentum and an electrical quadrupole moment. Atomic nuclei are in general characterized by a spin or angular momentum, a magnetic moment, and sometimes an electric quadrupole moment, although some or all of these quantities are zero in certain nuclei.   When a certain nucleus possesses an electric quadrupole moment, its electrical field exhibits a deviation from spherical symmetry.   In the tunneling process in ammonia, the orientation of the nuclear angular momentum is specified by a new quantum number, subject to a selection rule.   Correspondingly, the energy-level diagram embodies an additional degree of complexity because of the energy term arising from interaction between the field of the nitrogen nucleus and the inhomogeneous field arising from the three hydrogens. The net effect is to give the observed spectrum a quadrupole-moment fine structure. Microwave spectroscopy is yielding a wealth of information on the symmetry, or lack of it, of the fields of atomic nuclei. The electric field surrounding a nucleus may be represented as an oblate or as a prolate spheroid, depending on the nucleus in question. However, the calculation of the quadrupole moment of a nucleus on the basis of the separation of the satellite lines from the main rotational lines is not a simple matter; another piece of information is needed, namely, the field inhomogeneity at the position of the nucleus, and at the moment this information is not particularly accurate.

The fine-structure story would be incomplete without mention of the Zeeman effect in ammonia. Each of the main lines, and each satellite as well, is split into two displaced lines when absorption is measured with the gas in a strong (10,000 gauss) magnetic field.

Let us recapitulate the story for ammonia. The inversion spectrum first observed by Cleeton and Williams, consisting of one line at the pressure they employed, actually represents a very minute energy difference which was first suspected to exist because of a fine structure in the infrared spectrum of this gas that could barely be resolved when using infrared techniques at 100 μ. This one line was duly found at microwave frequencies at reduced pressure, and the high resolution realizable in the microwave spectroscope showed it to consist of 30 lines. These lines represent the rotational fine structure. Each line in this 30-line spectrum—with one notable and significant exception—was next found to consist of a main line and four smaller satellite lines. This fine structure is the quadrupole-moment fine structure. Finally, each of these latter lines can be broken up into its Zeeman components by a magnetic field. At this point, a classical quotation is in order: "Great fleas have smaller fleas upon their backs to bite 'em, and little fleas have lesser fleas, and so *ad infinitum.*"

Molecular properties which can be studied to advantage by the microwave method include molecular geometry, *i.e.*, bond lengths and angles, moments of inertia, dipole moments, and changes in these quantities as the quantum state of the molecule changes. Dipole moments are conveniently studied by employing the Stark effect in which an electric field is applied to the gas under study. Nuclear spin and quadrupole moment can also be found, while information on nuclear magnetic moments is obtained by related techniques at much lower radio frequencies.

Application of this work to the stabilization of frequency deserves mention. The absorption lines observed are quite narrow, line Q's of 100,000 or higher being readily realized experimentally. Moreover, the frequency of a given line cannot be altered significantly by anything one chooses to do to a molecule, which is a most fortunate circumstance.   In contrast, the frequency of a quartz crystal, or of a tuning fork, or of a pendulum depends upon its history, method of fabrication, source of the material, and other factors.   The (3.3) line of ammonia is the strongest one observed to date.   It occurs at the frequency 23,870.11 Mc/sec irrespective of the source of the ammonia.   The effects of gas pressure and temperature and of stray electric or magnetic fields are well known, so that these external operating conditions may readily be chosen to make optimum use both of the high Q and of the inherent stability of the absorbing molecule.   This principle has been applied, first, to the control of frequency of klystrons and, later, to the control of a clock. Stability to better than 1 part in 10^7 has been obtained,[6] and with the development of improved lock-in techniques, the means of minimizing the difficulties which arise from the Doppler effect, and the use of lines with higher inherent Q, still further improvement seems assured for the future.   A servo system is at present in use in which electronic search techniques are used to make a cyclic comparison between klystron or clock frequency and the frequency of an absorption line, the error information being fed back to the klystron to control its frequency.   The ammonia molecule as a standard of frequency (or time) has the same advantages over a frequency standard such as a quartz bar as a cadmium or mercury line has over a standard meter bar as a standard of length. It speaks well for spectroscopy that it should be expected to furnish the ultimate in standards, both for time and for length.

In attempting to secure frequency information from an absorption line, one meets a species of uncertainty principle.   If one attempts to collect the frequency information by scanning the line with a swept-frequency oscillator, several time constants should be spent in sweeping over the line itself, which limits the interrogation rate.   Accordingly, for a very narrow line, the sweeping rate must be kept low in order to maintain an acceptable signal-to-noise (S/N) ratio.   If one insists nonetheless in interrogating the line very frequently, he is faced with two alternatives. Either he may sacrifice S/N ratio and impair the performance of his stabilizing system, or if he wishes to work both with high S/N ratio and a high scanning rate, he may do so by reducing line Q, for example, by increasing gas pressure above the optimum value.   In short, with a given line characterized by its noise, he may have frequency information of high precision a limited number of times in each second or lower-precision frequency information more often.   The ideal spectrum line for use in a stabilizing system must have both a high Q and a favorable signal-to-noise ratio to begin with.

The microwave energy that is absorbed reappears as heat; if the microwave power is modulated, the energy reappears as sound. Heat conversion may be demonstrated by absorbing the microwave energy in a sample of ammonia contained in a resonant cavity which communicates with a U tube full of a light fluid such as kerosene. The kerosene level will change by 1 ft in less than a second when the power from a magnetron with 10 watts average power is absorbed by the ammonia. The response time is set by the thermal lag introduced by the ammonia gas and by the inertia of the kerosene column.

Sound conversion may be demonstrated by causing modulated microwaves to impinge on a container, such as a rubber balloon, filled with ammonia. Such a balloon will sing with an audible note which corresponds to the modulation frequency. What one does with a talking balloon after he has it may be a question without an easy answer, but these ideas have led to a patent.[7]

5.3 Paramagnetic Resonance

Microwave spectroscopy applied to gases yields information on the structure and geometry of molecules and on the spins and quadrupole moments of nuclei. A second aspect of microwave spectroscopy, involving "paramagnetic resonance," is useful in giving information on the energy levels of electrons in solids. As in gases, line-absorption spectra are found, but only when the material is placed in an appropriate magnetic field. The topic will be treated by first considering the properties attributed to the electron which make the experiments intelligible, then describing the experimental arrangements used in making measurements, and finally discussing complexities found in observed spectra in materials of interest.

The practicing engineer probably is familiar with the experiments which led to the assignment of a definite mass and charge to the electron. These experiments deal with the trajectories of electrons in a beam which traverses deflecting electric and magnetic fields. Some of the classical experiments may readily be repeated in a modern cathode-ray oscilloscope. Such deflection experiments, in conjunction with Millikan's experiments on the charge of a single electron, have enabled the determination of the mass and the charge of the electron. As a result of studies of the Zeeman effect in conventional spectroscopy, additional properties of the electron were discovered, namely, magnetic moment and angular momentum or spin. In the Bohr atom, the electrons occupy well-defined orbits, the magnetic moment due to orbital motion can be calculated readily, and quantitative predictions of the effect of a magnetic field on optical spectra can be made. In the predicted Zeeman effect, a single emission line may, for example, split into a group of lines when the field is applied. However, it was found experimentally that "normal" Zeeman spectra in agreement with the simple theory are quite rare, while "anomalous" Zeeman spectra inconsistent with the simple theory are common. The difficulty was resolved by attributing to the electron an "internal" degree of freedom in addition to the external degrees of freedom associated with its mobility and its orbital motion about a nucleus.   To the electron is assigned an intrinsic angular momentum of $\sqrt{\frac{1}{2}(\frac{1}{2} + 1)}\, h/2\pi$, with the component of angular momentum along the direction in space determined by an external field equal to $\pm\frac{1}{2}(h/2\pi)$.   The associated magnetic moment is $2\mu_B$, where μ_B is called the *Bohr magneton;* it is the orbital magnetic moment of an electron in the lowest-energy Bohr orbit, and has the value $eh/4\pi mc$.   The Bohr atom model has now been superseded, but the terminology based on the model is too useful to be abandoned. The factor 2, which is required to achieve agreement with experiment, at first appeared quite arbitrary, but it is predicted in Dirac's theory of the electron.   The intrinsic angular momentum of the electron may be compounded with its orbital angular momentum to give a net angular momentum; similarly, orbital magnetic moment is combined with intrinsic magnetic moment in the appropriate fashion to yield a net magnetic moment.   When an electron is placed in a magnetic field, it behaves (speaking pictorially rather than accurately) like a gyroscope to whose frame a torque is applied.   Its axis precesses about the direction of the magnetic field at a frequency which we term the *gyromagnetic frequency.* This frequency is the frequency for paramagnetic absorption.   The frequency condition for resonance is

$$h\nu = g\mu_B H$$

where h = Planck's constant

ν = frequency

g = Landé g factor

$\mu_B = eh/4\pi mc$ = Bohr magneton

H = applied magnetic field

The resonance frequency is 9375 Mc/sec for an applied magnetic field of 3350 gauss and a g of 2.   The value of g is 2 for free electrons; this bespeaks the absence of both orbital magnetic moment and orbital angular momentum.   However, the g value appropriate to paramagnetic-resonance experiments actually is $2[1 + (\alpha/2\pi)]$, where α is the "fine-structure constant."   Hence, strictly speaking, the free-spin value to be expected is 2.0023, rather than 2.   The term "orbital" as used here refers not to an orbit in the sense of the Bohr atom model, but to an orbit in the wave-mechanical sense.   The analogy based on motion of a gyroscope is not to be taken literally; the rigorous procedure is to treat paramagnetic-resonance absorption as arising from transitions between Zeeman levels of the pertinent energy-level diagram.

The experimental equipment[8] used for obtaining paramagnetic spectra is similar in many respects to that used in the absorption spectroscopy of gases. For reasons of convenience, a high-Q resonant cavity is employed to hold the sample; this permits effective use to be made of a small sample of material in a magnetic field of limited cross section. To meet the condition for paramagnetic resonance, the external applied magnetic field must be maintained perpendicular to the exciting microwave field applied to the sample. A material containing electrons whose spin is "free" will exhibit a selective absorption either if the applied magnetic field is held constant and frequency is varied, or if the technically simpler procedure is followed of holding frequency constant and varying the magnetic field. An effective method of conducting the experiment is to sweep the magnetic field slowly through a range of perhaps 500 gauss in 5 min, superposing on this slowly changing field an alternating field of amplitude 2 to 5 gauss and frequency of 30 or 40 cycles/sec. Absorption occurs when the resonance condition is met. Depending upon the material studied, resonance curves may have widths from 0.040 to 1000 gauss or more.

The question now arises as to when electrons in solids may have "free" or "almost-free" spins. In a variety of materials, one should not expect to find free spins and corresponding paramagnetic spectra. We interpret the periodic table in terms of filled and partially filled electron shells. The element neon, for example, has two completely filled electron shells: the K shell of two electrons and the L shell of eight electrons. For all these electrons, the spins are so paired that the individual magnetic effects cancel out. Moreover, in shared electron bonds, as for example H:H or the single carbon-to-carbon bond found in many organic compounds whose molecules contain an even number of electrons, all magnetic moments effectively cancel each other. However, there are a limited number of molecules in which an odd number of electrons occur. One example is the material diphenyl-trinitrophenyl-hydrazyl, which has 203 electrons. All but one of these are paired, and the odd electron that is left unpaired is responsible for the paramagnetism displayed by the molecule. The molecule is large—it has 41 atoms—so that the electrons with unpaired spins are relatively far apart. The material displays a strong paramagnetic absorption at a field value corresponding to a g value of 2.0036, the resonance curve is 1.4 gauss wide, and the absorption itself is so intense that in a measuring equipment a sample one-tenth the size of a matchhead yields a spectrum with a signal-to-noise ratio in excess of 100.

A much larger class of compounds displaying either paramagnetic or ferromagnetic spectra are those containing atoms of the transition group of elements in which the M shell has an incomplete quota of $3d$ electrons. Here one finds the ferromagnetic elements nickel, cobalt, and iron, as well as the elements manganese, chromium, vanadium, titanium, and copper, which, depending on the valence state in a given compound, have a variety of incomplete electron shells. The rare-earth elements, which lack $4f$ electrons in the N shell, similarly display paramagnetic resonance, but only at liquid-air temperature or lower, since at room temperature the lines are too wide for observation.

Experiments on paramagnetic resonance are currently under way in a number of laboratories.[10]   The range of topics under study is large; some of the topics will be mentioned to indicate the present and future possibilities of the method. For example, work on ferromagnetic materials is under way, and g values greater than 2 by 10 or 15 per cent are found. Ferrites are being investigated; in these materials large Faraday rotations have been found and applied to a new microwave component.[9]   Here a ferrite sample several inches long and perhaps $\frac{1}{4}$ in. in diameter is placed along the axis of a circular waveguide transmitting a plane polarized wave. It is found that the plane of polarization is rotated through 90° or more if the ferrite sample is magnetized in a direction parallel to its axis. Moreover, if the wave whose plane of polarization has been rotated is reflected back through the ferrite in a direction opposite to that for the first traversal, the original rotation is not canceled out, but rather is doubled. This microwave element violates the law of reciprocity usually followed by networks or wave transmission systems; thus a new switch with unique properties becomes available for the designer of microwave transmission systems. The device is termed a *gyrator;* the effect arises from the precession in a magnetic field of electrons with unpaired spins.

Chemists are employing paramagnetic resonance not only to study "odd" molecules but also to explore the materials termed *biradicals*, as well as investigate the character of chemical bonds. Some chemical bonds appear to be mixed in character. In others, the electron structure is in doubt. Paramagnetic studies based on bulk ponderomotive effects have been used to good advantage in studying such compounds. The paramagnetic-resonance method is now in use in several laboratories to examine such problems in chemical-bond types more closely and precisely than has been possible heretofore. In biradicals, two unpaired electrons occur in a single molecule, and spectra for these have been found. In addition, the semiconductors formed when sodium or lithium is dissolved in liquid ammonia or in one of the amines have been found to contain unpaired electrons as revealed by the paramagnetic-resonance method. Much of this work is still unpublished or has been published only in fragmentary form.

One class of materials in which the paramagnetic-resonance method promises to be useful comprises those materials known in the electronics industry as *electronically active*. These include electron-emitting materials, photoemitting and photoconducting substances, and the phosphors used in television picture tubes and in fluorescent lamps. For example, a phosphor may be synthesized by beginning with a pure host crystal, such as zinc sulfide, and introducing a small trace of an impurity known as an *activator*. After processing, the material is converted into a phosphor capable of converting the energy of an electron beam or of ultraviolet excitation into light in the visible range. The energy-transfer process is imperfectly understood even though 100,000 different phosphors have been synthesized and more than 100 tons of these spectroscopically pure materials are made in a year. Among the activators in common use are various members of the transition group of elements, which lack $3d$ electrons, and also rare earths, which lack $4f$ electrons.

In one experimental study the paramagnetic spectra[11] of 32 manganese-activated phosphors were studied. The manganese may be present to 1 part in 100 or 1 part in 100,000, depending on the phosphor. The doubly ionized manganese ion (Mn^{++}) is in an S state, which means that in the exposed $3d$ shell there is no orbital angular momentum and no orbital magnetic moment; thus the observed magnetic moment arises solely from that of the electrons themselves. Three kinds of spectra have been observed in these phosphors. In the first, a single strong broad absorption curve, perhaps 750 gauss wide, is observed. Here the g value is 2 within the limit of accuracy of the measurements. Two factors may conspire to give us wide lines: (1) a short relaxation time for the excited state which arises from irradiation of the material by the microwaves and (2) perturbation of the energy levels by an anisotropic crystal field to which the Mn^{++} ions are subjected. The material is used in powder form, so that the crystal axes of the grains of powder are oriented at random with respect to the applied field. The first contribution to line broadening has to do with the ease or difficulty with which an ordered spin orientation due to the combined effects of the steady and microwave fields is degraded so that the energy reappears as heat or random lattice vibrations. For the Mn^{++} ion, this relaxation time is believed to be so long that the first factor does not contribute materially to line width.

Two other kinds of spectra are observed for Mn^{++}-activated phosphors. Both varieties may be demonstrated by using a concentration of Mn^{++} of 1 part in 100,000 of ZnS, but in one phosphor the ZnS host crystal is cubic and is known to mineralogists as sphalerite, while in the second the ZnS host crystal is hexagonal and is known as wurtzite. For the cubic crystal, a six-line spectrum is observed. A paramagnetic-resonance spectrum for manganese in zinc sulfide is shown in Fig. 5.3. Owing to the method used in taking observations, the slope of the absorption curve rather than the absorption curve itself is obtained. In the lower curve, the sign of the slope is preserved, while in the upper, it is lost because a square-law detection system was used. Each line is 6 gauss wide, the spacing between line centers is about 70 gauss, and the whole spectrum extends over a range of about 350 gauss. For the wurtzite, a 30-peak spectrum is found to extend over the same 350-gauss range. Obviously, the internal crystal field together with the applied magnetic field act quite differently for the two cases. There are five $3d$ electrons in the M shell of Mn^{++}, and this shell is spherically symmetrical. The hexagonal field squeezes the electron cloud out of shape, giving rise to a perturbed set of energy levels. There are $(2S + 1)$ or six such sublevels, since there are five electrons in the shell, each with a spin of $\frac{1}{2}$. In addi-

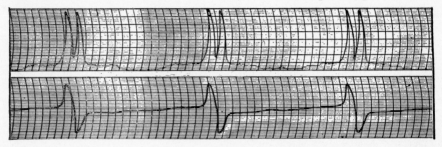

Fig. 5.3   A paramagnetic resonance spectrum for manganese in zinc sulfide.   Owing to the method used in taking observations, the slope of the absorption curve rather than the absorption curve itself is obtained.   In the lower curve, the sign of the slope is preserved, while in the upper it is lost because a square-law detection system was used.   (*By permission from the Physical Review.*)

tion, the Mn^{++} nucleus itself has a spin $I = \frac{5}{2}$, and when the electron spins are flipped over by the fields, the nuclear orientation is unaltered. The Mn^{++} nucleus itself has a limited number of permitted orientations in the field. The hexagonal crystal field with the external magnetic field is sufficient to remove both the $(2I + 1)$ and the $(2S + 1)$ degeneracy, but for the cubic crystal, only the $(2I + 1)$ degeneracy is removed. Other cubic crystals including zinc aluminate and magnesium oxide also give rise to six-peak spectra. These results are given to indicate the use of paramagnetic resonance in studying fields inside crystals.

To summarize, the paramagnetic-resonance method promises to be useful in a variety of fields: (1) to the person interested in studying internal fields in crystals; (2) to chemists concerned with "odd" molecules, biradicals, and the study of chemical bonds whose electronic make-up is in doubt; and (3) to those who have to deal with the specialized materials, such as phosphors, of considerable technical interest, in which electrons may occupy states with spins unpaired. The method appears to be particularly useful in studying deep-lying electrons within a material rather than those concerned with surface behavior, and it depends for its effectiveness on spin and magnetic moment rather than on the mobility of an electron as a carrier of charge.

REFERENCES

1. The reader interested in review articles and detailed specific information on the microwave spectroscopy of gases is referred to:

   Gordy, *Revs. Mod. Phys.*, **20:** 668 (1948).
   Coles, "Advances in Electronics," Vol. II, Academic Press, Inc., New York, 1950.
   Gordy, Smith, and Trambarulo, "Microwave Spectroscopy," John Wiley & Sons, Inc., New York, 1953.
   Kisliuk and Townes, Molecular Microwave Tables, *Nat. Bur. Standards Circ.* 518, June 23, 1952.
   The paper by Gordy lists 182 references; that by Coles, 92 references.
   The NBS tables list some 1800 spectral lines.
2. Cleeton and Williams, *Phys. Rev.*, **45:** 234 (1934).
3. Van Vleck, *Phys. Rev.*, **71:** 413 (1947).
4. Bleaney and Penrose, *Nature*, **157:** 339 (1946).
5. Good, *Phys. Rev.*, **69:** 539 (1946).
6. Hershberger and Norton, *RCA Rev.*, **9:** 38 (1948).
7. U.S. Patent 2,483,768, issued Oct. 4, 1949.
8. A review article by Kikuchi and Spence, *Am. J. Phys.*, **18:** 167 (1950), gives 46 references on paramagnetic resonance beginning with the first successful work by Zavoisky, *J. Phys. USSR*, **9:** 211, 245, and 447 (1945).
9. Hogan, *Bell System Tech. J.* **31:** 1 (1952).
10. An entire issue of *Physica*, April, 1951, Vol. 17, is devoted to "Spectroscopy at Radio Frequencies." It contains a wealth of theoretical and experimental papers on paramagnetic resonance.
11. Hershberger and Leifer, *Phys. Rev.*, **88:** 714 (1952).

6

Nuclear Structure and Transmutation

W. A. FOWLER

PROFESSOR OF PHYSICS

CALIFORNIA INSTITUTE OF TECHNOLOGY

6.1 Atoms and Nuclei

Nuclear physics is that branch of physics concerned with the study and investigation of the properties of the nuclei of atoms. The words *nucleus* and *nuclei* are used in many different senses in modern science, but in the physical sciences they refer to the positively charged bodies which were shown in 1911 by Lord Rutherford to exist at the center of the atoms of all substances. They are the "suns" of atoms and are surrounded by negatively charged electrons in somewhat the same way that the sun is surrounded by the planets in the solar system. The forces of attraction which hold together atomic systems and the solar system are of course quite different; in the atomic case they are the electrical attraction between oppositely charged bodies, whereas the planets and the sun interact through gravitational forces between their masses.

It is known that the distinguishing chemical, mechanical, and electrical properties of all elements depend on the number of electrons in their constituent atoms and do not depend directly to any great extent on the properties of the atomic nuclei. The nuclei do contain most of the mass of the atom (all but 1 part in 1837 in the hydrogen atom and all but 1 part in 4750 in the uranium atom), but the density of material in bulk depends not only on the atomic mass but also on the spacing between atoms, and the latter is an electronic rather than a nuclear property. However, the number of electrons in atoms, which under normal circumstances are electrically neutral, is just sufficient to neutralize the positive electric charge on the nuclei. Hence their charge is the distinguishing property of the nuclei of the various elements from hydrogen through uranium to the artificially produced transuranic elements. This charge, in units of the absolute value of the electron charge, is an integer, usually designated by Z. In many cases several nuclei with the same Z but different masses are found in nature; they are called *isotopes*. However, the properties of all the isotopes of the different elements are determined directly by the behavior of the extranuclear electrons. In the ordinary phenomena with which we are accustomed in our everyday life, nuclei play no important part. In electrical as well as chemical phenomena it is electrons which are important; *e.g.*, electrons carry the current in electrical circuits, and electrons make the valence bonds in chemical combination. In fact, in these ordinary phenomena, nuclei are immutable and unchangeable. This fact is responsible for the immutability of atoms no matter what chemical reactions and combinations they undergo, in which their electronic structures are considerably changed and distorted. Throughout the chemical transformation of an atom its nucleus remains immutable, and when the atom returns to its elemental state its electronic structure returns to that demanded by its nuclear charge. In recent years it has been shown that chemical combination as well as external pressure does influence very slightly the activity of radioactive nuclei and moreover that radioactivity has important effects on chemical structure. These effects are irrelevant in the ordinary behavior of atoms having stable nuclei.

In view of this aloofness of nuclei from ordinary interactions, it might be asked why nuclear physics has been so vigorously pursued in recent years. The answer lies in the fact that, in accordance with Einstein's equivalence of mass and energy, the relatively massive nuclei of atoms are the repository of much larger amounts of energy than the electronic structure of these same atoms. In World War II this energy was released in an explosive fashion by exploiting the fission of uranium and plutonium nuclei. In addition, it is known that the source of the energy of the sun and many other stars is the fusion of hydrogen nuclei into helium nuclei. Furthermore, the fusion of helium nuclei into heavier nuclei up to iron is probably a further stage in the ultimate fate of most stars. There is considerable promise, especially in England, that nuclear processes can be employed terrestrially for the controlled generation of usable power. In addition, nuclei are of interest since for some years naturally radioactive nuclei have been useful as tracers and therapeutic agents in the technical and medical professions. In recent years, applications of this type have been greatly augmented by the ability of the nuclear physicist and chemist to produce a great variety of radioactive nuclei in great quantities, by artificial means. As a last point, the citizen should be interested in nuclei and nuclear physics, if for no other reason than because billions of his tax dollars are expended in nuclear enterprise every year by the Federal government. As long as he is paying for a monopoly, he ought to have some understanding of what is being monopolized.

6.2   Elementary Particles and Nuclear Constituents

The study of the properties of nuclei has led to many ramifications in the study of associated phenomena, particularly in the elucidation of the nature of nuclear radiations and of the fundamental particles of the universe.   At this point we wish to discuss these matters briefly.   We do this to make meaningful the later discussion of the properties of nuclei. We first refer to the radiations of natural radioactivity, α, β, and γ rays, which were discovered soon after the turn of the twentieth century (see Fig. 6.1).   At that time it was shown that α rays are fast-moving nuclei of the element helium, which had first been detected in the sun (see Fig. 6.2).   As α rays, these helium nuclei were observed to be ejected

Alpha Rays (*Easily absorbed*)	High velocity nuclei of Helium	Used in first successful transmutation experiments
Beta Rays (*Intermediate absorption*)	High velocity electrons (*Electricity*)	Too light to be effective as nuclear projectiles
Gamma Rays (*Very penetrating*)	High energy photons (*Light*)	Not very effective as nuclear projectiles

Fig. 6.1   The radiations from naturally radioactive materials.

with high velocity from heavy elements such as uranium, radium, and thorium. β rays, also ejected with high velocity, were found at about the same time to be identical with the negative electrons which as noted previously surround all nuclei to make *neutral* atoms and are the bearers of the currents in electrical circuits.   Modern experiments have established this identity within extremely small limits of error.   In this same early period γ rays were found and were shown to move with the highest of all attainable velocities—that of light—and indeed they proved to be high-energy photons or light quanta, several million times higher in frequency and energy than visible light quanta.

In connection with γ radiation it is to be noted that nuclear physicists under many circumstances treat photons as particles, albeit with zero rest mass and charge, but still subject to the particle-conservation laws involving charge, mass-energy, momentum, and angular momentum.   It must simultaneously be noted that the wave nature of all particles regardless of their charge and mass is also of the greatest importance in nuclear physics.   In no other branch of physics is the dual nature—particle and wave—of the elementary entities so prominent and so essential for a clear understanding of its subject matter.

We refer next to the belief established about 1932 that all nuclei are composed of two types of building blocks—protons and neutrons (see Fig. 6.3).   In this connection protons and neutrons taken together are called *nucleons*. Protons had previously been identified as the nuclei of hydrogen; the neutral hydrogen atom contains one proton and one electron; the proton being 1836.13 times as massive as the electron. Neu-

trons were first discovered by nuclear physicists in 1932 and were found to be particles of almost exactly the same mass (1838.66 electron masses) as the proton but of zero electrical charge. Moreover they have been found to be radioactive in the free state, emitting a negative electron with a half-life* of 12.8 min and changing into a proton. This fact and their affinity for atomic nuclei make neutrons undetectable in ordinary phenomena; only on their release in nuclear transmutations can they be detected and studied. Inside stable atomic nuclei, neutrons themselves are stable, and the belief that they are nuclear building blocks is firmly held today even though it is not by any means completely understood.

The radioactivity of the neutron is presumed to be responsible for the activity of the natural and artificially produced negative-electron emitters among radioactive nuclei. In stable nuclei there are roughly equal numbers of protons and neutrons. Nuclei, natural or artificially produced, which have an excess of neutrons over the number characterizing the stable type are found to be negative-electron emitters. This is not too surprising, but in 1933 was

Fig. 6.2 Cloud-chamber photograph showing a "billiard ball" collision of an α particle with a helium nucleus in the helium gas of the cloud chamber. The angle of 90° between the two particles of the collision shows that they have equal mass and shows the identity of the α particle with helium nuclei. This simple but elegant photograph is typical of the methods employed to identify nuclear radiations. (*From Rutherford, Chadwick, and Ellis, "Radiations from Radioactive Substances," p. 246, Cambridge University Press, New York, 1930.*)

made the somewhat surprising discovery that artificially produced nuclei having a proton excess (none of these occur naturally) also emit electrons but in this case positive electrons or *positrons*. These positrons had been discovered in 1932 in cosmic radiation. The positron radioactivity of protons in nuclei indicates that protons share many of the properties of neutrons. The fact that neutrons are heavier than protons is what determines that neutrons, not protons, are radioactive in the free state.

An essential idea which must be emphasized at this point is that elec-

*In the decay of radioactive nuclei the *half-life* is the period in which one-half of a given number of the nuclei will decay.

trons and positrons do not exist as such in nuclei; only neutrons and protons, in so far as we now know, retain their identity in nuclei.   Neither do photons exist as such in nuclei or for that matter in atoms; they are emitted when protons and neutrons change their energy in a nucleus or when electrons change their energy in atoms.   The question whether α particles exist as such in nuclei has not been conclusively answered. α particles or helium nuclei consist of two protons and two neutrons very

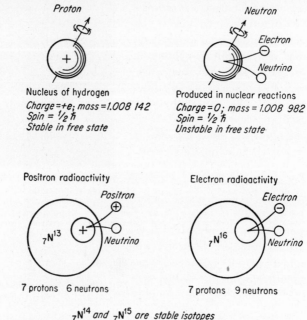

Proton

Nucleus of hydrogen
Charge =+e; mass =1.008 142
Spin = 1/2 ℏ
Stable in free state

Neutron

Electron

Neutrino

Produced in nuclear reactions
Charge =0; mass = 1.008 982
Spin = 1/2 ℏ
Unstable in free state

Positron radioactivity

Positron

$_7N^{13}$ *Neutrino*

7 protons   6 neutrons

Electron radioactivity

Electron

$_7N^{16}$ *Neutrino*

7 protons   9 neutrons

$_7N^{14}$ and $_7N^{15}$ are stable isotopes

Fig. 6.3 Protons and neutrons as nucleons or nuclear "building blocks" and their part in the β radioactivity of nuclei.   The positron activity of $_7N^{13}$ and the electron activity of $_7N^{16}$ are illustrated here.

tightly bound together.   It is clear that these four nucleons must amalgamate before α activity is possible, but whether they constitute a distinguishable unit in stable nuclei is not known at the present state of our knowledge.

Returning for the moment to the process of beta radiation, it has been realized almost from the time of its discovery that the conservation laws of energy, linear momentum, and angular momentum cannot be satisfied by the hypothesis that a negative electron alone is emitted in the process. In recent years, painstaking effort has shown that the conservation laws are all satisfied if we postulate that a particle known as the *neutrino* is emitted with the β-ray electron or positron (see Fig. 6.4).   This particle has zero rest mass and charge, just as the photon, but exhibits none of the properties of light interacting with matter.   Theory predicts only a very weak interaction of neutrinos in passing through matter, that of inverse beta decay. For example, a proton on absorbing a neutrino of sufficient energy would emit a positron and change to a neutron. Recent experiments at Los Alamos indicate that this probably does occur. At the present time it is generally assumed that the neutrino is one of the

Fig. 6.4 In this cloud-chamber photograph of the disintegration of Li^8, three disintegration products are observed: one electron and two α particles. The electron track is curved in the magnetic field which was normal to the plane of the photograph while the two α-particle tracks exhibit the characteristic dense ionization and definite "range" of such tracks. The Li^8 decays by electron emission to Be^8 which subsequently breaks up into two α particles. The angle between the two α tracks (6° less than 180°) indicates a considerable recoil of the Be^8 from the Li^8 disintegration. The momentum of this recoil is greater than that of the observed electron and is presumably balanced by that of a neutrino which produces no ionization and hence cannot be observed in the chamber.

fundamental particles of nuclear physics. In fact it is even sometimes assumed that the particle emitted with positron decay may be different from that emitted with electron decay. The two particles are conventionally referred to as *neutrino* (+ decay) and *antineutrino* (− decay).

In the study of cosmic radiation it has been discovered that there are several types of particles, originally called mesotrons but now called *mesons*, which are intermediate in mass between the electron and proton mass. Further, there are even some, called V particles, which are slightly heavier than protons. The mesons and V particles will be discussed in considerably more detail in Chap. 9. Of primary interest to the nuclear physicist are the so-called π mesons, positive, negative, and neutral, which can be produced and studied in the laboratory and are believed to be closely related to the forces between nucleons. The charged π mesons have positive or negative charges equal in magnitude to that of the electron and a rest mass 273 times that of the electron. The neutral π meson has no charge but a rest mass 262 times that of the electron. Also of interest to the nuclear physicist are the μ mesons, positive and negative, which, along with neutrinos, are the products of the decay of the positive and negative π mesons. These μ mesons have single electronic charges and rest masses equal to 207 electron masses. They decay into electrons, either positive or negative, along with a pair of neutrinos. Neutral μ mesons have not been detected. Neutral π mesons decay with the emission of two high-energy photons.

6.3 Notation of Nuclear Physics

We conclude these preliminaries by making a few comments on nuclear symbols and notations which have been borrowed in large measure from chemistry. The symbols used to designate chemical elements and compounds, such as H for hydrogen, O for oxygen, and H_2O for water, have been taken over in nuclear physics with the addition of a right-hand superscript to designate the closest integer to the atomic weight and of a left-hand subscript to designate the integral atomic number or charge. Thus the atom of light hydrogen is designated in detail by $_1H^1$, while that of heavy hydrogen, the deuterium atom, is designated by $_1H^2$ or $_1D^2$ and that of the heaviest hydrogen, tritium, by $_1H^3$ or $_1T^3$. The helium atom, with a nucleus of mass 4 and charge 2, is designated by $_2He^4$. The name tralphium has been suggested for the helium atom with a nucleus of mass 3, $_2He^3$. The three known stable isotopes of oxygen are $_8O^{16}$, $_8O^{17}$, $_8O^{18}$, and the two naturally occurring isotopes of uranium are $_{92}U^{235}$ and $_{92}U^{238}$. European physicists often write the atomic-weight superscript on the left-hand side, e.g., $_1^1H$. Since the chemical symbol and charge number are actually redundant, the charge subscript is often omitted, e.g., O^{16}. On the other hand, whenever the neutron number is of particular interest, it is sometimes added as a subscript on the right-hand side, e.g., $_{92}U^{235}_{143}$ and $_{92}U^{238}_{146}$. By tradition, the symbols here under discussion refer strictly to neutral atoms or atoms in neutral molecules. The nuclear physicist often uses them loosely to designate nuclei, although, in the case of light nuclei, letters such as p for the proton, n for the neutron, d for the deuteron, t for the triton, and α for the α particle are commonly used. Capital P and N are often used to designate the proton and neutron as nucleons inside the nucleus. The deuteron is the nucleus of heavy hydrogen. It consists of a proton and neutron bound together by their mutual attraction.   The triton is a still heavier hydrogen nucleus, that of tritium, made up of one proton and two neutrons.

In describing ionized atoms, the atomic hydrogen ion (which is actually just a proton, deuteron, or triton) is designated by H^+, D^+, or T^+, while the molecular hydrogen ion is designated by HH^+, HD^+, or DD^+, etc. Ions of helium are He^+ and He^{++}, the latter just being an α particle. In the high-energy hydrogen beams produced by accelerators, the H^+ or proton beam is referred to as the mass-one beam, the HH^+ beam as the mass-two beam, and the HHH^+ beam as the mass-three beam.   This last ion, HHH^+, is unstable against dissociation but has a lifetime long enough for acceleration to high energy in the accelerating device.

6.4   Techniques of Nuclear Research

Research in nuclear physics has required the development of techniques which can reveal information about the properties of nuclei in spite of the fact that they are impervious to ordinary chemical, mechanical, and electrical changes.   One of the basic difficulties resides in the small size of nuclei; the largest nucleus found naturally, that of uranium, is only 10^{-12} cm in radius, while the helium nucleus is only slightly larger than 10^{-13} cm.   This means that microscopes using visible light (which reach down to 10^{-5} cm) and electron microscopes (which reach to 10^{-8} cm) cannot be used to "see" a nucleus.   We have no means of making a direct visual presentation of the image of a nucleus.   Our nuclear information comes (1) from studies of the small interactions of nuclei with their surrounding electron structures and with externally applied electromagnetic fields, (2) from investigations of natural radioactivity, and (3) from causing nuclei to interact with each other or with the fundamental particles and drawing conclusions from the nuclear processes which take place.   The small size of nuclei, about 10^{-4} that of their atoms, combined with their relatively large mass, practically all that of the atom, indicate that nuclear densities are much larger than that of matter in the bulk.   The density of all nuclei is found to be about the same and corresponds to 3×10^9 tons/cu in.   With reference to its constituent nuclei, bulk matter is very porous, but it must be borne in mind that the space between nuclei is filled by electron clouds which bind the whole assemblage.   On the basis of the equivalence of mass and energy, we see that the concentration of energy is much greater in nuclei than in bulk material.

The actual difficulty associated with the small size of nuclei arises from the fact that all nuclei are positively charged.   The charge on an atomic nucleus has some integral value between unity for hydrogen and 92 for uranium, in units of the electronic charge.   Since the potential energy between two charges $Z_0 e$ and $Z_1 e$ at a separation r is $+Z_1 Z_0 e^2/r$, we note that, for large Z and small r, a very large amount of energy is necessary to bring two nuclei close enough together so that they may interact. If we replace r by the sum of the radii of the two interacting nuclei, the potential energy is known as *the height of the classical potential barrier* between the two nuclei. It is true that, in the quantum mechanics, which nuclei presumably obey, such a barrier can be penetrated when the particles have relative kinetic energies less than the height of the barrier, but this penetration is improbable at energies much below the barrier energy. In classical mechanics, penetration is impossible below the barrier energy.

Since all the nuclear species found in nature are positively charged, we can see the fundamental reason for the failure of the alchemists to transmute the elements. The techniques which they employed were essentially those of high pressure and temperature. We now know that the kinetic energies necessary to bring about reactions between even the light nuclei are of the order of 10^5 electron volts* except in a very few cases. If we try to concentrate this amount of energy on a single nucleus by heating bulk matter, we find from the Maxwell-Boltzmann equation $\bar{E} = \frac{3}{2}kT$ that the necessary temperature is $10^{9\circ}$K, which is very hot indeed. Actually, because at temperature T some particles have much more energy than $\frac{3}{2}kT$, and because of the quantum-mechanical penetration of barriers with some probability even at very low energies, the temperature at which nuclear processes take place as a source of energy in the sun is as low as $1.5 \times 10^{7\circ}$K and even lower in cooler stars. Even these temperatures are unattainable terrestrially except in actual nuclear detonations.

In terms of pressure effects on nuclei, the alchemist's failure was even more fantastic. If we could exert pressure on a single nucleus, we would find, using $E = P\,\Delta V$, that the pressure necessary to make even a 2 per cent change in the volume of a nucleus is 10^{23} tons/sq in. All that the alchemists were able to do was bring about chemical reactions involving the electronic structure of atoms, and of course much of what they did laid the basis for the science of chemistry which grew out of their attempts. With their techniques they could not and did not transmute nuclei.

We have noted that the only successful techniques involve studies of the small interaction of nuclei with their electronic structure or with applied magnetic fields and the concentration of large amounts of energy on a nucleus so that it can be made to interact with other nuclei. We will discuss further only the second of these techniques. This technique boils down essentially to a kind of nuclear "target practice," as shown in Fig. 6.5. Many nuclei of one kind, usually light nuclei such as the

---

* The electron volt (ev) is the energy of an electron after being accelerated through a potential of one volt. It is the customary unit of energy in nuclear physics. Kilo electron volts (Kev) and million electron volts (Mev) are also employed as units.

proton, are accelerated in some kind of nuclear machine to form a high-velocity beam of particles, and these are allowed to impinge on "targets" consisting of other nuclei in bulk matter.   All the bombarding particles lose energy gradually to the electrons in the target material, but occasionally one of them makes a direct collision with a target nucleus.   Such a collision results either in a scattering or deflection of the incident particle, or else in a nuclear transmutation in which another type of particle is emitted and a new nucleus remains in place of the original one.   Our

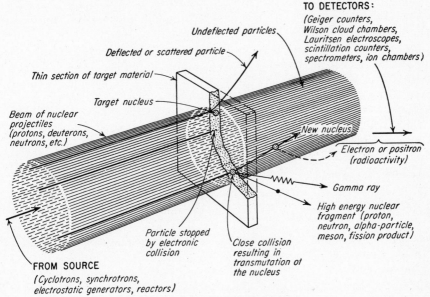

Fig. 6.5 Nuclear "target practice."

terminology here is quite arbitrary.   In most transmutations two fragments result, and we refer to the lighter one as a particle and the heavier one as a residual nucleus.   When they are of about the same mass, we refer to the transmutation as fission and to the products as fission fragments.   The essential point is that in the nuclear collisions, scattering as well as transmutation, we learn something about the constitution and structure of the interacting nuclei.

This technique of bombarding nuclear targets with high-velocity nuclear projectiles was first employed by using as projectiles the high-energy α particles emitted naturally by heavy nuclei.   Lord Rutherford found that these α particles, passing through nitrogen, transmuted some nitrogen nuclei into oxygen with the emission of protons.   Lord Rutherford and other investigators found that other nuclei could also be transmuted in this way.   The first artificially induced transmutation was brought about by Cockcroft and Walton in 1932.   They accelerated protons in a vacuum tube connected to a high-voltage source. When the protons struck a target of lithium, two α particles were ejected for each proton which made a nuclear "hit." The discovery of deuterons by Urey soon led to the additional discovery that the deuteron serves as a very efficient nuclear projectile.

At this point, the question will certainly be raised as to why negatively charged particles, such as electrons which are electrostatically attracted by nuclei, or neutral particles, such as neutrons, are not used as nuclear projectiles. In the case of neutrons the answer is very simple—they are used and, because they are not repelled by potential barriers, are found to interact strongly with all nuclei. The catch is the fact that neutrons do not exist in the free state in nature—they are rapidly captured by nuclei, and even in vacuum they decay into protons. Thus neutrons themselves are available only as the products of reactions induced among the nuclei which exist in nature; these are all positively charged and thus must have large relative kinetic energies to interact. The first neutrons were actually produced in the transmutation of beryllium into carbon by α-particle bombardment. It was soon found that high-velocity deuterons accelerated in cyclotrons were the most effective projectiles for the production of neutrons. Later it was found that neutrons could be produced without first accelerating charged particles to high energy. In the process of the fission of uranium 235 or plutonium, which is induced by neutron bombardment, it was found that two to three neutrons were emitted in each event along with the fission fragments. This leads directly to the possibility of a chain reaction if enough uranium or plutonium can be assembled in such a way that some of the excess neutrons from one event of fission are absorbed in another fissionable nucleus. In the chain-reacting pile, one of the neutrons from each fission event initiates another fission process to keep the pile operating at a given level while the other excess neutrons (one or two), except for unavoidable losses, can be used for transmutation experiments. In order to be chain-reacting, piles have a minimum possible size and a minimum content of fissionable material; thus even this source of neutrons is a device of substantial dimensions and cost.

The answer in regard to electrons is much more difficult. It is true that they are electrostatically attracted by nuclei, but this is not enough. In what we have said about transmutations of nuclei by protons, deuterons, α particles, and neutrons it has been implied that once they were brought close enough together they would interact strongly. This is indeed known to be the case. Strong attractive forces between nucleons —protons and neutrons—have been observed. They exist only at short ranges, $\sim 1.4 \times 10^{-13}$ cm, and are very strong, corresponding to potential energies of the order of 25 Mev. They have come to be called *nuclear forces.* Attractive forces of this magnitude do not seem to exist between electrons and nucleons. The interactions between electrons and nucleons, except for the Coulomb forces, are of the order of 4 Kev, and thus the interaction processes are very slow and are primarily manifested in the process of *delayed β* decay where the observed half-lives vary from 10^{-2} sec to many years. The times for the *prompt* nuclear reactions between nucleons are, on the other hand, as short as 10^{-22} sec. Electrons can be used to bombard atomic nuclei, but they induce nuclear transmutation only with a very low probability. This is also true for photons, which seem to have no interactions with nuclei other than those weak ones characteristic of the action of light on any system of charged or magnetic particles. Photons actually have stronger electrical and magnetic interactions with nuclei than do electrons, and at very high energies they can be used effectively in nuclear transmutations. However, such high-energy photons must first be produced either as X rays or as transmutation products in machines capable of accelerating electrons or protons to high energy, or else as by-products in the chain-reacting piles which produce neutrons. High-energy electrons are scattered electrostatically by the protons in nuclei and thus serve as a probe of high resolution for determining the spatial distribution of protons in nuclei. Recently experiments have been carried out taking advantage of this fact. Even though electrons rarely disintegrate nuclei, electrons do tell us something about the internal structure of nuclei.

The devices for accelerating charged particles to high energy for use as nuclear projectiles will be discussed in Chap. 7 and will not be treated further here. A second set of techniques necessary in nuclear physics is concerned with the detection of the reaction products or nuclear fragments. Many different detection devices have been developed: ionization chambers, Geiger counters, Lauritsen electroscopes, Wilson cloud chambers (including the recent development of continuously acting chambers), thick-emulsion photographic films, and crystal and scintillation counters. All these depend for their operation on the fact that charged particles produce ionization and light by interacting with the electronic structure of the atoms which compose the matter they traverse. The ions or the light so produced can be detected by ordinary electrical or photographic processes, and in this way nuclear fragments can be *indirectly* detected by their effects. Again neutrons introduce special difficulties; because they do not interact with electrons directly, they can be detected only when they transmit energy to protons or other nuclei through collisions or transmutations. Photons are detected through the high-energy electrons or positrons they produce in the photoelectric effect (ionization of atoms), Compton effect (collisions with free electrons), or pair formation (production of a positive and negative electron pair). We will not discuss detecting devices in detail. Suffice it to note that they make it possible to determine the identity, number, energy, and direction of motion of the particles produced in nuclear transmutations. The determination of the identity of a particle involves the prior determination by the same techniques of all its characteristics such as charge, mass, spin, and magnetic moment.

6.5   Protons and Neutrons as Nucleons

The experimental results which have been obtained from the study of nuclei constitute at the present time an imposing bulk of empirical knowledge. A considerable amount of theoretical research has been done in nuclear physics, and as a consequence many of the experimental results can be understood in terms of adequate theory. However, the situation is by no means similar to that in atomic spectroscopy, where the quantum or wave-mechanical theory of the Rutherford atom (nucleus plus electrons) has a very precise and apparently complete correspondence with experimental facts. We do not have today a theory of nuclear structure or of nuclear particles which is by any means complete. In what follows we will adopt a very simple model—that of nuclei consisting of protons and neutrons as nucleons—and attempt to understand certain features of nuclear structure and transmutation in terms of this model. Without the model our discourse would consist of a long list of apparently unrelated empirical facts.

Before proceeding further we must catalogue the most important of the known properties of the proton and neutron. We have already noted that the proton has a unit positive charge in terms of the absolute value of the charge of the electron (4.802×10^{-10} esu), while the neutron (as its name implies) is electrically neutral. The mass of the hydrogen atom has been found from mass spectroscopy and the mass-energy balance in nuclear reactions to be 1.008142 AMU with a probable error of three parts in the last figure. The abbreviation AMU stands for the *atomic mass unit* which has been arbitrarily taken as one-sixteenth the mass of the neutral O^{16} isotope of oxygen. It is often shortened to MU and corresponds to 1.660×10^{-24} g. The mass of the electron on this scale is 0.000549 AMU. One will rarely see the mass of the proton or of any other stripped nucleus listed in the literature, since it has been traditional to list neutral atomic weights in chemistry. Since there is one electron in the atom for every proton in the nucleus and since *atomic binding energies* are small compared to nuclear energies, the nuclear physicist has gone along with this tradition. The mass of the proton can be calculated from the difference between the masses of the hydrogen atom and the electron; it is 1.007593 AMU. The atomic binding energy of 13.6 ev $\sim 10^{-8}$ AMU is completely negligible in this case.

From the mass-energy balance in nuclear reactions the mass of the neutron is found to be 1.008982 AMU, again with a probable error of three parts in the last figure. We note that it is heavier than a proton plus an electron and neutrino, and we have already indicated that this is the reason for its decay in the free state. This is expressed in the traditional notation by

$$_0n^1 \rightarrow {}_1H^1 + \beta^- + \nu$$

and in a newer notation which is coming into use by

$$n(-, \beta^-\nu)H^1$$

or, more briefly,

$$n(\beta^-\nu)H^1$$

The negative electron is designated by β^- and the neutrino by ν. It is really more accurate to use p rather than H^1 or $_1H^1$, and this will often be found in the literature. With the help of Einstein's mass-energy law we can now calculate the energy which will be distributed among the proton, electron, and neutrino if a neutron decays after coming to rest in the laboratory in high vacuum. The law gives the energy E in ergs released on the conversion of a mass M in grams by

$$E = Mc^2$$

where $c = 3 \times 10^{10}$ cm/sec is the velocity of light. In the customary units of nuclear physics one finds the conversion factor to be

$$E \text{ (Mev)} = 931.162M \text{ (AMU)}$$

or

$$1 \text{ AMU} = 931.162 \text{ Mev}$$

As a rough rule, one mass unit corresponds to one billion electron volts (Bev) and one milli-mass unit (mMU) corresponds to one million electron volts (Mev).

In the neutron decay the mass difference, taking the neutrino rest mass as zero, is 0.840 mMU or 0.782 Mev. A direct measurement of this quantity can be made by measuring the maximum energy of the electron when it obtains practically all the energy released. This has now been checked accurately in the actual neutron decay and in many other β-decay processes. The essential point is that the mass of the neutron, as measured by mass-energy balance in the reactions in which it is produced, is consistent with the energy released in its decay. We note at this point that in all β-decay processes the mass-energy balance is satisfied only if we employ the maximum observed energy of the electron or positron plus the small recoil energy of the daughter nucleus. The observed energy spectrum of the β particles is actually continuous; this is one of the reasons for postulating the simultaneous emission of the neutrino, which can carry off energy in a form that is undetectable in so far as ordinary techniques are concerned. In a few events, the neutrino receives no energy. This will be the case when the electron energy has its maximum value.

One other property of protons and neutrons of interest in nuclear physics is their intrinsic angular momentum or spin. The unit of angular momentum used in nuclear physics is Planck's constant h divided by 2π; it is designated by $\hbar = h/2\pi$ (h bar). We must emphasize that the fundamental unit of angular momentum is $\hbar$, not h. Orbital angular momentum always occurs in integral multiples of this unit: $0\hbar$, $1\hbar$, $2\hbar$, $3\hbar$, etc. Intrinsic spin angular momentum can occur in both integral and half-integral multiples: $0\hbar$, $\frac{1}{2}\hbar$, $1\hbar$, $\frac{3}{2}\hbar$, etc. Planck's constant h first came into use because it gives the energy of a quantum in terms of its frequency ν as $E = h\nu$. However, if one uses the angular or circular frequency $\omega = 2\pi\nu$ which occurs most naturally in the expression for a sinusoidally time-varying quantity (sin ωt compared to sin $2\pi\nu t$), then the quantum energy is $E = \hbar\omega$. In terms of $\hbar$, the proton and neutron as well as the electron and neutrino have an intrinsic spin of one-half unit. In the literature, the spin is said to be $\frac{1}{2}\hbar$ or quite often just $\frac{1}{2}$. On our model the total angular momentum of any nucleus is made up vectorially of the intrinsic spins of its constituent nucleons plus the orbital angular momentum which arises from their internal motion in the nucleus. As noted previously, the possible orbital angular momenta for nucleons are quantized such that only integral multiples of $\hbar$ occur. Experimentally, pairs of neutrons and pairs of protons in complex nuclei seem to line up to give a vector sum of their angular momenta equal to zero, so that the resultant angular momentum for the nucleus is just that of the unpaired or odd nucleon such as that of the odd neutron in $_8O^{17}$. The observed spin for $_8O^{17}$ is $\frac{5}{2}$, and this is thought to arise from the odd neutron having an orbital angular momentum 2 parallel to its intrinsic spin $\frac{1}{2}$. The theory of nuclear-shell structure makes this result plausible, and to the experimental physicist the measured results are useful in indicating the orbital angular momentum of the odd nucleons in the nucleus under study, since this tells a great deal about the internal structure and dynamics of the nucleus. An empirical rule worthy of note is that all nuclei with an even number of protons and an even number of neutrons have zero spin. Because of the cancellation of neutron-proton pairs, the intrinsic spins even of the heavy nuclei do not become very large; the largest observed value that occurs with any frequency is $\frac{9}{2}$.

When taken as nucleons, protons and neutrons are often considered to be different manifestations of the same particle. This particle is said to have a total *isotopic spin* of one-half (similar to the possible value one-half for rotational spin). This isotopic spin can have a projection in "charge space" of plus one-half in which case it manifests itself as a proton or minus one-half in which case it manifests itself as a neutron. Abstruse as this concept is, it is really no more abstruse than intrinsic rotational spin, and it has been very fruitful in explaining some experimental results.

6.6 The Deuteron and Nuclear Forces

The simplest of compound nuclei is the deuteron which, with an electron, constitutes an atom of heavy hydrogen or deuterium. The simplest of interactions in nuclear physics are those between two protons or between a neutron and a proton. The interaction between two neutrons cannot be studied directly in the laboratory because we cannot obtain free neutrons as targets. These "two-body" problems of nuclear physics have been studied extensively, and they have led to a considerable amount of empirical knowledge about the nuclear forces between pairs of nucleons. These two-body forces are the basis of current theories of nuclear structure which assume that the nucleons in a complex nucleus interact with each other in such a way that each interaction is independent of the other nucleons (except for exclusion-principle effects which will be discussed later). To date it has not been necessary to include many-body forces in nuclear theory, although it may eventually prove to be necessary to do so in order to understand nuclear structure fully.

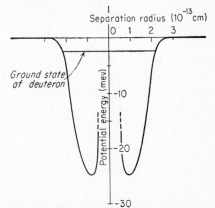

Fig. 6.6 The interaction potentials between nucleons and the ground state of the deuteron.

The properties of the deuteron are in themselves very revealing. It has a spin of 1; this is generally assumed to indicate that the constituent proton and neutron are in the lowest possible energy states of zero orbital angular momentum with their intrinsic spins parallel. The mass of deuterium $_1D^2$ is 2.014735 (± 6) AMU, and that of the deuteron is 2.014186 (± 6) AMU. This latter value is just 2.389 mMU or 2.225 Mev less than the combined mass of the proton and the neutron. In other words, the nuclear forces between a proton and a neutron bind them together into a stable configuration with a "binding energy" of 2.225 Mev. This can be accounted for by assuming that at short distances there exist strong attractive forces between a proton and a neutron. These forces are characterized by a negative potential energy of several tens of Mev. This is illustrated in Fig. 6.6. The short range is indicated by numerous experimental observations, such as the small size of nuclei and the fact that neutrons and protons fired at hydrogen nuclei do not interact till very close to them. The range or extent of the negative potential well is dependent on the exact spatial shape assumed for it but is about 1.4×10^{-13} cm on any model. Recently, evidence has been found that nuclear forces become repulsive at still smaller separations $(0.5 \times 10^{-13}$ cm), but this does not prevent the formation of the deuteron or other nuclei from protons and neutrons. Quantum mechanics dictates that a proton and neutron interacting in a potential well will have allowed energy states of a discrete nature, the exact number of bound states and their energy values depending on the width and depth of the well. The fact that the deuteron has only one state, at -2.225 Mev, fixes the well depth at about 25 Mev with some uncertainty that depends on the exact shape assumed. The induced interactions between protons and neutrons (scattering and capture) are consistent with this picture and indicate in addition an unbound state just above zero energy with spin 0 having proton and neutron spins antiparallel. The potential well consistent with this state has about the same range but only half the depth of the well previously discussed. Thus we find the magnitude of the potential interaction between a proton and neutron to depend on the relative orientation of their spins; thus, the nuclear forces are said to be *spin-dependent*. One additional point should be noted. Quantum mechanics indicates that two protons or two neutrons with zero relative orbital angular momentum cannot exist in a state with parallel spin as a proton and neutron can, so that *pp* forces and *nn* forces include only the weaker of the two *pn* forces described above. Considerable indirect experimental evidence indicates that the *nn* forces are identical with the *pp* forces except for the influence of the electrostatic forces between the proton charges. *Mirror nuclei*, in which the number of protons and neutrons is interchanged, have similar structures. Examples of these mirror nuclei are $_6C_5^{11}$ and $_5B_6^{11}$. Careful measurements show that the binding energies of such nuclei differ only by the difference in the Coulomb energies of their differing numbers of protons. The essential nuclear forces in the two cases are identical. Another type of similar *isobaric* nuclei is represented by the triad $_6C_8^{14}$, $_7N_7^{14}$, $_8O_6^{14}$.

6.7   Nuclear Binding Energy and Stability

Nuclei heavier than the deuteron become increasingly complicated in structure. Their integral positive charge Z is just equal to the number of protons they contain.   Their atomic weights A are almost integral in terms of AMU; this is to be understood on the basis that

$$A \approx N + Z$$

where N is the number of neutrons in the nucleus.   The fact that A is almost an integer for all nuclei (just as it is by definition for O^{16}) is very interesting.   It indicates that each proton and each neutron has a mass of almost unity in nuclear combinations.   Thus they have a *mass defect* of 8 to 9 mMU or a *binding energy* of about 8 Mev apiece.   This is a remarkable fact about nuclei.   It indicates that a given nucleon does not interact with all the other nucleons in a nucleus; for, if it did, the binding energy *per particle* would increase linearly with the number of nucleons in a nucleus, on the basis of attractive forces between each pair. Nucleons apparently interact only with their immediate neighbors (about three of them), much as molecules in a liquid or gas interact only with neighboring molecules.   This is known as the *saturation* of nuclear forces and is consistent with their short range, the forces falling to zero for large separations.   Nuclei do not collapse to radii so small that all nucleons are within the range of the nuclear forces; instead, only immediate neighbors are within this range.   As a consequence, each nucleon occupies a cell or element of volume in the nucleus having a radius of about the range of the nuclear forces.   Thus the total volume of the nucleus is proportional to the number of nucleons which it contains or (what is the same thing) to A, the atomic weight. This means that the radius of a nucleus of atomic weight A should be

$$R = A^{1/3} \times 1.4 \times 10^{-13} \text{ cm}$$

and in those nuclear experiments where the classical concept of a target cross section can be employed, as for fast neutrons, it is found that this cross section is just given by $\pi R^2 \sim 2A^{2/3} \times 10^{-26}$ cm^2, both in terms of its magnitude and its dependence on A (see Fig. 6.7).   We can calculate the den-

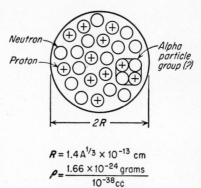

$$R = 1.4 A^{1/3} \times 10^{-13} \text{ cm}$$
$$\rho = \frac{1.66 \times 10^{-24} \text{ grams}}{10^{-38} \text{cc}}$$
$$= 3 \times 10^9 \text{ tons/cu in.}$$

Fig. 6.7   Nuclear size and density.

sity of matter inside a nucleus from these considerations by noting that we have approximately one mass unit of 1.660×10^{-24} g in an element of volume of $\frac{4}{3}\pi(1.4 \times 10^{-13})^3 \sim 10^{-38}$ cc.   The density is thus 1.6×10^{14} g/cc or about 3 billion tons/cu in.   Recent experiments on electron scattering by nuclei indicate that the numerical coefficient in the above equation for the nuclear radius may have to be lowered by about 25 per cent.

If one looks carefully at the atomic weights of the known nuclei, as shown in Table 6.1, it is found that the deviation of A from an exact integral value follows a smooth curve in general. The deviation from an integral value is called the *mass excess* when positive or *mass defect* when negative. When expressed as a fraction of the total atomic weight,

Table 6.1   Table of Atomic Masses from Nuclear Data

A, mass no.		M, atomic mass (AMU)*	A, mass no.		M, atomic mass (AMU)*
n	1	1.008982	F	17	17.007505
			F	18	18.006651
H	1	1.008142	F	19	19.004456
H	2	2.014735	F	20	20.006350
H	3	3.016997			
			Ne	19	19.007952
He	3	3.016977	Ne	20	19.998777
He	4	4.003873	Ne	21	21.000504
He	6	6.020833	Ne	22	21.998358
			Ne	23	23.001768
Li	6	6.017021			
Li	7	7.018223	Na	21	21.004286
Li	8	8.025018	Na	22	22.001409
			Na	23	22.997055
Be	7	7.019150	Na	24	23.998568
Be	8	8.007850			
Be	9	9.015043	Mg	23	23.001453
Be	10	10.016711	Mg	24	23.992628
			Mg	25	24.993745
B	9	9.016190	Mg	26	25.990802
B	10	10.016114	Mg	27	26.992876
B	11	11.012789			
B	12	12.018162	Al	27	26.990071
			Al	28	27.990760
C	11	11.014916			
C	12	12.003804	Si	27	26.995256
C	13	13.007473	Si	28	27.985767
C	14	14.007682	Si	29	28.985650
			Si	30	29.983237
N	13	13.009858	Si	31	30.985140
N	14	14.007515			
N	15	15.004863	P	31	30.983550
			P	32	31.984016
O	15	15.007768	P	33	32.982166
O	16	16.000000			
O	17	17.004533	S	32	31.982183
O	18	18.004857	S	33	32.981881

* 1 AMU = 931.152 Mev in this table.
Probable errors vary from 3 ppm early in the table to 1.5 ppm at the end.

this excess or defect is known as the *packing fraction*. The packing-fraction curve (see Fig. 6.8) starts at $(1.009 - 1)/1 = 0.9$ per cent for the neutron, 0.8 per cent for the proton, drops to 0.1 per cent at He^4, goes through zero at O^{16} by definition, reaches a minimum of -0.07 per cent for Fe, and then rises to $+0.06$ per cent for U. The binding energy per particle varies correspondingly. It is zero for the free proton and neutron, about 7 Mev for He^4, about 8 Mev for O^{16}, 8.5 Mev for Fe, and 7.5 Mev for U, as can be found by multiplying the difference in the fractions given above by 931 Mev according to Einstein's relation. In both the packing fraction and the binding energy per particle the total number of particles has been divided out.

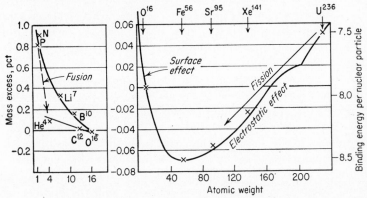

Fig. 6.8 Packing-fraction curve showing the decrease in mass and release of energy in the fission and fusion processes. Note that the left-hand portion lies above the right-hand portion and that its ordinate has been scaled down by a factor of 10.

The smooth variation in the packing-fraction and binding-energy curves can be understood qualitatively as follows. Each nucleon in the nuclear interior has a binding energy of about 8.5 Mev arising from its nuclear interactions with its neighbors; *i.e.*, 8.5 Mev must be introduced to free it from its neighbors. The nucleons on the nuclear surface, however, have fewer neighbors than those in the interior; thus, their binding energy is less than that of the nucleons in the interior volume. Light nuclei with their small radii have a greater surface-to-volume ratio than the heavy nuclei. Thus they contain relatively more surface particles and on the average have a smaller binding energy per particle. This explains the observed increase in binding energy from low atomic weights up to Fe. There is another effect, however, namely, the electrostatic repulsive force between protons. This repulsive force gives a negative binding energy which increases with the square of the number of protons and decreases the binding energy per particle in the heaviest nuclei. The combined surface and electrostatic effects explain the observed curve which has a maximum in the binding energy or a minimum in the packing fraction at Fe.

The electrostatic repulsions between protons have another marked effect on nuclear constitution. This has to do with the determination of the number of protons Z and the number of neutrons N which make up the atomic weight A, or more accurately the *mass number*, the closest integer to A. From the standpoint of nuclear structure, nuclei having the same mass number have the most similar characteristics and properties. Such nuclei are called *isobars*. Examples are A^{40} and Ca^{40} or Hg^{204} and Pb^{204}. They differ only in the number of constituent protons and neutrons but not in the sum of the two. The importance of A in *internal* nuclear considerations is in marked contrast to the situation regarding the extranuclear electronic structure and the chemical properties, which depend only on Z. One of the primary nuclear problems involves an attempt to understand why the isobars found in nature are the most stable configurations of protons and neutrons for a given atomic weight. We expect only the most stable configurations to occur in nature, since β-decay processes, although slow, will have reduced the less stable nuclei to the stable ones in the known lifetime of the universe ($\sim 4 \times 10^9$ yr). We will now investigate this point in more detail. As noted previously, the attractive nuclear forces between protons and neutrons are stronger than those between two protons or two neutrons. This means that the most stable configuration for a collection of A nucleons will occur when the number of protons (Z) equals the number of neutrons (N) so that $N = Z = A/2$. Among the light nuclei, the equality or near equality of the number of protons and neutrons is actually observed. Thus Ca^{40} has 20 protons and 20 neutrons, while A^{40} has 19 protons and 21 neutrons. However, as we go to heavier nuclei the increasing electrostatic repulsion between protons decreases their binding energies, and the most stable configurations involve an excess of neutrons. Thus Hg^{204} consists of 124 neutrons and 80 protons, while Pb^{204} consists of 122 neutrons and 82 protons. Even in the very light nuclei, the electrostatic repulsion has the effect of making the form with one excess neutron stable as well as that with equal number of protons and neutrons. A fairly smooth curve of neutron excess, called the *isotopic number* $I = N - Z = A - 2Z$, can be drawn as a function of A. The isotopic number has the value 0 or 1 for small A and reaches $(238 - 92) - 92 = 54$ at U^{238}.

The observed stability in light nuclei is very illustrative; *e.g.*, the stable forms of nitrogen found in nature are N^{14}, which constitutes 99.6 per cent of natural nitrogen, and N^{15}, which constitutes 0.4 per cent of natural nitrogen. Thus 7 protons + 7 neutrons form a stable configuration as do 7 protons + 8 neutrons. However, in the laboratory we can produce other isotopes of nitrogen by means of nuclear transformations; these are found to be radioactive (see Fig. 6.3).   If they had ever existed in the universe, they have now disappeared because of their radioactivity.   The first such isotope produced was N^{13} consisting of 7 protons and 6 neutrons. This was found to be unstable; it decays to C^{13} consisting of 6 protons and 7 neutrons according to the reaction equation

$$_7N^{13} \rightarrow {}_6C^{13} + \beta^+ + \nu$$

The half-life is 10.1 min and the maximum decay energy 1.200 Mev.   In other words, the smaller binding in N^{13} makes it energetically unstable relative to C^{13} which is a known stable isotope of carbon.   This decay process is typical of that found in all *light* isobars of *odd* integral mass number.   *The stable configuration involves an excess of one neutron, while an excess of one proton is always unstable even though the electrostatic forces are small compared with the nuclear forces.*   The second radioactive isotope of nitrogen to be produced was $_7N^{16}$, having 7 protons and 9 neutrons. It was found to decay according to

$$_7N^{16} \rightarrow {}_8O^{16} + \beta^- + \nu$$

where $_8O^{16}$ is a known stable isotope of oxygen consisting of 8 protons and 8 neutrons.   The half-life is 7.35 sec and the maximum decay energy 10.3 Mev.   This decay process is typical of all *light* isotopes of *even* integral mass number.   *The stable configuration is an equal number of neutrons and protons, the electrostatic forces not being strong enough to make an excess of two neutrons the stable form.*   For heavier nuclei they do push the stability in this direction.

In recent years still more unstable forms of nitrogen have been produced. $_7N^{12}$ decays very energetically (16.6 Mev) and rapidly (0.0125 sec) by positron emission to $_6C^{12}$. $_7N^{17}$ decays somewhat energetically (3.7 Mev) and rapidly (4.14 sec) by electron emission to $_8O^{17}$.   In terms of our proton-neutron model we see that in isobars with an excess of nuclear charge over that of the stable nucleus found in nature a proton will change over to a neutron with positron emission; in those nuclei with too great an excess of neutrons, a neutron will decay to a proton with electron emission.

In Fig. 6.9 we show graphically a similar analysis of the atomic and nuclear structure of the isotopes of carbon.   Two isotopes are not illustrated: $_6C^{10}$, which is a positron emitter, and $_6C^{15}$, which is an electron emitter.

The alert reader will perhaps have noted that the greater abundance of N^{14} in nature may imply that it is more stable than N^{15}.   This is indeed true, the average binding energy per particle in N^{14} being 7.48 Mev, while it is 7.08 Mev in N^{15}.   The N^{15} is the stable form for $A \approx 15$

because the alternative O^{15} is even less stable and because the $_7N^{15}$ does not contain enough mass energy to break up into N^{14} and a neutron. However, under the conditions of high pressure and temperature which probably existed when the natural abundances were determined, the equilibrium among the nuclear reactions then taking place apparently led, as one might qualitatively expect, to a lower abundance of the less stable form. This possibility forms a fascinating link between astrophysics and nuclear physics and one on which a considerable amount of research effort

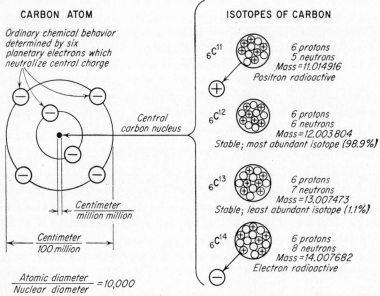

Fig. 6.9 The atomic and nuclear structure of the isotopes of carbon. Note the difference in atomic and nuclear diameters. Two radioactive isotopes are not illustrated: $_6C^{10}$, which is a positron emitter, and $_6C^{15}$, which is an electron emitter.

is concentrated at the present time (Chap. 10). The relation between nuclear reaction rates and isotope abundances is by no means completely understood at our present stage of knowledge.

6.8   Nuclear-energy Release

We now return to an important aspect of the packing-fraction curve (Fig. 6.8), that having to do with the release of nuclear energy. It is clear from the curve that the smallest energy content per nucleon occurs at the minimum near Fe and that higher energy contents occur on either side. Thus the general process of building up the heavier nuclei (up to Fe) from the lighter ones results in the release of energy. The fusion of hydrogen into helium, which we will discuss in more detail in what follows, is an example of such a process. Similarly, the general process of breaking down the heavy nuclei (above Fe) into lighter ones results in the release of energy. The fission or division of U^{235} is an example of such a process. We note that in the fusion processes at most about 1 per cent of the mass can be converted into energy while in the process of fission still less, only about 0.1 per cent, can be so converted. This is an important point. To date in nuclear-energy release we have succeeded only in releasing the energy available as protons and neutrons are bound together into more stable nuclei from less stable ones. Nuclear physicists have not succeeded in transforming the full mass of a proton or neutron into the form of energy. This may ultimately be possible and will mark a hundredfold increase in effectiveness over fusion processes which are, in turn, ten times as effective in this regard as fission processes. The energetics of all these transformations are well understood now; the problem is to discover the specific processes by which the mass-energy transformation can be brought about under terrestrial circumstances and at the will of the scientist and engineer.

6.9 Nuclear Transformations

The proton-neutron nuclear model is useful not only in the study of nuclear structure but also in that of nuclear transformations. This is primarily true in those laboratory-induced reactions which occur at bombarding energies below the threshold (≈ 133 Mev) for the production of mesons. Meson production involves the rapid interchange of protons and neutrons and will be discussed in detail in Chap. 9. Here we will confine ourselves to those nuclear processes in which protons and neutrons remain immutable during the process and in all of which the protons and neutrons are merely reshuffled into new and different nuclear configurations. It is true that many of the nuclei formed in nuclear transformations are radioactive by $\beta^{\pm}$ decay, as discussed above, but this decay is *slow* compared to the rate of the *prompt* nuclear reactions which we are now considering. The fastest known β decay is that of N^{12} (0.0125 sec), while the nuclear reactions induced by bombardment techniques can be shown by indirect methods to occur in times ranging from 10^{-13} to 10^{-22} sec.

It is of interest to consider first the original transformation induced by Lord Rutherford, which has been noted previously. In the notation of nuclear-reaction equations we have

$$_7N^{14} + {}_2He^4 \rightarrow {}_8O^{17} + {}_1H^1$$

The fast α particles which Rutherford employed overcame the electrostatic barrier of N^{14} and amalgamated with it to produce an intermediate aggregate which was energetically able to break up with the emission of a proton, leaving O^{17} as the residual nucleus. In the forms of $_7N^{14}$ and

$_2$He^4, Rutherford brought 18 nucleons (9 protons and 9 neutrons) together and found that they could reform as 8 protons and 9 neutrons in $_8$O^{17} with the energetic emission of a free proton.   It has been found in low-energy nuclear processes (bombarding energies <35 Mev) that the reactions do indeed proceed in two distinct and independent stages: the formation of the so-called *compound nucleus* from the initial nuclei and its subsequent breakdown into the final products.   This is indicated in detail by

$$_7N^{14} + {}_2He^4 \rightarrow ({}_9F^{18}) \rightarrow O^{17} + {}_1H^1$$

where parentheses have been employed to indicate the short-lived compound nucleus of fluorine produced as an intermediate stage in the process.   For reasons of simplicity we will omit this stage in what follows.   In high-energy nuclear reactions the intermediate stage in which the energy is shared by all the nucleons of the compound nucleus does not occur since the nuclei are almost "transparent" to the incident nuclear projectiles.   The reactions occur as more localized events involving the stripping of portions from one nucleus and their amalgamation with the other.   In deuteron bombardments even at relatively low energies the (dn) reaction can be described as the *stripping* of the proton from the incident deuteron by the target nucleus while the neutron continues to move with only small deflection from the original direction of motion of the deuteron.   The *diffraction patterns* or *angular distributions* over small forward angles of these neutrons reveal many spectroscopic details of the states of the residual nucleus into which the stripped proton is captured. [To describe the (dp) reaction, interchange the words "proton" and "neutron".]

The first artificially induced transmutation, that of Cockcroft and Walton, can be represented by

$$_3Li^7 + {}_1H^1 \rightarrow {}_2He^4 + {}_2He^4$$

in which a proton is shot into a nucleus of lithium and two energetic α particles are released.   The sum of the subscripts and superscripts on the two sides indicates that the number of nucleons and the number of protons (and thus the number of neutrons) has remained unchanged. As this was the first nuclear reaction on which the mass-energy balance of Einstein's relation was shown to hold within experimental error, we will investigate it in a little detail.   We will use modern values for the masses and energies.   By mass-spectroscopic methods the masses involved on the two sides of the equation are found to be

Li^7	7.01820 (± 10)	He^4	4.00388 (± 3)
H^1	1.00813 (± 1)	He^4	4.00388 (± 3)
	8.02633 (± 10)		8.00776 (± 6)

The difference is 0.01857 (± 12) mass units; when converted into energy units this becomes 17.29 ± 0.11 Mev and is known as the Q *value* of the reaction. Q is often written in a nuclear-reaction equation as

$$Li^7 + H^1 = He^4 + He^4 + Q$$

where the symbols represent the mass of the atoms indicated. (Since four electrons are needed on *each* side to make atoms from the nuclei involved, it is satisfactory to use atomic masses instead of nuclear masses. This is what is usually done since the mass spectroscopists tabulate atomic, not nuclear, masses.) Modern measurements show that if protons of 1.000 Mev are employed to initiate the reaction, the two α particles fly apart with a total energy of 18.34 ± 0.01 Mev. The energy difference is just 17.34 ± 0.01 Mev, and this energy release is thus equal within the experimental error to the energy equivalent of the mass which disappeared.

The accuracy with which nuclear reactions among the light nuclei have been measured makes it possible to construct a table of masses relative to O^{16} from the neutron to sulfur without use of mass-spectroscopic data. Such a list of atomic masses is given in Table 6.1.

Many hundreds of nuclear transformations have been produced since Rutherford's first example. In the interest of studying the simplest things first, the light nuclei of hydrogen and helium and neutrons have in general been employed as the nuclear projectiles. The transmutation of Li^6, the light stable isotope of lithium, by neutrons to form an α particle and a radioactive triton is illustrated as a reshuffling of nucleons in Fig. 6.10. Photons (in the form of γ rays and X rays), electrons, and lately mesons have also been used as nuclear projectiles. Under low-energy bombardment the light nuclei are also commonly emitted as the lighter fragment of the two-body breakups. At higher energies (>100 Mev) the breakup results in the emission of more and more fragments. These processes are called *spallation*, and an example is the reaction describing the results of the bombardment of arsenic by 400 Mev α particles, *viz*,

$$As^{75} + He^4 \rightarrow Cl^{38} + 6He^4 + 6H^1 + 11n^1$$

The vast variety of nuclear transmutations is a fruitful source of information on the properties of nuclei, and the study of such transmutations and the search for new ones are a major part of research in nuclear physics today.

The production of artificially radioactive nuclei follows the pattern of processes in which stable nuclei are produced. A reaction in which N^{13} can be produced is

$$C^{12} + D^2 \rightarrow N^{13} + n^1$$

We start with the relatively "proton-rich" isotope of carbon, bombard it with a proton and neutron in the form of the deuteron, emit a neutron, and leave N^{13} which has an excess of one proton and is unstable against positron emission.   A reaction in which N^{16} can be produced is

$$N^{15} + D^2 \rightarrow N^{16} + H^1$$

We start with N^{15} with one excess neutron, and on absorbing the neutron from the deuteron we make N^{16} with two excess neutrons which is unstable.   So it goes.

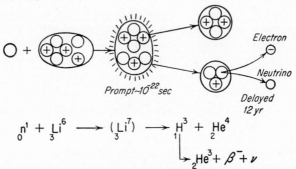

$$\underset{0}{n}{}^1 + \underset{3}{Li}{}^6 \longrightarrow (\underset{3}{Li}{}^7) \longrightarrow \underset{1}{H}{}^3 + \underset{2}{He}{}^4$$
$$\longrightarrow \underset{2}{He}{}^3 + \beta^- + \nu$$

Fig. 6.10   The transmutation of Li^6 by neutrons, which is typical of nuclear reactions with bombarding energies up to 150 Mev in which only a reshuffling of the original protons and neutrons occurs in the prompt reaction, *i.e.*, both the number of protons and the number of neutrons remain constant throughout the reaction.   If one of the resulting products is unstable, as is the H^3 in this reaction, the slow process of β radioactivity will result in the change of a neutron into a proton, or vice versa.   Above 150 Mev, the production of mesons makes possible the exchange of protons and neutrons even in the prompt reaction.   The intermediate formation of the compound nucleus ($_3Li^7$) is indicated in this reaction.   This two-stage mechanism is characteristic of nuclear reactions up to bombarding energies of about 35 Mev.   Above 35 Mev the reactions occur as more localized events involving the stripping of portions from one nucleus and their amalgamation with the other.   Also at higher energies the number of fragments can be considerably greater than two, as in the spallation process.

One of the most fascinating discoveries, yet not too difficult to understand, was that neutrons, once produced, were very effective as nuclear projectiles (no barrier) and that they were particularly effective when they had been slowed down to thermal velocities by collisions with protons in hydrogenous substances.   The neutron-capture cross section was found to be inversely proportional to the velocity of the neutron; this can be roughly understood on the basis that the more slowly a neutron passes by a nucleus, the longer time it has to interact with it.   Thus the interaction cross section increases with decreasing neutron velocity.

The process of nuclear fission which has been mentioned previously is probably the best known of all nuclear processes.   It was the first example of a transmutation in which not just small fragments were emitted, but

NUCLEAR STRUCTURE AND TRANSMUTATION

the whole nucleus split into two nearly equal parts, with consequent large total energy release, even though the energy release per nucleon was not particularly great. Just as important as the large energy release was the fact that two or three neutron fragments were simultaneously emitted, making a chain reaction possible. This can all be indicated in the reaction

$$_{92}U^{235} + {_0}n^1 \rightarrow {_{38}}Sr^{94} + {_{54}}Xe^{140} + {_0}n^1 + {_0}n^1 + 200 \text{ Mev}$$

which is actually only one of the many fission processes which can take place. It will be noted that the strontium and xenon produced in this reaction are not the stable isotopes of these elements but have a neutron excess. Thus they are β^- radioactive, and actually several decays are necessary to bring them to stable nuclei. Thus a by-product of the fission process is the formation of many radioactive nuclei of varying half-lives and energies which are very useful as tracer and therapeutic agents. In this radioactive chain a few of the decay products are even unstable to neutron emission. These neutrons are delayed by the slow β decays which precede them, but they are very essential to the operation of nuclear reactors, in which the control of the reaction rate must be accomplished by moving rods of neutron-absorbing materials such as cadmium in and out of the reactors at a finite rate of speed. The fission of U^{235} is of particular importance because it is initiated by slow neutrons and is thus a very probable reaction. The fission of U^{238}, the more abundant isotope of uranium, is initiated only by fast neutrons and then not so rapidly as in the case of U^{235}. For this reason it has been desirable to separate the rare isotope from the more abundant one. These and other matters are discussed in Chap. 8.

Another important source of nuclear energy is the fusion of four nuclei of hydrogen into a nucleus of helium with the release of two positrons and two neutrinos. It is known that this can be accomplished directly through reactions in which the protons amalgamate to form deuterium and He^3 at intermediate stages (see Fig. 6.11) or indirectly through a catalytic cycle involving isotopes of carbon and nitrogen through the reactions

$$C^{12} + H^1 \rightarrow N^{13} + \gamma$$
$$N^{13} \rightarrow C^{13} + \beta^+ + \nu$$
$$C^{13} + H^1 \rightarrow N^{14} + \gamma$$
$$N^{14} + H^1 \rightarrow O^{15} + \gamma$$
$$O^{15} \rightarrow N^{15} + \beta^+ + \nu$$
$$N^{15} + H^1 \rightarrow C^{12} + He^4$$

In either case the over-all process can be written as

$$4_1H^1 \rightarrow {_2}He^4 + 2\beta^+ + 2\nu + 26.7 \text{ Mev}$$

The neutrinos carry off less than 2 Mev in the form of energy which cannot be usefully absorbed. The energy release is less than that in fission, but it is about 6.5 Mev per nucleon involved compared to less than 1 Mev per nucleon in fission. Complete annihilation would release 931 Mev per nucleon. The fusion of hydrogen by the direct process is thought to be the source of energy of the sun and cooler stars. For stars

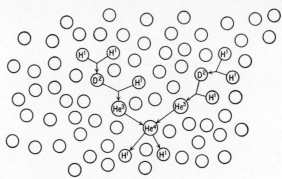

Overall result: 4 hydrogen nuclei⟶helium nucleus
Energy release = 100 million killowatt-hours per pound converted
Fig. 6.11   The fusion of ordinary hydrogen as in the sun.

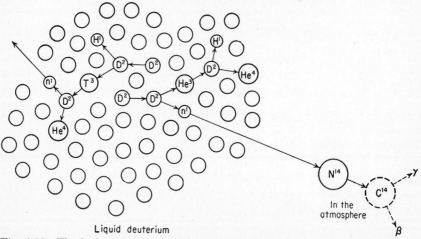

Liquid deuterium
Fig. 6.12   The fusion of heavy hydrogen. Note the release of neutrons which are absorbed by the nitrogen of the atmosphere to form radioactive C^{14}.

hotter than the sun, the CN cycle is thought to be the mechanism of energy release. The fusion into helium of the other isotopes of hydrogen, deuterium (see Fig. 6.12) and tritium, also results in energy release, and it is the search for specific processes, initiating mechanisms, containment and control measures, and so forth which constitutes thermonuclear research at this time.

6.10 Excited States of Nuclei

In many nuclear transmutations the residual nuclei are not produced in their most stable states or ground states. They are often produced as residual nuclei in excited states which usually decay fairly rapidly (10^{-13} to 10^{-17} sec) by γ-ray emission to their ground state. In some cases the excited states decay much more slowly and live long enough to be studied over reasonable periods in the laboratory. Such long-lived excited states are called *isomeric states*, and nuclei when in those states are called *isomers* of similar nuclei in their ground states. Often excited

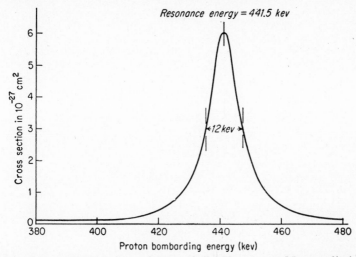

Fig. 6.13 Cross section for the production of 17.6 Mev + 14.8 Mev γ radiation from the reaction Li^7 (p, γ) showing resonance at a proton bombarding energy of 441.5 Kev with a width of 12 Kev. The corresponding state in Be^8 made by the amalgamation of the proton and the lithium is at an excitation of 17.6 Mev; this excess energy is radiated mainly as γ rays.

states of nuclei are unstable enough to decay by particle emission and thus can form one stage of a multibody decay scheme. The compound nuclei formed as first stages in a nuclear reaction also sometimes decay by γ-ray emission rather than particle emission, yielding what is known as *capture* radiation, since it results from the capture of the incident particle by the target nucleus. The formation of the compound nucleus in the first stage of a nuclear reaction is often characterized by *resonance* phenomena in the vicinity of the excited states of this nucleus. The cross section for the nuclear process goes through a marked maximum in close analogy to the large currents which flow and the corresponding large energy dissipation which occurs in an electrical or mechanical circuit at its resonant frequency. One of the first resonance reactions discovered is illustrated in Fig. 6.13. It shows resonance in the γ-ray production from the reaction Li⁷ (pγ) at a proton energy of 441.5 Kev with a width of 12 Kev.

Resonance occurs in the case of nuclei at resonant energies rather than at resonant frequencies. This can be understood from the very intimate relationship between energy and frequency in quantum mechanics. The

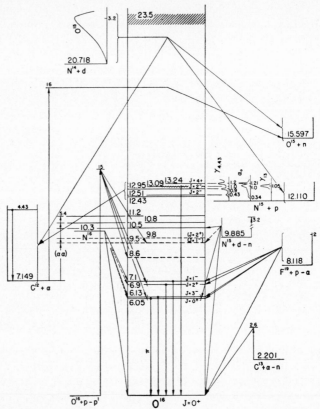

Fig. 6.14 The excited states of the nucleus O¹⁶. In these diagrams, energy values are plotted vertically in Mev, based on the ground state as zero. Uncertain levels or transitions are indicated by dashed lines; levels which are known to be particularly broad are crosshatched. For reactions in which O¹⁶ is the compound nucleus, thin-target excitation functions are shown schematically (where known), with the yield plotted horizontally and the bombarding energy vertically. Bombarding energies are indicated in laboratory coordinates and plotted to scale in center-of-mass coordinates. Values of total angular momentum (J) and parity which appear to be reasonably well established are indicated on the levels; less certain assignments are enclosed in parentheses. Excited states of the residual nuclei involved in these reactions have generally not been shown.

For reactions in which the present nucleus occurs as a residual product, excitation functions have not been shown; a vertical arrow with a number indicating some bombarding energy—usually the highest—at which the reaction has been studied is used instead.

nuclear physicist studies the resonance phenomena as a function of energy input with great detail through high resolution in the control of the bombarding energies of the particles which he employs. It is this fact that makes low-energy but high-resolution devices such as electrostatic generators as useful in nuclear physics as the high-energy devices such as cyclotrons and synchrotrons in which comparable resolution cannot be obtained.

The study of the excited states of nuclei has become known as *nuclear spectroscopy*, and it has lead to the elucidation of many facts about nuclei, just as the study of excited atomic states has been so fruitful in atomic theory. The excited states of the O^{16} nucleus are illustrated in Fig. 6.14. It must be emphasized, however, that there is still no comprehensive theory of nuclear excited states comparable with the Bohr theory of the Rutherford nuclear atom. It remains for more experimental and theoretical research to lead to such a theory.

6.11 Nuclear Shell Structure

A promising beginning in nuclear theory has been made by Mayer and Jensen, whose theory of nuclear shell structure describes many of the properties of the ground states and lowest excited states of the medium and heavy nuclei. The theory is similar to that of electronic shells in atoms. In atoms, each electron moves in the electrostatic field of the central nucleus and of the other electrons. The radial and orbital motions of the electrons are limited by quantum-mechanical laws to certain quantized states of discrete energies. These states are often referred to as shells and are characteristic of the potential in which the particle moves—in this case the potential of the electrostatic field of the nucleus and other electrons. In addition, by the action of the *exclusion principle*, only limited numbers of electrons can go into these states or shells. When a shell is filled, the next electron must go into a next higher state where it is not so tightly bound. A filled shell forms a particularly stable structure. This is indicated in the atomic case by the stability or inertness of the noble gases, He, Ne, A, Kr, Xe, and Rn; we see that electronic shells are filled at 2, 10, 18, 36, 54, or 86 electrons. The individual shells contain 2, 8, 8, 18, 18, and 32 electrons, and this can be understood theoretically from quantum theory. Once filled, a shell remains practically inert and the chemical properties of the elements show a *periodic arrangement* as the number of electrons outside the closed shells—the number of valence electrons—returns to zero and builds up through the low integers; *e.g.*, Na with one electron outside the second shell has properties similar to those of Li, which has one electron outside the first shell.

The essential difference in the nuclear case is that the potential or field in which the nucleons move cannot be stipulated with the exactness of the electrostatic field in the case of electrons in atoms. However, Mayer and Jensen have made the simplest possible assumption: that each nucleon does not interact outside the nuclear radius but has a strong and practically constant interaction inside. By rounding off the interaction at the nuclear surface, they obtain a potential which is very similar to that of a simple oscillator. They solve for the quantized radial and orbital motions of protons and neutrons in this potential and find results considerably different than in the atomic case for electrons. In addition they assume a spin-orbit force which lowers the energy of a state when the orbital and intrinsic spins of the nucleon in it are parallel and raises it when they are antiparallel. With this they find that the "magic numbers" for filled shells for both neutrons and protons are 2, 8, 20, 50, 82, and 126, in agreement with experiment. This explains why the "doubly magic" nuclei such as $_2He_2^4$, $_8O_8^{16}$, $_{20}Ca_{20}^{40}$, $_{82}Pb_{126}^{208}$ have greater binding energies than their immediate neighbors. The correspondence with experiment is complicated by the fact that in medium or heavy nuclei the filled shell will not occur simultaneously for both protons and neutrons. Even so, $_{50}Sn_{70}^{120}$ and $_{38}Sr_{50}^{88}$ are more stable than their immediate neighbors. The current ramifications of nuclear-shell theory are very numerous, especially in correlating the myriad properties of the ground states of nuclei. We must close our discourse at this point, fortunately on the note that a very real and substantial beginning has already been made in an understanding of nuclear structure.

7

Electronuclear Machines

R. V. LANGMUIR

ASSOCIATE PROFESSOR OF ELECTRICAL ENGINEERING
CALIFORNIA INSTITUTE OF TECHNOLOGY

7.1 Historical Introduction

Experimental nuclear physics is mainly concerned with high-energy interactions between nuclei and elementary particles or other light nuclei. The first nuclear disintegration experiments were done by Lord Rutherford in 1919 at Cambridge, England. The experiment consisted of bombarding nitrogen gas with the very energetic α particles (He nuclei) emitted during the decay of radium and its daughter radioelements. The reaction resulted in the breakup of the nitrogen nucleus and the emission of energetic protons. This was the first artificial transmutation experiment. Other similar experiments followed during the next decade, all using naturally occurring radioactive materials as a source of energetic α particles.

In 1932 Cockcroft and Walton succeeded in producing nuclear reactions by bombarding a lithium target with protons which had been accelerated to high energies by a high-voltage rectifier attached to a vacuum tube in which the protons were given energies of nearly 1 Mev. About the same time Van de Graaff at Princeton and later at MIT started the construction of the electrostatic accelerator which now bears his name. Within a few years the energy available to accelerate particles in the laboratory had been increased to about 2 Mev.

Handling such high voltages directly was so difficult that it was clear the energy range would be restricted to only a few Mev. The first solution of this difficulty was the invention of the *cyclotron* by E. O. Lawrence in 1930. In this machine the particle being accelerated is forced by a magnetic field to travel in a circular orbit and is repetitively accelerated by a small voltage each time it has made a half revolution in the magnetic field. The early cyclotrons enabled energies of over 10 Mev to be

173

obtained, although (as we shall see) the onset of the relativistic increase in mass of the accelerated particles limited the maximum energy to about this value.

About 1940 another circular accelerator, the *betatron*, was developed by D. W. Kerst at Illinois. This electron accelerator is capable of energies reaching as high as 300 Mev. Its limitation to about this energy arises from another relativistic effect.

The advent of World War II put a stop to further accelerator construction, but the development of atomic energy created a great interest in nuclear physics, and the discovery of mesons in cosmic rays showed that accelerators of still higher energy were needed. The time was ripe for an invention. As often happens at such a time, the invention was made independently and simultaneously by two people living on almost opposite sides of the world. The principle of phase stability was discovered in 1945 by E. M. McMillan at Berkeley and by V. Veksler in Russia.

Application of this principle permitted the extension of cyclotron energies up to almost 500 Mev through a relatively simple design modification. It also led to several new machines, the *electron synchrotron*, the *proton synchrotron* (or *bevatron*), and the *electron cyclotron*. These permit acceleration of electrons up to energies of about 1 Bev ($= 10^9$ ev) and protons up to energies of some 10 Bev.

At about the same time an old idea, that of the *linear accelerator*, was rendered practical by the advances in high-frequency techniques brought about by the development of radar during the war. A linear accelerator accelerates particles repetitively, but the particles move in a straight line rather than in circular orbits. Large amounts of r-f power are needed, but a large magnet is not required. Proton energies of 50 Mev or more are possible, and electron energies of 1 Bev should be reached soon. In the following pages the physical principles underlying the various types of accelerators will be set forth, and some of the existing accelerators will be described as examples.

7.2 The Van de Graaff Generator

The Van de Graaff generator, sometimes called an electrostatic machine or *statitron*, is in effect a redesign of a Wimshurst machine so as to make it suitable for very high voltages. As shown in Fig. 7.1, electric charges are sprayed onto a rapidly moving insulating belt and mechanically moved up to the top roller where they are removed from the belt, thus charging up the insulated terminal at the top. The voltage of this top terminal can be controlled by resistors or corona discharge to give the desired value. The energy required to charge the terminal capacity to the oper-

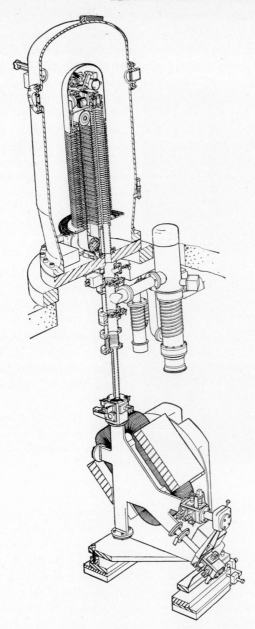

Fig. 7.1   Cutaway view of Van de Graaff machine with energy analyzer for emergent particles.   (*Courtesy of High Voltage Engineering Corp.*)

ating voltage and supply the losses due to corona, resistor current, and beam current are supplied by the motor driving the bottom roller. Between the terminal and ground is placed the accelerating column, and usually the voltage gradient down both the charging belt and the acceler-

Fig. 7.2 Six-Mev Van de Graaff posi-tive-ion accelerator. Units are in-stalled at Oak Ridge National Labo-ratory and at the Rice Institute. (*Courtesy of High Voltage Engineering Corp.*)

ating column is kept constant by a set of metal rings supported by insulators. These rings are kept at constant voltage differences either by resistors or corona gaps. The whole machine is usually kept at a pressure of several hundred pounds per square inch in order to reduce corona losses and inhibit electrical breakdown through the air. Sometimes special gases are used to reduce corona further; gases of high electron affinity, such as freon and sulfur hexafluoride, are most useful. The ion source involves an arc in hydrogen, usually with an electron-emitting cathode to keep the discharge going. Ions of various masses and charges emerge from the ion source through a very small hole and are accelerated down the column. One of the important design considerations in a Van de Graaff generator is to supply enough pumping speed to keep high vacuum throughout the accelerating column even in the presence of considerable amounts of gas streaming down from the ion source. This can be accomplished either by having an accelerating column of rather large diameter or by having several columns from ground to the high-voltage terminal, one of which is used as an accelerating column while the others are used as parallel pumping channels.

Van de Graaff accelerators are used mostly for very accurate and detailed investigation of nuclear-energy levels. For this purpose the emergent beam should be extremely stable and homogeneous in energy to better than 0.1 per cent. To accomplish this they are usually fitted with an energy-sensitive analyzer at the exit; a servo system is so arranged that, if the beam energy departs slightly from the value to which the analyzer is set, the error voltage is fed back to change the voltage of the high-voltage terminal. The analyzer can be magnetic or electrostatic or a combination of the two. Changes in the beam energy are sensed by causing the beam to pass through a slit with insulated jaws. An increase in current to one of the slit jaws controls the regulating servo system. A practical Van de Graaff machine, complete with analyzer, is shown in Fig. 7.1.

In a Van de Graaff machine, very high voltages must be maintained down the accelerating column and across the air gap from the terminal to the pressure tank. The problems associated with handling these high voltages have been solved below about 6 million volts, and commercial machines of such voltage can be purchased. Van de Graaff machines expected to reach an energy of 15 Mev are under construction at MIT and Los Alamos. The major problem at these high voltages seems to be breakdown inside the vacuum of the accelerating column. Van de Graaff generators can accelerate any charged particle. For nuclear-physics work, protons or deuterons are ordinarily used, while for industrial purposes electrons are often used either directly or else to provide a source of high-energy X rays. The direct electron beam can be brought out of the accelerating tube through a thin foil and used for biological experiments.

7.3 The Betatron

The betatron is an electron accelerator that works in the region from 10 to 300 Mev. Usually the electrons are made to hit an internal target in order to produce X rays, although a small fraction of the electron beam can be brought outside the machine when this is desired.

The betatron involves a central accelerating magnetic field surrounded by a guide magnetic field passing through a ring-shaped vacuum tube in which the electrons are accelerated. These two magnetic fields are in phase and change with

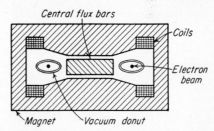

Fig. 7.3 Schematic cross section of a betatron.

time, usually at a frequency of 60 cycles/sec or some multiple thereof. A simplified diagram of a betatron is shown in Fig. 7.3.

The simple theory of the betatron will be presented here, together with some discussion of the focusing properties of the guide field.

Let p = momentum of electron
$\quad v$ = velocity of electron
$\quad e$ = charge of electron
$\quad m$ = mass of electron
$\quad B_0$ = magnetic field at orbit
$\quad \Phi$ = total flux linking orbit
$\quad r$ = radius of orbit

Then

$$\text{Centrifugal force} = Bev = \frac{mv^2}{r}$$

so that

$$mv = p = Ber \qquad (7.1)$$

If the magnetic field is increasing at rate $\dot{B}$, we have for an electron in an orbit of constant radius

$$\dot{p} = \dot{B}_0 er \qquad (7.2)$$

However, by the laws of electromagnetic induction $E2\pi r = \dot{\Phi}$ and $\dot{p} = eE$ by definition. Thus

$$\dot{p} = eE = \frac{e\dot{\Phi}}{2\pi r} \qquad (7.3)$$

so that

$$\dot{B}_0 r = \frac{\dot{\Phi}}{2\pi r} \qquad (7.4)$$

Rearranging,

$$\dot{\Phi} = 2\pi r^2 \dot{B}_0 \qquad (7.5)$$

Integrating,

$$\Phi - \Phi_0 = 2\pi r^2 B_0 \qquad (7.6)$$

Thus, if Φ_0 is zero, the average magnetic field inside the orbit must be twice the magnetic field at the orbit in order to keep the particle moving in a path of constant radius. The presence of the integration constant Φ_0 shows that only the *change* in the central flux is important, not its absolute value. Thus, if B_0 goes from 0 to 5000 gauss, the average flux inside an orbit can go either from 0 to 10,000 gauss or from -5000 to $+5000$ gauss. Some saving may be effected by the latter regime; betatrons so operated are called *biased* betatrons.

In a betatron, and also in synchrotrons and cyclotrons, the magnetic field at the orbit must decrease with radius to provide radial and vertical focusing of particles during acceleration. For stable particle orbits, there must be some force which will return to the orbit a particle which has wandered slightly away from the orbit. If the magnetic field decreases with increasing radius, then the magnetic lines of force must be slightly bowed outward.   Then, above and below the plane of the orbit there will be a small radial component of the magnetic field in addition to the large vertical field.   The magnitude of this radial field, for small displacements from the orbit, is proportional to the departure of a particle from the median plane; its direction is such as to exert a force on the particle tending to return it to the median plane.   Under these conditions, simple harmonic oscillations will take place; they are called *vertical betatron oscillations*.   They are quite rapid; usually one full period of the oscillations occurs in a few rotations of the particle in its orbit.   A somewhat similar oscillation takes place in the radial direction.   If the magnetic field falls off inversely with the radius, it can be seen from Eq. (7.1) that, when a particle of given momentum travels in a circle, the radius of that circle is independent of the momentum.   In other words, there is no focusing force tending to constrain the particle to any given radius.   If the magnetic field falls off slower with radius, the difference between this magnetic field and one which falls off inversely with radius will supply a focusing force that tends to restore the particle to an equilibrium orbit, giving rise to *radial betatron oscillations*.   The details of this action will now be given.

Let the magnetic field in the median plane be given by $B_z = B_0(r/r_0)^{-n}$. Since the time rate of change of the magnetic field is very small, curl B is zero and the ϑ component of this equation gives $\partial B_r/\partial z = \partial B_z/\partial r$. Thus we have $\partial B_z/\partial r$ at $r = r_0$ given by $\partial B_z/\partial r = -nB_0/r_0$, and hence $\partial B_r/\partial z = -nB_0/r_0$.   Of course, $B_r = 0$ at $z = 0$; so, if we restrict ourselves to small excursions Δz, above and below the median plane, we have $B_r = (-nB_0/r_0)\,\Delta z$.   The force returning the particle to the median plane is $F = B_r ev = B_r e r_0 \Omega$, where $\Omega = v/r_0$, the angular velocity of the particle, which is also eB/m, the angular frequency of any charged particle of charge e and mass m moving in a magnetic field B.   We thus have the force constant of the oscillating system, which corresponds to the Hooke's law constant k of a simple harmonic oscillator.   Here k is seen to be $nB_0 e\Omega$.   In a simple oscillator, the angular frequency of the oscillation is given by $\omega = \sqrt{k/m}$.   Similarly here we have

$$\omega = \left(\frac{Be\Omega n}{m}\right)^{1/2} = \Omega \sqrt{n}$$

This action is shown in Fig. 7.4.   If n is negative (*i.e.*, if the vertical field increases with increasing radius), the motion will be unstable and no focusing will occur.   Thus n must be greater than zero to yield stable vertical oscillations.

A somewhat similar situation exists in the case of the radial oscillations. Here the magnetic field available for returning the particle to the design orbit of radius r_0 is the difference between the field actually present and one which falls off inversely with radius (this is the condition for no focusing forces at all). This situation is shown in Fig. 7.5. It will be convenient to consider only small excursions from r_0 and to expand in terms of δ where $r = r_0(1 + \delta)$. Using this expansion, $B = B_0(1 - n\delta)$. The focusing magnetic field B_f is given by $B_f = B_0\left[\left(\dfrac{r}{r_0}\right)^{-n} - \left(\dfrac{r}{r_0}\right)^{-1}\right]$ or, approximately, $B_f = B_0(1 - n)\delta$. The restoring force here is $F = -B_f ev = -B_f e\Omega r_0 = -B_0\delta(1 - n)e\Omega r_0$. The Hooke's law force

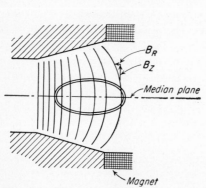

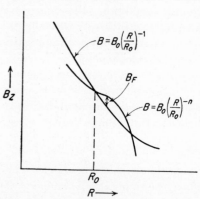

Fig. 7.4 Diagram showing the radial magnetic field necessary to make the vertical betatron oscillations stable.

Fig. 7.5 Plot of the magnetic field in the median plane of a betatron, $B = B_0(r/r_0)^{-n}$. B_F is the net magnetic field available for radial focusing.

constant is thus $B_0(1 - n)e\Omega$. The angular frequency of the radial oscillations is then

$$\omega = \left[\frac{B_0 e}{m}\,\Omega(1 - n)\right]^{\frac{1}{2}} = \Omega\sqrt{1 - n} \qquad (7.7)$$

It is clear from this result that the radial motion will be unstable if n is greater than 1. Thus, since both radial and vertical stability must exist in a successful machine, the permitted values of n lie between 0 and 1. This restriction is somewhat unfortunate, since, if larger absolute values of n could be used, much stronger focusing forces would exist, the amplitude of the betatron oscillations would be reduced, and the volume of the magnetic field needed to contain these oscillations could then be greatly reduced with consequent saving in the cost of the accelerator. This is precisely the point of a new accelerator recently suggested by Courant and others at the Brookhaven National Laboratory, in which it is proposed to use an n of several hundred for both radial and axial oscillations, stability being obtained in a different manner.

We shall now consider the actual constructional details of a typical

Fig. 7.6 (*a*) Professor D. W. Kerst, of the University of Illinois, with the first betatron ever built. This machine accelerated electrons to 2.3 Mev. (*b*) The second betatron ever built, capable of producing 20-Mev electrons. The injector filament can be seen glowing on the right of the vacuum tube between the magnet poles. (*c*) Professor D. W. Kerst and the 300-Mev betatron, largest in the world, built at the University of Illinois.

betatron.　Changing magnetic fields are needed; so these machines are usually driven by alternating current at power-line frequency or some multiple thereof.　Laminated iron is used in constructing the magnet, whose appearance is quite similar to that of a transformer (see Fig. 7.6a, b, and c).　Large amounts of energy are stored in the inductance of this magnet; in order to keep the power factor near unity, the magnet is resonated by a large bank of condensers.　The losses are then quite small compared with the stored energy.　Losses in the magnet and in the capacitors are about equal; both must be cooled.　The power circuit of a typical betatron is shown in Fig. 7.7.　Betatrons are available commercially in the energy range from 10 to 100 Mev.　Electrons are injected into the orbit at an energy of about 50 Kev, and the X-ray output of a typical machine is some hundreds of roentgens per minute 1 m from the target, being higher the greater the peak energy of the electrons.　About 10^8 electrons are successfully accelerated per acceleration cycle.

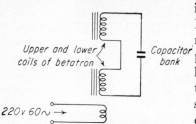

Upper and lower coils of betatron

Capacitor bank

220v 60~

Fig. 7.7　Power circuit of a betatron.　A bank of power-factor-correction condensers resonates the inductance of the betatron magnet. Typical capacitor, iron, and copper losses in a 50-Mev machine might total a few tens of kilowatts.

When the electrons are at peak energy, a few turns of wire inside the orbit are energized by a thyratron so as to reduce the central magnetic flux momentarily.　This causes the electron orbits to contract; the electrons then strike a small tungsten wire placed near the inner wall of the accelerating tube. The resulting X-ray beam is contained in a narrow cone whose axis is pointed in the same direction as the electrons were traveling when they struck the target.

The betatron is a simple and efficient source of high-energy X rays up to energies of about 100 Mev.　Above this energy range, several new factors enter which make the successful design of such a machine difficult. The foremost difficulty is caused by the fact that at energies above 100 Mev electrons traveling in a circle of radius a meter or so will radiate a considerable amount of energy as a result of the very high centripetal accelerations needed to keep them moving in a circular orbit.　This is merely an unfamiliar manifestation of the well-known physical principle that whenever a charged particle is accelerated it will radiate electromagnetic energy.　The theory of the radiation from centripetal acceleration is rather complicated, but its results can be simply stated.　In a typical high-energy accelerator, the radiation will consist of harmonics of the revolution frequency of the particle in its orbit.　The amplitude of these components will increase with harmonic number up to a harmonic number approximately equal to $\frac{3}{2}(E/m_0c^2)^3$, where E is the total energy of the particle and m_0c^2 is 0.511 Mev for an electron. Beyond this harmonic number, the energy associated with any harmonic drops off exponentially with increasing energy. In the case of electron accelerators of energy over 50 Mev, operating at revolution frequencies of a few hundred megacycles per second, the radiation is strong in the visible region and can be easily observed as a bright white light. Of more interest to the designer of such a machine is the energy per turn radiated by an electron. This is given by $W_{rad} = 712B^4r^3$ ev per turn, where B is in webers/m² and r in meters. This can also be put into the form $W_{rad} = 8.8 \times 10^{-8}E^4/r$ where E = the energy of the electron in Mev. Thus, for a constant-radius betatron, an additional changing flux must be supplied to make up radiation losses, and this additional flux increases as the fourth power of the electron energy. If this extra flux is not supplied, the orbit radius will gradually decrease as the electron energy rises, and the electrons will then strike the target before they have been fully accelerated. The complication of adding this extra flux is quite expensive, and the problem is usually avoided by using a synchrotron for energies much above 100 Mev.

7.4 The Fixed-frequency Cyclotron

The fixed-frequency cyclotron is the oldest of the circular accelerators, having been first built by a group of physicists working with E. O. Lawrence at Berkeley in the early 1930's. The principle is simple, and a schematic diagram of such a machine is shown in Fig. 7.8a and b. An r-f voltage at a frequency in the range of 10 to 20 Mc/sec is applied across the gap between the two "dees"; this establishes a spatially limited acceleration region for positive ions crossing the gap. After crossing this gap, the ion makes a half circle in the field-free space inside the dee and returns again to the gap. If the time taken by an ion to traverse a half circle is equal to one half period of the r-f voltage, the particle will again be accelerated when it crosses the gap. The mathematics of this system is

$$\frac{mv^2}{r} = Bev \qquad \text{or} \qquad \omega = \frac{v}{r} = \frac{eB}{m} \qquad (7.8)$$

The angular velocity ω of the particle is independent of the particle's linear velocity (and therefore of its energy) so long as e, B, and m remain constant. Thus a constant-frequency oscillator can be used to drive the dees; the particle motion is a sort of spiral gradually increasing in radius as the particle is accelerated.

Targets can be bombarded inside the magnet gap, or various electric and magnetic fields can be used to divert outside the cyclotron a weaker external beam.

The fixed-frequency cyclotron begins to experience difficulties at energies above about 10 Mev.   At these energies, the constancy of m assumed in Eq. (7.8) no longer holds.   Relativistic changes in the mass of the particles being accelerated begin to occur, in accordance with the relation $m = m_0/(1 - v^2/c^2)^{1/2}$.   The value of ω is correspondingly decreased by about 1 per cent for 10-Mev protons.

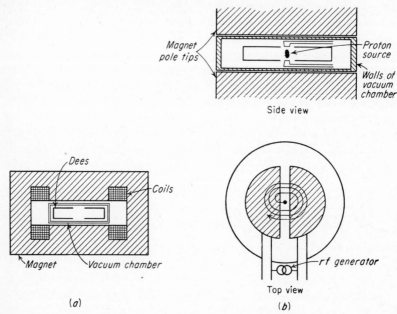

Fig. 7.8   (*a*) Cross section of a fixed-frequency cyclotron.   The magnet is excited with direct current to produce a constant magnetic field.   Positive ions are accelerated in an evacuated chamber between the pole tips of the magnet.   (*b*) Details of the dee structure in a cyclotron.

To provide vertical focusing in a cyclotron, just as in the betatron, the magnetic field must decrease slightly as the radius increases.   The decrease in B is usually rather small, perhaps 1 per cent or so from the center to the outside of the magnet.   This decrease in magnetic field produces a corresponding decrease in the angular velocity of the particle as it spirals out, so that the particle will gradually drift out of full synchronism with the constant frequency of the driving r-f voltage.   The difficulty can be eased by completing the full acceleration in as few r-f cycles as possible, but this requires the use of extremely high voltages.

7.5   The Principle of Phase Stability

The various troubles with the betatron and cyclotron, mostly due to relativistic effects occurring at high energy, were overcome by the independent discovery of the principle of phase stability by E. M. McMillan and V. Veksler in 1945. Consider a charged particle of given energy circling in a magnetic field, as in Fig. 7.9. Each time it goes around the circle it will cross the gap of an r-f cavity and will be accelerated, in its transit through the gap, by whatever voltage is present at the gap. The action here is quite similar to that of an electron crossing the gap of a klystron cavity. If the angular frequency of the particle is equal to or near the resonant frequency of the cavity, a strong interaction will take place. If the particle crosses the gap just as the gap voltage is zero and changing from accelerating to decelerating, then the particle will receive no acceleration; if the angular frequencies of the particle's orbit and of the r-f field are the same, then the particle will return to the gap one r-f cycle later. Let us now ask whether this motion is stable in the presence

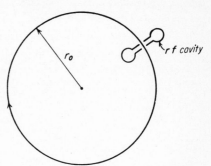

Fig. 7.9 A constant magnetic field is perpendicular to the plane of the figure. A charged particle executing a circular orbit in this field passes once each revolution through a gap in a resonant cavity excited by r-f power.

of small energy or timing errors. We see that it is from Fig. 7.10. Suppose a particle crosses the gap at 0° with a small excess of energy over the energy corresponding to resonance. This particle will then travel in

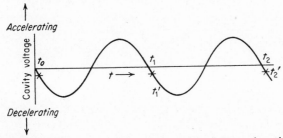

Fig. 7.10 Voltage across the gap in the cavity of Fig. 7.9 as a function of time. A particle crossing the gap at t_0, t_1, or t_2 neither gains nor loses energy. A particle crossing the gap at time t_0 but having an energy slightly higher than that required for resonance with the r-f field will take more than one r-f period to return to the gap and will come back, for example, at t_1. It is then decelerated by the r-f field existing in the gap, so that part of its excess energy will be removed. This process returns the particle to resonance with the r-f field.

a circle of larger radius than normal and will take a longer time to return to the gap. On its second transit through the gap, it will thus arrive after the r-f voltage has gone through zero; the particle will thus be slightly decelerated. This excursion into the decelerating phases of the r-f voltage will continue until the particle has lost its excess energy; it will then overshoot so that it has an energy smaller than the normal energy. The particle thus will execute phase oscillations about its stable phase angle, in this case 0°. It is clear that this motion is stable.

The principle of phase stability is applied in accelerators by slowly changing the conditions to which the particles are subjected, such as the magnetic field, the cavity frequency, or both. Under these conditions, the particle motion will remain stable as long as any significant change in the external conditions takes place in a time longer than the period of a phase oscillation. Several new types of accelerators have been developed from this principle, all of which have been put into actual operation since the war.

In the *electron synchrotron*, the cavity frequency is kept constant and the magnetic field is gradually increased. Electrons are injected at an energy of 1 to 2 Mev, and hence at a velocity differing from that of light by only a few per cent. Thus, while the energy of the electrons is increased to several hundred Mev, the velocity during the whole of the acceleration period remains approximately constant at that of light. Since the angular frequency of the electrons ($\omega = v/r$) is kept constant and equal to that of the cavity, the acceleration takes place at approximately constant radius. Thus only a small region of magnetic field need be provided.

On the average, the increasing magnetic field will require that the electron gain a certain energy per turn in order to remain in synchronism with the oscillator. This fixes the stable phase angle about which phase oscillations will take place. If V_0 is the peak r-f voltage and V_e the energy per turn needed to keep the particle in step with the magnetic field, then $V_e = V_0 \sin \phi$, where ϕ is the stable phase angle. If there is any other source of energy loss, such as radiation at high energies, then the stable phase angle will slowly change in such a way that this extra energy is extracted from the cavity and delivered to the electron. The system is thus self-regulating for radiation effects.

The construction of a synchrotron is similar to that of a betatron. Larger synchrotrons inject electrons directly at energies of 1 Mev or more. However, for smaller machines it is more convenient to construct a small betatron integral with the regular synchrotron magnet. This involves adding some flux bars in the center of the magnet to carry the required central flux for betatron action. Injection into this "preliminary" betatron is at about 50 Kev from a small electron gun. When the electrons have been accelerated to an energy of 1 or 2 Mev by betatron action, the cavity is turned on and synchrotron acceleration takes over. Shortly thereafter the small central flux bars will saturate and no longer play any role in acceleration. The principle of phase stability permits this transition from betatron to synchrotron action to occur without any detailed programming of the magnetic field or r-f voltage.

If the oscillator frequency is gradually lowered while the magnetic field is kept constant, the particle motion is still stable. This fact is exploited in the f-m cyclotron, or *synchrocyclotron*. The angular frequency of a particle such as a proton is given by $\omega = eB/m$. If the particle is injected at the center of a simple cyclotron whose oscillator runs at an angular frequency $\omega = eB/m_0$, where m_0 is the rest mass of the particle, the particle will be accelerated until the relativistic increase in mass becomes important. If, however, the frequency of the oscillator is gradually decreased, the principle of phase stability states that the particle will remain in synchronism with the oscillator. This requires the mass of the particle to increase, and hence its energy rises. The action is quite similar to that of a synchrotron, except that the particle orbit is a spiral rather than a circle of constant radius. The acceleration can take place quite slowly, and high dee voltages are not needed. This accelerator will operate satisfactorily at energy levels considerably in excess of those attainable by the fixed-frequency cyclotron. Indeed, the restriction on maximum energy is economic rather than physical in this case.

The output from the synchrocyclotron occurs in pulses rather than being continuous as it is in the fixed-frequency cyclotron. Particles are accelerated only when they leave the ion source at the beginning of the f-m cycle of the oscillator. This leads to a rather low average output current, although pulsed ion sources which can supply high current are often used. Frequency modulation of the r-f system is accomplished by means of a rotating variable condenser used to tune the oscillator. Since high dee voltages are not needed, a single dee is often used in place of the usual two. This simplifies extraction of the beam and provides a clear space inside the magnet for experiments using the internal circulating beam. Several synchrocyclotrons have been built for operation in the region of 400 Mev.

At energies much above 400 Mev, accelerators become so expensive that economic considerations are paramount. The major cost of a circular accelerator is related to the construction of the large magnet, and the cost of the magnet will be roughly proportional to the volume of the magnetic field required. The large volume needed for the spiraling orbits of a cyclotron clearly is wasteful when compared with the much smaller volume of the annular magnetic field of a synchrotron. The orbits in the cyclotron can be made circular if the magnetic field and the oscillator frequency are *both* changed during the acceleration time in such a way as to confine the orbits of protons to an annular region. A machine in which this is done is called by various names, the most popular of which are *bevatron* (referring to operation in the energy region of several Bev), *cosmotron* (referring to cosmic rays), and *proton synchrotron*. These gigantic machines have an orbit radius of about 50 ft and use several thousand tons of iron in the magnet. The oscillator frequency must track the rising magnetic field quite accurately in order to confine the particles to a small annular region. Such a machine operating at the Brookhaven National Laboratory had reached an energy of over 2 Bev in 1952 (see Fig. 7.11). A still larger machine to reach about 6 Bev was under construction at Berkeley in 1953. A further reduction in the vol-

Fig. 7.11 View of cosmotron. Two layers of shielding visible in foreground. Farther back, projecting from the ring-shaped accelerating tube, are 3 of the 12 vacuum pumps which exhaust it. In the center background can be seen (partly obscured by the magnet) the 3.6-Mev Van de Graaff machine used as a proton injector. (*Courtesy of Brookhaven National Laboratory.*)

ume of magnetic field needed can be obtained in the future from a new focusing principle developed at Brookhaven in 1952.

7.6 Synchrotron Oscillations

In this section a simplified discussion of phase oscillations will be given. As an example, consider an electron synchrotron operating at energies sufficiently high so that the rest energy of the electron can be neglected. It will further be assumed that the amplitude of the phase oscillations is small and that the stable phase angle is zero, a restriction that will later be relaxed slightly. Since the energy of the electron is large, its velocity will be approximately c, the velocity of light. As in the previous discussion of radial oscillations in the betatron, we will expand r as $r = r_0(1 + \delta)$. Let the angular position of the particle be ϑ and the applied frequency from the cavity be $\omega_0 = c/r_0$. Thus at high energies we have

$$\dot{\vartheta} = \frac{v}{r} \approx \frac{c}{r} \approx \left(\frac{c}{r_0}\right)(1 - \delta) = \omega_0(1 - \delta)$$

Thus the rate of change of the phase angle of the r-f voltage ϕ at which the particle crosses the accelerating gap is

$$\dot{\phi} = \dot{\vartheta} - \omega_0 = -\delta\omega_0 \tag{7.9}$$

If the peak voltage across the accelerating gap is V_0, then the rate of increase in the energy E of the particle is

$$\frac{dE}{dt} = \frac{eV_0}{2\pi}\omega_0 \sin\phi \approx \frac{eV_0\omega_0}{2\pi}\phi$$

if ϕ is small. Differentiating, we have

$$\frac{d^2E}{dt^2} = \frac{eV_0\omega_0}{2\pi}\dot{\phi} = \frac{-eV_0\omega_0{}^2}{2\pi}\delta$$

However, at high energies we have $E = eBcr$, and since

$$B = B_0\left(\frac{r}{r_0}\right)^{-n} \approx B_0(1 - n\delta)$$

we have

$$E = ecB_0r_0[1 + (1 - n)\delta]$$

and

$$\frac{d^2E}{dt^2} = ecB_0r_0(1 - n)\ddot{\delta}$$

Equating the two expressions for d^2E/dt^2, we have

$$ecB_0r_0(1 - n)\ddot{\delta} = -\frac{eV_0}{2\pi}\omega_0{}^2\delta$$

This is the differential equation of simple harmonic motion and shows that there are stable radial synchrotron oscillations of angular frequency

$$\omega_{synch} = \omega_0\left(\frac{V_0}{cB_0r_0(1 - n)2\pi}\right)^{1/2} = \omega_0\left(\frac{V_0}{2\pi(1 - n)E_0}\right)^{1/2}$$

These frequencies are considerably lower than the revolution frequency of the particle in its orbit. There is a corresponding phase oscillation, as can be seen from Eq. (7.9). The phase oscillations are also sinusoidal and are of course just another manifestation of the radial oscillations. It should be noted that the synchrotron oscillations involve oscillations in the energy of the particle, while the betatron oscillations do not.

A similar treatment holds for the cyclotron. The statement that a fixed-frequency cyclotron must finish the work of acceleration before the particle has dropped out of phase with the dee voltage can now be put more exactly. Referring to Fig. 7.12, the frequency of the dee voltage is set to be equal to the angular frequency of the particle when the particle has an energy less than its final energy but at a value greater than the natural frequency $\omega_0 = eB/m_0$ corresponding to the rest mass of the particle. Initially, then, the particle slowly drifts back in phase until the two frequencies match. From this point on the particle increases its

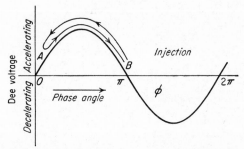

Fig. 7.12   Phase relations between particle and accelerating field in a fixed-frequency cyclotron. Particles are injected at all phase angles of the r-f voltage, but those successfully accelerated to high energy enter at a phase angle almost 180° ahead of that of the field. The phase at which the particles cross the gap between the dees slowly decreases because the initial angular frequency in the particle orbit is slightly greater than that of the r-f oscillator. As the particle acquires energy, the corresponding relativistic increase in its mass lowers its angular velocity, which becomes equal to that of the r-f field at the point A. As the energy rises still further, the frequency of the particle in its orbit is lower than the oscillator frequency and the phase gradually increases. By the time the particle has reached the point B, acceleration is over; at later times the further increase in the phase would bring the particle into the gap between dees at a time when it would see a decelerating field.

phase angle with respect to the dee voltage until it is eventually decelerated. The proper regime of operation of a fixed-frequency cyclotron is thus seen to be just the first half period of a synchrotron phase oscillation.

In all cyclotrons and synchrotrons, methods of radial and vertical focusing must be provided. Vertical focusing is accomplished in cyclotrons by causing the magnetic field to fall off slowly with increasing radius. A detailed analysis of the operation of a cyclotron shows that, during the early part of the acceleration, considerable vertical focusing is provided by the lens action at the dee gap; as the particle gains energy, the effect of this electrostatic focusing becomes small and magnetic focusing, using a bulging magnetic field, must be used. In the synchrocyclotron, the magnetic field can fall off with increasing radius much faster than is permissible in a fixed-frequency cyclotron; this provides stronger vertical focusing forces. The radial focusing forces are quite strong in a cyclotron, as can be seen from Eq. (7.7), in which the value of n appropriate to a cyclotron magnet may be about 0.05.

7.7 Linear Accelerators

The operation of a linear accelerator is somewhat like that of a cyclotron whose particle orbit has been unwound from a spiral form and laid in a straight line. An r-f voltage is applied across a succession of gaps arranged in a straight line. Between the accelerating gaps the particles pass through tubes which provide an essentially field-free drift space. The length of the drift tubes and the frequency of the r-f voltage applied

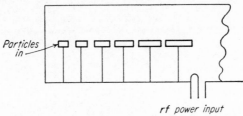

Particles in

rf power input

Fig. 7.13 Simple linear accelerator for heavy particles. The diameter of the cavity is typically several feet and it may be 40 ft long. Typical resonance frequency is about 200 Mc/sec.

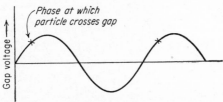

Phase at which particle crosses gap

Gap voltage

Fig. 7.14 Phase stability in a linear accelerator. Particles which cross the gap between electrodes at a moment corresponding to the first quarter cycle of the r-f accelerating voltage are stable in phase.

to the gaps are so proportioned to the speed of the particles that acceleration takes place at each gap. Each section must also have its diameter fixed in such a way that all sections resonate at the same frequency.

A schematic diagram of a linear accelerator is shown in Fig. 7.13. For stability in the particle motion in a linear accelerator, the accelerating gap should provide not only phase focusing but also position focusing which can overcome small radial motions of the particles. This latter type of focusing is automatic in a circular machine such as a synchrotron, but must be considered separately here. Figure 7.14 shows that phase stability obtains on the rising part of the acceleration phase, for if a particle crosses at a time slightly later than normal, it receives a small extra acceleration and the time of transit to the next gap is somewhat less. Thus the phase is retarded, and stable phase oscillations take place about the normal phase angle just as in a synchrotron.

Unfortunately, however, the electron lens formed by the gap is diverging for these phase angles, as can be seen from Fig. 7.15. The accelerating voltage is increasing during the time of transit of the particle through the gap; hence the effect of the diverging radial electric field in the second half of the gap will be stronger than that of the converging field in the first part of the gap. This presumes that the particle velocity does not change much while going through the gap, as will usually be the case once the particle is at high energy. Thus the linear accelerator

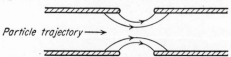

Particle trajectory ⟶

Fig. 7.15 Lines of force at the electrostatic lens corresponding to a gap between neighboring electrodes in a linear accelerator. If the voltage across the gap is increasing while a particle passes through (as is necessary for phase stability), the defocusing effect of the diverging field at the right will be greater than the focusing effect of the converging part of the field, leading to radial instability.

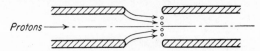

Protons ⟶

Fig. 7.16 First-order focusing obtained at an accelerating gap by placing a coarse grid across the entrance of the second drift tube.

seems to be inoperable unless some method of radial focusing can be devised. The actual solution for heavy particles such as protons is to cover the entrance of the drift tube with a coarse screen, as shown in Fig. 7.16. This essentially removes the defocusing part of the electron lens and leaves the first-order focusing which is converging. An objection to this procedure is that a small fraction of the particles will be intercepted by each grid; if many gaps are needed, the beam intensity will be considerably reduced. However, proton linear accelerators use this principle and operate quite satisfactorily.

The situation is somewhat different in the case of an electron accelerator. The particle velocity is close to that of light throughout the whole trajectory, and relativistic effects are very prominent. A detailed study of the motion shows that an electron injected with a velocity approximating that of light will have a neutral stability, the stable phase angle approaching 90° where the acceleration is maximum. Because of relativistic effects, the radial focusing forces approach zero. This is not important, as can be seen in two ways. One sophisticated view is that the FitzGerald contraction at high velocities makes an observer moving with the electron beam see an accelerator such as the one at Stanford (which is several hundred feet long) as only about 8 in. long. An electron beam will not diverge much in 8 in.; so there is no need for any strong radial focusing. Another way to look at the problem is to consider the radial motion of an electron as it gains energy rapidly. The radial momentum will remain constant, but the mass of the electron is increasing almost linearly as the particle is accelerated. Thus the radial velocity diminishes inversely with the distance traveled down the tube. This leads to a slow logarithmic expansion of the beam. The actual formula is

$$r_2 - r_1 = \vartheta_0 z_1 \log \frac{z_2}{z_1}$$

where r_2 and r_1 are the radii of the beam at points z_2 and z_1 along the tube and ϑ_0 is the initial angle of divergence at z_1. A typical electron accelerator might operate at about a million volts per 30 cm of length, and its electron injector might be capable of injecting a beam of initial energy 1 Mev through a 1-mm hole at 1 m distance, corresponding to $\vartheta_0 = 10^{-3}$. For a 300-Mev accelerator, which would be about 300 ft long, we then have $z_2/z_1 = 300$ and $z_1 = 30$ cm. Thus $r_2 - r_1 = 1.71$ mm, and the beam has somewhat more than doubled its size in going the whole length of the accelerator.

The actual construction of a linear accelerator is a somewhat exacting mechanical job. All but the first few sections of an electron accelerator will be constructed for acceleration of particles traveling at the velocity of light, so that most of the sections will be identical.

It is sometimes convenient to consider the accelerator tube as providing an electromagnetic wave traveling down the tube at the velocity of light. The particle rides with this wave in such a phase that it is continuously accelerated. Any other waves that are present will be traveling with a much different phase velocity, and their effects will average out over the path and give no net acceleration to the electron. Thus we can consider the gaps and drift tubes of a high-energy electron accelerator as agencies for obtaining a wave that travels down the tube at exactly the velocity of light in free space. The equipment added to a circular tube to make an electron accelerator can be thought of as artificial loading of a circular waveguide which makes the phase velocity of one of the modes exactly the velocity of light. This is normally done by adding disks with small holes in them at equally spaced intervals along the pipe, as shown in Fig. 7.17.

The wave which accelerates the electrons may be either a standing wave or a traveling wave, depending on whether there is or is not a termination at the end of the loaded waveguide. The choice between these two types of wave depends on the energy and length of the accelerator and is also related to the method of supplying r-f power to the loaded waveguide. Small electron accelerators operating below about 10 Mev use a single power oscillator and are often built to use standing

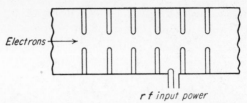

Fig. 7.17 Cross section of a high-energy linear accelerator for electrons. The diameter of the loaded waveguide is typically a few inches.

Fig. 7.18 General view of the 220-ft-long electron linear accelerator built at Stanford University. At 10-ft intervals, waveguide inputs bring 10-cm energy from the 15-megawatt klystrons shown to the right of the accelerator tube. The pulse voltage applied to the klystrons is about 350 kv.

waves. Longer accelerators, such as the one at Stanford, are of the traveling-wave type. In this case, the various power oscillators that are spaced about every 10 ft down the tube must be kept exactly in phase with one another. This is accomplished by means of a master-oscillator-power-amplifier arrangement.

Some general consideration will show that linear accelerators can be operated only at rather small duty cycles. This follows from the equation for the power P required to drive to V volts a cavity having a characteristic impedance Z_0 and merit factor Q, which is

$$P = \frac{V^2}{2QZ_0}$$

In a linear accelerator, the V across the cavity is much higher than that across the accelerating gap of a corresponding circular accelerator such as a synchrotron, and the power required is hence larger. Another important factor is the frequency of operation. The Q of a cavity operating at an angular frequency ω is defined as

$$Q = \frac{\omega(\text{peak stored energy})}{(\text{watts lost})}$$

Thus for a given peak stored energy and Q, the power lost is proportional to the operating frequency. Since electron linear accelerators are usually operated at the high frequency of about 3000 Mc/sec, the losses in the cavity are quite high.

It is interesting to digress at this point and invert the above argument to ask how one should design a single-cavity accelerator so as to obtain the highest voltage for the smallest input power. High Q is very important, but a much greater gain can be obtained by operating at as high a Z_0 as possible (and hence at low capacity) and at the lowest possible frequency. The practical embodiment of this idea is the *resonant transformer*, shown in Fig. 7.19. Here the accelerating column is similar to that of a Van de Graaff generator, but the voltage is derived from resonating the high inductance of the coil wound around the column with the distributed capacitance of the terminal and column to ground. The values turn out to be about 15,000 henrys resonating with somewhat less than 100 $\mu\mu$f capacity at a frequency of about 180 cycles/sec. This accelerator is driven with a few kilowatts of power obtained from a frequency tripler connected to the 60-cycle/sec power lines.

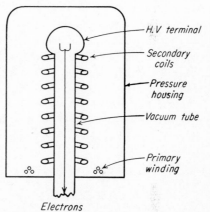

Fig. 7.19 Resonant transformer. The secondary coils are random-wound pancakes of many turns of thin wire. Their aggregate inductance may be as high as 15,000 henrys. This resonates with the 100 $\mu\mu$f of the terminal at about 180 cps.

A duty factor of about 10^{-4} is used in the electron linear accelerator. The peak power used may be about 10 megawatts, on for about a microsecond sixty times each second.   Small accelerators (below 10 Mev) use a single magnetron supplying somewhat less than 10 megawatts at 3000 Mc/sec for 1 μsec.   High-power klystrons are used in larger accelerators; these provide peak powers of 10 megawatts or more at 3000 Mc/sec. These remarkable tubes were developed at Stanford for use in the large accelerator built there.   The difficulties of handling such high microwave powers have not been completely overcome, but enough of the large klystrons were operating during 1952 to permit operation of the Stanford linear accelerator at energies over 300 Mev.

In 1953, electron synchrotrons were in operation at energies as high as 500 Mev, and one was planned for operation at 1 Bev.   At this high energy, the loss of energy through electromagnetic radiation caused by high centripetal acceleration makes such severe demands on the r-f power supply that electron energies much higher than 1 Bev probably should not be attempted with circular machines.   The only type of electron accelerator that is practical in the energy region above 1 Bev is the linear accelerator, whose success in 1954 awaited the solution of several engineering difficulties in the construction of high-power klystrons.   A synchrocyclotron yielding proton energies in the region of 5 Bev began operation at Berkeley in 1954.   A proposal to improve the construction of proton synchrotrons by using strong focusing was made in 1952. This promises to make possible the construction of a 100-Bev proton accelerator at a cost comparable with that of the larger proton accelerators already in existence.   One such machine may be built by 1960.

8

The Actinide Elements and Nuclear Power

GLENN T. SEABORG

PROFESSOR OF CHEMISTRY
UNIVERSITY OF CALIFORNIA, BERKELEY

8.1 Introduction

The 14 elements following actinium (atomic number 89) in the periodic system, *i.e.*, the elements with atomic numbers 90 through 103, constitute a transition series analogous to the rare-earth elements and are designated as the *actinide elements*. These include the naturally occurring elements thorium, protactinium, and uranium and the presently known, as well as a number of undiscovered, synthetic transuranium elements.

The term *transuranium elements* designates the chemical elements lying beyond uranium in the periodic table and hence including all the elements with atomic number higher than 92, the atomic number of uranium. All the transuranium elements are radioactive, do not occur in appreciable amount in nature, and have been discovered and investigated as a result of their syntheses by transmutation reactions starting with uranium as the primary material (Sec. 8.2). All those known are members of the group of chemically similar elements, the actinide transition series of elements, a group which is chemically similar to the rare-earth or lanthanide group of elements (Sec. 8.3).

Plutonium has assumed the position of dominant importance among the transuranium elements because of its successful use as an explosive ingredient in the nuclear weapon and the excellent prospects which it offers as the base material for the development of industrial uses of atomic (nuclear) power or energy (Sec. 8.4). This depends on the property of Pu^{239} of being readily fissionable and hence capable of undergoing a nuclear chain reaction and its availability in proper quantities. Plutonium is the only member of this synthetic group of elements

197

for which methods have been developed for production in kilogram amounts. From a purely scientific point of view, however, the other transuranium elements are of nearly as great interest as plutonium.

There has been a great deal of speculation concerning the upper limit of atomic number for the existence of transuranium elements, with considerations that such a limit might arise from either atomic or nuclear (radioactivity or spontaneous fission) instability. If the former is not the limiting factor, it appears likely, on the basis of extrapolation from the nuclear properties of the heaviest elements, that a few elements above atomic number 100 will have isotopes of sufficiently long life to make possible their physical investigation when the problem of their production in detectable amounts is solved. Unfortunately, predictions based on the systematics of radioactivity and spontaneous fission and the shape of the nuclear-energy surface in the heavy region suggest that the half-lives for even the longest lived (heavy-mass) isotopes of the elements with atomic number over 100 will be so short as to make tracer chemical investigations difficult.

8.2 Transuranium Elements

The known transuranium elements are described in the order of their increasing atomic numbers in the following discussion.

8.2.1 *Neptunium* (*Atomic Number* 93). Neptunium was the first transuranium element to be discovered. Using the neutrons from the University of California, Berkeley, 60-in. cyclotron, E. M. McMillan and P. H. Abelson in 1940 were able to show with the help of their chemical work that the irradiation of uranium leads to the production of the isotope Np^{239}. This isotope, which has a half-life of 2.3 days, is the decay product of the 23-min U^{239} formed by radiative neutron capture in U^{238}. Their experiments on the tracer scale of investigation enabled them to show that neptunium is similar in chemical properties to uranium. They named the element which they had discovered *neptunium*, following uranium in the same order as the corresponding planets Uranus and Neptune. Later the symbol Np was suggested for this element.

Another important isotope of neptunium, Np^{237}, was discovered by A. C. Wahl and G. T. Seaborg early in 1942 by bombarding uranium with fast neutrons, using the Berkeley 60-in. cyclotron. This isotope is the decay product of the previously known 7-day β-particle-emitting U^{237} which is formed as the result of an $(n, 2n)$ reaction on U^{238}. The isotope Np^{237} is of particular importance because it is long-lived, emitting α particles with a half-life of 2.20×10^6 years, and because it is available in weighable amounts. The first pure neptunium in the form of compounds of the isotope Np^{237} was isolated by L. B. Magnusson and T. J. LaChapelle at the wartime Metallurgical Laboratory of the University of Chicago (now the Argonne National Laboratory) in October, 1944, in experiments on the ultramicroscale with amounts ranging from 1 to 50 micrograms. This isotope is produced during the operation of the large uranium chain-reacting units, a very fortunate circumstance for otherwise it is probable that the element neptunium would not be available for study in the macroscopic state.

With this material, it has been possible to make an intensive study of the chemical properties of neptunium, leading to the establishment of its oxidation states and the properties of a large number of its compounds. This work has shown that neptunium has the oxidation states VI, V, IV, and III with a general shift in stability toward the lower oxidation states as compared with uranium.

The relatively low specific α activity of the isotope Np^{237} places the element neptunium in a class by itself in the transuranium group because it is relatively safe to handle from the health standpoint. The other transuranium elements are so highly α radioactive that special techniques and precautions are mandatory when they are handled in ordinary amounts. However, the half-life of Np^{237}, 2.20×10^6 years, corresponds to a specific α-particle activity of some $1\frac{1}{2}$ million α particles per min per mg, only about 1000 times that of ordinary uranium. Material of this level of radioactivity can be handled without special equipment, provided reasonable care and precautions are observed.

In addition to Np^{239} and Np^{237} there are nine other isotopes of neptunium now known. These are all listed in Table 8.1, which also includes all the presently known isotopes of the other transuranium elements.

8.2.2 *Plutonium (Atomic Number* 94). Plutonium was discovered late in 1940 by G. T. Seaborg, E. M. McMillan, J. W. Kennedy, and A. C. Wahl as a result of bombarding uranium with deuterons in the Berkeley 60-in. cyclotron. This particular isotope was later shown to be Pu^{238}. Early in 1941 the isotope of major interest, Pu^{239}, was discovered by J. W. Kennedy, G. T. Seaborg, E. Segrè, and A. C. Wahl in uranium bombarded with neutrons produced in the same Berkeley cyclotron. The nuclear reactions for the production of Pu^{239} are as follows:

$$U^{238}(n,\ \gamma)U^{239} \xrightarrow{\ \beta^-\ } Np^{239} \xrightarrow{\ \beta^-\ } Pu^{239}$$

Element 94 was given the name *plutonium* (symbol Pu) by the discoverers after the planet Pluto to follow uranium and the previously discovered neptunium in the same order as the corresponding planets.

The chemistry of plutonium was first investigated by the tracer technique, using the isotope Pu^{238}. These experiments showed that the chemical properties of this element are similar to those of neptunium and uranium, differing in that the lower oxidation states of plutonium are more stable.

The Plutonium Project of the Manhattan Engineer District was organized for the purpose of producing the isotope Pu^{239}, the explosive ingredient for the atomic weapon. The first pure plutonium in the form of compounds of the isotope Pu^{239} was isolated by B. B. Cunningham and L. B. Werner at the wartime Metallurgical Laboratory of the University of Chicago on Aug. 18, 1942, in experiments on the ultramicroscale, using material prepared by means of bombardment with cyclotron neutrons; they made the first weighing of a plutonium compound on Sept. 10, 1942. This is the first synthetic element to be isolated in pure form. It is interesting to note that chemical plants costing hundreds of millions of dollars were designed and constructed on the basis of early experiments involving only microgram quantities of plutonium. The availability of the relatively large amounts of plutonium, as the result of the successful operation of the chain-reacting piles, has made it possible to make complete investigations of its chemical properties, using methods which can be considered to be those of ordinary chemistry except for the health precautions that are necessary. This work has established that plutonium has the oxidation states VI, V, IV, and III and that there is a shift in stability toward the III state as compared with neptunium and uranium. A large number of compounds of plutonium have been prepared and their properties determined. It may be said that the chemistry of plutonium today is as well or better understood than is that of most of the elements in the periodic system, even though its chemistry is very complex, as can be judged by the multiple oxidation states and their oxidation potentials.

Because of its relatively high specific α radioactivity, amounting to about 140 million α disintegrations per min per mg, special equipment and precautions are necessary in the investigations of its properties. This high α radioactivity makes it expedient to continue to use rather small amounts—i.e., milligram amounts—for a number of these investigations even though large amounts might be available. Even if there were no other reasons, its high α radioactivity places plutonium outside the class of elements which might eventually find widespread distribution among chemists for investigation of its chemical properties.

The knowledge of the chemical properties of neptunium and plutonium which had become available as a result of the discovery and study of these elements made it possible to conduct effective searches for these elements in various minerals. Early in 1942, G. T. Seaborg and M. L. Perlman in Berkeley undertook a search for these elements in pitchblende ore, the primary purpose at that time being to establish whether such a source of a fissionable transuranium isotope might serve as a practical substitute for, at that time, the undeveloped and questionable nuclear chain reaction for production purposes.   The amount of plutonium found in pitchblende corresponded to about 1 part in 10^{12}, an amount which could not possibly have been found had the chemical properties been unknown, and this was too small to be of practical value.   Subsequent work on numerous uranium ores has confirmed the existence of such small concentrations of plutonium, which is continuously formed by the absorption in the uranium of neutrons from various natural sources.   Other transuranium elements, other than Np^{237} which is present in uranium ores in slightly smaller concentration than Pu^{239}, are present in nature at concentrations too small to measure.

The presently known isotopes of plutonium are summarized in Table 8.1.

8.2.3   *Americium* (*Atomic Number* 95).   Americium, the element with atomic number 95, was the fourth transuranium element to be discovered, its first identification taking place late in 1944 and early in 1945.   The first isotope of this element was identified in the experiments of G. T. Seaborg, R. A. James, and L. O. Morgan at the wartime Metallurgical Laboratory of the University of Chicago.   They showed that the bombardment of Pu^{239} with neutrons leads to the formation of Pu^{241} as the result of the successive capture of two neutrons.   The Am^{241} is the daughter of 13-year β-particle-emitting Pu^{241}.   The reactions therefore are as follows:

$$Pu^{239} + n \rightarrow Pu^{240} + n \rightarrow Pu^{241}$$

$$Pu^{241} \xrightarrow[\text{13 yr}]{\beta^-} Am^{241}$$

The isotope Am^{241} emits α particles with a half-life of 470 years.   This element was named *americium*, symbol Am (after the Americas), by analogy to the naming of the chemically homologous rare-earth element europium (named after Europe).

The availability of this isotope of americium made it possible to study the chemical properties of this element, using the tracer technique in the first experiments.   It has been possible also to isolate americium in the form of pure compounds and to study its chemical properties in macroscopic concentrations.   B. B. Cunningham, working at the Metallurgical Laboratory, succeeded in the fall of 1945 in isolating this element and studying its chemical properties using a weighable amount on the ultramicrochemical scale.   This, then, is the third synthetic element to be isolated in pure form.   Following its initial isolation a great deal of later work has been done in the study of its properties using milligram amounts.   The work with pure americium in aqueous solution has confirmed the tracer work by showing that the III oxidation state is very stable in solution and is the predominant and most important state. Americium can be oxidized with strong oxidizing agents to the IV, V, and VI states.

Americium, in the form of Am^{241} with its 470-year half-life, has a higher specific α activity than even Pu^{239}. Its specific α activity amounts to some 7 billion α disintegrations per min per mg. Thus even if this isotope should become available in ordinary amounts, it will always be necessary to conduct its investigation with special precautions and using the special techniques for handling highly α-active material. Future chemical investigations may use longer-lived isotopes such as Am^{243} in order to lessen this difficulty.

A number of additional isotopes are known and are listed in Table 8.1.

8.2.4 *Curium (Atomic Number 96)*. Curium was the third transuranium element to be discovered. The first isotope of this element was Cm^{242}, which was identified in the summer of 1944 by G. T. Seaborg, R. A. James, and A. Ghiorso at the Metallurgical Laboratory as the result of its production in the Berkeley 60-in. cyclotron by the following reaction:

$$Pu^{239}(\alpha,n)Cm^{242}$$

The isotope Cm^{242} is an α-particle emitter with a half-life of about 162 days. This element was given the name *curium*, symbol Cm (after Pierre and Marie Curie, pioneer investigators in radioactivity), by analogy to the naming of gadolinium, the chemically homologous rare-earth element (named after Johan Gadolin, pioneer rare-earth chemist).

The availability of this isotope of curium made it possible to study the chemical properties of this element by use of the tracer technique. Extensive investigations have led to the conclusion that curium probably exists exclusively in the III oxidation state in aqueous solution. It is carried quantitatively by the rare-earth fluorides in precipitation reactions and can be separated from them only with difficulty.

The isotope Cm^{242} is formed in weighable amounts as the result of the strong neutron irradiation of Am^{241}. The Am^{241} absorbs neutrons to form the short-lived (16-hr half-life) β emitter Am^{242}, which in turn decays to the Cm^{242}. These nuclear reactions may be summarized as follows:

$$Am^{241} + n \rightarrow Am^{242} + \gamma$$

$$Am^{242} \xrightarrow[16\ hr]{\beta^-} Cm^{242}$$

I. Perlman and L. B. Werner succeeded in the fall of 1947 at the University of California in isolating curium (as Cm^{242}) in the form of a pure compound by work on the ultramicrochemical scale. The isotope Cm^{242} with its 162-day half-life has a specific α-activity corresponding to about

10^{13} α disintegrations per min per mg. Among the difficulties in working with this isotope are the rapid decomposition of the water in the solution, the formation of hydrogen peroxide in the solution, heating of the solution, and other effects. However, it has been possible to study the chemical properties of curium by work on the ultramicrochemical scale, and this work has confirmed the fact that this element exists exclusively in the III oxidation state in aqueous solution. Future chemical studies of curium will make use of longer-lived isotopes such as Cm^{244} in order to lessen this difficulty.

All the presently known curium isotopes are given in Table 8.1.

8.2.5 *Berkelium (Atomic Number 97).* Berkelium (Bk) was the fifth transuranium element to be discovered. This was accomplished in December, 1949, at the University of California, Berkeley, by S. G. Thompson, A. Ghiorso, and G. T. Seaborg as a result of the bombardment of americium (Am^{241}) with helium ions in the 60-in. cyclotron. Like the other transuranium elements, all its isotopes are radioactive, and the first one to be discovered, that with the mass number 243, has a half-life of about 4.6 hr. This element is the eighth member of the actinide transition series and was given its name after the city of Berkeley, California, in a manner similar to that used in naming its chemical homologue terbium (rare earth with atomic number 65) whose name was derived from the town of Ytterby, Sweden, where the rare-earth minerals were first found. This element has not been isolated in weighable amounts, and therefore its chemical properties are studied solely with invisible amounts through the use of its radioactive properties for detection purposes. It has valence states of III and IV and rare-earth-like properties in aqueous solution.

The known isotopes of berkelium are summarized in Table 8.1.

8.2.6 *Californium (Atomic Number 98).* Californium (Cf) was discovered in February, 1950, by S. G. Thompson, K. Street, Jr., A. Ghiorso, and G. T. Seaborg at the University of California, Berkeley, as a result of the bombardment of curium (Cm^{242}) with helium ions in the 60-in. cyclotron. This element is the ninth member of the actinide transition series, chemically homologous to the rare-earth dysprosium, and is named after the university and state where the work was done. Since this element, like berkelium, has not been isolated in weighable amounts, its chemical properties are studied with invisible amounts through the use of its radioactive properties for detection purposes. It has a valence state of III with rare-earth-like properties in aqueous solution. The first isotope which was discovered (mass number 244) has a half-life of about 45 min.

The known isotopes of californium are summarized in Table 8.1.

Table 8.1 Summary of Isotopes of Transuranium Elements

Isotope	Half-life	Radiations	Isotope	Half-life	Radiations
Neptunium:			Curium:		
Np^{231}.....	~50 min	α	Cm^{238}.....	~2.5 hr	α, EC
Np^{232}.....	~13 min	EC	Cm^{239}.....	~3 hr	EC
Np^{233}.....	35 min	EC, α	Cm^{240}.....	26.8 days	α
Np^{234}.....	4.40 days	EC	Cm^{241}.....	35 days	EC, α
Np^{235}.....	410 days	EC, α	Cm^{242}.....	162.5 days	α
Np^{236}.....	22 hr	EC, β^-	Cm^{243}.....	~100 yr	α
Np^{237}....	2.20 $\times$ 10^6 yr	α	Cm^{244}.....	19 yr	α
Np^{238}.....	2.10 days	β^-	Cm^{245}.....	~10^4 yr	α
Np^{239}.....	2.33 days	β^-	Berkelium:		
Np^{240}.....	60 min	β^-	Bk^{243}.....	4.6 hr	EC, α
Np^{240m}....	7.3 min	β^-	Bk^{244}.....	~5 hr	EC
Np^{241}.....	minutes	β^-	Bk^{245}.....	4.95 days	EC, α
Plutonium:			Bk^{246}.....	~2 days	
Pu^{232}......	36 min	EC, α	Bk^{249}.....	~1 yr	β^-, α
Pu^{234}......	9.0 hr	EC, α	Bk^{250}.....	3.1 hr	β^-
Pu^{235}......	26 min	EC, α	Californium:		
Pu^{236}......	2.7 yr	α	Cf^{244}......	45 min	α, EC?
Pu^{237}......	~40 days	EC	Cf^{246}......	35.7 hr	α
Pu^{238}......	90 yr	α	Cf^{247}......	~3 hr	EC
Pu^{239}......	24,400 yr	α	Cf^{248}......	225 days	α
Pu^{240}......	6,600 yr	α	Cf^{249}......	~500 yr	α
Pu^{241}......	13.0 yr	β^-, α	Cf^{250}......	~10 yr	α
Pu^{242}......	10^6 yr	α	Cf^{251}......	long	α pred.
Pu^{243}......	4.98 hr	β^-	Cf^{252}......	2.1 yr	α
Americium:			Cf^{253}......	~20 days	β^-
Am^{237}.....	~1.3 hr	EC, α	Element 99:		
Am^{238}.....	2.1 hr	EC	99^{246}......	minutes	EC
Am^{239}.....	12 hr	EC, α	99^{247}......	7.3 min	EC, α
Am^{240}.....	47 hr	EC	99^{253}......	~20 days	α
Am^{241}.....	470 yr	α	99^{254}......	36 hr	β^-
Am^{242}.....	~100 yr	β^-, α	99^{255}......	30 days	β^-
Am^{242m}....	16 hr	β^-, EC	Element 100:		
Am^{243}.....	7.6 $\times$ 10^3 yr	α	100^{249,250}..	~30 min	α
Am^{244}.....	26 min	β^-	100^{254}.....	3.2 hr	α
			100^{255}.....	~15 hr	α

α—alpha particle.
EC—electron capture.
β—beta particle.

8.2.7 *Elements 99 and 100.* Although the elements with atomic numbers 99 and 100 had been previously produced, isotopes of these elements were announced for the first time early in 1954. Element 99 was chemically identified among the products formed in the bombardment of natural uranium with 100-Mev nitrogen ions ($_7$N^{14}); the isotope, tentatively assigned as 99^{247}, has a half-life of 7.3 min. The two nuclides 99^{253}

(20 days) and 100^{254} (3.2 hr) are among the isotopes which were chemically identified as a result of the intensive neutron bombardment of Pu^{239} in the Materials Testing Reactor at Arco, Idaho.

The known isotopes of elements 99 and 100 are summarized in Table 8.1.

8.3 Actinide Transition Series

The discovery of the transuranium elements and the study of their properties, especially the chemical properties, led to a more satisfactory elucidation of the electronic structure of the heaviest elements and of their position in the periodic system (Fig. 8.1). The evidence currently available leads naturally to the view that in these elements the $5f$ electron shell is being filled. The evidence seems sufficient to suggest that this rare-earth-like series begins with actinium in the same sense that the "lanthanide" or rare-earth series (where the $4f$ electron shell is being filled) begins with lanthanum, and this evidence will be briefly reviewed here.

The heaviest naturally occurring elements, thorium, protactinium, and uranium, atomic numbers 90, 91, and 92, respectively, have been in corresponding positions below the sixth-period "transition" elements, hafnium, tantalum, and tungsten, in which the $5d$ electron shell is being filled. The elements hafnium, tantalum, and tungsten are similar in their chemical properties to the corresponding transition elements in the fifth period, zirconium, niobium, and molybdenum, in which the $4d$ shell is being filled. It has been known that thorium, protactinium, and to a much smaller extent uranium show some resemblance in chemical properties to these $4d$ and $5d$ elements, and for this reason most of the pre–World War II textbooks and standard works on chemistry and physics in which electronic structure was discussed accepted the view that it is the $6d$ shell which is being filled in the case of the heaviest elements. Thus, the structure of the elements above radon (element 86) through uranium has been written to show the addition of the next two electrons in the $7s$ shell for element 87 (francium) and element 88 (radium) and addition in the $6d$ shell for the following four elements: actinium, thorium, protactinium, and uranium.

Some of the early papers which appeared after N. Bohr's classical work on the quantized nuclear atom suggested, in contrast to this view, that it is the $5f$ electron shell which is being filled in the neighborhood of uranium. There was a wide divergence of opinion as to just what element constituted the beginning of such a transition series, with suggestions ranging all the way from element 90 to element 96 or higher.

The recent work on the heaviest elements, and particularly the transuranium elements, suggests that the tripositive oxidation state is impor-

1 H 1.008																		2 He 4.003
3 Li 6.940	4 Be 9.02											5 B 10.82	6 C 12.010	7 N 14.008	8 O 16.000	9 F 19.00	10 Ne 20.183	
11 Na 22.997	12 Mg 24.32											13 Al 26.97	14 Si 28.06	15 P 30.98	16 S 32.06	17 Cl 35.457	18 A 39.944	
19 K 39.096	20 Ca 40.08	21 Sc 45.10	22 Ti 47.90	23 V 50.95	24 Cr 52.01	25 Mn 54.93	26 Fe 55.85	27 Co 58.94	28 Ni 58.69	29 Cu 63.57	30 Zn 65.38	31 Ga 69.72	32 Ge 72.60	33 As 74.91	34 Se 78.96	35 Br 79.916	36 Kr 83.7	
37 Rb 85.48	38 Sr 87.63	39 Y 88.92	40 Zr 91.22	41 Nb 92.91	42 Mo 95.95	43 Tc	44 Ru 101.7	45 Rh 102.91	46 Pd 106.7	47 Ag 107.880	48 Cd 112.41	49 In 114.76	50 Sn 118.70	51 Sb 121.76	52 Te 127.61	53 I 126.92	54 Xe 131.3	
55 Cs 132.91	56 Ba 137.36	57 La 138.92	58-71 See La series	72 Hf 178.6	73 Ta 180.88	74 W 183.92	75 Re 186.31	76 Os 190.2	77 Ir 193.1	78 Pt 195.23	79 Au 197.2	80 Hg 200.61	81 Tl 204.39	82 Pb 207.21	83 Bi 209.00	84 Po	85 At	86 Rn
87 Fr	88 Ra	89 Ac	See Ac series	(104)	(105)	(106)												

Lanthanide series:

57 La 138.92	58 Ce 140.13	59 Pr 140.92	60 Nd 144.27	61 Pm	62 Sm 150.43	63 Eu 152.0	64 Gd 156.9	65 Tb 159.2	66 Dy 162.46	67 Ho 163.5	68 Er 167.2	69 Tm 169.4	70 Yb 173.04	71 Lu 174.99

Actinide series:

89 Ac	90 Th 232.12	91 Pa 231	92 U 238.07	93 Np 237	94 Pu	95 Am	96 Cm	97 Bk	98 Cf	99	100	(101)	(102)	(103)

Fig. 8.1 Periodic table showing heavy elements as members of an actinide series. (Predicted positions in parentheses.)

tant here and points to a beginning of the series with actinium in the same sense that the rare-earth series begins with lanthanum. However, there is the important difference that the first elements in the heavy series exhibit the property of oxidation to higher states with much greater ease than is the case for the corresponding elements in the rare-earth series. The most important criterion for this classification is the probable presence of seven $5f$ electrons (analogous to the stable gadolinium structure) in tripositive curium (element 96) rather than the presence of the first $5f$ electron in thorium. In fact, there might not be any such electrons in thorium with, for example, their first appearance in protactinium (two $5f$ electrons) or in uranium (three $5f$ electrons). An important aspect of these considerations is the probability that the $5f$ and $6d$ shells of the elements in this heaviest region lie so close together that the energy necessary for the shift from one shell to the other may in some cases be within the range of chemical binding energies.

The earliest element in this series which clearly exhibits the characteristic oxidation state of III is uranium, the third element in the series. In going up the series from uranium, each of the successive elements exhibits a more stable III oxidation state than the preceding element. When the elements americium and curium are reached, the III state is the predominant one and, in fact, seems to be the only state of these latter elements which is thermodynamically stable in acidic aqueous solution. In the cases of berkelium and californium only tracer experiments have been done, and therefore the information is less certain. These experiments indicate that berkelium exhibits stable III and IV oxidation states and californium exists solely in the III state, which behavior is in entire conformity with their expected analogy with their rare-earth homologues, terbium and dysprosium, respectively.

Table 8.2 summarizes the known oxidation states of the lanthanide and actinide elements in such a way as to bring out the analogy between the two groups and to show the greater ease of oxidation for the members of the latter group. The uncertain or unusual states are designated with parentheses (omitting those states with metallic or possibility of metallic character in their bonding which have oxidation numbers less than III). Such a table has only limited meaning in that oxidation states of solid compounds formed only under drastic conditions, varying in their severity, are included. However, to list only those states which are stable in aqueous solution also has shortcomings since the existence of an aqueous ion, besides being limited by the ionization potentials of the electrons, is affected by the specific chemical processes of hydration and complex formation and is arbitrarily confined within the limits of its oxidation or reduction by water. The oxidation states of the actinide elements in the table are underlined in such a manner as to show the variation in their stability in going across the series. These considerations are further illustrated in Table 8.3 which lists all the nonoxygenated halides of actinium, thorium, protactinium, uranium, neptunium, plutonium, americium, and curium which have been prepared and maintained as stable in the solid state.

Like the rare-earth elements, the elements in the actinide series are in general colored in those oxidation states in which two or more f electrons are present. The absorption bands are sharp and are to be ascribed to shielded electronic transitions within the $5f$ shell, in which the $5f^n$ configuration is preserved in the upper and lower states for a particular ion. The absorption spectra may be used for the qualitative and semiquantitative determination of many of the elements in the series.

Table 8.2 Oxidation States of Lanthanide and Actinide Elements

Atomic number	57	58	59	60	61	62	63	64	65	66
Element	La	Ce	Pr	Nd	Pm	Sm	Eu	Gd	Tb	Dy
Oxidation states						2	2			
	3	3	3	3	3	3	3	3	3	3
		4	4						4	

Atomic number	89	90	91	92	93	94	95	96	97	98
Element	Ac	Th	Pa	U	Np	Pu	Am	Cm	Bk	Cf
Oxidation states							(2)			
	3	(3)	(3)	3	3	3	3	3	3	3
		4	4	4	4	4	(4)		4	
			5	5	5	5	5			
				6	6	6	6			

As the number of the electrons in the f shell increases, there is a contraction of the ionic radius as noted for the rare-earth elements. W. H. Zachariasen finds that practically all the various halide types have structural identity; e.g., all members of the group ThF_4-PaF_4-UF_4-NpF_4-PuF_4 are of the same structure type, all members of the group UF_3-NpF_3-PuF_3-AmF_3 are also isostructural with each other, and the same is true for the group UCl_3-$NpCl_3$-$PuCl_3$-$AmCl_3$, etc. To be sure, in some cases (e.g., UBr_3-$NpBr_3$-$PuBr_3$-$AmBr_3$), there is a change in structure type in proceeding up the group, but this is to be expected on the basis of the contraction and change of ionic radius ratio which takes place and is entirely consistent with the addition of the successive electrons to the $5f$ shell. Table 8.4 gives the ionic radii of the actinide and, for comparison, the lanthanide elements with interpolated values given in parentheses.

Magnetic susceptibility measurements on compounds of the heaviest

Table 8.3   Halides of Some of the Heaviest Elements

Element	Fluorides	Chlorides	Bromides	Iodides
89—Ac	AcF_3	$AcCl_3$	$AcBr_3$	AcI_3
90—Th	ThF_4	$ThCl_4$	$ThBr_4$	ThI_4 ThI_3
91—Pa	PaF_5 PaF_4	$PaCl_5$ $PaCl_4$	$PaBr_5$	PaI_5
92—U	UF_6 UF_5 UF_4 UF_3	UCl_6 UCl_5 UCl_4 UCl_3	UBr_4 UBr_3	UI_4 UI_3
93—Np	NpF_6 $NpF_5(?)$ NpF_4 NpF_3	$NpCl_4$ $NpCl_3$	$NpBr_4$ $NpBr_3$	NpI_3
94—Pu	PuF_6 PuF_4 PuF_3	$PuCl_3$	$PuBr_3$	PuI_3
95—Am	AmF_4 AmF_3	$AmCl_3$	$AmBr_3$	AmI_3
96—Cm	CmF_3			

Table 8.4 Ionic Radii of Actinide and Lanthanide Elements

No. of 4f or 5f electrons	Actinide series				Lanthanide series	
0	Ac^{+3}	1.11 A	Th^{+4}	0.99 A	La^{+3}	1.04 A
1	(Th^{+3})	(1.08)	Pa^{+4}	0.96	Ce^{+3}	1.02
2	(Pa^{+3})	(1.06)	U^{+4}	0.93	Pr^{+3}	1.00
3	U^{+3}	1.03	Np^{+4}	0.92	Nd^{+3}	0.99
4	Np^{+3}	1.01	Pu^{+4}	0.90	Pm^{+3}	(0.98)
5	Pu^{+3}	1.00	Am^{+4}	0.89	Sm^{+3}	0.97
6	Am^{+3}	0.99			Eu^{+3}	0.96

elements ideally should lead to the resultant magnetic moments in fundamental units and in this way give information on the quantum states of the responsible electrons.   Actually, as evidenced by the rare-earth elements, the situation is rather complex, and the exact behavior expected

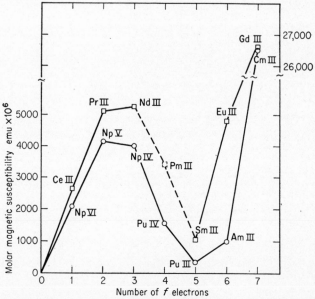

Fig. 8.2   Plot of molar magnetic susceptibilities of some actinide and lanthanide ions.

for the heaviest elements, on the basis of the presence of either 5f or 6d electrons, cannot be, or at least has not been, predicted.   Nevertheless, such measurements should give, and have given, some information on this point.

Figure 8.2 shows a plot comparing the room-temperature experimental magnetic susceptibilities of the lanthanide and actinide cations in such a way as to show their remarkable analogy in this property.   This plot is admittedly rough because data are used from both aqueous solutions and solid compounds; these are not strictly comparable, and even data from different solid compounds of the same oxidation state of an element differ somewhat because of exchange effects and the effects of the crystal fields. Nevertheless, the comparison is sufficiently reliable to show that the magnetic measurements point toward the filling of the $5f$ shell in the manner expected on the basis of the actinide concept.

Perhaps the most striking chemical evidence as to the course taken in the filling of the $5f$ electron shell in this region is that offered by the work on the separation of the tripositive actinides and lanthanides by the ion-exchange-column method.   The use of a cation-exchange resin with an eluting agent such as ammonium citrate solution, as developed on the Plutonium Project, has led to a satisfactory solution of the difficult problem of separating the rare-earth elements from each other in pure form.   The tripositive actinide elements are equally difficult to separate from each other and from the rare earths because of their great similarity to the rare-earth elements.   However, the analogy in behavior of the actinide and lanthanide elements here is much greater than results from a similarity in the difficulty of separation, as can be seen from Fig. 8.3, where the data have been normalized to show equal amounts for purposes of clarity.   The data for the actinides shown here are those of K. Street, Jr., S. G. Thompson, and G. T. Seaborg, in which the cation-exchange resin Dowex-50 was used and the elution performed at 87°C with ammonium citrate buffered with citric acid to a pH of 3.5 (total citrate concentration $0.2M$).   The data on the lanthanide elements are those of B. H. Ketelle and G. E. Boyd, in which the same resin was used in a somewhat longer column and the elution performed at 100°C, using a similar citrate buffer solution (pH 3.28).   (The dotted lines show the predicted elution positions for elements 99 and 100, which have been essentially confirmed in the experiments on these elements.) A remarkable analogy in the spacing can be seen between the group californium-berkelium-curium-americium and their rare-earth homologues dysprosium-terbium-gadolinium-europium.   The spacings here reflect the relative changes in ionic radii which determine the relative separations in the ion-exchange adsorption method.   It can be seen that the same sequence of changes in the ionic radius is encountered on filling in the $5f$ electrons as occurs on filling the $4f$ shell, and therefore it seems quite clear that curium represents the midway point in the actinide transition series of elements in view of its position analogous to gadolinium.

The experimental evidence is not sufficient to make definite statements as to the electronic structure of each of the elements in this group.   On the basis of the available evidence, however, certain surmises can be made, and these are summarized in Table 8.5.

The direct spectrographic evidence available is also consistent with this point of view for the electronic structure of the heaviest elements. C. C. Kiess, C. J. Humphreys, and D. D. Laun investigated the spectrum of the neutral uranium atom which they interpret to have the electron

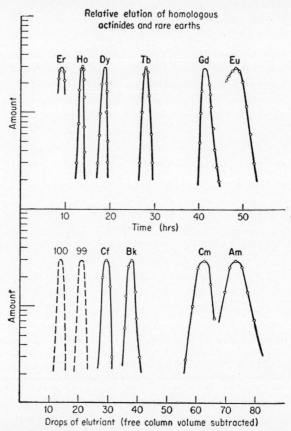

Fig. 8.3 Relative elution of homologous actinides and lanthanides.

configuration $5f^36d7s^2$ (beyond radon) for the lowest state of uranium. This is the configuration to be expected for the third element in an actinide series. Other work on the spectrum of uranium II has given results which are consistent with this structure for the neutral uranium atom, while work on the thorium II spectrum indicates that the $5f$ is very close to the $6d$ electron in binding energy in this atom.

It is interesting to speculate about the chemical properties of the undiscovered higher transuranium elements. The elements through atomic number 103 should complete the rare-earth-like (actinide) transition group. The hypothetical element with atomic number 104 should be chemically similar to hafnium (atomic number 72), *i.e.*, should be an eka-hafnium. The 14 hypothetical elements with atomic numbers 105

Table 8.5 Suggested Electron Configurations (beyond Radon) for Gaseous Atoms of Actinide Elements

89—Ac............	$6d7s^2$	94—Pu............	$5f^67s^2$ (or $5f^56d7s^2$)
90—Th............	$6d^27s^2$ (or $5f6d7s^2$)	95—Am............	$5f^77s^2$
91—Pa............	$5f^26d7s^2$ (or $5f6d^27s^2$)	96—Cm............	$5f^76d7s^2$
92—U.............	$5f^36d7s^2$	97—Bk............	$5f^97s^2$
93—Np............	$5f^57s^2$ (or $5f^46d7s^2$)	98—Cf............	$5f^{10}7s^2$

through 118 should, consecutively, be chemical homologues to the 14 known elements with atomic numbers 73 (tantalum) through 86 (emanation or radon).

8.4 Nuclear Energy for Power

8.4.1 *General Considerations.* It is fortunately a characteristic of the nuclear chain reaction operating on fissionable material that tremendous amounts of energy can be released in a slow controlled fashion as well as instantaneously as is the case for the nuclear weapon. The same amounts of energy can be released under controlled conditions in nuclear-energy machines or *nuclear reactors* or *piles* as they are called. Thus under suitable arrangements it is possible to have a controlled self-sustaining chain reaction in which the nuclear-fission process repeats itself until large amounts of the fissionable material are consumed with conversion to energy.

The basic concept upon which the nuclear-energy development is based, the principle of the equivalence of mass and energy, as first stated by Einstein in 1905, is given in the equation $E = mc^2$, where c is the velocity of light and E is the amount of energy equivalent to the mass m. In nuclear reactions the amount of energy produced can be enormous compared to that produced in ordinary chemical reactions because in nuclear transformations appreciable amounts of mass are converted to energy, whereas in chemical reactions the change in mass which is converted to energy is very small. Einstein's relation shows that 1 kg (2.2 lb) of matter if converted entirely into energy would give 25 billion kwhr of energy. Since in the nuclear-fission reaction not all the mass of the nucleus but only about 0.1 per cent is converted to energy, we find that 1 kg of fissionable material is equivalent to about 25 million kwhr of heat-energy equivalent. Thus, 1 lb of fissionable material burned per day with the conversion of heat energy to electrical energy could supply the needs in power and light for a city of some hundreds of thousands of people. The heat is generated within the material and, by flowing a cooling agent over it, can be brought outside the reactor or pile and converted into useful energy by conventional means.

There are three potential fuels for such nuclear-energy machines, and these are the three fissionable isotopes or *nuclear fuels* U^{235}, Pu^{239}, and U^{233}. The first of these is produced by the method of isotope separation in plants of the type which are in operation in Oak Ridge, Tennessee. The second is produced by the absorption of neutrons in U^{238} according to the reaction

$$U^{238} + n \rightarrow U^{239} \xrightarrow[23 \text{ min}]{\beta^-} Np^{239} \xrightarrow[2.3 \text{ day}]{\beta^-} Pu^{239}$$

in production plants of types such as are in operation at Hanford, Washington. The isotope U^{233} is produced by the absorption of neutrons in Th^{232} according to the reaction

$$Th^{232} + n \rightarrow Th^{233} \xrightarrow[23 \text{ min}]{\beta^-} Pa^{233} \xrightarrow[27.4 \text{ day}]{\beta^-} U^{233}$$

The U^{233} can be produced in quantity only by irradiating thorium with neutrons in conjunction with a chain reactor operating on one or another of the three nuclear fuels U^{235}, Pu^{239}, or U^{233}, while Pu^{239} can be produced by the operation of the nuclear chain reaction in the natural mixture of uranium isotopes. The element thorium itself consists in macroscopic quantities of only the one isotope Th^{232}, and thus, since this isotope is not readily fissionable, the element thorium cannot sustain a chain reaction as is the case for the natural mixture of isotopes in uranium.

Thus it can be seen that, although U^{235} is the only naturally occurring fissionable substance, it is possible to burn indirectly the more abundant isotope U^{238} by means of its intermediate conversion to fissionable Pu^{239}. This means that the potential amount of nuclear fuel is considerably larger than that which corresponds to the rare isotope U^{235}. There exists the interesting possibility, after the accumulation of a sufficient amount of Pu^{239} so that it may be used to operate chain reactors, of producing more Pu^{239} by the absorption of the excess neutrons in U^{238}. The reactions would be as follows:

$$Pu^{239} + n \rightarrow \text{fission products} + \text{energy} + \text{neutrons}$$
$$U^{238} + n \rightarrow U^{239} \rightarrow Np^{239} \rightarrow Pu^{239}$$

If it should prove possible to produce more Pu^{239} according to the second reaction than is consumed in the same time by the first reaction, we should have the possibility of *breeding* Pu^{239} or, in other words, of making available all the uranium as nuclear fuel and not just the small amount of U^{235}. This would have the effect of multiplying one-hundredfold the amount of energy which can be realized from uranium.

The same breeding possibility exists in principle with respect to the thorium-U^{233} pair. Here we would have the reactions

$$U^{233} + n \rightarrow \text{fission products} + \text{energy} + \text{neutrons}$$
$$Th^{232} + n \rightarrow Th^{233} \rightarrow Pa^{233} \rightarrow U^{233}$$

If it should prove possible to produce more U^{233} according to the second reaction than is consumed at the same time according to the first, it would be possible to use all the thorium as a nuclear fuel. It is because of the possibility of utilizing, at least in part, the nuclear energy of thorium indirectly through its conversion to fissionable U^{233} that the element thorium is subject to the same controls in its mining and processing as is uranium. The U^{238} and Th^{232} are known as *fertile* material.

A chain-reaction system, *i.e.*, a nuclear reactor, can take various forms depending upon its neutron spectrum, its construction, its composition, and the purpose for which it is required. The reaction may operate with predominantly slow (thermal), intermediate (epithermal), or fast neutrons as the main source of fission. In the case of operation with slow neutrons, known as *thermal reactors*, perhaps the most important, the neutrons emitted in the fission reaction are slowed to thermal energy through collisions with the nuclei of material placed in the proximity of the fissionable substance. This neutron-slowing material is known as the *moderator*. The moderator material to be most efficient should have a low atomic weight in order that the maximum neutron energy may be lost per collision and should, of course, have a low cross section for the absorption of neutrons. Thus materials such as deuterium, helium, beryllium, and carbon are good moderators, and hydrogen (*e.g.*, in the form of water) is useful for some types of reactors in spite of its relatively large neutron-absorption cross section. Reactors which operate with fast neutrons, *i.e.*, *fast reactors*, are similar in principle to the atomic bomb, but they release their energy in a controlled rather than in an uncontrolled manner. The reactors operating with intermediate-energy neutrons have properties between those of the slow and fast reactors, with their position determined by the average energy of the neutrons which may be anywhere from just above the thermal region to just below the energy region of the completely unmoderated fission neutrons. The construction may be of the *homogeneous* or *heterogeneous* type. A homogeneous reactor is one in which the uranium is dissolved in the moderator, while a heterogeneous reactor is characterized by having the fissionable material and the moderator in separate phases. The composition of a reactor is determined not only by its particular type of nuclear fuel and moderator, but also by the subsidiary material such as that required for structural strength, heat removal, corrosion protection, etc.   The three main purposes for nuclear reactors are for research and development, production of fissionable material, or the practical utilization of fission energy as power.   These objectives are, of course, not mutually exclusive, and nearly all reactors have overlapping applications.

8.4.2   *Reproduction Factor and Critical Size.*   There are a number of fundamental concepts and terms which should be reviewed prior to the discussion of the various types of reactors themselves.   Chief among these is the condition that must be met for the maintenance of a nuclear chain reaction.   The minimum condition is that for each nucleus undergoing fission there shall be produced, on the average, at least one neutron which causes fission of another nucleus.   This condition is conveniently expressed in terms of a *reproduction factor* or *multiplication factor* of the system, defined as the ratio of the number of neutrons of any one generation to the number of the immediately preceding generation. If the multiplication factor, represented by k, is exactly equal to or somewhat greater than unity, a chain reaction will be possible, but if k is less than unity, even by a very small amount, the chain cannot be maintained.

A convenient expression of k, for the important case of thermal reactors, is given in the following.   Thus k can be defined by the equation

$$k = \eta \epsilon p f$$

where the symbols have the following meaning.   The average number of fast neutrons produced by fission for each thermal neutron absorbed by fissionable nuclei is represented by η.   This number is increased by ϵ which may be called the *fast fission factor*, having a value slightly in excess of unity, and is the factor by which η must be multiplied in order to account for the additional fast neutrons which are produced by the fission processes that take place before the neutrons have their velocity decreased appreciably.   The factor p, named the *resonance escape probability*, is a measure of the probability that any fast neutron will reach the thermal region without suffering nonfission capture and thus is always less than unity.   The factor f, referred to as the *thermal utilization factor*, is the fraction of the thermal neutrons taken up by the fissionable nuclei to produce the fission reaction and is therefore less than unity.   The thermal utilization factor, like the resonance escape probability, is governed by the composition of the system and by the fission and nonfission capture cross sections of the fissionable nuclei and the neutron capture cross sections of the other material in the reactor.   In the design of a self-sustaining chain reacting system it is, of course, necessary to make it possible for this quantity k to be somewhat greater than unity.

It can be seen from the definition of k, in which the fate of a particular generation of neutrons is considered, that it is assumed that none of the neutrons escape entirely, *i.e.*, a system of infinite size is postulated. In actual practice some neutrons are lost through the boundaries of the system, so that k must be somewhat larger than 1 in order that the size of the reactor be finite. The *critical size* of a given design of reactor with fissionable material is defined as the size for which the number of neutrons produced in the fission process just balances those lost by escape and by the above-mentioned capture processes. Thus the critical size is the smaller, the larger the value of k for a given system.

Another important aspect of the nuclear reactor is, of course, the problem of the controls to prevent the chain reaction from going out of hand. If in a given system exactly one neutron per generation is consumed in the fission reaction, the number of neutrons present would not increase from one generation to the next. However, if this is exceeded, no matter by how small an amount, there is an increase in the number of neutrons in each successive generation and the growth must be checked in order that the system be stable. In order to maintain the neutron density constant once the desired energy level has been reached, control rods made of high neutron-absorbing material, such as cadmium or boron steel, are used. These rods are inserted in the reactor in such a position as will permit them to absorb all the excess neutrons. Thus the control rods can be adjusted in position so as to keep the reactor at the desired power level, and if it is desired to increase or decrease the power, the controls are partially removed or further inserted. It is a fortunate circumstance that a certain fraction of the neutrons liberated in the fission process, amounting to some 0.5 per cent of the total, are emitted with a delay of the average order of an appreciable fraction of a minute. As a result of this, the neutron density and the power output do not undergo sudden changes, either up or down, and control by means of neutron absorbers is a relatively simple matter.

8.4.3 *Scientific and Engineering Problems.* As mentioned above, there are a number of purposes for which nuclear reactors can be contemplated. For the industrial utilization of nuclear energy, the two important types are the power piles and the production piles. Before going on to a consideration of these, the present section will be devoted to some of the general considerations pertinent to both, especially the difficulties which are inherent in their construction and operation.

The power output of a nuclear reactor depends, of course, on the rate at which fission takes place, which in turn is proportional to the mean neutron density. Nuclear reactors with power outputs from a fraction of a watt to megawatts are possible, and in fact there is no theoretical upper limit but only the practical one set by the limitations on the materials of construction. In order to obtain a high thermodynamic efficiency for power production, it is necessary to operate the power pile at as high a temperature as possible, which adds to the complexity of the many problems.

A great number of very difficult scientific and engineering problems must be solved before a nuclear-energy industry can be fully developed. An attempt will be made here to indicate briefly what some of these problems are.

There is first of all the problem of the materials of construction including the fuel, the moderator, and the structural members for holding the reactor together. The nuclear fuel must somehow be put in a form where large amounts of heat can be removed while at the same time its physical form, upon which continued operation of the reaction depends, is not destroyed. The moderator, which is to be made from light elements such as deuterium, beryllium, carbon, etc., must be prepared very pure so as not to absorb too many neutrons and must somehow be able to withstand the high temperature and the radiation. The structural materials must be made to meet conditions that have hitherto never been encountered in structural engineering, since they must be carefully selected on the basis of their nuclear properties as well as their mechanical properties. In particular they must have as low an affinity for capturing neutrons as possible, and this indispensable requirement may not easily be made consistent with structural strength. Since the reactors must operate at high temperatures in order that there might be good efficiency for the conversion of the heat energy to the useful form of electrical energy and since intense radiation will be present, the problems which are posed are very formidable indeed.

One of the knottiest problems of pile construction is that of the removal and utilization of the heat energy, the primary form in which the energy appears. Besides liquids like water, such materials as permanent gases, which have some advantages in handling but have low heat capacities, and molten metals, which have high heat capacities but are difficult to handle, are possibilities. One is again faced with the necessity of considering only such coolants as have the proper nuclear properties. In connection with the coolant, there is, of course, the problem of possible reaction with the nuclear fuel, and in order to prevent this, it may be necessary to place the latter in a jacket. In any case, there has to be considered the corrosive and erosive action of the coolant, effects which are considerably aggravated by the presence of intense radiation.

An especially critical component of a reactor is the control system, the mechanism which allows the machine to be turned on or off and which keeps it at the desired operating level without either dying or running away. The reactor control system operates on the simple principle of draining off neutrons by absorption.   Thus there must be extremely reliable mechanisms for inserting and withdrawing control rods, and therefore the development of completely foolproof apparatus is paramount here.

The radiation emanating from a pile operating at a high power level is of extremely high intensity.   Neutrons escape from the surface, and γ rays emanate from the nuclear reactions which take place in the uranium and other material and from the fission products.   This amounts to a staggering level of radiation, unheard of in previous experience, and the whole of the power pile must therefore be enclosed in very thick walls of concrete, steel, or other absorbing material.   This shielding material must be constructed in a manner which is consistent with the loading and unloading of the reactor and in such a manner as to make it possible to carry the coolant in and out.   The shields must not only be radiation-tight but possibly also airtight, since air exposed to the radiation of the pile would become radioactive.

There is also the large problem of the chemical processing.   It will be necessary from time to time to remove the "clinkers," $i.e.$, the fission products, by reprocessing the fissionable material.   For each different type of pile or mode of operation, a chemical-extraction process tailored to suit the situation will be required.   The success or failure of the breeding process will depend in large measure on the solution of this problem, since in this case the repetitive nature of the chemical-separation procedures demands an almost fabulously high recovery yield in each of the many chemical cycles required in the course of a single turnover of the fuel material.   The radiation dangers which require shielding in the pile are present in a large part in the chemical-separation plant.   Perhaps the most difficult problem of all is the question of how to dispose of these highly radioactive wastes.

8.4.4   *Production Reactors.*   The purpose of a production reactor is to make available new fissionable material to act as a fuel in another chain-reacting system.   An example may be found in the reactors which are operated with natural uranium, $i.e.$, uranium containing its isotopes in the proportion found in nature, in order to produce the nuclear fuel Pu^{239}. The U^{235} in the natural uranium is the nuclear fuel in this example, and such a reactor may also be referred to as a *converter*, since it converts the nuclear fuel U^{235} into the new nuclear fuel Pu^{239}.   Converters can, of course, also operate on enriched U^{235}, $i.e.$, uranium in which the proportion of U^{235} is higher than in natural uranium, or on the other nuclear fuels.   In the example mentioned above with natural uranium, the U^{238} is itself not a fuel, since it cannot sustain a chain reaction, and is called the *fertile material*.   As mentioned above another possible fertile material is the more abundant Th^{232}.

There is the interesting possibility in which more fissionable material might be formed in each generation than is used up in fission. A nuclear chain reactor in which fertile material is converted into more fissionable material than is consumed is called a *breeder*. By the use of the breeding process the stockpile of fissionable material could be steadily increased, or in other words, all the fertile, nonfissionable material could be converted into fuel material. Although it is not known whether fuel breeding is practical or not, it is undoubtedly possible in principle, since the necessary condition that more than two neutrons be produced per neutron absorbed in fissionable nuclei appears to be met with at least some of the known nuclear fuels.

Many of the above-mentioned problems are aggravated in the case of breeder operation because of the great importance for neutron economy in this case. This makes the problem of the materials of construction especially difficult since only substances with very low neutron absorption cross sections can be tolerated, and an even greater difficulty is that of the repetitive chemical purification which is required. Thus after a certain amount of operation the reactor core will contain an amount of fission products sufficient to compete for the precious neutrons, and these must be removed. The spent fuel must consequently be purified from the fission products at rather frequent intervals, and since the chemical losses thus are compounded, the chemical losses must be kept exceptionally low.

In the construction of a breeder reactor, the fertile material may be part of the fuel units, or it may form a blanket or reflecting shield surrounding the core of fuel, thus capturing some of the neutrons which might otherwise escape. The fission reaction may be carried on by slow, intermediate, or fast neutrons.

8.4.5 *Power Reactors.* The production and power aspects of nuclear reactors cannot be separated, since the energy released in a breeder reactor may be utilized and there may be some regeneration of fuel during the operation of a power reactor. However, it is convenient to classify as power reactors those which are primarily intended for the production of usable power.

The aim of a power reactor is to transform the heat which is produced from the energy released in fission into some usable form such as electrical power. The heat energy can be transferred to a fluid, liquid, or gas passing through the core of the reactor, and this fluid can also pass through a heat exchanger where the energy may be transferred and utilized by more or less conventional means. A sketch of an example of such a nuclear-power plant is shown in Fig. 8.4.

Because of the shielding requirements, nuclear-reactor power plants must be associated with a great bulk and weight of material and therefore will be better suited to stationary structures. Thus this source of power may be used more profitably in regions which are somewhat isolated and where there is a need for additional power. Such power plants may of course be used for mobile units where the limits on space and weight are not too stringent, such as large ocean-going ships, submarines, and very large airplanes.

8.4.6   *Economic Considerations.*   Although a detailed discussion of the economic aspects of nuclear energy is outside the scope of this discussion, it is desirable to make a few remarks in this connection. Of foremost importance is the question of the availability and cost of uranium and thorium. The best available estimate of the average uranium content of the earth's crust is about 4 ppm, while that for thorium is about 12 g of thorium per million grams of rock. Thus the earth's crust consists of some 16 ppm of potentially fissionable material, and if one takes into account the factor of about 2.5×10^6 greater heat-energy equivalent of

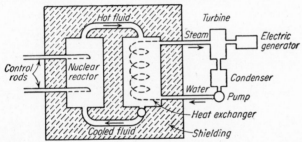

Fig. 8.4   Outline sketch of a method for production of electric power from nuclear energy.

fissionable material as compared to an equal weight of coal, one finds that 1 ton of the earth's crust has an energy content from this source equivalent to some 40 tons of coal.

However, this is a gross oversimplification and ignores the question of economics. The extraction of the uranium and thorium from this source is a matter of great expense and therefore questionable feasibility. The proportion of the uranium and thorium on the earth which lies in relatively rich ore deposits is rather small. However, the accessible sources probably run into millions of tons, especially if sources with concentrations of the order of a fraction of a per cent, from which extraction may be feasible, are considered. It can be calculated, on the basis that all the fertile material can be utilized, that the energy consumption of the world could be taken care of through the use of some thousands of tons per year.

These considerations are gone into merely in order to give an idea as to the order of magnitudes involved in the nuclear-fuel-source problem. It does not appear likely that the energy of fission will be used as a substitute for the existing energy sources, but rather will be used to supplement them.

Although some estimates as to the cost of producing nuclear power have been made, it does not seem possible to make any very sensible statements on this point at the present time.   Important to this matter is the question of ore supply and whether or not breeding will be successful.   It is not out of the question that the nuclear sources will eventually compete economically with coal as a source of energy, but it is also quite possible that this will never be the case except for localities where the price of coal is high because of transportation difficulties.

Even should the atomic source never provide cheaper energy than the present common sources, it will still have an important future because of its advantages as a compact and almost inexhaustible source of energy, characteristics which give it advantages which no other fuel can come close to equaling, advantages which cannot be evaluated in terms of dollar values because there is no alternate way of accomplishing the same things at any price.

REFERENCES

Seaborg, G. T., J. J. Katz, and W. M. Manning, eds., "The Transuranium Elements: Research Papers," National Nuclear Energy Series, Plutonium Project Record, Vol. 14B, McGraw-Hill Book Company, Inc., New York, 1949.

Seaborg, G. T., and J. J. Katz, eds., "The Actinide Elements," National Nuclear Energy Series, Plutonium Project Record, Vol. 14A, McGraw-Hill Book Company, Inc., New York, 1954.

Glasstone, Samuel, "Sourcebook on Atomic Energy," D. Van Nostrand Company, Inc., New York, 1950.

9

Elementary Particles

W. K. H. PANOFSKY

PROFESSOR OF PHYSICS, STANFORD UNIVERSITY

9.1 Introduction

This is a particularly inopportune time to write about "elementary particles." As you well know, the number of particles now known has been increasing at a formidable rate, and it is indeed presumptuous to make any statements at this time as to which may be more "elementary" than others.

It is certainly likely that our present knowledge of particles is incomplete. I remind you of the story of the fisherman who was fishing with a net of 6-in. mesh: he concluded that all fish in the sea were larger than 6 in. Our situation in physics is very similar: our instruments for detection of subatomic particles have associated with them certain "characteristic dimensions" or "characteristic times"; the probability of particle detection will in general be related to these quantities. Without going into detail, I think it is generally admitted that the recent discovery of new particles in the cosmic radiation was "lucky," being due to the "accidental" match between the properties of these particles and the characteristics of the detecting apparatus. The inference that our knowledge of these particles is still quite spotty therefore lies near.

Our present aim is thus considerably more limited than to determine which particles are or are not "fundamental" or "elementary." We shall simply list the most important subatomic particles and look into some of the known relationships between them.

One of the facts which makes the term *fundamental* or *elementary particle* meaningless is the existence of processes by which each of the known particles can turn into others. As an example, I might mention here the process of β decay which effectively converts a neutron into a proton with the emission of additional particles.

Despite the "changeability" of the basic particles, it is indeed not true that any one particle can turn into any other or any group of others.

223

There exist certain rules which permit only those processes to occur which fulfill particular conditions related to the *intrinsic properties* of each particle. Such rules, which define whether a certain process can "go" or not "go," are called *selection rules*. Some of such rules I shall mention will be quite obvious to you, others are based on fairly elaborate reasoning, and at least one is not understood at all at this time.

To recapitulate: the purpose of this chapter is to summarize the rules governing possible processes among the particles in terms of their properties. We shall then discuss the intrinsic properties of the most important particles and finally illustrate the connection between these two groups of facts by presenting the important physical processes which are known to occur.

9.2   Selection Rules on Transformation Processes

Let us then return to our selection rules in detail. These are as follows:

a. The law of conservation of energy (and therefore mass). This law implies that the sum of the rest masses of the resultant constituents in a spontaneous reaction must be less than that of the particles comprising the initial system. Hence, if the rest masses (an intrinsic property) of the fundamental particles are known, then certain reactions are ruled out immediately. As an example, the neutron is heavier than the proton; hence the neutron can become a proton as a result of β decay, but the reverse reaction cannot occur.

b. The law of conservation of charge. All particles have a charge which is an integral multiple of the electronic charge

$$e = 4.8022 \times 10^{-10} \text{ esu} = 1.6019 \times 10^{-19} \text{ coulomb}$$

The total charge must be conserved in any permitted process.

c. The law of conservation of linear momentum. The total momentum of a system cannot change. This prevents, for example, one particle from disintegrating into another single particle with kinetic energy, since momentum would then have to be created. Disintegration of a single particle into two particles is, however, possible if it is permitted by the other rules.

d. The law of conservation of angular momentum. Each particle has associated with it an intrinsic angular momentum which, by fundamental rules of quantum mechanics, must be an *integral* or *half-integral* multiple of a fundamental physical constant ($\hbar$) which equals 1.0542×10^{-27} erg sec. This multiplier is called the *spin* of the particle. In a reaction the total angular momentum must be conserved. It must be remembered that, if enough kinetic energy is available, either the initial or final products may carry "orbital" angular momentum, which will add vectorially to the intrinsic angular momentum of the particles involved.

It can be shown by fundamental quantum mechanics that such orbital angular momenta must always be *integral* (*not* half-integral) multipliers of $\hbar$. We thus have the following selection rule: *The sum of the spins of the initial and final products of a permitted process may differ by an integer but not a half integer.*

All nonelectric subatomic forces are characterized by the fact that they act over a limited "range" of roughly 3×10^{-13} cm, which happens to be equal to $e^2/m_e c^2$, where e = charge on the electron, m_e = mass of the electron, c = velocity of light. Hence, in order to yield an angular momentum $\hbar$, a particle of mass m must have a velocity

$$v = \frac{\hbar}{m}\, \frac{m_e c^2}{e^2} \tag{9.1}$$

and a kinetic energy (assuming ordinary mechanics)

$$E = \frac{1}{2}\, mv^2 = \frac{1}{2}\, \frac{\hbar^2}{m}\, \frac{m_e^2 c^4}{e^2} = \frac{1}{2} \left(\frac{\hbar c}{e^2}\right)^2 \left(\frac{m_e}{m}\right) (m_e c^2) \tag{9.2}$$

$e^2/\hbar c$ is a famous number, called the *fine-structure constant;* it has very closely the value $\frac{1}{137}$. It is the only pure number (no units) which can be made out of the fundamental atomic constants. $m_e c^2$ is equal to the rest energy of the electron, which is $\frac{1}{2}$ Mev. Hence,

$$E = \frac{1}{2} \times \frac{1}{2} \times (137)^2 \times \frac{m_e}{m} = 4.7 \times 10^3 \frac{m_e}{m} \qquad \text{Mev} \tag{9.3}$$

Hence a particle interacting in a nuclear system must have at least this energy to produce an angular momentum change $\hbar$, four times this energy to produce a change $2\hbar$, etc. For a proton this energy is 2.6 Mev for an angular momentum change $\hbar$.

Hence, the permitted difference in angular momentum between the initial and final state is not in general an arbitrary large multiple of $\hbar$, but the highest multiple depends on the energy available in the particular process.

e. The law of conservation of parity. There exists a further restriction on permitted processes which unfortunately we cannot discuss here in any intelligible detail. Each particle has a property known as *intrinsic parity* which for all integral-spin particles is either positive or negative. In addition, if sufficient energy is available, there is also "orbital parity" which can add to the "intrinsic parity." The over-all "parity" must be conserved.

f. The law of conservation of nucleons. It is often convenient to designate the neutron and proton, which are the fundamental constituents of nuclei, as *nucleons*. It is an empirical fact that as yet no process has been found in which the *total* number of nucleons is altered. This rule may rest upon a much more fundamental basis than is now known; it can certainly not be understood in terms of the five rules above which do have a sound foundation.   I might mention that, if this rule (or a more fundamental one with similar consequences) did not exist, absurd conclusions on the stability of matter as we know it would result.

Armed with this set of rules, we can now see why particles are "different" from one another.   Their mass, charge, spin, and parity define what processes they can undergo.   It is a general fact in particle physics that all processes which are permitted to go, under these rules, do in fact occur.   These rules can thus serve as a guide in supplementing the reactions which I shall discuss below.

9.3   Forces of Interaction between Particles

In processes involving subatomic particles, different kinds of forces are active.   You are probably familiar with one of these, namely, the ordinary electrical attraction and repulsion.   In addition to this force, there exist at least two other interactions of importance, namely, the specific "nuclear forces" and the β-decay forces.   Let me list these roughly in order of their "strength," i.e., their interaction energy at comparable distances:

Table 9.1

Type of Force	Approximate Relative Strength
Nuclear force	1
Electric (coulomb) force	10^{-2}
β-decay force	10^{-12}
Gravitation	10^{-45}

If more than one process is permitted by the selection rules discussed in Sec. 9.2, the one which is in general observed is the one driven by the strongest force listed above.

9.4   Catalogue of Familiar Particles

9.4.1   *Negative Electrons, Neutrons, and Protons.*   I shall assume that you are familiar with the negative electron and the neutron and proton from previous chapters.   Let me enter them into a table of "intrinsic properties."

Table 9.2

Particle	Charge, units of e	Mass, units of electron mass $= 9.107 \times 10^{-28}$ g	Spin, units of $\hbar$
p	$+1$	1836.13	$\frac{1}{2}$
n	0	1838.66	$\frac{1}{2}$
e^-	-1	1	$\frac{1}{2}$

9.4.2   *The Neutrino.*   You have been introduced to electrons as the extranuclear component of the atom.   It was observed in the early days of radioactivity that "β rays," soon recognized as very energetic electrons, were emitted spontaneously by a large number of radioactive materials.   Energy measurements on these electrons showed that they were not homogeneous in energy, but rather formed a continuous spectrum. Also their energy is, in general, too high to come from extranuclear sources.   A set of puzzling questions arose from these observations:

a. If electrons are not normally in the nucleus, how can they be emitted from the nucleus?

b. If electrons can be "created" by the basic process $n \rightarrow p^+ + e^-$, then the selection rule 9.2*d* is clearly violated.

c. Since all masses involved are definite, how can a continuous range of energy values be observed?

These questions were resolved by the postulate (due to Pauli) that there exists a particle, called the *neutrino*, of the following "intrinsic properties."

Particle	Charge	Mass	Spin
ν (neutrino)	0	Approximately 0	$\frac{1}{2}$

The fundamental process involved, now called β decay, is then

$$n \rightarrow p^+ + e^- + \nu \tag{9.4}$$

The reason the electron energy is variable here is that the electron and neutrino can divide the available energy in arbitrary proportions.   Note that the postulate of the neutrino makes the process conform to all the rules given in Sec. 9.2.

The neutrino has never been observed directly, since it does not interact with matter in any appreciable way.*   Nevertheless, the circumstantial evidence concerning its existence is so strong that we may admit it into the list of established particles without further question.

9.4.3   *The Positron.*   We shall discuss later in more detail the properties of the positive electron, or *positron*.   Suffice it to say here that in its "intrinsic properties" it is identical to the negative electron except for charge.

Particle	Charge	Mass	Spin
e^+	+1	1	$\frac{1}{2}$

The analogous process to the neutron β decay

$$p \rightarrow n + e^+ + \nu \tag{9.5}$$

---

* A neutrino passing through the earth's diameter would have only one chance in 10^{11} of interacting.

is impossible for a free proton by energy conservation—very luckily, or we would have no hydrogen. However, this process *can* take place in the presence of other nucleons if enough energy is available to make up the energy defect of (9.5). For instance, the β^+ decay of C^{11}

$$_6C^{11} \rightarrow {}_5B^{11} + e^+ + \nu + \text{energy} \tag{9.6}$$

is essentially process (9.5).

There is a real question whether the neutrinos appearing in processes (9.4) and (9.5) are the same particle. Present experimental information is insufficient to resolve this problem.

9.4.4 *Photons.* In processes involving fundamental particles interacting with the electromagnetic field, it can be shown that the electromagnetic field can be treated as a particle called a *photon*. The photon concept is a rather difficult one to comprehend fully, since the properties of a photon are not always the same. In quantum mechanics, the strength of an electromagnetic field cannot be changed by arbitrary amounts; instead, only definite "states" of the field are possible. In its lowest state the field is said to contain one photon. Since the electromagnetic field can be plane polarized, circularly polarized, etc., we will also have plane and circularly polarized photons. This is conceptually reasonable, since the photon represents the entire field. It can be shown that a photon behaves exactly like a particle of rest mass zero so far as its energy and momentum relationships are concerned. It can also be shown that emission or absorption of a photon can change the angular momentum of a system only by integral multiples of $\hbar$; it can, but need not, change the parity of the system, depending on the type of field it represents. Which of these various things the photon does do will depend on the type of classical electromagnetic field it represents. We can therefore enter the photon into our table as

Particle	Charge	Mass	Spin
γ (photon)	0	0	Integral

This completes our summary of the fundamental particles of importance in processes involving energy exchanges of less than 100 Mev. Before adding to our table some of the particles of importance in high-energy processes, let us look at some of the reactions which involve the particles thus far described.

9.5 Processes Involving These Particles

We have already described the β-decay process [reactions (9.4) and (9.5)]. Now consider the process

$$\gamma \rightleftarrows e^+ + e^- \tag{9.7}$$

This decay balances charge, spin, and, if sufficient initial energy is available, it satisfies the energy-conservation law. However, some simple arithmetic shows that momentum can in general *not* be conserved unless an additional particle is present which can absorb the "recoil." Hence this process cannot occur spontaneously in free space. This process, when going in the right-hand direction, is called *pair production;* it occurs with good probability, particularly in heavy elements, when γ rays of energy greater than twice the electron rest energy strike a nucleus.

The reverse process, called *pair annihilation*, occurs always when positrons are slowed down in matter; if this happens they spend enough time near the negative electrons to permit annihilation to take place. Note that this process releases about 1 Mev of energy.

Positive and negative electrons act entirely symmetrically in this process, just as they do in β decay. The stability of the negative electron, as compared to the "death by annihilation" of the positive electron, is not basic in the theory but is due only to the circumstance that our part of the universe has more negative electrons than positive ones in it. No presently known fact in physics indicates any *basic* asymmetry between positive and negative charge.

Let us digress momentarily and talk about the conceptual nature of the electromagnetic interaction between two particles. Consider two electrons repelling one another. The common description is as follows: One of the electrons produces an electric "field"; when exposed to this field, the other suffers a force. How does the photon representation of the field fit into this picture? A qualitatively useful concept in reconciling this problem is the following. Let the first electron emit a photon, and let the second electron absorb it

$$e_1 \rightarrow e_1 + \gamma \qquad \gamma + e_2 \rightarrow e_2 \tag{9.8}$$

a short time afterward, and vice versa. The virtual interchange of photons between two systems undergoing electromagnetic interaction is thus a description of electromagnetic forces in terms of a particle picture.

9.6 Mesons and Their Reactions

We know that in nuclear physics electromagnetic forces are not the most important sources of interaction. Rather, there are specifically "nuclear" forces which are responsible for the stability of nuclei. For example, the deuteron, consisting of a neutron and a proton, is evidently held together by nonelectrical forces. What then is the "photon" of this specifically nuclear field? In 1935, Yukawa, a Japanese theoretical physicist, analyzed the character of such a hypothetical particle and named it a *meson;* he predicted that its mass should be 200 to 300 electron masses. The term meson is now applied to any particle whose rest mass is intermediate between that of the electron and that of the proton.

A particle of approximately the correct mass value was discovered in cosmic rays shortly after Yukawa's prediction. Cloud-chamber tracks of various cosmic-ray particles were shown to be incompatible in behavior with the particles known at the time (1936–1938). Further detailed studies of the properties of these new particles made it more and more difficult to reconcile their behavior with the particles predicted by Yukawa. This difficulty was resolved by the recent discovery (1947) that the mesons seen in the cloud chamber at sea level are actually decay products of short-lived mesons of larger mass. These latter mesons, called π mesons, occur in cosmic rays only at high altitude since they decay into the lighter so-called μ mesons before reaching sea level. The mesons originally detected are thus μ mesons. It was soon shown, particularly with the aid of mesons produced in electronuclear machines, that the π mesons do conform in their essential properties to the carriers of the nuclear force predicted by Yukawa.

The process by which charged π mesons decay into μ mesons with a mean life of $\sim 2.65 \times 10^{-8}$ sec is almost certainly

$$\pi^{\pm} \rightarrow \mu^{\pm} + \nu \qquad (9.9)$$

Both signs of charged π and μ mesons are observed; in addition a neutral π meson was discovered which decays as follows (mean life $\sim 10^{-14}$ sec):

$$\pi^0 \rightarrow 2\gamma \qquad \text{(2 photons)} \qquad (9.10)$$

or

$$\pi^0 \rightarrow \gamma + e^+ + e^-$$

The second process takes place only in one in a hundred disintegrations.

The μ meson itself is also unstable and is found to decay by the process

$$\mu^{\pm} \rightarrow e^{\pm} + \nu + \nu \qquad (9.11)$$

The lifetime (mean life $\sim 2 \times 10^{-6}$ sec) of this decay is, however, much longer than that of process (9.9), thus accounting for the preponderance of μ mesons at sea level. Each of these particles thus has its own decay scheme. In addition to these processes involving the "free" particles, many studies have been made concerning the interaction of these particles with nuclei. The most fundamental of these are, of course, the basic reactions

$$\left. \begin{array}{l} p \rightleftarrows n + \pi^+ \\ p \rightarrow p + \pi^0 \\ n \rightleftarrows p + \pi^- \\ n \rightarrow n + \pi^0 \end{array} \right\} \begin{array}{c} \text{production of } \pi\text{'s} \\ \text{and} \\ \text{absorption of } \pi\text{'s} \end{array} \qquad (9.12)$$

which are the analogous processes to the photon processes (9.8). These processes have been observed to take place in nuclei by numerous experiments which we unfortunately cannot discuss here in detail. On the other hand, experiments involving the interaction of μ mesons with nuclei have always shown that this interaction is very weak, in fact of the "β type." The process which has been observed, or rather inferred, is

$$\mu^- + p \rightarrow n + \nu \tag{9.13}$$

From these reactions, we can easily enter the π and μ mesons into our "intrinsic-property" table:

Particle	Charge	Mass	Spin
π^+	$+1$	273	0
π^-	-1	273	0
π^0	0	265	0
μ^+	$+1$	207	$\frac{1}{2}$
μ^-	-1	207	$\frac{1}{2}$

The story of the definite assignment of these values is a long one. Let me here only point out how the spin assignment fits the reactions (9.9) to (9.12); in fact, the half-integral spin of the μ meson makes the presence of the neutrino necessary when the μ meson reacts with nuclei, entirely in analogy with β decay.

The difference in mass between the negative and neutral π mesons has made the following process possible:

$$\pi^- + p \rightarrow \pi^0 + n \qquad \text{(charge-exchange absorption)} \tag{9.14}$$

In fact, it is from this process that we know that such a mass difference exists.

The existence of mesons has forced the necessity of our last and unexplained selection rule, namely, the *law of conservation of nucleons.* Were it not for that (empirical) rule, then decay processes like

$$p \rightarrow \mu^+ + \pi^0 \qquad n \rightarrow \pi^- + \mu^+ \tag{9.15}$$

would *not* be forbidden by any of the known laws of physics. As the result, matter as we know it would be unstable.

As you have seen, even the group of particles I have discussed represents a fairly complete picture. Let me not convey the impression that this picture is well understood. In particular, the detailed theoretical treatment of meson processes has met many serious difficulties. To these has been added the discovery of further unstable particles, such as V particles, τ mesons, and κ mesons, in the cosmic radiation. Their properties cannot at present be definitely assigned. It would only increase the complexity if I would add them to our table in their presently highly tentative and controversial status.

The question naturally arises whether we are close to the end in this process of discovering particles or, conversely, whether the number of particles discoverable is finite. If it were true that several of the particles treated separately are actually modifications or "states" of some other particles, then simplification of the picture would result. Attempts have been made to classify particles into groups and to introduce additional selection rules which would include the law of conservation of nucleons and the behavior of the new particles. Clearly, some further systematization is necessary as the number of particles increases. At this time the information on the particles not discussed here in detail is sufficiently tenuous that their consistent classification into groups will be most uncertain.

We must therefore conclude that progress toward simplification of the "fundamental-particle" picture must first pass through a further phase of complication by the addition of new data.

Table 9.3 Summary of Elementary-particle Properties

Symbol	Name	Rest mass, units of electron mass = 9.107×10^{-28} g	Charge, units of electron charge	Spin
p	Proton	1836.13	+1	$\frac{1}{2}$
n	Neutron	1838.66	0	$\frac{1}{2}$
e^-	Negative electron	1	−1	$\frac{1}{2}$
e^+	Positive electron	1	+1	$\frac{1}{2}$
ν	Neutrino	~0	0	$\frac{1}{2}$
γ	Photon	0	0	Integral
π^+	Positive pion	273	+1	0
π^-	Negative pion	273	−1	0
π^0	Neutral pion	265	0	0
μ^+	Positive muon	207	+1	$\frac{1}{2}$
μ^-	Negative muon	207	−1	$\frac{1}{2}$

PART 2

Man's Physical Environment

10
Astrophysics

JESSE L. GREENSTEIN

MOUNT WILSON AND PALOMAR OBSERVATORIES
AND CALIFORNIA INSTITUTE OF TECHNOLOGY

10.1 Introduction

The word *astrophysics* carries with it the connotation of a mixed science, linking astronomy with modern physics. But modern physics is in continuous flux, and the border between astronomy and astrophysics moves forward continuously. Newton was a physicist and astronomer, but we would not now call him an astrophysicist. Similarly, the astrophysics of the last generation is the classical astronomy of the present. We should therefore realize the narrowness of any definition of present-day astrophysics. I shall cover a few broad fields in which atomic and nuclear physics are applied to stellar situations; I must omit other fields of modern science (such as aerodynamics and magnetohydrodynamics) which are lively parts of modern astrophysics.

The difficult and precise observations of several generations of astronomers have given us a broad outline of the universe in which we live. Our planet is a dead rock circulating about an average star; our sun is one of 10^{11} suns in a rather large galaxy (spiral nebula) whose diameter is at least 100,000 light-years. Our galaxy is one of an uncounted number of other systems of stars, which now have been seen out to a distance of over a billion light-years. These galaxies contain stars and gas and dust clouds, as does our own. They are made of the same materials, (having spectra like those of an average star) to the limit of the observable universe. Their one peculiarity, the red shift, now observed out to one-fifth the velocity of light (61,000 km/sec), is generally accepted to be the result of a real expansion; with relativistic corrections, Tolman derived an age of the universe amounting to 1.3 billion years. Current observations indicate that the distance scale should be substantially corrected and that an age of 5 billion years seems probable. By *age* we mean that

235

a point in time existed before which the universe was substantially different with regard to the existence of planets, stars, galaxies, and atoms.

10.2 The Stars

From this broad picture, let us return to a star. In a deep sense, we can understand a star better than we can understand the structure of the earth or of a protein molecule. The laws of physics are simple under stellar conditions. A small fraction of a star's mass, at the center of the star, is hot enough to undergo nuclear transmutation. Another small fraction, at the surface, is cool enough to show spectral lines. Molecules are rare, diatomic, and confined to the surface of cool stars. The enormous bulk of the mass is a hot, highly ionized, perfect gas in hydrostatic equilibrium, through which radiation generated in the center slowly diffuses outward. The mean temperature of stellar matter is a few million degrees, its mean density about that of water; the ionization makes the perfect-gas laws valid even at high density. There is an enormous store of radiant energy and of energy of ionization. In the energy-generating region the most abundant element, hydrogen, is transmuted into the second most abundant, helium; other nuclear processes may also change the composition slightly. A fundamental problem is the degree of mixing of the elements between the core and the surface. Normal diffusion of heavy elements to the center is prevented by even slight convective stirring. Slow circulation currents, of periods nearly 10^8 years, may be started by the rotation of the star. At present, many believe that mixing does not occur (except in rapidly rotating or otherwise unstable stars) and that the composition of the surface and the interior may differ appreciably.

Astronomical observations of apparent stellar brightnesses and colors have been obtained by visual, photographic, and now by photoelectric techniques. The intrinsic brightness, or "luminosity," of the star is derived from its apparent brightness and its distance. The sun has the luminosity $L\odot = 4 \times 10^{33}$ ergs/sec, which we shall use as our unit. The masses of double or multiple stars are derived from the Newtonian law of gravitation; the solar mass $M\odot$ is 2×10^{33} g. The radii of the stars are derived in a few cases by direct observation but mostly are inferred from eclipses of close double stars or by deduction from the luminosity and temperature. The radius of the sun $R\odot$ is 6.9×10^{10} cm. It has a color temperature of between 5000 and 7000°K, dependent on the wavelength region used. The "effective temperature" of the sun is 5700°K; the theory of radiative transfer gives us a relation between the color and effective temperature of a star. Table 10.1 gives a brief résumé of the approximate mean physical properties of the stars.

The "spectral types" listed in Table 10.1 are used to order stars in a temperature sequence.   Spectra of several hundred thousand stars have been classified at low dispersion.   The classes, in order of decreasing temperature, are O, B, A, F, G, K, M, with decimal subdivisions.   O and B stars are "early" hot stars, K and M "late" cool stars.   (The terms *hot* and *cool* refer to the surface only.)   The luminosity can also be estimated approximately from the spectra; such estimates prove to be well correlated with the measured luminosity.   Peculiar stars exist in most classes; an offshoot containing stars with strong carbon lines and bands exists in types R and N, and a group with strong ZrO bands exists in type S.

10.3   Stellar Lifetimes and Evolution

Table 10.1 reveals a general feature of normal stars, the steep increase of luminosity with increasing mass.   The white dwarfs are an exceptional group of underluminous stars of small radius and fantastic density (in the rather mild example given, about 2 tons/cu in.).   Excluding the white dwarfs, which provide a separate astrophysical problem, there are three main groups of stars: (1) the main-sequence or normal dwarf stars, by far the most common group in space; (2) the supergiant stars, rare but of

Table 10.1   Numerical Data of Standard Stellar Types in Solar Units

Luminosity class	Spectral type	$L/L\odot$	$R/R\odot$	$M/M\odot$	Effective temperature, °K
Main sequence..	B	7500	7	10	20,000
Main sequence..	A	40	2	2	10,000
Main sequence..	G	1	1	1	6,000
Main sequence..	M	0.04	0.76	0.4	3,000
Supergiant......	B	10^5	50	40	25,000
Supergiant......	M	10^5	1500	30?	2,500
Red giant.......	K	100	16	4	4,700
White dwarf....	A	0.0025	0.022	1	9,000

enormous luminosity; (3) the red giant stars.   Low effective temperature means very low density for the red giants and supergiants.   Since an elementary result of the theory of stellar interiors is that the mean temperature $\bar{T}$ (in degrees Kelvin) exceeds, but is of the order of, $4.6 \times 10^6 \mu M/R$, where μ is the mean molecular weight per particle (0.5 for ionized pure hydrogen, 2.0 for ionized helium or heavy elements), the mean temperature of the red supergiants is very low, and their source of energy is an outstanding problem.   Recently, substantial advances have been made in the theory of the internal structure of the red giants, on the assumption that no mixing occurs between their center and surface; the conversion of hydrogen to helium at the center results in a variation of molecular weight with depth and in the enormous radii and low density observed. On the other hand, the very common main-sequence stars have nearly constant M/R (Table 10.1) and therefore could be a rather homogeneous group. Main-sequence stars like the sun, or fainter, can be shown to be substantially unchanged by nuclear-energy generation in 3×10^9 years. Stars of very large L/M exhaust their hydrogen quickly, however. The maximum life of a star converting pure hydrogen into pure helium (the fundamental process, see Chap. 6) is given by

$$\text{Life} = 9.8 \times 10^{10} \frac{M}{L} \text{ yr} \qquad (10.1)$$

A supergiant B star has $M/L = 4 \times 10^{-4}$, so that it cannot have radiated at its present rate for more than 40 million years, while a main-sequence class A star has a life of at most 5 billion years. But these lives are definitely upper limits; the study of stellar interiors indicates that exhaustion of hydrogen in about 20 per cent of the mass changes the stellar structure radically. Thus we may confidently say that, even among main-sequence stars, the high-luminosity objects are "new" stars, while the low-luminosity objects may be new or old. The requirement for stellar formation is real; it is needed to rescue astrophysics from a serious impasse. We now turn to a brief consideration of the structure of our galaxy and of the results yielded by a classical astronomical subject, stellar kinematics.

10.4 Structure of the Galaxy. Interstellar Gas and Dust

Our own galaxy, the Milky Way, is a flattened, rotating system of stars, gas, and dust. The stars move, under the influence of their joint gravitational potential field, in orbits around the galactic center, 25,000 light-years distant from us. The solar orbit is nearly circular, with a period of about 3×10^8 years. Nearby stars with other nearly circular orbits show low velocity relative to the sun. Stars moving in eccentric or inclined orbits pass the sun with relatively high velocity. It has been known for a long time that various types of stars could be characterized by different velocity dispersions with respect to the sun. Recently it has been shown by Baade that there exist at least two different stellar "populations." Type I contains the sun, many main-sequence stars (including the blue O and B stars of high luminosity), supergiants, ordinary red giants, open clusters (like the Pleiades), and interstellar gas and dust. Type I stars have small velocity dispersion, are highly concentrated to the main plane of the Galaxy, and in that plane are bunched in the spiral arms. Type II stars are characterized by large velocity dispersion. This type includes bright red giants, subgiants (stars intermediate between the main sequence and giants), subdwarfs (stars fainter than main-sequence stars), and globular clusters.   Figure 10.1 shows the nature of the correlation between luminosity and surface temperature (or spectral type) for population types I and II.   Figure 10.2 shows a resolved typical spiral galaxy rich in blue type I stars (up to $10^6 L \odot$) and gas clouds; also shown (Fig. 10.3) is an ellipsoidal type II galaxy, barely

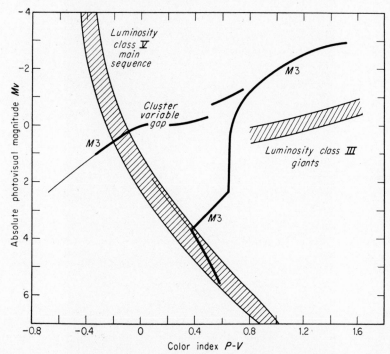

Fig. 10.1 A schematic diagram showing the absolute magnitude of the stars as a function of their color, in the type I population (shaded) and in the globular cluster Messier 3 (M3), typical of the type II population.   In the latter, note the blue stars near $M_v = 0$ and the bright red giants, which are rare in type I.   The color index $P - V$ is a measure of temperature, -0.4 corresponding to $25,000°K$ and $+1.2$ to $5000°K$.   The absolute magnitude $M_v = 5 - 2.5 \log_{10} (L/L\odot)$.   (*Mount Wilson and Palomar Observatories; Astronomical Journal.*)

resolved into stars the brightest of which are only 1000 times the luminosity of the sun.   The type II population includes little or no gas and dust, and it has no stars of very high luminosity.

Interstellar gas has a mass comparable to that of the stars in our part of our galaxy.   We live in a region rich in stars of high luminosity, which cannot be old.   The association of high-luminosity stars with gas and dust clouds is remarkably close.   The spiral arms of our own system are now being mapped in three ways: first, by the location of clouds of ionized hydrogen, glowing because of the recombination of protons and electrons; second, by detection of clouds of neutral hydrogen through their r-f emission of the hyperfine-structure line at 1421 Mc/sec; third, by detection of clouds of other gases through their interstellar absorption lines.

Fig. 10.2   The spiral galaxy, Messier 33, a giant and distant stellar system containing 10^{11} stars, as seen through our own system, by the 200-in telescope.   M33 contains large amounts of dust (dark clouds), hot gaseous nebulae (bright patches), and many blue supergiant stars of short life.   A photograph taken 100 million years from now would show a rotation of about 180 degrees but completely different high-luminosity stars, because of the exhaustion of nuclear-energy sources.   The sun, at the distance of M33, would be too faint to be seen on this photograph.   (*Mount Wilson and Palomar Observatories.*)

The existence of gas and dust is graphically shown in Fig. 10.4, a photograph of a diffuse emission-line nebula, *i.e.*, a region of our own Milky Way containing hot O and B stars, gas, and dust.

This clue has led, in the last few years, to the growth of two theories proposing either (1) the continuous formation of stars from gas and dust clouds or (2) the refueling of stars by accretion (capture) of hydrogen from interstellar space.   The high velocities of the population type II

Fig. 10.3 The type II ellipsoidal galaxy, NGC 147, a system of stars completely lacking in dust, gas, or stars of high luminosity.   Its brightest stars are like the bright red giants in the globular cluster (see Fig. 10.1).   The bright images on this photograph are those of stars in our own system. (*Mount Wilson and Palomar Observatories.*)

Fig. 10.4 The gaseous nebula, M16, about 3000 light-years distant, in our own galaxy.   It is a cloud of dust and gas, 40 light-years in diameter.   Note the bright cluster of stars in the upper right.   These make the gas shine by fluorescence.   Note also the black dust clouds silhouetted against the bright gas; some of the small dense globules of dust may condense to form stars. (*Mount Wilson and Palomar Observatories*)

stars and the apparent absence of gas from type II galaxies prevent the above processes from working effectively. Thus type II stars are presumably all old, while type I stars are of mixed ages. A consequence of the first theory is that type I may have a relatively higher abundance than type II of the elements C, N, O and the metals, as compared with hydrogen. The lower concentration of hydrogen in type I may arise from the evaporation of hydrogen from the interstellar dust, which is supposed to condense into new stars. The dust is now pictured as consisting mainly of frozen simple gases and simple metallic compounds (*e.g.*, solid CH_4, NH_3, CO_2, H_2O, and metallic hydrates), since even at the low temperatures of space, hydrogen and helium will evaporate. We can expect population I stars to differ among themselves in the ratio of hydrogen to the metals, for example, although we should not expect great variations in the ratio of one metal to another. The type II stars should be relatively poor in metals and might be expected to show other signs of age.

The capture radius of the star for interstellar matter is normally too small to provide effective refueling. At low relative velocity of star and gas, however, and at high gas densities, the capture radius is greatly increased, according to the accretion theory advanced by Hoyle and the Cambridge group of astrophysicists. Unfortunately, little evidence exists for such favorable conditions. In addition, the accretion hypothesis has been less fruitful in explaining correlations between stellar composition and velocity than has the hypothesis of star formation.

The properties of the interstellar matter are of intrinsic interest. In population type I regions, where gas is present, the mean space density is about one hydrogen atom per cm^3. Even the denser gas clouds shown in photographs seldom exceed 1000 atoms/cm^3. The relative abundances in the gaseous substratum of hydrogen, helium, the oxygen group, and the metals are about the same as those characterizing the stars. The dust has a lower space density than the gas and is subject to larger density fluctuations; the great dark clouds of dust have masses several hundred times that of the sun. The dust grains have radii near the wavelength of light; they absorb light preferentially at shorter wavelengths so that transmitted starlight is both weakened and reddened. The extraordinary observation has recently been made that the transmitted light is not only reddened but often plane-polarized. The attempt to explain "interstellar Polaroid" leads to the hypothesis that the dust grains are elongated, rather than spherical, and that their longer axes have a tendency toward common alignment over great volumes of space. The most successful explanations require the existence of a magnetic field in space; its magnitude is uncomfortably large (at least 10^{-5} gauss), and if it is real, the magnetic field represents an unexpectedly large fraction of the energy of the Galaxy.

10.5   The Theory of the Spectroscopic Analysis of the Stars

Against this broad background of astronomical facts and hypotheses we shall attempt the analysis of a stellar atmosphere.   The methods of laboratory spectroscopic analysis are familiar; the methods of stellar analysis are less familiar and unfortunately more complex.   Radiation diffuses outward through the stellar atmosphere from the interior. Atoms and ions absorb and reemit this radiation.   The outward flow of radiation is maintained by a temperature gradient; our first step is to understand how radiation transfer occurs.

Deep in the star, the mixture of quanta and atoms is very close to the state of thermal equilibrium.   The energy distribution of the radiation is given by Planck's black-body formula for the local temperature, and the velocities of the atoms follow the Maxwellian distribution.   Absorption and reemission occur in accordance with Kirchhoff's law.   As a consequence, the spectrum is *continuous;* no absorption or emission lines exist. The outward flux is small compared with the total energy of the radiation field.   But, at the boundary of the star, radiation flows outward only, and its energy distribution cannot be described by the Planck formula. The outward flux and the total energy content become comparable.   The one-sided nature of the radiation field at the boundary results in a temperature differential.   Two points in the outer atmosphere which are separated vertically by about one free path for an average quantum in the continuous spectrum differ by about 20 per cent in temperature.   In this outer region the absorption lines are formed.   If we could set our spectrograph inside the star at a depth of several free paths, no lines would be observed; they would gradually strengthen as we rose toward the boundary.   The strength of an absorption line depends on the magnitude of the temperature gradient, on the continuous absorption coefficient of the stellar atmosphere, on the position with respect to the black-body energy maximum, and finally on the concentration and motion of the atoms and their atomic transition probabilities.   The astronomical situation is much more complex than that obtaining in laboratory arc or flame emission-line spectra, where only the last two factors enter.

The rigorous solution of the stellar problem requires (1) the construction of a model of the stellar atmosphere, which gives the temperature T, pressure P, and continuous absorption coefficient k_ν at each depth; (2) the computation for each point of the number of atoms n of an element in the lower energy state which produces the given line; (3) the computation of the line-absorption coefficient per atom l_ν which is not monochromatic, of course, but has a shape given by the thermal agitation, pressure broadening, and radiation-damping broadening.   The solution of the equation of radiative transfer finally gives the effect of the line in depressing the continuous spectrum in terms of an integration through the model atmosphere of the ratio nl_ν/k_ν. The result is the depth of the line, defined as $A_\nu = (1 - F_\nu/F_c)$ where F_ν is the emergent flux at frequency ν in the line and F_c is the flux in the neighboring continuous spectrum. We can measure the profile A_ν or, more usually, its integral over the line $W_\nu = \int A_\nu \, d\nu$, where W_ν is the "equivalent width" or strength of the

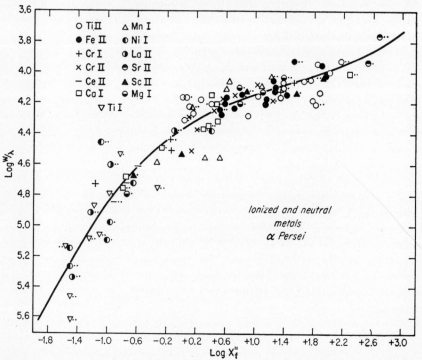

Fig. 10.5 A curve of growth for a supergiant star, showing the relation between the observed absorption line intensities W and the theoretical transition probabilities X''_f. The near-horizontal section arises from the saturation of strong lines. (*McDonald Observatory; Astrophysical Journal.*)

absorption line. The most conspicuous result is that the strength W_ν proves to be a complicated function of the ratio $X_0 = nl_\nu(0)/k_\nu$, where $l_\nu(0)$ is the line-absorption coefficient at the center of the line. W_ν is a linear function of X_0 only when the line is very weak; as X_0 increases the line becomes saturated, and W_ν increases only slowly; eventually, for very strong lines in which the pressure or radiation-damping wings are prominent, W_ν increases as $(\Gamma X_0)^{\frac{1}{2}}$, where Γ is the damping constant. The result is a "curve of growth" which relates the strength of an absorption line to the effective line-absorption coefficient X_0; the latter is pro-

portional to the atomic transition probability and the concentration of
the atoms.   A typical theoretical curve of growth is shown in Fig. 10.5
together with observed equivalent widths in a star.

The curve-of-growth method is not a rigorous one, and the use of a
model stellar atmosphere is properly followed by the matching of observed
profiles of strong lines with the line profile predicted by the integration

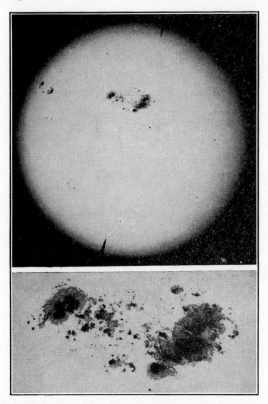

Fig. 10.6   A direct photograph of the sun, showing its mottled surface, bright patch-
work near the limb, and a major sunspot group nearly 200,000 miles long.   The
enlargement shows the complicated pattern of the turbulent gases and the filamentary
structure of hotter gas clouds bridging the cooler areas of the spot.   (*Mount Wilson
and Palomar Observatories.*)

through the atmosphere.   A combined approach will provide some or
all of the following data about the star: boundary, excitation and effective temperatures, surface gravity, macro- or microturbulence, electron
pressures and gas pressures, the presence of the Stark effect (random
electric-field broadening due to ions and electrons) and Zeeman effect
(stellar magnetic fields), hyperfine structure, and finally the abundances
of the elements.

So ambitious a program cannot always be carried out, and various approximation methods have been introduced in the work on the stellar abundances of the elements.   One main obstacle to exact analysis is not astronomical but is the lack of sufficient physical data on the transition probabilities and damping constants for the lines.   In principle, quantum mechanics provides methods for computation of the wave functions for any atom in any state of ionization or excitation.   From the wave functions for the initial and final atomic states the transition probability can be computed.   In fact, except for hydrogen, helium, hydrogen-like ions, and atoms in excited hydrogenic states, almost no reliable transition probabilities exist.   Even relatively simple problems, such as transition probabilities in the helium atom, require elaborate computations; a complex atom such as iron would represent a major effort for the largest electronic computers, even if a practicable computing scheme could be invented.   Thus we must turn to laboratory investigations of transition probabilities.   While simple in principle, the laboratory work has been meager; it is mainly due to A. S. and R. B. King.   Materials are vaporized in an electric vacuum furnace of known (and constant) temperature. If the vapor-pressure data are reliable, the number of atoms will be known, and the emission or absorption intensities of the lines can be measured.   If the furnace approaches conditions of thermal equilibrium, the Boltzmann equation may be used to compute the concentration of atoms in a given excited state, and consequently the observed line strength gives the transition probability.   It is considerably simpler to obtain the relative transition probability of one line with respect to another than to obtain absolute transition probabilities.

Some progress has recently been made in obtaining absolute transition probabilities for simple diatomic radicles in the spectra of flames and jets. Certain simple radicles appear in late-type stellar spectra (notably CH, CN, NH, C_2, and TiO).   Further progress in the analysis of the sun and cooler stars depends greatly on this new technical advance.

10.6   The Technique and Limitations of Astronomical Spectroscopy

A telescope can be used as a light-gathering device to feed spectrographs of various sizes and dispersions.   Approximately one-half the observing time of the 200- and 100-in. reflectors is used for detailed spectroscopic examination of the stars.   Photography of the spectrum provides a simultaneous record of both the position and intensity of the lines; intensities are calibrated by photometric devices.   Wavelengths can be measured with an accuracy of ± 0.001 A (angstroms) in favorable cases; line intensities have accuracies limited by the photographic process to several per cent, at best.

The normal wavelength range covered in astronomy is 3000 to 9000 A. Atmospheric ozone prevents observation at shorter and water vapor at longer wavelengths; photographic emulsions are slow in the infrared. The sun is sufficiently bright to permit scanning of the infrared spectrum to 35,000 A, using the lead sulfide photoconductive cell and electronic recording. Low-dispersion PbS scanning of spectra of the planets and

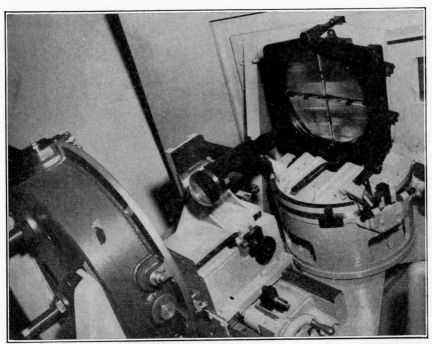

Fig. 10.7 Part of the coudé spectrograph at Palomar. Note the composite plane-grating mount, with a beam aperture of 13 in. An aspheric Schmidt correcting plate is located nearly in contact with the gratings. At the left is the spherical mirror, and in the center the plateholder and aplanatic quartz sphere. (*Mount Wilson and Palomar Observatories; Astrophysical Journal.*)

of some stars has proved successful (leading, for example, to the detection of ice in the polar cap of Mars and probably in the rings of Saturn). The astronomer must not be accused of ignorance of modern techniques, however, if he fails to use photoelectric scanning of spectra; to obtain high spectral resolution for line profiles, the photocell must provide a satisfactory signal-to-noise ratio on light perhaps equal to one-millionth the total light of the star. The statistical fluctuation in this small fraction of the already small number of quanta arriving from a star sets the ultimate limit of scanning speed.

The photographic spectrographs used vary enormously in dispersion,

depending on the brightness of the star.   Solar spectroscopy at very high
dispersion, up to 0.1 A/mm and resolving power up to 500,000, is easy.
The highest dispersions now used for stars are 2.8 A/mm at Mount Wilson
and 2.1 A/mm at Palomar.   All naked-eye stars can easily be observed
at this scale.   The lowest useful dispersion for classification purposes is
about 150 A/mm; the red-shift measures of faint galaxies are carried out
at 300 A/mm.   At Palomar, fairly detailed spectroscopic investigations

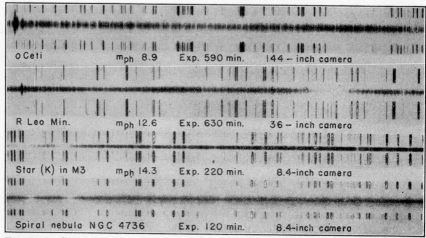

Fig. 10.8 Spectra taken with the Palomar coudé; these are negatives, so that stellar
absorption lines appear white on the black continuous background.   Above and
below are the black lines of the comparison spectrum of the iron arc.   Long wavelengths are to the right.   The uppermost spectrum, at the highest stellar dispersion,
is of Mira, omicron Ceti, a cool variable star.   It has (black) emission lines, as does
R Leo Min., another variable star.   In the third spectrum, that of a red giant in the
globular cluster M3, the shift toward shorter wavelengths of the stellar iron lines
corresponds to about 150 km/sec relative velocity.   The broad lines in the spectrum
of the spiral nebula arise from the internal motions of its stars.   (*Mount Wilson and
Palomar Observatories; Astrophysical Journal.*)

can be carried out on stars 10,000 times fainter than the limit of naked-
eye vision.

The modern astronomical spectrograph is a remarkable instrument;
a brief outline of the design principles of the new coudé spectrograph at
Palomar may be of interest.   The over-all size, about 30 ft, requires that
it be fixed in position.   Consequently, two (and at times, four) auxiliary
mirrors reflect the light from the 200-in. mirror into a large room below
the south pier, at which point the equivalent focal length of the telescope
is 500 ft and the focal ratio is $f/30$.   The star image is centered on a slit,
and trailed back and forth to provide a widened spectrum.   The $f/30$
beam then travels 30 ft to the off-axis parabolic collimator at the far end of

the spectrograph room. The parallel beam returns to a mount containing four plane diffraction gratings, each $5\frac{1}{2} \times 7$ in. These gratings, ruled by Dr. Horace Babcock at the Mount Wilson Observatory, have 10,000 lines to the inch and throw about 60 to 70 per cent of the light into one order; they are used in the third-order violet or second-order red. The

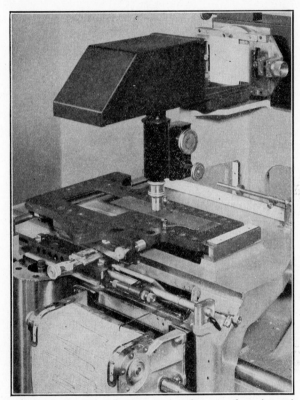

Fig. 10.9 Portion of the microphotometer used to produce intensity tracings of stellar spectra. A servomechanism drives the pen and rapidly plots the intensity of the star's radiation as a function of wavelength. The servoamplifier is controlled by a photo-multiplier tube, which records the varying transmission of a light beam through the moving photograph of the stellar spectrum. (*Mount Wilson and Palomar Observatories.*)

composite grating mount is of extreme rigidity but permits adjustment of the gratings so that the spectra formed by all gratings coincide. To permit observation at different dispersions of stars of a wide range of brightness, five cameras with focal lengths from 144 to 8 in. can be placed into the beam from the gratings. Four are Schmidt cameras, consisting of a spherical mirror and an aspheric correcting plate placed nearly in contact with the grating; the focal ratios range from $f/12$ to $f/1.5$. The

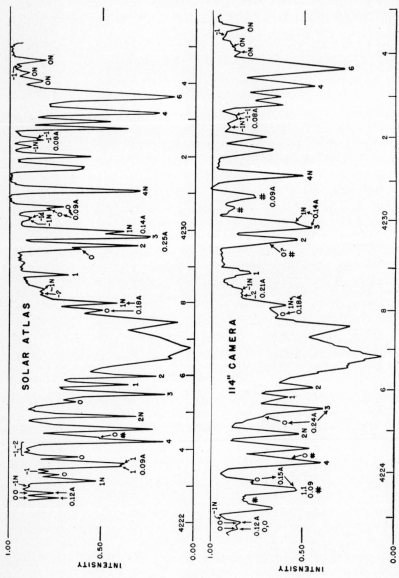

Fig. 10.10 Tracings of the solar spectrum, showing intensity (vertical) as a function of wavelength. The upper record is from a plate taken with the highest available astronomical dispersion (original 0.3 A/mm); the lower is with the dispersion used at Mount Wilson to study stellar composition (2.8 A/mm). Stars down to the limit of naked-eye visibility can be studied on this scale. The very strong line is that of neutral calcium (at 4227 A). Its breadth arises from atomic collisions and measures the pressure in the solar atmosphere. (*Mount Wilson and Palomar Observatories.*)

shortest camera, the 8 in. $f/0.7$, contains in addition an aplanatic sphere of fused quartz and represents about the ultimate in camera speed for the large aperture of the beam used, 13 in.   Figure 10.7 shows the composite grating, aspheric corrector plate, mirror, and aplanatic quartz lens. The camera of highest dispersion requires a mirror 4 ft in diameter, *i.e.*, one comparable to those used in good-sized telescopes.   Spectra taken with different cameras are shown in Fig. 10.8.

Line intensities are measured on microphotometer records of the spectra.   The problem of photometric reduction of spectra is greatly lessened by the use of an elaborate microphotometer designed by Babcock which produces a record of the spectrum on an intensity scale.   A servo-mechanism drives a linear calibration wedge to match the density on the photographic plate.   The speed of response is high enough to record an inch of very complex spectrum in about 5 min.   Figure 10.10 shows a typical tracing of a spectrum as compared with the "Utrecht Atlas of the Solar Spectrum."   The latter was obtained at ten times the dispersion possible on the stars; while it reveals somewhat more detail, the gain is not very large.

10.7   Spectral Classification; Ionization and Excitation in Normal Stars

Spectra of low dispersion have been taken on almost half a million stars.   While at first sight the variety seemed bewildering, it soon was possible to arrange the spectra in a sequence which proved to be one of decreasing temperature.   As an example, consider the spectral changes at the high-temperature end of the sequence.   The hottest stars, the O stars, show lines of He II, He I, Si IV, and of several ions of C, N, and O.   The B0 to B2 stars show He I, Si III, H, and O II and weak lines of Fe III. At B8 only H, Si II, and weak He I remain; at A0 we find H, Si II, Mg II, Ca II, and weak lines of Fe I.   Obviously, we must not assume that the A0 stars ($T \approx 10,000°K$) are of different composition from the B0 stars ($T \approx 25,000°K$).   The gradual transition from a highly ionized element to its neutral form, for example, can be understood as an effect of the lower temperature.   The average energy of a quantum, or of a colliding atom, is of the order of 1 ev (electron volt) at $11,600°K$ and is proportional to the temperature.   The average energy is not a good measure of the level of ionization; for a rough guess, a certain stage of ionization requiring I ev will actually dominate when $11,600I/T$ is approximately 15.   The actual equilibrium between two successive stages of ionization is given by the same formula as physical chemists use to compute the degree of dissociation of a molecule, except that for our problem the ionization by quanta, or by collisions, is balanced by the recombination of the free electrons and ions.   The Saha ionization formula gives the ratio of ions (n_1) to neutral atoms (n_0) in terms of the electron pressure P_e as

$$\frac{n_1 P_e}{n_0} = \frac{(2\pi m)^{3/2}(kT)^{5/2}}{h^3} \exp\left(\frac{-I_0}{kT}\right) \qquad (10.2)$$

(We neglect the correction for statistical weights.) The equilibrium equations can also be applied to the ratio of successively higher stages of ionization, with the relevant value of I inserted. Thus the fraction of an element appearing in a given stage of ionization can be obtained.

A further application of statistical mechanics gives us the fraction of the population of a certain ion excited into a given atomic energy state, located E ev above the ground state. Again neglecting statistical weights, the Boltzmann equation is

$$\frac{n \text{ (excited)}}{n \text{ (ground state)}} = e^{-E/kT} \qquad (10.3)$$

For example, commonly observed subordinate lines of Si IV ($\lambda\lambda$ 4089 and 4116) require $E = 24$ ev, and ionization of Si III (yielding Si IV) is measured by $I = 45$ ev. Computation of typical observable subordinate lines of various ions of silicon can be made using the Saha and Boltzmann formulas, and with $P_e = 100$ bar, show that Si IV lines appear between 22,000 and 30,000°K, Si III between 17,000 and 23,000°K, Si II between 9000 and 15,000°K, Si I below 8000°K. These temperatures depend somewhat on the electron pressure, most sensitively so at low temperatures. In consequence, a two-dimensional classification can be made of stellar spectra; the leading parameter is the temperature T, while a secondary parameter is the electron pressure P_e. At a given T, P_e is proportional to surface gravity $g = GM/R^2$. Inspection of Table 10.1 shows that supergiant stars have small surface gravity compared to main-sequence stars, as do red-giant stars. Consequently, examination of spectra of a given T for the second-order effects dependent on P_e should permit us to estimate the star's surface gravity and therefore its luminosity. This has been done successfully, both empirically and by theory, and provides a powerful tool for estimating the distance of faint stars for which other methods fail.

We have used the words *temperature* and *electron pressure* very loosely in this discussion. The temperature varies appreciably within the stellar atmosphere, and P_e must go to zero at the boundary of every star. Integration through a model atmosphere including the changes of ionization and excitation permits us to obtain meaningful definitions of the average temperature and pressure at which the absorption lines are formed. In general, first-order agreement can be obtained between the results based on an exact model and those obtained from an equivalent isothermal, isobaric atmosphere. Obvious exceptions to this statement must be made; *e.g.*, if we consider a line arising from a highly excited state, the population of this state will increase steeply inward, as compared with the population of the ground state.

The resultant "stratification" of different lines is quite conspicuous, *e.g.*, in the Balmer lines of hydrogen. These require $E = 10.16$ ev, *i.e.*, a high temperature; but since hydrogen is the most abundant element in the stars, it shows strong lines even at the solar temperature, $6000°K$. These lines must be produced many free paths below lines of low E, that is, at higher temperatures and pressures. Further, the hydrogen lines show large Stark-effect broadening by the electrostatic field of nearby ionized particles; this statistical broadening (Holtsmark theory) produces hydrogen-line wings that extend for 10 A in the sun, 40 A in A stars, and 200 A in high-pressure white dwarfs. On the other hand, in supergiant A stars the pressure is low, so that even with stratification the hydrogen lines remain relatively narrow. Thus, sharpness of the hydrogen lines provides a useful method of luminosity classification, in which the mean electron pressure is the parameter. Another important effect is the pressure broadening of strong resonance lines of neutral elements in the cooler stars. In particular, Na I and Ca I are sensitive to the total gas pressure P_g. We can in principle determine both P_e and P_g from observations of the line profiles. In a star of $6000°K$ temperature, hydrogen proves to be nearly completely neutral. Since hydrogen is extremely abundant, P_g essentially is the partial pressure of hydrogen, p_H. The metals and Al, Si, and Mg are the only elements which are substantially ionized at $6000°K$, so that P_e is the partial pressure of the metals p_M. As a result we can use P_g/P_e to determine $A = p_H/p_M$, the abundance ratio of hydrogen to the metals.

Besides the evidence based only on pressure broadening, we use the opacity of the stellar atmosphere to determine A. The discussion of the equation of radiative transfer showed that the strength of an absorption line depends on the ratio nl_ν/k_ν. Once it became clear that hydrogen was the most abundant element, it was possible to show that the sources of opacity are as follows:

Stellar Type	*Absorption Processes in Stellar Atmosphere*
O5–B5	Electron scattering, bound-free and free-free transitions in hydrogen and helium
B5–F5	Bound-free transitions in hydrogen
A5–K0	Bound-free and free-free transitions in the negative hydrogen ion H^-
Later than G5	Probably H^- and molecular continua of unknown nature

The rigorous theory of the continuous absorption by H, He II, and electrons and an approximate theory for He I and H^- now exist. The negative hydrogen ion H⁻ suggested by Wildt dominates in many stars. The ion is very loosely bound, with a dissociation potential of only 0.7 ev; the equilibrium equation, like the Saha ionization equation, permits us to compute $n_H n_e/n_{H^-}$, which proves to be a slowly varying function of temperature. Note that the concentration of H^-/H is proportional to n_e; that is, to P_e. Under solar conditions only one hydrogen atom in 10^7 is a negative ion, but this concentration exceeds the fraction of hydrogen atoms excited to the second and third quantum states (one in 10^8 and 10^{10}, respectively). Quanta of energy greater than 0.7 ev ($\lambda < 18,000$ A) dissociate H⁻. The absorption coefficient has been computed from the wave function of H⁻, a system containing a proton and two electrons, by Chandrasekhar. The absorption is strong from the near infrared to the ultraviolet. In addition, the absorption by a free electron in the field of a neutral hydrogen atom (free-free transitions of H⁻) dominates in the far infrared. An important feature is the effect of the H⁻ concentration on the strength of metallic lines. A weak neutral metallic line has the quantity X_0 proportional to the concentration of the particular metal relative to hydrogen. A strong ionized line of the same metal has X_0 proportional only to the concentration of the metal relative to the concentration of all metals. Consequently, the abundance ratio A of hydrogen to all metals can be determined. Application of this and other methods yields a value of A of 6000 to 8000 for the sun.

The H⁻ ion also dictates the energy distribution in the continuous spectrum of stars cooler than 8000°K. The measured and theoretical energy distributions deviate from that of a black body; the color temperature of a star depends on the wavelength and is usually higher than its effective temperature. The absorption by H⁻ has never been detected in the laboratory; the agreement between its computed value and the value deduced from solar and stellar observation, however, is quite satisfactory. In hotter stars, hydrogen is the source of opacity. Stellar spectra show continuous absorption edges at the Paschen limit (8206 A) and the Balmer limit (3647 A). Observation of the "Balmer jump" in the continuous spectrum provides important information about the star's temperature and electron pressure, as well as about its atmospheric temperature gradient.

10.8 Abundances of the Elements in Normal Stars

The limited spectral region observable seriously limits astronomical abundance determinations. The strongest (resonance) lines arise from the ground state of the element, and many are in the ultraviolet. Ionized elements have resonance lines in the vacuum ultraviolet. The most abundant elements, H, He, C, N, O, and Ne, show only lines from highly excited states in the observable region. One result is that the Boltzmann factor is very small; another difficulty is that the temperature critically affects the ratio of the number of excited atoms to atoms in the ground state. As a consequence the abundances of He, C, N, O, and of most of the nonmetals are well determined only in the hot stars and in the planetary nebulae, in which low-lying forbidden lines can be used. For O an accurate abundance determination can be made in the sun, through the presence of forbidden absorption lines. The bands of CN, CH, OH, and

Table 10.2 Elemental Abundances in the Stars and in Meteorites
(The number given is $\log_{10}$ of the number of atoms, with hydrogen normalized to +12. The meteorite abundances have been fitted by adding 3.5.)

| Element | Sun | Meteorites | | Element | Sun | Meteorites | |
		Brown	Urey			Brown	Urey
H.........	12.00	....	....	Ge.........	2.6	3.90	3.54
Li.........	1.26	3.30	3.50	Sr.........	2.88	3.11	3.11
Be.........	2.18	2.67	2.70	Y.........	2.7	2.50	2.49
O.........	8.58	....	....	Zr.........	2.3	3.68	3.65
Na.........	6.28	6.16	6.21	Nb.........	2.2	2.45	2.35
Mg.........	7.40	7.45	7.44	Mo.........	1.8	2.78	2.27
Al.........	6.06	5.45	5.41	Ru.........	1.3	2.47	1.82
Si.........	7.15	7.50	7.50	Rh.........	0.1	2.04	1.35
S.........	6.9	7.04	6.49	Ag.........	0.6	1.93	1.78
K.........	5.15	5.34	5.04	Ba.........	2.21	2.09	2.02
Ca.........	6.28	6.33	6.25	La.........	1.2	1.82	1.82
Sc.........	3.1	2.76	2.73	Ce.........	2.0	1.86	1.86
Ti.........	4.96	4.92	4.76	Nd.........	1.6	2.02	2.02
V.........	4.05	3.90	3.68	Sm.........	1.1	1.58	1.54
Cr.........	5.20	5.48	5.41	Eu.........	1.0	0.95	0.95
Mn.........	5.40	5.39	5.33	W.........	−0.2	2.77	2.61
Fe.........	7.14	7.76	7.33	Pt.........	1.2	2.44	1.68
Co.........	5.2	5.50	4.96	Hg.........	3.0	...	>−0.72
Ni.........	6.2	6.63	6.09	Pb.........	1.7	<1.8	<1.8
Cu.........	4.9	4.16	4.12				
Zn.........	4.53	3.70	3.76				

NH should ultimately permit abundance determinations for C, N, and O in the sun and other cool stars, but the pertinent transition probabilities are still too poorly known. The spectra of cool stars, however, contain large numbers of lines of the heavier elements; many arise from the ground state and others from low-lying excited states for which the Boltzmann factor is moderately well determined. Transition probabilities are not always available; for some elements only rough estimates can be made based on the f-sum rule. Not all heavy elements are observable, even in the sun, in which about 20,000 spectral lines have been recorded. The heavier elements have such complex spectra that only a small fraction of the strength of a given electronic transition appears in any line. Elements up to an atomic number of about 40 are fairly well observable with understandable exceptions. From $Z = 40$ to $Z = 70$, except for some elements with simple spectra and a few rare earths, the situation worsens, but progress may still be possible. The heaviest elements and the unstable uranium group have extremely complex spectra, and little can probably ever be done with them. A total of 70 of the 92 stable elements have been identified.

The linkage of the abundance determinations of H, He, C, N, and O in the hot stars with those of H and the metals in the cool stars is quite difficult. Only H, O, Mg, Si, and Fe are common to both groups, and the techniques of analysis differ so widely that we should not expect too

Table 10.3   Elemental Abundances from High-temperature Objects

Element	Stars	Planetary nebulae
H.............	12.00	12.00
He............	10.75	11.18
C.............	7.7	7.7
N.............	8.0	8.0
O.............	8.6	8.7
F.............		<4.7
Ne............	8.5	8.7
S.............	7.1	7.7
Cl............	<6.7	<6.7
A.............	7.0	6.7

great an accuracy. As a consequence I give two separate tables which may be viewed as independent. I give also two determinations of the elemental abundances in meteorites, by Harrison Brown and by Harold Urey. Meteorites are our only tangible sample of nonterrestrial matter. Direct chemical or nuclear chemical abundance determinations in meteorites are very accurate. Unfortunately, meteorites occur in two main divisions: the "irons" (nearly pure nickel-iron alloys) and the "stones" (complex silicates). Two methods provide estimates of the relative frequency of the metallic, the sulfide, and the silicate phases in the original source from which meteorites come. Brown assumes that the source was a planetoid like the earth, containing a high-density metallic core and a stony mantle, and uses the terrestrial data to adjust the relative masses of these two phases. Urey has recently suggested that certain structures in meteorites (chondrites), which have about the same density as the moon, should represent a good average. The uncertainty of the astronomical data is not easy to estimate. Some fairly gross adjustment of the abundances of H/He/oxygen group/iron is not impossible. Readjustments for well-determined light metals should not be large. My personal hope is that changes by a factor of 3 will not occur. However, in Table 10.2, the uncertainties of the elements beyond Fe are quite large and can be decreased by further work.

Finally, isotope abundances can be briefly reviewed. No deuterium or tritium has been detected, in spite of the high abundance of hydrogen. The isotope C^{13} has been found, from its bands, in certain cool stars with the remarkably high abundance $C^{13}/C^{12} = \frac{1}{4}$. Search for other isotopes has led to negative results, but these were expected in most cases (Ti and Li). The He^3/He^4 ratio, which has significance in energy-generation processes, is known only to be less than 1 per cent. The isotope abundances in meteorites have so far proved similar to those on the earth.

The general behavior of the abundances of the elements in stars and in meteorites is similar to that on the earth, with certain interesting and obvious exceptions. For example, except for the part found as water, most hydrogen has escaped from the earth. So have the lighter inert gases like He and Ne, and any theory of the formation of the earth involves selective chemical processes that may have produced fractionation of chemically active elements or of heavy elements. On the other hand, Li and Be are being destroyed by nuclear reaction in the stars. (This is the reason for the drop of almost 10^{10} in abundance between H, He and Li, Be.) The characteristic features of the abundance curve are the general decrease toward heavy elements; the high abundance of C, N, O, and Fe, which after H and He dominate stellar spectra; and the negligible mass of the heavy elements. If we compute the abundances by weight, H = 75 per cent; He = 24 per cent; C, N, O, Ne about 1.2 per cent; and heavy elements about 0.3 per cent. Thus the earth, if formed out of stellar material, retained only 1 per cent of its initial mass. The stars are mainly H and He with an impurity of C, N, and O and only "traces" of the other 90 elements. Theories of the formation of elements should apparently start with processes which build complex atoms out of simple particles, protons and neutrons. In fact, several theories have already been advanced by Chandrasekhar, Gamow, Teller, ter Haar, and Hoyle. Neutrons and protons at high density and very high temperature coalesced to form the heavier elements in some primeval nuclear cookery, 5 billion years ago, at the epoch when the galaxies, stars, and atoms we know were new. The probability of multiple collisions leading to formation of heavy elements was obviously low, so that their abundance is low. The flattening out of the abundance curve for the heavy elements has been explained (Gamow, Alpher, Herman) as a reflection of the neutron-capture cross section of the heavy elements. It would be unwise to dismiss such theories as pure speculation; the near constancy of the relative abundance of the elements through the entire cosmos we observe cannot be an accident.

The absolute abundances given are subject to revision. Another approach to the chemical composition of the stars, however, is much more precise and more positive in its results. If we compare two stars, we obtain relative abundances of the elements in one as compared with the other. The transition probabilities, which are poorly known, cancel out as does the numerically large ratio of hydrogen to the metals. The relative abundances can be determined accurately. We need know only the temperature and surface-gravity difference between the two objects. Several major investigations of this nature have recently been made. In one, a group of normal F stars showed relative abundance ratios for about 20 elements differing by less than a factor of 2 from the mean. A larger investigation now nearing completion at Mount Wilson includes 10 stars of spectral type G covering a range of luminosity of 1000. Increased accuracy will permit abundance ratios to be determined within 25 per cent; preliminary results confirm the assertion that the relative abundances of the metals remain constant from star to star, except for a systematic difference between population type I and type II stars. This difference is particularly striking in the "subdwarfs," which are underluminous stars of very high velocity.

10.9   The Spectra of Abnormal Stars

Table 10.4 contains a list of the principal types of unusual objects, recognized first on low-dispersion spectra. The number of abnormal objects is small, less than 1 per cent of the total known spectra; their frequency in space is even smaller. But, as in the study of biological evolution, the unusual objects give valuable insights into the processes of stellar evolution. An attempt has been made to correlate some of these peculiarities with the nuclear processes which we will discuss below.

The determination of elemental abundances in stars with peculiar spectra has never been carried through with the accuracy attainable for the normal stars. Many of the peculiarities are obvious on direct examination of the spectra and are undoubtedly real. Quantitative data on the luminosities, masses, radii, and temperatures of the peculiar stars are almost nonexistent. Models for the atmospheric structure cannot be constructed; the source of continuous opacity is not known in the carbon stars and other late-type stars. Variations in the abundance ratio of He/H, of C/H, or of Zr/Ti in the so-called helium, carbon, or zirconium stars must be by at least a factor of 10 in order to be detected by inspection. Consequently, we shall consider them as gross effects requiring a radically different origin or evolution.

Table 10.4 Stellar Types with Apparent or Real Abundance Peculiarities

WN–WC sequences....... Very high temperature unstable objects, with widely different ratios of nitrogen to carbon. Possibly a consequence of CN cycle and mixing.

Helium stars............ Exhaustion of hydrogen in high-luminosity stars in either the CN or pp reaction.

Carbon stars............ The stars rich in carbon may be so by origin or by nuclear processes. Two types exist:

  $C^{12}/C^{13} = 4$, carbon more abundant than normal, mixing effective.

  $C^{12}/C^{13} > 30$, possibly extreme hydrogen-poor objects.

Magnetic stars.......... Hot stars with constant or rapidly varying magnetic fields show apparent anomalous abundances of Si, Mn, Sr, Cr, and especially the rare earths. Spectroscopic peculiarity or magnetic sorting of elements?

Metallic-line stars........ Apparent high abundance of some metals, weakness of Sc, Zr, Mg, Ca, Ti. Possibly spurious, owing to physical conditions in atmosphere affecting ionization.

S stars................. Cool stars with high-ratio ZrO/TiO bands, Tc I lines (unstable element, half-life 3×10^5 yr), and strengthened Y, Nb, Mo, Ba. Fifth and sixth periods strengthened with respect to the fourth-period elements. Speculatively, neutron-capture processes recently active.

Li stars................ Two cool stars with strong Li. No mixing since origin?

High-velocity stars....... In most spectral types. Low abundance of the metals with respect to hydrogen and also of the C, N, O group in the majority of cases. Subdwarfs show extreme variation of H/metals by factor of more than 10. "Old" stars.

White dwarfs............ Very low interior hydrogen content. Possible squeezing of hydrogen to surface. Very weak metallic lines. Degenerate interiors, presumably helium-rich.

10.10 The Internal Structure of a Star

At the high temperatures of normal stars the dominant elements (H through O) are highly ionized. As a consequence we consider a perfect gas of protons, α particles, electrons, and a fraction of 1 per cent of partly ionized heavy elements.

The energy content at a typical point inside a star is made up of kinetic energy of the particles, ionization energy, and radiation. (At very high temperatures the energy density of radiation is about the same as that of the matter.) Energy normally flows outward through the star by radiative transfer, rather than by conduction or convection. In certain regions where the ratio of specific heats is favorable, or where nuclear energy is being produced, convection occurs and helps to transport energy outward. Energy transport by convection produces a temperature gradient close to the adiabatic one. Radiative transport requires a temperature gradient which is computed from the opacity of the gas. The opacity of an ionized gas to radiation depends on the composition of the material and especially on the abundance of oxygen and metals, which alone retain bound electrons. At 10 million degrees the average quantum has an energy of 1000 ev, *i.e.*, of an X ray; the X-ray opacity is known both experimentally and theoretically (Kramers's law). Thus we can, in principle at least, compute the temperature gradient dT/dr through the star.

If convection or turbulence is slow, the weight of the gas above a given point in the star at a distance r from the center must be balanced by the gas pressure P at that point. This leads to the equation of hydrostatic equilibrium:

$$\frac{dP}{dr} = -\frac{GM(r)\rho}{r^2} \tag{10.4}$$

The quantity $M(r)$ is the mass interior to the point r,

$$\frac{dM(r)}{dr} = 4\pi\rho r^2 \tag{10.5}$$

and ρ is the density. We shall also use the perfect-gas law, which states that

$$P = \frac{k}{\mu H}\rho T \tag{10.6}$$

Here k is Boltzmann's constant, H the mass of a proton, and μ the mean molecular weight per free particle. Since the material is highly ionized, μ would be $\frac{1}{2}$ for pure hydrogen, $\frac{4}{3}$ for pure helium, and $A/Z + 1$ for an ionized heavy element of weight A and charge Z. In general, $A/Z + 1$ is about 2. If X is the abundance of hydrogen by weight, Y that of helium, and $1 - X - Y$ that of heavy elements,

$$\mu = \frac{2}{1 + 3X + 0.5Y} \tag{10.7}$$

We see that the detailed composition of the star does not affect μ, which depends mainly on the hydrogen abundance; the equation of state is therefore quite simple.

Two stages existed in the development of the theory of stellar interiors. In the first, the gas law was assumed that of a polytrope, *i.e.*, one which through the entire star could be written as

$$P = K\rho^\gamma = K\rho^{(1+n)/n} \tag{10.8}$$

where n is the polytropic index and γ the ratio of specific heats. The equations of equilibrium lead to the second-order nonlinear differential equation

$$\frac{1}{r^2}\frac{d}{dr}\left(\frac{r^2}{\rho}\frac{dP}{dr}\right) = -4\pi G\rho \tag{10.9}$$

Inserting the polytropic relation and normalizing the variables, we obtain the Lane-Emden equation:

$$\frac{1}{x^2}\frac{d}{dx}\left(x^2\frac{dy}{dx}\right) = -y^n \tag{10.10}$$

This equation has been solved numerically for all useful values of n, so that P, ρ, T, and $M(r)$ are known for every point in the star; i.e., a complete model of a star is obtained in tabular form. Boundary conditions are required at the center and at the outer boundary, where $P = \rho = T = 0$. The latter, however, is a mere formalism, since we can stop the integration and require the density to vanish at a finite T, so long as T is very small compared to its value in the interior. For various values of n we find the ratio of the temperature and density at the center T_c and ρ_c to the mean values for the star $\bar{T}$ and $\bar{\rho}$. With certain rather special, but reasonable, assumptions, this approach, using a constant "polytropic index," leads to a mass-luminosity law. Thirty years ago it was found that the predicted and observed luminosities of the stars agreed. (Roughly, the observed relation is that the luminosity L is proportional to a power of the mass $M^{3.4}$.)

The extraordinary feature of the above approach is that it required no knowledge of the source of the energy in the star; only the mean molecular weight was adjustable. It provided a self-consistent model, in which the temperature gradient maintained an energy flow equal to the observed luminosity, and the weight of the star was supported by the pressure at every point. If energy could be supplied to balance the outward flow, a physically sensible model could be said to exist. Essentially, one equation is still lacking, to give the luminosity of the star produced interior to the point r; this is

$$L(r) = 4\pi \int_0^r \epsilon \rho r^2 \, dr \tag{10.11}$$

where $L(R) = L$, the observed luminosity of the star. Here ϵ is the energy produced per gram of material. The physical requirement is that if ϵ is a function of ρ and T, known from the laws of physics, our model which gave ρ and T should also predict the correct luminosity. It would be surprising if the self-consistent model derived without the use of the above luminosity equation gave the correct luminosity to support the temperature gradient in that model. Fortunately the energy-generation proves to be a very steep function of temperature, so that we get the correct luminosity if we can alter the central temperature slightly. Almost all the energy is generated in the central 10 per cent of the mass of a normal star, so conditions at the center control the luminosity.

Current research is devoted to finding a stellar model which satisfies the requirements of both the internal equilibrium and the energy generation. The first requirement leads to a single condition on both the hydrogen and helium contents; the energy-generation formula provides still another condition; the simultaneous solution of both gives X and Y separately. The abundance of the elements that participate in the energy-generation process of course must be known, but the final model is not very sensitive to their concentration, because of the steep temperature dependence of ϵ. The temperature is determined mainly by X and Y, for a given L, M, and R.

The analytical approach, using the Lane-Emden functions, has been abandoned for step-by-step simultaneous numerical integration of the system of equations given above. A set of postulates describing the model is needed to start. For example, should we assume radiative equilibrium or convective equilibrium? Once we obtain a preliminary solution, we test whether in fact the radiative or convective temperature gradient is the stable one and change our integration from one based on the equation for radiative transfer to that for convective equilibrium, whenever required. The former is

$$\frac{dT}{dr} = -\frac{3K\rho L(r)}{16\pi acr^2 T^3} \tag{10.12}$$

The convective solution is the polytropic equation of index $n = \frac{3}{2}$. Another assumption required for a model concerns the chemical composition, which we need not assume to be independent of r. As a consequence of the fundamental energy-generation process, hydrogen is converted into helium. In a star that is completely stirred to homogeneous composition (say by rotationally induced circulation currents), X is slowly decreasing with time. On the other hand, in a star in which there is no mixing between the interior and the envelope, the value of X decreases rapidly at the center; the mean molecular weight increases inward, and very radical changes occur in the equilibrium of the star.

The system of differential equations used in the numerical integration process leads to an eigenvalue problem, and the particular set of assumptions leads to the determination of an eigenvalue parameter C in a luminosity formula:

$$L = \frac{A}{K_0 C}\frac{M^{5.5}\mu^{7.5}}{R^{0.5}} \tag{10.13}$$

In this formula, K_0 is a constant from the theory of opacity and involves $(1 + X)(1 - X - Y)$; A is a known physical constant. The assumptions made in the theory of stellar interiors have their effect on C, the model parameter in the mass-luminosity formula. Variation of the molecular weight with depth results in a large change in the model constant C, and the central temperature can be a larger multiple of the mean temperature of the star than in models with constant μ. This permits us to compensate for the fact that large R normally produces low T_c. Recent work on the theory of red-giant stars suggests that they have cores of small X (due to the exhaustion of H by conversion into He) surrounded by envelopes of normal composition (Bondi, Schwarzschild). A critical stage in certain problems of stellar interiors has currently been reached. The structure depends strongly on certain controversial assumptions as to the degree of mixing and as to the composition of the central exhausted core, if it exists. On the other hand, the structure of main-sequence well-mixed stars is fairly well understood. Even fairly large changes in the energy-generation rates given by nuclear physics will not appreciably alter the determination of X and Y for the sun, for example, nor its T_c and ρ_c.

10.11 The Energy-generation Processes in Normal Stars

Two alternate ways of combining four protons into an α particle are shown in Table 10.5. The first, Bethe's well-known CN cycle, uses carbon as a catalyst; it is the main source of energy when T_c exceeds 15 million degrees. All reactions have been observed in the laboratory.

Table 10.5
CN Cycle

Reaction	Time
$C^{12}(p, \gamma)N^{13}(\beta^+\nu)C^{13}$............	1.3×10^7 yr
$C^{13}(p, \gamma)N^{14}$...................	2.7×10^6 yr
$N^{14}(p, \gamma)O^{15}(\beta^+\nu)N^{15}$...........	3.2×10^8 yr
$N^{15}(p, \alpha)C^{12}$...................	1.1×10^5 yr

Time is given for a temperature of 13×10^6 degrees and a density of 150 g/cm³. Predicted $C^{12}/C^{13} = 4$; $N^{14}/C^{12} = 26$; $N^{14}/N^{15} = 2800$.

Direct pp Process

Reaction	Time
$H^1(p, \beta^+\nu)D^2$.................	14×10^9 yr
$D^2(p, \gamma)He^3$...................	6 sec
$He^3(He^3, 2p)He^4$..............	10^6 yr

Time is given for a temperature of 13×10^6 degrees and a density of 100 g/cm³. Predicted H/He is a function of age; $He^3/H = 10^{-4}$; $D^2/H = 3 \times 10^{-17}$; Li/H = 10^{-16}.

The second, the proton-proton process, has as its first step a very slow nuclear reaction for which the rate can be computed only from the theory of β decay; the other steps are observable at laboratory energies. Current work at the Kellogg Radiation Laboratory of the California Institute of Technology by W. A. Fowler (see Chap. 6) and his colleagues has provided the most recent experimental data for the CN cycle. Theoretical work by Motz, Frieman, and Salpeter is the best available for the $H^1(p, \beta^+\nu)D^2$ process; the theory has been subject to considerable change in the last few years; only in 1950 was it realized that the pp process is more important than the CN process in the sun.

Only a brief explanation of thermonuclear processes is possible here. They have a complex dependence on temperature. The positively charged nucleus repels the incident proton; the probability of a low-energy proton leaking through the high repulsive potential barrier of the positive nucleus is measured by the Gamow penetration factor. In addition, at a given T, thermal protons have a wide range of energies. While the mean proton energy at 15 million degrees is only 1.3 Kev, the maximum yield is obtained from the few protons with energy near 10 Kev, because the Gamow factor depends exponentially on proton energy. In addition, nuclear resonance makes the probability of a proton being captured, once it has entered the nucleus, depend on the difference between its energy and that of the resonance level and also on the width of the resonance. Certain nuclei have low-lying resonance levels, making capture much more probable. Direct observation of proton capture cannot be carried out in the laboratory because of the small yield below 100 Kev, which is still far above stellar energies. All important resonances in the processes in Table 10.5 are well known with the exception of those of the $N^{14}(p, \gamma)O^{15}$ reaction. As far as is *now* known, there is no low-lying resonance, and the reaction seems to be the slowest one in the CN cycle. But if it is the bottleneck, N^{14} will be very abundant compared with C^{12}, since C^{12} will be relatively rapidly destroyed. (In general, in an equilibrium state between reacting components, the abundance of a given component will be inversely proportional to its lifetime.) On this basis the ratio N^{14}/C^{12} should be about 26; in few stars, except possibly the peculiar WN Wolf-Rayet stars, is nitrogen so abundant. It could be argued that nonmixing prevents us from seeing a sample of the reacting interior, but this seems an assumption *ad hoc*. Consequently, it may also be assumed in the present state of knowledge that an unknown resonance speeds up the $N^{14}(p, \gamma)O^{15}$ process and that the Bethe cycle rate is determined by the $C^{12}(p,\gamma)N^{13}$ step. This provides two extreme limits to the energy-generation formula for the CN cycle. Fowler has evaluated the energy output per gram of material at the center of the sun as ϵ_c, given for the CN cycle (with the present laboratory data) by

$$\epsilon_c = 1.7 \left(\frac{\rho X}{100}\right) \left(\frac{X(C + N)}{0.01}\right) \left(\frac{T}{13 \times 10^6}\right)^{20} \text{ erg/g sec} \quad (10.14)$$

The quantity $X(C + N)$ is the abundance by weight of carbon plus nitrogen. The rate for the pp process is

$$\epsilon_c = 28 \left(\frac{\rho}{100}\right) X^2 \left(\frac{T}{13 \times 10^6}\right)^{4.1} \text{ erg/g sec} \quad (10.15)$$

Note the less steep temperature dependence of the pp process. These formulas have been derived for conditions such as those holding at the center of the sun, where $T_c = 13$ million degrees K and the density is about 150 g/cm^3. They can be extrapolated over a moderate range of T_c; note that to obtain a CN rate 10,000 times that in the sun we need raise the temperature only by $(10^4)^{1/20}$, *i.e.*, to 24 million degrees. The entire range in luminosity up the main sequence can be explained by an increase in T_c of 60 per cent. Since the mean temperature varies as M/R, it is obvious that T_c could increase by this amount in stars built on the same model as the sun, but with larger M/R. (The steep temperature dependence of ϵ also provides a safety valve for a star. If the star contracts slightly, T_c increases, as do ϵ_c and L; the star then expands, finally lowering T_c to a safe value. Pulsation of a star can be initiated by such a process, but not an explosion. Explosion, or more properly implosion, would occur if endothermic nuclear reactions strongly absorbed energy as the star contracted.)

10.12   Correlations of Energy-generation Processes and the Spectroscopic Features of the Star

Nuclear penetration of the heavy elements by protons is difficult; the barrier factor (which occurs in the exponential) is proportional to $Z_1 Z_2 / T^{1/2}$, where Z_1 and Z_2 are the atomic numbers of the reacting nuclei. Since the Bethe process, which involves protons ($Z_1 = 1$) and carbon ($Z_2 = 6$), is slow at 13 million degrees, reactions between protons and iron ($Z_2 = 26$) would occur only at 300 million degrees and between α particles ($Z_1 = 2$) and carbon ($Z_2 = 6$) only at 60 million degrees. Thermonuclear processes involving hydrogen usually stop at about $Z_2 = 8$; they do not occur between heavier elements. At the low stellar energies, processes affecting heavy elements must involve neutrons, since they have zero charge and therefore are not repelled by the potential barrier. But stellar pressures are normally not high enough to form neutrons, and none of the above reactions produces neutrons.

In normal stars, the major predictions based on the energy-producing reactions of main-sequence stars can now be briefly summarized.

a. Stars of high luminosity are either young, or if near the end of their life, they have a relatively high He/H ratio.

b. In the time required for the Bethe cycle to go around a few times for any given C^{12} nucleus, the equilibrium ratios should be attained, *i.e.*, $C^{12}/C^{13} = 4$, $N^{14}/C^{12} = 26$ (or about unity if a low-lying resonance level actually exists in N^{14}), and N^{15} very rare. As a second-order effect, the ratio of N^{14}/C^{12} might be lower in stars with high T_c, dropping to 2.

c. In any star in which thermonuclear reactions occur, D^2, Li, Be, and B should be rapidly destroyed.

d. Faint dwarf stars in which the CN cycle has not gone around even once since the star's formation may still have the primeval abundance of C^{12}, C^{13}, N^{14}, N^{15}, etc. However, only the very faintest stars are cool enough in their interior to permit Li and Be to retain any original high abundance.

e. The $He^3(He^3, 2p)He^4$ process, which was only recently suggested, results in a low abundance of He^3 in any star.

f. Stars in which mixing is complete should display the above effects. Incomplete mixing, however, might result in the disappearance from the atmosphere of some of the primeval D^2, Li, and Be but might occur without establishing the C^{12}/C^{13} ratio of 4, or the N^{14}/C^{12} ratio of 26.

g. The carbon-rich stars cannot arise from the simple reactions listed for the CN or *pp* process.

If we now consult Table 10.4, which lists some of the principal types of peculiar stars, we see that at least some predictions as to effects of thermonuclear reactions in the interiors can be matched with observations of stellar atmospheres. Let us consider items *a* to *e* above. (*a*) Stars having an abnormally high abundance of helium are known. Two are supergiants, *i.e.*, stars rapidly exhausting their hydrogen. The luminosities of the others are still unknown; one shows no hydrogen lines at all, in a spectrum dominated by helium. Some white dwarfs appear to be helium-rich. (*b*) The prediction of the N^{14}/C^{12} ratio is not definite at present. If we take the best known value of the N^{14} cross section, then N^{14}/C^{12} is about 26. Let us assume that 26 is correct; then the Wolf-Rayet WN and WC sequences can be interpreted as representing two different degrees of mixing of interior and surface; the WN stars give us a true sample of the interior, while the WC stars either show the possibly high primeval abundance of carbon or else have produced carbon by Salpeter's process, which we will discuss below. Slow mixing of the solar atmosphere and interior is confirmed by the fact that $C^{12}/C^{13} > 40$ in the sun, although there is little doubt that the Bethe cycle has set up the predicted equilibrium ratio of $C^{12}/C^{13} = 4$ in the interior. We shall postpone the discussion of the carbon-rich stars, which provide a separate thermonuclear problem. (*c*) The elements of small nuclear charge are weak or absent in all stars, except only for two red-giant stars in which Li is about ten times as abundant as in normal stars. The solar abundance of Li is less than a hundredth of the terrestrial value (see Table 10.2), and Be has the terrestrial value; the presence of any Li shows that in the sun and normal stars mixing is very slow and cannot penetrate to a depth where the temperature exceeds 3×10^6 degrees. It is also possible that Li and Be may exist in stellar atmospheres only through accretion from interstellar space or formation by cosmic rays. (*d*) As yet, we have unfortunately been unable to devise methods for determining the C/N ratio in the late faint main-sequence stars. (e) No He³ has yet been found in any star nor, after a careful search, in the sun.

We must briefly consider the problem of the white dwarfs. These stars have a different equation of state, that of a degenerate electron gas. The model is such that they should have normal or even high central temperatures. Thus their luminosity should be that of normal stars, while in fact it is 10^{-4} as great. The usual explanation is that they have completely lost their hydrogen through its conversion into helium, so that nuclear-energy generation is low or zero. Their life expectancy, without nuclear-energy sources, is still very great on the basis of their contraction and the consequent conversion of gravitational potential energy into heat.

Table 10.6 Other Energy Sources or Processes

1. Gravitational contraction; exothermic.

   Life $\approx 2.4 \times 10^7 \dfrac{M^2}{LR}$ yr

2. Partially endothermic nuclear processes:
   - (a) $He^4(\alpha, \gamma)Be^8$ (-95 Kev)
     $Be^8(\alpha, \gamma)C^{12}$ ($+7.4$ Mev)
   - (b) and possibly $C^{12}(\alpha, \gamma)O^{16}$; $O^{16}(\alpha, \gamma)Ne^{20}$ . . .
   - (c) $He^4(\alpha, n)Be^7$ (-19 Mev)
     $Be^7(\beta^+\nu)Li^7$

3. Production of heavy elements by neutrons, in final stages of very hot star. Normally not an energy source. $C^{13}(\alpha, n)O^{16}$. Neutron sources in stellar atmospheres?

4. Destruction of elements of small Z. Very rapid.
   $Li^6(p, \alpha)He^3$
   $Li^7(p, \alpha)He^4$
   $Be^9(p, \alpha)Li^6$ and $Be^9(p, 2\alpha)D^2$

We cannot use spectral observations of the atmosphere to make deductions about the interior composition, because the light elements have been squeezed to the surface by the intense gravitational field.

The possible existence of an inert, hydrogen-free core in a contracting star brings us to the more extreme nuclear processes that may occur in this end stage of stellar evolution. Table 10.6 lists some of the currently suggested ones. Note that gravitational contraction (1) gives a long life for a star of small L and R, like the white dwarfs. But, as contraction occurs, pressures and temperatures will rise until thermonuclear processes occur for elements of larger nuclear charge than a proton. The most interesting process is 2a, which is essentially a triple collision of α particles. Be^8 has a life of only 10^{-18} sec, decaying into two α particles. If another α-particle collision occurred within 10^{-18} sec, C^{12} would be produced. Salpeter recently showed that, at reasonably high densities and temperatures for the core, process 2a would produce C^{12} and some energy. At 200 million degrees and 25,000 g/cm³ the rate would be

1000 Y^2 ergs/g sec, where Y is the abundance of helium by weight. While not sufficient to provide long life for stars of high luminosity, this reaction suffices for a transition stage in old red-giant stars, and it may be the explanation of the carbon-rich stars. Only C^{12} is produced. A nonmixed main-sequence star might evolve an inert core while energy production continues in the outer regions where hydrogen still exists. At a later epoch, when the hydrogen of the entire star is also depleted, a collapse of the star might bring the carbon-rich material to the surface. The further history of the carbon stars is still unpredictable. But, since they are a rare group, it is possible that they have only a short life as luminous objects. The most common type of carbon star is observed to show the ratio $C^{12}/C^{13} = 4$, nearly that predicted by the CN reaction. Consequently it appears that the carbon after formation has traversed a zone in which Bethe's cycle operates. A small number of carbon stars show almost zero atmospheric hydrogen, and these have $C^{12}/C^{13} > 30$. These rare objects may have consumed all their hydrogen before the mixing occurred.

Process 4 in Table 10.6 had been suggested many years ago as a possible short-term source of the energy to initiate other thermonuclear reactions in new stars contracting out of the interstellar matter. Process 3, on the other hand, is still to be viewed as an extremely speculative one, since neutrons do not occur in sufficient numbers in normal stars. But at either extremely high pressures (degenerate gases) or high temperatures (above 10^9 degrees), the number of neutrons in equilibrium with protons and electrons may become appreciable. In that case, the building of heavy elements may occur by successive neutron captures, since repulsive forces are not present. Neutron-capture cross sections are quite large and increase with atomic weight, eventually becoming constant. The abundance of heavy nuclei in an equilibrium mixture with neutrons would be the reciprocal of the neutron-capture probability curve. Nuclei formed by a succession of neutron captures will have A/Z greatly in excess of 2, the ratio for stable elements, but spontaneous β-decay processes will ultimately make stable elements of them. Neutrons will thus produce radical changes in the abundance of the heavy elements. If a star runs out of all energy sources and radiates only by contraction, it may reach this neutron stage, and its ultimate fate is probably explosion. On the other hand, if the hydrogen-poor core of a nonmixed star reaches the neutron stage and forms heavy elements, it may find a less radical way out, by mixing the newly formed heavy elements with the rest of the star. This process is one very speculative possibility for explaining the S stars, which apparently have technetium in their atmospheres. Technetium (Tc) is an artificially produced element which does not occur naturally on earth, being commonly made as a product of uranium fission. The longest life of any known Tc isotope is 300,000 years.   In 3×10^6 years, less than one-ten-thousandth of the original amount of Tc would be left; this is a very short life span astronomically, so that an S star would represent a rare and transitory phase in the life of a red-giant star which had exhausted its hydrogen.

I should like to indulge in one final speculation as to neutron capture. A few stars have been found to have very strong magnetic fields (up to 5000 gauss) which vary with time.   Changing magnetic fields require an intense flow of electric currents, and these may accelerate atoms to very high energies in the outer atmospheres of the stars.   Such "betatron" processes might produce high-energy nuclear transmutations in stellar atmospheres.   Disintegration of the heavy elements would produce some unstable light elements and possibly neutrons.   Neutrons could also be involved in processes which would build up unstable heavy elements and isotopes not producible by proton capture.   Thus, the appearance of unstable elements in a few stars may reflect recent effects of such magnetic fields.

10.13   Abundance Differences Depending on the Origin of the Stars

Among the most recent advances in the study of stellar abundances has been the discovery of differences in composition which characterize the population types.   Stars of low velocity, belonging to type I, have been the subject of most spectroscopic research, and our abundance tables refer to them.   Type II lacks bright hot stars, and little can be learned about the ratios H/He, or H/C, N, O.   Scattered investigations have so far led to the general impression that the principal difference is a higher ratio in type II of hydrogen to the metals.   In some main-sequence type II stars, this difference was found to amount only to a factor of 2. Inspection of the spectra of extreme high-velocity stars, stars in globular clusters, and subdwarfs suggests that larger differences exist.   In the subdwarfs, the metals seem to be as much as twenty times rarer than they are in the sun.   We do not know whether the high-velocity stars form a homogeneous group; the ratio of hydrogen to the metals may be quite variable.   The relative abundances of the metals are still to be determined, but they seem normal in the less extreme type II stars that are now being investigated.   Answers to some of these problems will come from the Palomar spectrograph, which for the first time permits observation of the faint stars at moderately high dispersion.   The subdwarfs are intrinsically faint as well as apparently faint; the interesting stars in globular clusters, which are intrinsically very luminous, are so distant that their spectra will require exposures lasting several nights, even with the 200-in. telescope.   The globular-cluster stars seem to be extreme type II objects, with peculiar spectra. No method has yet been suggested for current creation of type II stars or for their accretion of interstellar gas. It is quite possible that type II stars will show most clearly the signs of aging through exhaustion of energy sources, in spite of their apparently high hydrogen abundance.*

Fig. 10.11 A region of our galaxy in which many stars of population type I are present. Note the close association with clouds of gas and dust, in which star formation may be occurring. The rings and crosses around the brighter stars are caused by photographic halation and by diffraction. (*Mount Wilson and Palomar Observatories.*)

We have already mentioned one possible origin for the differences between the two populations. Type I objects may have condensed out of dust clouds in interstellar space, rather recently; they will initially have high abundances, relative to hydrogen, of the metals and of readily frozen gases. This aspect of type I has been explored by Spitzer and Schwarzschild, but still another difference in original composition may

*Since this chapter was written, underluminous hot stars of type II have been found. They show peculiar composition, being rich in He and in N, in agreement with the predictions of Sec. 10.12.

exist.   The type I stars we have studied are at the outer edge of our Galaxy; type II stars, especially those in globular clusters, are more closely related to the center of the Galaxy.   We have no reason to believe that the original processes occurring in the great melting pot from which

Fig. 10.12   A closeup of part of the relatively nearby giant spiral system, the Andromeda nebula.   The brighter stars belong to our own system.   The central unresolved region contains type II stars and is relatively free from dust and very bright stars. The spiral arms are partly resolved into bright blue stars, especially near the center of the left-hand edge of the picture.   Note the dark dust clouds in the spiral arms. (*Mount Wilson and Palomar Observatories.*)

the elements were formed had the same results everywhere or everywhere led to the same abundance curve of atomic nuclei.   Stars may have condensed in different ways in the center of our system and at its edges. Perhaps future spectroscopic analysis will give us a new insight into such fascinating cosmogonical problems.

11

High-pressure Phenomena
with Applications to
Geophysics

DAVID T. GRIGGS

PROFESSOR OF GEOPHYSICS
UNIVERSITY OF CALIFORNIA, LOS ANGELES

11.1 Introduction

The investigation of phenomena at high pressures is unique among the fields of physics in that it has been dominated for the last forty-five years by the work of one man. As a graduate student at Harvard University in 1906, Percy Williams Bridgman made the first of a long series of discoveries in technique which extended the useful range of pressures in which significant physical measurements could be made. The maximum working pressure consistently achieved prior to Bridgman was 4000 bars.[*] The chronology of increasing "working pressures"—all first achieved by Bridgman—is as follows:

1906	12,000 bars	with liquid pressure medium
1912	20,000 bars	with liquid pressure medium
1935	50,000 bars	with solid pressure medium
1938	30,000 bars	with liquid pressure medium
1940	100,000 bars	with solid pressure medium

100,000 bars is equal to the pressure which occurs in the earth at a depth of 300 km. It should be emphasized that a "working pressure" is always lower than the maximum that can be achieved. Bridgman, for instance,

---

[*] The *bar* is the fundamental unit of pressure.

$$1 \text{ bar} = 10^6 \text{ dynes/cm}^2 = 1.02 \text{ kg/cm}^2 = 0.987 \text{ atmosphere} = 14.5 \text{ psi}$$

In this chapter, hydrostatic pressures will be given in bars, differential pressures in kg/cm².

272

has achieved a pressure of 425,000 bars (equal to that at a depth in the earth of more than 1000 km). This was accomplished by employment of local stress concentrations on an exceedingly small volume of test material and only qualitative effects—such as the change from graphite to diamond—could be sought.

Clearly higher pressures than this can be, and have been, reached. The detonation of an explosive, momentarily confined by the inertia of massive walls, will yield a pressure of the order of 100,000 bars. Converging shock waves in a shaped charge can develop higher pressures than this in the shock front itself. The limit to such pressures is set only by the uniformity of the converging shock. Pressures of the order of megabars should be attainable by this method.

The initial pressure in an atomic-bomb explosion greatly exceeds this. The order of magnitude of such pressures may readily be estimated in the following way: Consider the explosion of a 20-KT atomic bomb in which the efficiency is 1 per cent. Because of the critical dependence of neutron multiplication rate on the density of the supercritical mass, the energy of fission will practically all have been released before the mass has expanded appreciably. Roughly half of the total will be in the form of PV energy at this very early stage of the explosion. The average pressure may then be calculated using the Einstein relation:

$$E = mc^2 = 20,000 \text{ tons high-explosive equivalent} \simeq 10^{21} \text{ ergs}$$

It is shown in Chap. 6 that about one one-thousandth of the mass of U^{235} is released as energy in the fission process. The mass of U^{235} which undergoes fission is thus

$$M \simeq 1000m = 1000 \times \frac{10^{21}}{9 \times 10^{20}} \simeq 1 \text{ kg}$$

Since we have assumed an efficiency of 1 per cent, the total volume of uranium in which the PV energy appears at this early stage is

$$V = \frac{100M}{\rho} = \frac{10^5 \text{ g}}{18.7} \simeq 5 \times 10^3 \text{ cc}$$

$$P \sim \frac{1}{2} \frac{E}{V} \simeq \frac{10^{21}}{10^4} = 10^{17} \text{ dynes/cm}^2 = 10^{11} \text{ bars} = 10^5 \text{ megabars}$$

For comparison, the pressure at the center of the earth is 3.5 megabars, that at the center of the sun is of the order of 2×10^5 megabars.

Transient pressures of the latter three types may be used for the determination of certain physical properties, e.g., the equation of state of matter at high pressure and high temperature. The degrees of freedom of such experiments are, however, severely limited by the interdependence of pressure and temperature.   It is hence impossible by these means to measure many of the parameters of interest to physics in these transient fields.   This chapter will be restricted to consideration of measurements under static pressure.

11.2   Elements of High-pressure Technique

High static pressures are achieved by the time-honored method of pushing a piston into a cylinder.   The chief difficulties encountered are leaking of the pressure fluid, failure of the piston or cylinder, and problems peculiar to the measurement of specific physical properties.

The problem of leaks was solved in principle by Bridgman's early development of the "principle of the unsupported area."   Figure 11.1 shows the simplest embodiment of this principle in a piston packing.

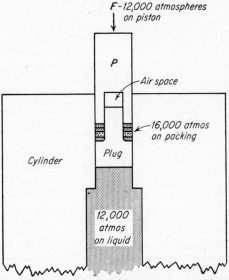

Fig. 11.1   Bridgman's high-pressure packing.

The packing is subject to the same force as the piston but, by virtue of its smaller cross-sectional area, is under a higher pressure than is the fluid. Thus the packing tends to extrude into the annulus between the piston and the cylinder—both out of the cylinder and, to a lesser extent, into the high-pressure chamber.   This extrusion is prevented or minimized by choice of packing materials having sufficient shear strength or work-hardening.   The shear strength must, however, be low enough so that the material will flow, thus forming the initial seal against the pressure fluid.   Typical materials for the intermediate-pressure range are neoprene between copper or mild steel washers.

It is obvious that this principle of the unsupported area can be applied in many different geometrical forms. It is the same principle that is used in flap valves or in the old-fashioned soft rubber disk used as a stopper for bathtub drains. All types of packing based on other principles will ultimately leak as pressure is increased. This packing just seals tighter and tighter as pressure is increased, until some element fails or the packing extrudes out of the system. Conscientious application of this principle to household plumbing fixtures would improve the pleasure of married life. One of the aggravations of high-pressure workers is constant leakage in the low-pressure end of the hydraulic systems, where commercial fittings are used for convenience.

Failure of materials is a far more fundamental limitation to the attainment of the highest pressures. All the research on metals has increased the maximum tensile strength of the strongest steel by less than a factor of 2 in the last fifty years. Prior to the discovery of Carboloy, this was not critical, since the compressive strength was but little higher, so that pistons failed about as regularly as cylinders. Sintered carbides, such as Carboloy, however, have compressive strengths as high as 70,000 kg/cm^2 and a Young's modulus three times that of steel. This permits the use of unsupported pistons to 60,000 bars pressure.

The bursting pressure of a steel cylinder can in principle be increased by winding it with wire under tension or by shrinking rings around it. The limit to which these

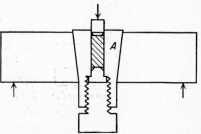

Fig. 11.2 Schematic representation of method of automatically subjecting the pressure vessel to external pressure. (*After Bridgman.*)

methods can be extended is set by inward flow at the bore of the cylinder. In practice, these methods have not resulted in more improvement than is obtained by cold-work (*autofrettage*), and the limiting bursting pressure is about 30,000 bars.

Bridgman overcame this weakness by making the cylinder conical and driving it into supporting rings to increase the outside pressure on the cylinder proportionally with the internal pressure. The simplest embodiment of this principle is shown in Fig. 11.2. Here the force on the piston pushes the cylinder into its conical supporting ring, automatically increasing the peripheral pressure on the cylinder as the internal pressure is increased. In practice, more freedom of design and better performance can be achieved by using an independently controlled press to push the cylinder into its supporting cone and to make this a multiple cone, so that the inner cones are also strengthened by external pressure. In this fashion, Bridgman has made routine measurements to 50,000 bars pressure. The fundamental limits to pressures which may be achieved in this way are (1) failure of the unsupported piston and (2) failure of the cylinder by annular extrusion.

To achieve higher pressures with present materials it is necessary to go to "cascade" apparatus in which the "supporting" pressure is hydrostatic, so that extrusion failure cannot occur. Here again Bridgman first achieved a proved solution, although there were many claimants to the title.* He first developed a liquid system operating to 30,000 bars.

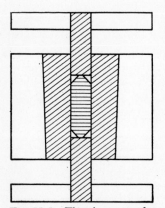

Fig. 11.3 The piezometer for volume measurements to 100,-000 kg/cm². The diagonally shaded regions are Carboloy, the horizontally shaded region is the charge whose compression is to be measured, and the unshaded regions are steel. (*After Bridgman.*)

He carefully calibrated his internal pressure gauge, developed an internal force gauge to measure the force applied to the piston of the second-stage cylinder, after considerable trouble found a liquid which did not freeze and retained a reasonably low viscosity to 30,000 bars, and modified his old internal extensometer to measure piston displacement. Perhaps the most difficult part of the development was getting seven electrical leads into the 30,000-atmosphere chamber.

Bridgman then inserted his second-stage cylinder and piston (optimistically called a *piezometer*) into this instrumented chamber at around 30,000 bars liquid pressure. The construction of the piezometer is shown in Fig. 11.3. The piston and cylinder are made of Carboloy. Each is supported not only by the liquid but also by the steel (shown unshaded in the diagram). The steel is initially pressed onto the Carboloy pistons and cylinder. Under the liquid pressure, because of the greater compressibility of the steel, it is strained beyond its elastic limit, providing the maximum supporting force that its strength will permit, in addition to the support from the pressure fluid. In this way, Bridgman has made routine measurements of compressibility to 100,000 bars. The whole apparatus is shown schematically in Fig. 11.4. The pressures attainable

---

* Goranson and Johnson, for example, working independently and at the same time, claimed to have reached a pressure of 200,000 bars. Their work was interrupted by the war. From their published data, it appears probable that their estimates of pressure were too high, because of friction in the apparatus. There is, incidentally, no direct way of measuring such high pressures. Pressure in the high-pressure element of the cascade must be inferred from external measurements. Friction is always present, and can easily lead to gross errors of interpretation.

in cascade apparatus are higher than the sum of the pressures which can be withstood by the separate chambers. This is due partly to the fact that the strength of materials is increased by pressure and partly to the decrease of brittleness caused by pressure. The former leads to a geometrical increase in pressure with the number of stages of the cascade. Practical difficulties have so far precluded more than a two-stage apparatus, however.

The hazards of high-pressure research have been overemphasized in the mind of the uninitiated. Actually the stored energy in a typical high-pressure research apparatus is the equivalent of the chemical energy in only a few grams of explosive. The ordinary impression of danger is heightened by some experimenters who refer to their high-pressure cylinders as "bombs." With a little care, there is no sensible danger to either personnel or property.

Perhaps the reader will pardon an anecdote about the type of precaution required: A distinguished scientist once arrived at the physics department office at Harvard in search of Bridgman, and was directed to his laboratory. He shortly returned to the office saying no one was down there except a funny little man in a lab coat, who occasionally ran across the room jumping high into the air in the middle of the room. No better description could have been given of Bridgman, who strives for simplicity of apparatus and eschews such expensive things as shields in the case of an apparatus of known weak points and predictable trajectories. On the other hand, Bridgman would not take an unnecessary chance; hence, it is entirely credible that he jumped the trajectory that might have been taken by his pressure-gauge stem—then a weak spot in his apparatus—had it let go. The effect of the story is heightened to the visitor by seeing fine holes drilled through Bridgman's windows by just such high-speed projectiles, but to my certain knowledge the windows were unrepaired for ten years.

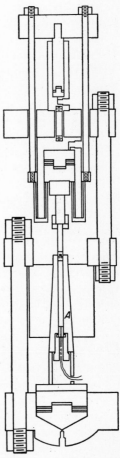

Fig. 11.4 Schematic diagram of apparatus for attaining 30,000 bars fluid pressure in chamber A. The 100,000-bar piezometer of Fig. 11.3 is inserted into this chamber. (*After Bridgman.*)

The third major problem of high-pressure research—measurement of physical properties—is too broad a subject to be summarized briefly.

Some of the physical properties which have been accurately measured at high pressure are the following:

Elastic constants of solids including PVT data
Phase changes in single and multicomponent systems
Viscosity of gases and liquids
Plastic properties of solids
Crystal structure
Thermal conductivity
Electrical conductivity
Dielectric constant
Thermoelectric effects
Magnetic properties
Radioactivity
Index of refraction
Photochemical effects
Rate of chemical reactions
Miscellaneous biological effects

It is readily apparent from this list that a great variety of techniques must be employed. In many cases, the design of the whole high-pressure apparatus is dictated by the requirements of the proposed means of measurement, *e.g.*, X-ray and optical systems.

Most work is done at or near room temperature because of the ease of operation. Temperatures ranging from near absolute zero to above 2000°C have been used in fairly routine fashion. Bridgman has achieved a temperature of the order of 3000°C at a pressure of about 45,000 bars, for a brief interval. Higher transient pressures and temperatures can of course be reached by using shock techniques, but the present discussion is limited to static conditions.

One fundamental difficulty in high-pressure investigations deserves special emphasis, for it is frequently overlooked even by experienced investigators. This is the behavior of the pressure-transmitting medium under the test conditions. Most liquids increase greatly in viscosity under pressure; all liquids will ultimately freeze if the pressure is high enough. Much laborious research has been invalidated either because the pressure medium became too viscous to transmit hydrostatic pressure throughout the apparatus or because the pressure medium froze without the knowledge of the investigator.

Most ordinary liquids freeze under moderate pressures. Water freezes at 190°C at 40,000 bars. Mercury freezes at 7500 bars at 0°C. Only a few substances remain liquids of moderately low viscosity at room temperature through the pressure range 1 to 30,000 bars. One such is pentane.

The only absolute method of measuring hydrostatic pressure is by use of the free-piston gauge, in which the piston friction is made as small as possible and pressure is determined by the force on the piston and its area.   Free-piston gauges are inconvenient in most applications, so that a secondary pressure gauge is used.   The most widely used is a loosely wound coil of manganin wire.   For calibration of these gauges, the most convenient method is usually the freezing point of mercury—measured by Bridgman to be 7490 bars at 0°C.   Bridgman has established a second fixed point as the pressure of transition between bismuth I and II at 30°C; this is 24,920 bars ±0.1 per cent.   The resistance of selected manganin wire is found by Bridgman to be a linear function of pressure within 1 per cent in the range 1 to 30,000 bars.   Higher accuracy requires calibration at two fixed points or by a free-piston gauge.

The best reference for high-pressure technique up to 1946 is the second edition of Bridgman's book "The Physics of High Pressure," or his survey article containing the same information.[1]   In addition to the text, 674 references to high-pressure work in the interval 1930–1945 are given.

EFFECTS OF PRESSURE ON
SOME SELECTED PHYSICAL PROPERTIES

11.3   Effects on Crystal Structure

Volume change with pressure has been measured by Bridgman for many crystalline elements and inorganic compounds up to 100,000 bars.   The least compressible substances have not been measured to 100,000 bars, since their compression is too small to be determined with any precision. Iridium is the least compressible of the elements that have been measured to 30,000 bars in the more precise apparatus.   Its volume is reduced by only 0.8 per cent at 30,000 bars, which would extrapolate to about 2.7 per cent at 100,000 bars.   The most compressible of the crystalline elements that have been measured to 100,000 bars is cesium, in which the volume is reduced by 63 per cent.

The qualitative variation of volume with pressure of some elements is shown in Fig. 11.5.   The absolute values of volume change in the high-pressure range are too high in this figure, which was made from early 100,000-bar results.   The shape of the curves is qualitatively correct. One notices immediately that the volume decrement is not linear with pressure in the smooth curves for Rb, K, Se, and Li.   Bridgman has found that the curves for most substances can be fitted within the experimental error by the following two-parameter relation:

$$\frac{\Delta V}{V_0} = -ap + bp^2 \qquad (11.1)$$

[1] Corresponding numbered bibliographic references appear at the end of the chapter.

This relation is obviously not applicable over a wide pressure range, since it would extrapolate to an increase of volume at sufficiently high pressures.

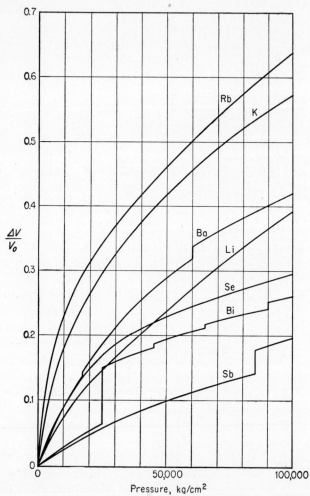

Fig. 11.5 The volume compressions of several elements to 100,000 kg/cm². The breaks in some of the curves indicate polymorphic transitions. (*After Bridgman.*)

At pressures above about 10 megabars, theory predicts that all matter will behave as a Thomas-Fermi electron gas, in which

$$PV = R^*T \tag{11.2}$$

where R^* may be called a universal electron-gas constant. In this condition, the electron shells have collapsed. The relative volumes of substances at a given pressure will depend to a first approximation only on the number of electrons associated with each nucleus, hence on Z, the atomic number. The experimental static-pressure range is not yet sufficient to approach this type of behavior. Figure 11.6 shows, however, that the observed change in volume in all cases except cesium is such as to make a transition into the degenerate electron gas plausible. The limiting slope for such a case is indicated. Bear in mind that on this

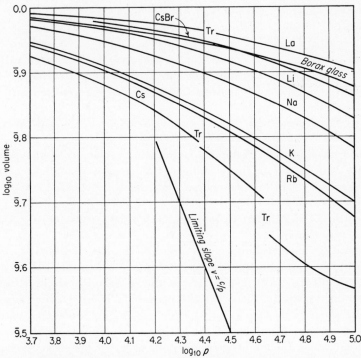

Fig. 11.6 Logarithm of the volume against logarithm of the pressure up to 100,000 kg/cm² for a range of substances. (*After Bridgman.*)

plot this limiting slope would not be reached until the abscissa was about 7.0. We shall return to the case of cesium later.

Returning now to Fig. 11.5, we note the discontinuities in the curves for Sb, Bi, and Ba. These represent polymorphic transitions—changes under pressure from one crystal form to another. Such changes would be expected by any student of elementary physical chemistry. A common example of such polymorphic crystal forms is the case of the element carbon: graphite and diamond both exist under normal conditions, with densities of 2.2 and 3.5, respectively. Diamond is the unstable form at room temperature and pressure, and exists in commerce only because of the slowness of the inversion to graphite.

Oddly enough, this is one of the few known polymorphic transitions that has not yet been produced in the high-pressure laboratory. Many of us were taught as schoolboys that Moissan had produced diamonds in the laboratory by quenching a molten mass of iron containing carbon at the center. The celebrated English inventor Parsons spent a fortune trying to duplicate these experiments and finally dug sufficiently deeply into the personalities surrounding Moissan to convince himself that it was a hoax of which Moissan was himself unaware.

It was my privilege to work in Bridgman's laboratory during the period when working pressures were increased from 20,000 to 100,000 bars. As each new apparatus was readied for trial, I noticed that Bridgman would become secretive and brusque. During the first run, kibitzers were not welcome. I subsequently learned that in each case graphite was the first substance tried.

During the war, with substantial backing by companies obviously interested in commercial prospects, a serious attempt to produce diamonds was made under Bridgman's direction.[2] The philosophy was that the rate of transition might be sufficiently increased by high temperature if the pressure were high enough so that diamond was the stable form. Massive apparatus developed 45,000 bars at something like 2000°C and temperatures varying up to perhaps 6000°C at 30,000 bars. No diamonds were formed.

Despite the intractability of the graphite-diamond transition, similar polymorphic crystal changes are most common at high pressure. Bridgman says (1945), "About one-third of the substances examined to date have transitions, and these transitions are distributed over the entire pressure range." H_2O is a fairly extreme example. Seven polymorphic forms of ice have been found. Ice VII melts at 190°C at 40,000 bars.

In many cases the high-pressure crystal structure has been determined and found to be consistent with the measured volume. In at least one case—cesium—a transition was predicted (by Bardeen) and found at 24,000 bars.

11.4 Effects on Atomic Structure

The transition in cesium just mentioned, according to Bardeen's theoretical treatment, is to the closest-packed crystal structure possible. Subsequently, another large transition was found at 46,000 bars, with a volume change of 11 per cent. If Bardeen is right, it is not possible to account for this as a simple change in crystal form. Sternheimer[3] tackled this problem with the encouragement of Fermi and Teller. He demonstrated convincingly that this volume change is due to a shift of the valence electron from the $6s$ orbit to the empty $5d$ orbit as the two orbits are compressed; they overlap at the point of transition.

Lawson and Tang[4] proposed a similar explanation for the transition in cerium at 12,500 bars, based on their discovery by X-ray analysis under pressure that the crystal structure was face-centered cubic both before and after the volume change.   In the case of cerium they propose a shift of the $4f$ valence electron into the $5d$ shell, changing from a quadrivalent to a trivalent element.

Such pressure-induced changes in electron configuration suggest that elements in general change their chemical character under sufficiently high pressure.   We know from the frequency of polymorphic transitions that the crystal structure of substances will usually be different under high enough pressure, and now it appears that even the chemical compounds formed at high pressure may be unfamiliar to us.   Other important changes will ensue in paramagnetic susceptibility, conductivity, and other properties.

11.5   Effects on Nuclear Structure

One is usually taught in elementary physics that properties of the nucleus, $e.g.$, radioactivity, are not affected by conditions of temperature and pressure accessible in the laboratory.   Bainbridge has shown, however, that pressure does produce a measurable effect on the radioactive lifetime of nuclei which are chosen to be most susceptible.   He subjected the metallic isomer Tc^{99m}, of 6-hr half-life, to a pressure of 100,000 bars and found that the radioactive decay was more rapid by 0.02 per cent, where the error of measurement was less than 0.01 per cent.[5]   It would appear desirable to study rather carefully the theoretically expected effects on nuclei at pressures of the magnitude attained in stars, to see if there would be any effect on the various nuclear fusion reactions proposed by Bethe and others.

11.6   Electrical Resistivity

The electrical resistance of 52 elements has been measured by Bridgman to 100,000 bars.[6]   The unusual pressure apparatus is shown in Fig. 11.7. The sample is in the form of a thin strip, insulated by AgCl which also serves as the pressure-transmitting medium.   The AgCl disk is retained by a narrow ring of pipestone—the remarkable rock which is indispensable in high-pressure work.   The electrical measuring equipment is conventional.

Forty-seven of the elements were metals.   Of these, 31 exhibited "normal" behavior, $i.e.$, a resistance decreasing with pressure along a curve convex to the pressure axis.   Other than this, there is little system to the observed resistance variations, and there is no adequate theory;

so no detail will be presented.   As an example of extreme behavior, Fig.
11.8 shows the behavior of cesium.   The first discontinuity corresponds
to the lattice transition from body-centered to face-centered cubic.   The
cusp corresponds to the above-mentioned "electronic" transition.   The

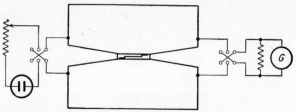

Fig. 11.7   Scheme of the method of measuring resistance.   (*After Bridgman.*)

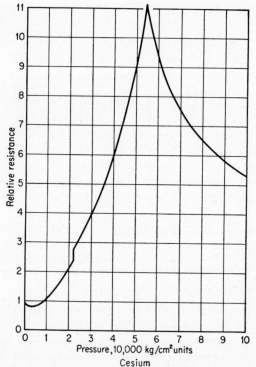

Fig. 11.8   The relative resistance of cesium to 100,000 kg/cm². (*After Bridgman.*)

electronic transition in cerium produces a sharp drop in the resistance
by a factor 2.

The resistance behavior of n- and p-type germanium is shown in Figs.
11.9 and 11.10, as measured by Bridgman to 30,000 bars in a different
apparatus.[7] This difference in behavior between the two types had not

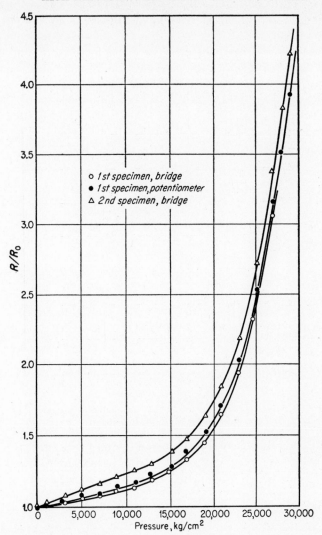

Fig. 11.9 The relative resistance of two specimens of n-type germanium at room temperature as a function of pressure.   (*After Bridgman.*)

been expected by theorists.   In this fast-moving and generally well-understood field of solid-state physics, it is to be anticipated that theory will shortly be forthcoming to explain this.[32]

Dr. S. K. Runcorn, of Cambridge University, recently attempted to measure the intrinsic conductivity of olivine, $(Fe, Mg)_2SiO_4$, in our laboratory.   This measurement is unique in that the absorption coefficient for ultraviolet light is used to measure the intrinsic conductivity.   The effect was just on the limit of experimental error (about 1 per cent) up to 10,000 bars.

Kurnick[8] has measured the pressure dependence of the ionic conductivity of AgBr to discriminate between the two different mechanisms

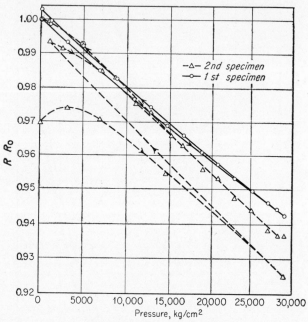

Fig. 11.10   The relative resistance of two specimens of p-type germanium at room temperature as a function of pressure.   (*After Bridgman.*)

proposed by Frenkel and Schottky.   Below 300°C the effect is consistent with Frenkel's theory.   Above 300°C, it is consistent with neither, and an attempt is made to explain the observations by a mixed theory.

11.7   Viscosity

The viscosity of liquids is more affected by pressure than is any other physical property.   A millionfold increase of viscosity at 10,000 bars is not exceptional.   In most of the liquids investigated, the viscosity increases exponentially with pressure, to a first approximation.   Another generalization is that complex molecules and polymers increase in viscosity more than do simple molecules.   An example is shown in Fig. 11.11, from Bridgman's work.[9]   Here it is seen that in the higher-pressure range there is about a tenfold greater increase in viscosity for each higher polymer of the series.   One other general feature also shows in this figure: the semilog curve initially is concave toward the pressure axis but at higher pressure becomes convex.

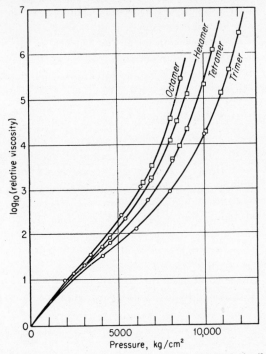

Fig. 11.11 Logarithm of relative viscosity of four dimethyl siloxane polymers. (*After Bridgman.*)

Bridgman has done most of the work on viscosities at the higher pressures—up to 30,000 bars—but other investigators too numerous to list have measured viscosities at lower pressures.

11.8 Elastic Constants

Elastic constants of solids have been measured under pressure by many different investigators and by a great variety of methods. One of the leaders in this field has been Francis Birch at Harvard. Many of his measurements are summarized in the "Handbook of the Physical Constants of Rocks."[10]   In general, the effect of pressure is to increase the elastic constants by a significant amount. The results have been found to be in close agreement with Murnaghan's theory of finite strain. Two elastic constants are necessary and sufficient to determine the elastic behavior of a homogeneous, isotropic, elastic solid. Compressibility has of course been measured over the whole pressure range to 100,000 bars. The measurement of other constants has been confined to pressures below 10,000 bars, so that there are not sufficient data to determine elasticity at higher pressures.

The recent work of Professor Darrell S. Hughes at the University of Texas is worthy of special mention. Hughes and his collaborators have developed pulse methods for dynamic measurement of the elastic constants, which provide an order of magnitude greater accuracy than any previous measurements. A variety of substances has been investigated to 10,000 bars and 400°C.

11.9   Strength and Plasticity

The behavior of crystalline solids in large plastic flow and fracture under high pressures has been investigated in classic experiments by von Kármán[11] and Böker[12] and more extensively by Bridgman under pressures approaching 30,000 bars[13]; certain aspects of this field applying to geophysical problems have been investigated by the author. Robertson[14] has done some recent and valuable work. Many other experimenters have made excursions into this field, but in all cases known to the author (at pressures in excess of, say, 2000 bars) the experimental conditions were such that the forces applied to the specimen were indeterminate and hence do not permit quantitative summarization.

Dr. John W. Handin and coworkers at the Shell research laboratory in Houston, Texas, have recently brought into operation a well-equipped and well-staffed laboratory dedicated to the investigation of flow and fracture in rocks under a variety of test conditions at temperatures up to 500°C and pressures to 10,000 bars. Some of their first results are reported in reference 31.

The most striking effect of high pressure on the behavior of crystalline solids under high stress differences is the increase of ductility. This was first demonstrated convincingly in von Kármán's experiments (1911). His stress-strain curves for marble at different values of the surrounding liquid pressure are shown in Fig. 11.12.

Bridgman has tested a great variety of materials under different stress fields at higher pressures. With few exceptions, he has found that normally brittle materials will suffer large plastic deformations without fracture under high pressure. Some examples are the following: (1) Carboloy: Under a hydrostatic pressure of 30,000 bars, the most brittle commercial grade of Carboloy (999) shortened 10 per cent before fracture under a superimposed compressive stress of 150,000 kg/cm^2—roughly twice its compressive strength at atmospheric pressure.   (2) Sapphire: Synthetic Al_2O_3 single crystals deformed plastically by twinning under a confining pressure of 25,000 bars and a superimposed compressive stress of 53,000 kg/cm^2.   (3) Hard Steel: "Glass-hard Teton Steel" (presumed to have a hardness of about Rockwell C-67) shortened plastically 9 per cent under a confining pressure of 26,000 bars and a superimposed compressive stress of 48,000 kg/cm^2.   Notable exceptions—materials that remain brittle under about 30,000 bars pressure—are quartz, glass, and diamond. The increase of ductility is markedly less when the differential stress is "tensile," *i.e.*, such as to produce elongation of the material. (Such a stress system, in which one of the principal stresses is lower than the common value of the other two, is hereafter called "extensile," since the absolute stress is usually compressive rather than tensile.) For example, Carboloy 999 and sapphire fail by brittle fracture with no plastic elongation under extensile stress at about 25,000 bars confining pressure.

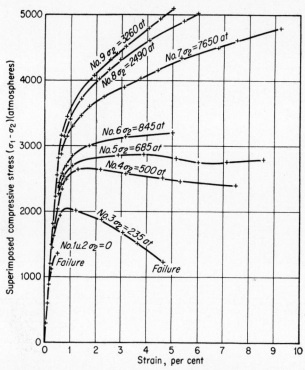

Fig. 11.12   Stress-strain curves of marble under hydrostatic pressure with a superimposed compressive stress $\sigma_1 - \sigma_2$. (*After von Kármán.*)

These observations are in agreement with a Griffith-type surface-flow theory of brittle fracture. Poncelet[15] has expressed such a theory in terms of molecular bonds; his theory shows excellent qualitative agreement with experimental results.

Bridgman has found that the elastic limit for normally ductile steels is increased by the order of 10 per cent under a pressure of 20,000 bars, whether the stress system is extensile or compressive. The outstanding effect of pressure on ductile materials is a further increase of their ductility. Figure 11.13 shows the difference in degree of necking before

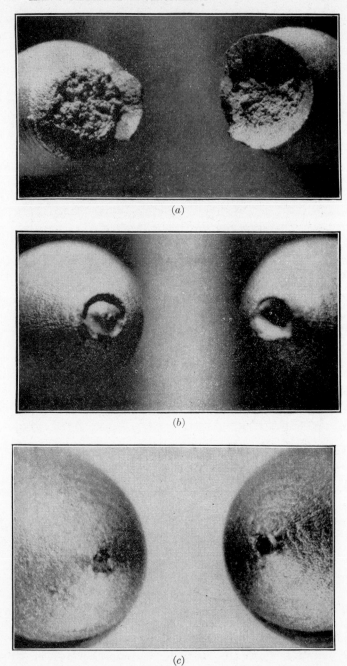

Fig. 11.13   The fracture of SAE 1045 steel, (a) broken at atmospheric pressure, (b) broken under 186,000 psi, (c) broken under 387.000 psi.   (*After Bridgman.*)

fracture in extension tests on SAE 1045 steel tempered to a Rockwell B hardness of 92, under varying hydrostatic pressures.

Experiments on deformation of single crystals of calcite up to 10,000 bars[16] have shown that the critical resolved shear stress for twinning is affected only slightly by the large normal component of stress. Twinning occurs in favorably oriented jacketed single crystals at a resolved shearing stress of 70 ± 20 kg/cm² when under a confining pressure of 10,000 bars, in experiments by the author. The critical resolved shear stress at atmospheric pressure is 15 ± 5 kg/cm². The increase of critical shear stress is thus about 0.5 per cent of the increase in normal stress. This is consistent with the dislocation theory of twinning and translation.

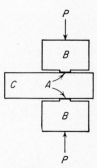

Fig. 11.14 Bridgman's shearing apparatus.

In a unique series of experiments, Bridgman investigated the shearing strengths of solids under high hydrostatic pressure and high shear strains (of the order of 100). The simple apparatus, shown in Fig. 11.14, consists of an anvil C rotated between two blocks B having cylindrical bosses. The material to be studied is placed between both bosses and the anvil. As the blocks are forced together, the material is extruded until it comes

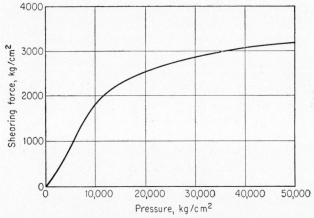

Fig. 11.15 Relation between shearing force and pressure for magnesium. At approximately the point with coordinates 10,000 and 2000 surface slip ceases and internal plastic shearing flow begins. (*After Bridgman.*)

to an equilibrium in which the high peripheral stress gradient balances the central nearly hydrostatic pressure. The anvil is then rotated and the torque measured. The torque generally assumes a steady value, independent of rate of rotation. A typical result is shown in Fig. 11.15.

At low pressure, slip occurs between the material and the steel, so that in Fig. 11.15 the curve below 10,000 bars is essentially a measure of friction. At higher pressures, the material shears internally, and the curve is a measure of the shear strength of the solid.

Many materials deform smoothly; in others, the flow is continually interrupted by "snapping" which is interpreted as due to internal "fracture" and rehealing. Bridgman has suggested that this "fracture" may be the mechanism of deep-focus earthquakes in the earth. This seems impossible to the author. At the higher pressures, fracture in the ordinary sense is precluded, since Coulomb friction between the surfaces of fracture would be higher than the internal shearing strength of the material, so that distributed flow would ensue. Under the extremely high shearing stresses and rates of shear in these experiments, however, the work done on the material is sufficiently great to cause local melting which would immediately relieve the shear stresses in the solid. Thermal conduction to the massive steel blocks would very rapidly reduce the temperature so that crystallization would occur almost immediately after relief of the high shear stresses. A similar process might operate in deep-focus earthquakes, where the rocks are near their melting temperatures.

The drastic shearing in these experiments occasionally produces irreversible transformations, as from red phosphorus to crystalline black—a transformation which Bridgman has been unable to induce under any other conditions. Some chemical reactions are produced, e.g., synthesis of Cu_2S from the separate elements. The crystalline lattice of most materials is broken up so that in many cases the crystallites are smaller than X-ray resolving power. A high degree of crystallographic orientation is usually produced, showing that the shear is controlled by the crystal lattice.

Other plastic properties have been investigated under pressure, but they do not lend themselves readily to summarization, and the above are the most noteworthy.

An interesting application of the change of ductility with pressure has been made by Rosenthal and Kaufman.[17] They investigated marble that had been deformed under high pressure and found X-ray line broadening but no shift in the lattice constant; presumably the residual stresses had been relieved by release of pressure. Since the deformed marble returned to its brittle state, it could be broken up by grinding in a mortar without inducing further plastic deformation. This allowed them to determine directly the size of the crystallites, by simply X-raying samples of smaller and smaller size until the X-ray line broadening vanished. They found the size of the crystallites to agree with Bragg's estimate of 3000 A.

Considerable commercial application is being made of the increase of ductility with pressure. An outstanding example is the cold-forming of metals. Shapes are now being made which were impossible until equipment was developed which would maintain the region of greatest strain at a high pressure. The pressure-induced ductility allows straining beyond the point at which fracture would normally occur. Previously, the required ductility had been obtained by raising the temperature. The advantage of cold-forming is that the work-hardening of the grains and the favorable texture are retained on release of pressure, yielding a stronger material than can be made by hot-forming. It appears to the author that high-pressure techniques have not been exploited to the full in this new and rapidly growing commercial art.

GEOPHYSICAL IMPLICATIONS OF HIGH-PRESSURE RESULTS

11.10   Composition of the Earth

Deductions as to the earth's interior are largely based on its mass, its moment of inertia, and the propagation of earthquake waves through it. The results of high-pressure research on compressibility and elastic constants are obviously of first-order importance. For example, in the earth's crust down to the first-order seismic discontinuity at about 30 km, the geological evidence indicates a granodioritic composition. Birch's studies of elastic constants over the appropriate range of pressure and temperature are consistent with this. Below that, petrologists prefer the ferromagnesian rock dunite. The observed elastic constants under pressure and temperature are consistent with this.

Similarly, a plausible extrapolation of Bridgman's data combined with solid-state theory yields physical properties not inconsistent with the hypothesis that the core of the earth (below 2900 km depth) is composed of molten iron.

With regard to the mantle, between 30 and 2900 km depth, Birch[18] has recently examined in detail the seismic evidence in the light of experimental results and concluded as follows: (1) The mantle from 900 to 2900 km is homogeneous, not composed of any crystal form found on the surface of the earth, suggesting a high-pressure modification of the orthosilicates. (2) The layer from 200 to 900 km is characterized by a gradual change of composition, or phase, or both. Verhoogen[19] has questioned Birch's second-order description of the strain energy and suggests that higher-order terms are important; he asserts that, if these are included, no change of phase or composition is necessary and the whole mantle may be comprised of dunite. It appears that there is at the moment insufficient experimental evidence to resolve this question.

11.11   Temperatures in the Earth

One of the major uncertainties about the interior of the earth is the distribution of temperature. The external shell of the earth is such a good insulating blanket that pronounced changes of temperature at a depth of a few hundred kilometers would not be observable at the surface of the earth for a billion years. One must therefore resort to indirect methods of measuring temperature deep in the earth. Fortunately one such method is available. Transient electric and magnetic fields induce currents within the earth as well as in the atmosphere. Measurements at the surface can, by classical methods, lead to an unequivocal determination of the electrical conductivity at depth. Since the penetration depth is small in wavelengths, however, one must resort to large-scale transient fields. Such fields are produced by "magnetic storms" caused by the emission of charged particles from the sun. From surface observations of the effects of such storms, Chapman and Price have deduced the electrical conductivity at depth. Since electrical conductivity is sensitive to temperature, this in principle sharply narrows the possible solutions for both temperature and composition at depth. Taken together with the elastic constraints considered above, it appears that we have sufficient evidence to determine uniquely the composition and temperature of the earth. What is needed is further experimental measurements of the effects of pressure and temperature on intrinsic electrical conductivity and on the elastic constants and a satisfactory theoretical explanation of both.

11.12   Origin of the Earth's Magnetic Field

It has been shown conclusively that the source of the main magnetic field of the earth is internal—located at the boundary of, or in, the core. The major component of the earth's field is varying, with an exceedingly short time constant by geological standards—of the order of 10,000 years —and it appears that secondary features of the earth's field vary with even shorter time constants, down to 25 years. Another major property of the earth has been observed to vary with a short time constant; the rate of rotation of the earth varies in a roughly periodic fashion with a period of the order of 25 years. To be sure, this change is small—1 part in 100 million—but the required change in moment of inertia to conserve angular momentum is large, and would correspond roughly to sinking the Himalayan mountain range to sea level and back. It is natural to associate this rapid change with the only other world-wide property known to change at the same rate—the magnetic field. Geophysicists are turning more and more to motions in the supposedly liquid iron core for explanations of both of these effects.[20]

An intense controversy is now in full swing among geologists and geophysicists as to the permanence of the earth's magnetic field. On the one hand, Hospers and Runcorn[21] have established that Tertiary lava flows of Iceland and the Columbia River plateau show reversals of the remanent magnetization at intervals of the order of a million years, which they cite as evidence that the main field of the earth has frequently changed 180° in direction. On the other hand, Balsley and Buddington,[22] examining similar reversals in intrusives of the Adirondacks, have found spatial distributions which appear to negate the possibility of reversal of the main field and, further, have found that such reversals always associate with a unique assemblage of minerals of high susceptibility and thermoremanent magnetization. Nagata[22] has found lavas in Japan which, when heated and cooled in a magnetic field, assume a magnetic polarization opposite to the applied field. It seems to be an open question as to whether the evidence demonstrates that the main field of the earth frequently reverses, or whether there is a physical process capable of inducing reversed remanent magnetization during the cooling of the lavas. Meanwhile, the main dipole component of the earth's field has decreased 5 per cent in the last fifty years, so that whether the field has ever reversed or not, it certainly is changing rapidly.

The only causal mechanism that promises to account for this rapid change is fluid motion in the earth's core. The viscosity required is of the order of 100 poises—that of glycerin under normal conditions. The most plausible energy source seems to be thermal: heat generated by radioactivity in the core. The combination of high pressure fields and important Coriolis accelerations, plus Cowling's theorem which restricts the possible mechanisms of producing magnetic fields, poses interesting problems for theory and experiment.

11.13   Fracture and Flow in the Earth

It is well known that rocks in the earth's crust deform plastically much like highly ductile metals, exhibiting crystal gliding and recrystallization. The same rocks under surface conditions are brittle and cannot be deformed plastically. Under other conditions, rocks fracture, causing earthquakes and the complicated fault structures which are universally associated with ore deposits and frequently with oil accumulations. The stresses available for rock fracture and flow are definitely limited, since it is well established that the earth's surface is to a good approximation in buoyant hydrostatic equilibrium, the lighter crust floating on the denser substratum. Further, any perturbation of this equilibrium— e.g., the comparatively sudden imposition of the extra load of an ice cap during glacial stages—causes flow in the substratum to return to equilibrium. When a glacier was formed, covering the Scandinavian peninsula, the crust sank because of substratum flow. Then when the glacier was suddenly removed, about five thousand years ago, the surface rose again, and the rate of this rise can be accurately determined from geological evidence. A hydrodynamic analysis shows that the variation of this rate with time and its spatial distribution are just what would be expected if the substratum behaved as a viscous fluid. Accordingly, the equivalent viscosity is calculated as 10^{22} poises. Such a viscosity is enormous compared with those encountered in ordinary experience. Even the slow creep of steel—say 0.1 per cent elongation in 1000 hr under a stress of 100,000 psi—would yield an equivalent viscosity of the order of 10^{19} poises.

On the other hand, earthquakes are normally associated with large-scale rock fracture (as in the case of the San Francisco earthquake), and they release enormous amounts of strain energy: perhaps of the order of 10^{24} ergs for large quakes, corresponding to a 20-megaton atomic bomb. Such earthquakes reach their highest intensity in the crust but also occur with indistinguishable characteristics down to depths of 700 km, where the confining pressure is of the order of 300,000 bars. Now fracture in the ordinary sense cannot occur at such confining pressures, since fracture implies release of strain energy and hence requires that the resistance to shearing motion on the fracture surface be substantially less than the shearing strength of the material. Coulomb friction would certainly occur in such motion, and since the normal stress is 300,000 kg/cm², the frictional resisting stress would be of the order of 100,000 kg/cm². We have seen, however, that the substratum is weak in response to long-continued stress, and it seems impossible to the author that rocks at 700 km depth, where the temperature would be of the order of 1000°C, can have a strength of more than 1000 kg/cm²; 100 kg/cm² is more likely. Similarly, no mechanism can be imagined which could suddenly accumulate such large stresses in a medium which flows so readily in response to secular stresses. Some mechanism other than conventional fracture must be sought to explain deep earthquakes, and the author favors phase change: either local melting or else polymorphic crystal transition which can release elastic stresses while readjusting the crystal bonds. The order of magnitude of stresses required by the known volume in which deep-focus earthquakes originate is 100 kg/cm².

The ancient puzzle as to how normally brittle rocks can deform plastically received a partial answer when von Kármán demonstrated in 1911 that pressure can induce ductility in marble. Major puzzles still remained, however; e.g., the texture of such artificially deformed rocks bore little resemblance to that produced by deformation in nature. Further, harder rocks, notably granite, had resisted all efforts to produce plastic deformation. Even at the highest pressures, Bridgman was unable to deform quartz plastically to a perceptible degree, while in nature quartz is one of the most readily deformed materials, deformed quartzites exhibiting textures similar to those of deformed metals at elevated temperatures.   In the high-pressure laboratory at the University of California, Los Angeles, we have recently achieved a second approximation to the solution of these problems.

Experiments have been conducted at temperatures up to 400°C at moderate confining pressures—5000 bars.   All rocks and minerals tested so far—including granite, dunite, basalt, and dolomite—have exhibited

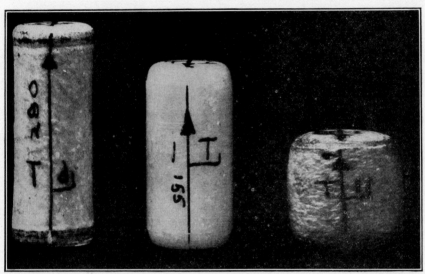

Fig. 11.16   Marble cylinders deformed at high pressure.   The specimen in the center is undeformed.   The specimen at the left has been extended 20 per cent at 300°C, 5000 bars confining pressure.   The specimen at the right has been compressed 40 per cent at 400°C, 3000 bars confining pressure.

definite plastic flow, although the amount of flow before fracture has been small.   We appear to be just at the threshold of the pressure and temperature required to induce large plastic flow in such rocks.

Further, in the readily deformed marble, increase in temperature causes progressive change in the texture in such a way that at 300°C and higher the texture closely approximates that of naturally deformed marbles. Figure 11.16 illustrates the uniformity of plastic flow which can be induced in marble specimens in the laboratory.   This marble cannot be deformed plastically at all under ordinary pressure.   Any degree of plastic strain can apparently be induced in marble without fracture if the combination of pressure and temperature is high enough.   There seems to be a qualitative relationship between the temperature and pressure required to induce a given amount of plastic flow such that doubling the absolute temperature roughly halves the required confining pressure.

Figure 11.17 shows the original texture of this marble. Figure 11.18 depicts the texture after deformation at room temperature. Here the deformation is largely intragranular, and the strain at grain boundaries is very inhomogeneous. Figure 11.19 shows the result after the same deformation at 150°C. Here the deformation within the grains is much more homogeneous. Figure 11.20 shows the texture at 300°C, all other test conditions being the same. Figure 11.21 shows the texture of a specimen

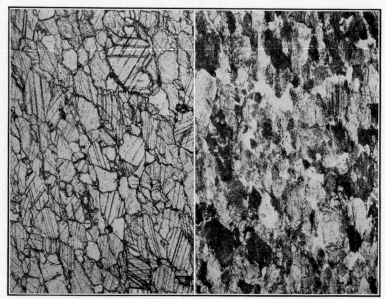

Fig. 11.17   Fig. 11.18

Fig. 11.17 Photomicrograph of marble (×20), undeformed.
Fig. 11.18 Photomicrograph of marble (×20), compressed (horizontally) 20 per cent at room temperature, 10,000 bars confining pressure.

deformed twice as much, over a 48-hr period, at 300°C. The texture in the latter two experiments closely resembles that of some natural, highly deformed marbles. Here, although intragranular flow is still important, intercrystalline flow and minor recrystallization are also evident.[24]

The strength of marble also decreases rapidly with temperature, other experimental conditions being the same. At 150°C the strength is two-thirds that at room temperature, at 400°C it is one-half.

The deformation of single crystals of calcite has been the subject of intensive study by F. J. Turner and the author.[25] Calcite has long been known to twin mechanically, and in our experiments at high pressure and at high temperature, it does so when the critical resolved shear stress

Fig. 11.19   Fig. 11.20

Fig. 11.19 Photomicrograph of marble (×20), compressed (horizontally) 20 per cent at 150°C, 5000 bars confining pressure.
Fig. 11.20 Photomicrograph of marble (×20), compressed (horizontally) 20 per cent at 300°C, 5000 bars confining pressure.

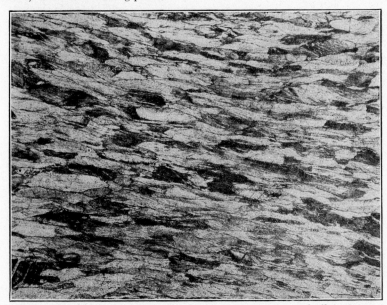

Fig. 11.21 Photomicrograph of marble (×15), compressed (vertically) 40 per cent at 300°C, 5000 bars confining pressure.   Duration of experiment was 48 hours.

in the proper sense is exceeded. This critical shear stress, as indicated above, is about 50 kg/cm². The appearance of a specimen deformed by twinning is shown in Fig. 11.22.

When single crystals of calcite are stressed so that they cannot twin at room temperature, they are twenty to forty times stronger than when they can twin. The mechanism of deformation under these conditions

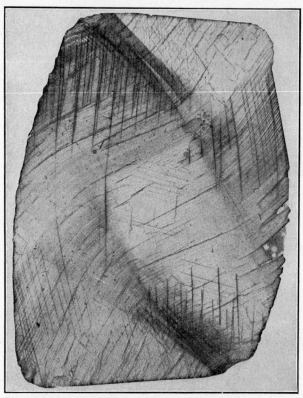

Fig. 11.22   Photomicrograph of single crystal of calcite (×5), compressed (vertically) 20 per cent normal to the C axis, at room temperature, 10,000 bars confining pressure. The central section has twinned completely. The twin planes are the curving lines from lower left to upper right. The ends are restricted from twinning by steel end caps.

is not certainly known. At 300°C, however, it has been possible to demonstrate unequivocally that the mechanism is translation on the normal cleavage plane in a direction parallel to the projection of the c axis on that plane. The critical resolved shear stress is 250 kg/cm² for this translation. A specimen so deformed is illustrated in Fig. 11.23. The light and dark bands are deformation bands, similar to those observed in some deformed metal single crystals. While the critical resolved shear stress for twinning does not vary with temperature within our experimental accuracy, that for translation decreases by a factor of 5 to 10 between 25 and 300°C and by another factor of 2 between 300 and 400°C, so that, at 400°, the critical stress for translation is only about twice as great as that for twinning. This difference in behavior of the crystals

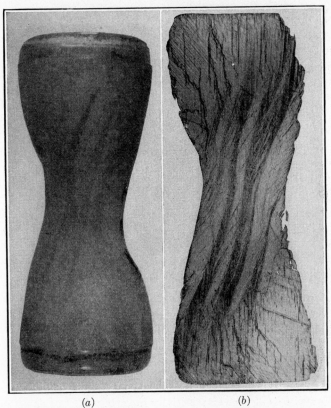

(a)   (b)

Fig. 11.23 Calcite single crystal (×3.3), extended 20 per cent parallel to the intersection of two cleavage planes, at 300°C, 5000 bars confining pressure. (a) External appearance of specimen. Steel end cups were fitted to the machined ends to prevent rupture of the copper jacket. (b) Thin section of specimen. The light and dark bands are deformation bands produced by different amounts of translation on the {10$\bar{1}$1} plane. The trace of this plane is shown at the ends, inclined about 20° to the end faces.

which compose marble must have important bearing on the differences observed in the behavior of marble with temperature.

Handin and coworkers are nearing completion of an extensive study of the deformation of dolomite rock and dolomite single crystals at 5000 bars and temperatures to 400°C. The primary mechanism of deformation in the single crystals appears to be translation on the basal plane. Contrary to our results with calcite, the critical resolved shear stress for translation is not markedly dependent on temperature (John Handin, personal communication).   F. J. Turner and the author have done a few experiments on dolomite rock which provide partial confirmation of their results.

Although granite is somewhat plastic at 300°C and 5000 bars confining pressure, its strength is enormous in short-time tests—14,500 kg/cm². This is stronger than most alloy steels.   In contrast, the strengths normally quoted for granites at atmospheric pressure average one-tenth of this.   A temperature of 300°C is believed to exist at the bottom of the average continental crust, and the pressure corresponds to that halfway down.   Doubling the pressure could only increase the strength.   Granite and basalt are the two rocks most commonly believed to make up the earth's crust.   Basalt has been found to be similarly strong at 300°C and 5000 bars: 14,000 kg/cm².   Dunite, which is supposed to be similar to the material of the subcrust, has been found in one preliminary test to have a strength of 9000 kg/cm² under similar conditions.   Interstitial solutions and rate of strain have not shown great effect in tests so far, though exploration of the effect of these variables has hardly begun.

These experiments would seem to point toward a strength of the crust and substratum some five to ten times as great as has previously been assumed.   The rate of strain in these laboratory experiments is so greatly in excess of that to be expected in natural deformations that any such conclusion would seem to the author to be premature.

11.14   Origin of the Earth's Surface Features

The time-honored hypothesis of the mechanism which repeatedly has deformed the great mountain belts of the earth is thermal contraction of an initially molten earth and consequent localized buckling of its constant-temperature crust.   At the time when this hypothesis was first enunciated, many important concepts were different: (1) It was thought that the earth was of necessity initially molten.   (2) It was believed that the earth had cooled to its present temperature in about 100 million years (radioactivity had not yet been discovered).   (3) Nothing was known about the viscosity of the substratum, except that the earth as a whole was a body in first-order hydrostatic equilibrium.

Today, the known heating capability of radioactive elements in the crust, which accounts for about half of the surface heat flow of the earth, plus their unknown distribution in depth, makes it indeterminate even whether the earth is cooling or heating, let alone at what rate.   Second, modern theories of the origin of the solar system offer the possibility that the primeval earth may have been *cooler* than the present earth, which has since been heated through radioactivity.   Finally, the greatest possible present rate of contraction—ignoring radioactive heating entirely—

is far too small to account for the recent surface features of the earth. The rate of contraction is given by

$$\frac{dr}{dt} = \frac{\alpha}{C_p} \frac{(q - q^*)}{\rho}$$ (11.3)

The ratio α/C_p is known from seismic velocities to be 1.7×10^{-4} g/cal at the top of the mantle, diminishing rapidly with depth. The density ρ is about 3.4, increasing downward. The heat flow q averages about 40 cal/(cm^2)(yr); q^* is the heat flow due to radioactivity and other sources. If this is taken to be zero, the maximum shortening of the radius of the earth in the last 100 million years is then 2 km.

If the forces of erosion and hydrostatic buoyancy alone operated on the crust, it would be eroded to a flat featureless plain near sea level in less than 100 million years, since the time constant for erosion is of the order of 10 million years and that of buoyant rise 1 million years. Hence, from the hypsographic curve of the earth—describing the topography—and from standard assumptions as to thickness of the crust and its density relative to the substratum, one can calculate the amount of shortening required to thicken the crust in the last 100 million years sufficiently to account for the present elevation of the land masses. The minimum amount of shortening of the earth's radius required is 200 km, or a hundred times the maximum amount available from thermal contraction.

The other principal hypothesis—thermal convection in the mantle—is not in much better shape. As shown above, Birch has adduced arguments favoring change of composition or change of phase through the 200 to 900 km depth in the mantle. Either would constitute at least a major obstacle to convection through this region and more probably would prevent it. On this point we shall have to await critical appraisal of Verhoogen's alternative proposal, which claims to eliminate the necessity for change in composition or in phase.

It seems wholly likely that thermal convection takes place within the presumably liquid core. Further, it seems inescapable that slow convection must occur in the lower mantle, as Jeffreys, Pekeris, Verhoogen, and others have indicated. In addition, if the solid mantle behaves in creep as do all solids in the laboratory, exhibiting plastic rather than Newtonian viscous flow, then it must follow, as the author originally suggested[26] and Brooks demonstrated theoretically,[27] that such convection must be in the form of a fairly rapid overturn followed by a long period of quiet while the unstable temperature gradient is reestablished by conduction. Such occasional convection overturns could cause folding of the mountain belts and would be expected to produce a pattern similar to that of the arcuate mountain belts. This is of no consequence, however, if Birch's theorem can be shown to preclude convection through the 200- to 900-km zone, since cells of 200 km depth will not suffice.

Two new developments seem to be of first-order importance to any theory of the earth's surface features: (1) The discovery by the Scripps Mid-Pacific expedition that heat flow through the Pacific floor is about the same as that through the land surface, implying a heat flow through the top of the mantle under the ocean crust some three to four times as great as under the continental crust, because of the fact that about three-fourths of the continental heat flow is believed to be due to radioactivity in the continental crust. Revelle and Maxwell[28] have indicated that no plausible distribution of radioactivity can account for the oceanic heat flow on a static equilibrium model. They infer that there must have been mass transport of hot material under the Pacific, as would be true in the case of convection. (2) Rubey[29] has reviewed the evidence as to the chemical history of sea water and shown that this evidence seems compatible only with a nearly constant growth of the ocean waters by continued supply of volcanic and hot-spring emanations which are themselves products of the fractional crystallization of magmas which can come only from the mantle. It follows that the continental crust must also have been growing in volume at a nearly constant rate through geologic time. Rubey[30] has reviewed the tectonic consequences of this hypothesis. He suggests that mountains may be formed as a result of such additions to the crust. In his hypothesis, the excess temperature at the roots of preexisting mountains would cause the temperature of the mantle to rise higher than normal, and selective fusion of the low-melting constituents of the mantle would occur. This melt would rise to the base of the crust. The thickened crust would then be unstable and would flow outward, compressing bordering geosynclines which have meanwhile accumulated a deep fill of sediments, thus forming new folded mountain chains adjacent to the older ones, as frequently occurs in nature.

This hypothesis has not yet been quantitatively tested. Whether it works exactly as Rubey postulates or not, it is clear that the hypothesis of continuous growth of the continents and oceans will have important tectonic consequences.

The final solution of this elusive riddle of the origin of continents and mountains must await more experimental and theoretical evidence on the equation of state of the deep earth, the temperature and composition of the mantle, the plastic properties of rocks at high pressures and temperatures, and more studies of the ocean basins of the type that the Scripps Institution of Oceanography and the Lamont Geological Laboratory are undertaking.

We conclude that the chief "geophysical implication" is that much work remains to be done.

REFERENCES

1. Bridgman, P. W., "The Physics of High Pressure," 2d ed., The Macmillan Company, New York, 1950; *Revs. Mod. Phys.*, **18:** 1–93 (1946).
2. *J. Chem. Phys.*, **15:** 92–98 (1947).
3. *Phys. Rev.*, **78:** 235–243 (1950).
4. *Phys. Rev.*, **76:** 301–302 (1949).
5. Personal communication from K. T. Bainbridge.
6. *Proc. Am. Acad. Arts Sci.*, **81:** 165–251 (1952).
7. *Proc. Am. Acad. Arts Sci.*, **79:** 125–179 (1951).
8. *J. Chem. Phys.*, **20:** 218 (1952).
9. *Proc. Am. Acad. Arts Sci.*, **77:** 115–128 (1949).
10. *Geol. Soc. Amer., Spec. Papers* 36, 1942.
11. *Z. Ver. deut. Ing.*, **55:** 1749–1757 (1911).
12. *Forsch. Gebiete Ingenieurw.*, **175:** 1–51 (1915).
13. Bridgman, P. W., "Studies in Large Plastic Flow and Fracture," McGraw-Hill Book Company, Inc., New York, 1952.
14. Robertson, E. C., Ph. D. thesis, Harvard University, 1951.
15. *Colloid Chem.*, **VI:** 77–88 (1945).
16. Robertson, E. C., Ph. D. thesis, Harvard University, 1951; Griggs, unpublished data.
17. *J. Appl. Phys.*, **23:** 600–601 (1952)
18. *J. Geophys. Research*, **57:** 227–286 (1952).
19. *J. Geophys. Research*, **58:** 337–346 (1953).
20. For an excellent review, see Elsasser, *Revs. Mod. Physics*, **22:** 1–35 (1950).
21. *Nature*, **168:** 1111–1112 (1951), and unpublished data.
22. Unpublished data.
23. *Nature*, **169:** 704–705 (1952).
24. *Bull. Geol. Soc. Amer.*, **64:** 1327–1342 (1953).
25. *Bull. Geol. Soc. Amer.* (in press).
26. *Am. J. Sci.*, **237:** 611–650 (1939).
27. *Trans. Am. Geophys. Union*, 548–551 (1941).
28. *Nature*, **170:** 199–200 (1952).
29. *Bull. Geol. Soc. Amer.*, **62:** 1111–1148 (1951).
30. *Trans. Am. Geophys. Union*, **34:** 350 (1953) (abstract).
31. *Trans. Am. Soc. Mech. Engrs.*, **75:** 315–324 (1953).
32. For the latest information up to the time of publication, see Paul, W., and H. Brooks, *Phys. Rev.*, **94:** 1128–1133 (1954).

12

The Earth beneath the Sea—
Geophysical Exploration
under the Ocean*

ROGER REVELLE

DIRECTOR, SCRIPPS INSTITUTION OF OCEANOGRAPHY
OF THE UNIVERSITY OF CALIFORNIA
LA JOLLA, CALIFORNIA

12.1 Introduction

Why are there continents and oceans? Have the deep-sea basins existed throughout geologic time with about their present shape and dimensions? Or have the continents and oceans gradually evolved over the past 3 billion years?

These questions are fundamental to an understanding of the origin and geologic history of the earth. They have not been satisfactorily answered. A description of the "first-order" features of the earth underneath the oceans must necessarily precede any attempt to answer them. The results from recent deep-sea exploring expeditions have made it clear that only five years ago our picture of these principal features was completely inadequate.

In the past, geologists comforted themselves with the belief that the sea was much more stable than the land, that little of geologic interest had happened there, that the broad expanses of the ocean floor were a monotonously uniform sea of mud over great distances, and that little could be learned about the earth's history from studies of the ocean. But they are now finding that the oceans have been the scene of intense and varied earth activity during the relatively recent geologic past, that the shape and structure of the sea floor are remarkably complex, and

*Contribution from the Scripps Institution of Oceanography, New Series, Number 684.

306

that within the upper layers of deep-sea sediments we have an unrivaled archive containing detailed records of climatic conditions during the last few million years.

The task of the geophysicist is not only to describe systematically what actually exists in the earth but also to determine why things are the way they are. He is concerned with the internal forces which have shaped the earth and which continually evidence their presence through earthquakes and volcanoes. These forces are surprisingly small. Table 12.1 compares the energy flux from within the earth with the average amount of energy received at the sea surface from the sun and the amounts utilized by plants and by our industrial civilization. It will be seen that the total flow of energy from within the earth is about 7000 times smaller in any given time interval than the energy received from the sun and about one-seventh of the energy utilized by land and marine plants in photosynthesis.

Table 12.1 Energy Flux from within the Earth

	10^9 ergs/yr/cm^2	10^{27} ergs/yr per entire earth
Heat conduction.................	1.6	8
Earthquakes....................	0.24	1.2
Volcanoes......................	0.008	0.04
Solar radiation.................	13,000	65,000
Photosynthesis..................	12	60
Human and industrial power......	0.1	0.5

The seagoing scientist labors under several disadvantages: First is the great disproportion between the area to be covered—almost three-quarters of the earth's surface—and the tiny number of scientists working on problems of the sea. Geologists frequently deplore the gross inadequacy of geologic mapping on land; yet the area of the world ocean is nearly three times that of the continental areas, while the ratio of professional oceanographers to geologists is roughly 1 to 20. Second is the great expense and difficulty of work at sea as compared to its immediate practical rewards—the fact that man is a land mammal will be enthusiastically confirmed by any one who has been seasick in the small, oily, and uncomfortable craft which are utilized as research laboratories by oceanographers. In this harsh environment the oceanographer must be as much seaman as scientist, and his instruments tend to be rugged and crude with attendant loss of precision and flexibility. Third is the stubborn opacity of the ocean to visible light—this has produced the paradox that we actually know more about the surface of the moon than about the topography of the ocean floor. The submarine geophysicist must probe blindly into the depths and can visualize only indirectly the performance of his instruments and the processes which he is investigating. Fourth, for the most part he must make measurements, at a series of discrete points in space and time, of parameters which vary widely and often unpredictably from point to point and from time to time. Finally the geophysicist is largely denied the benefits of controlled experiment, that peerless tool of the laboratory scientist. The ocean and the solid earth cannot be controlled. The forces involved are too large and the time scale too great. The methods of the geophysicist must be akin to those of the detective who patiently pieces together all possible clues in his attempt to reconstruct what has happened.

Surprisingly enough, however, many kinds of geophysical work at sea can be conducted with relative ease compared with corresponding investigations on land. In seismic work, consistent signals can be obtained through the sea floor out to distances of 60 miles with an 80-lb charge, and on occasion records up to 100 miles are obtained. On land, a distance of 10 miles with an 80-lb charge is considered very good. Measurements of heat flow through the sea floor, although somewhat difficult experimentally, are straightforward in interpretation because of the relatively uniform and constant temperature of the bottom waters over large areas of the oceans. In contrast, it is extremely difficult to obtain unequivocal determinations of heat flow on land because of migrating ground waters, uncertainties introduced by the circulation of drilling fluid in wells, and changing atmospheric temperatures. In magnetic and gravity measurements, the ability to use the sea surface as a reference plane and the simultaneous recording of a bottom depth profile considerably facilitate interpretation.

Moreover, experimentation does have its place in submarine geophysical investigations, particularly model experiments in which oceanic processes are studied on a reduced scale, and the conditions are varied, one by one, to establish a framework of analogy by which the full-scale phenomenon may be better understood. For example, many people now believe that sediment-laden waters flowing down submarine slopes have played a major part in the transportation of sediments and may have brought about the cutting of submarine canyons. Yet no one has observed such currents in the sea. Their existence has been deduced from model experiments in the laboratory and by analogy with somewhat similar phenomena in lakes and in the atmosphere, e.g., dust storms.

From its beginning 75 years ago in the great British *Challenger* expedition the scientific exploration of the deep sea has tended to run in cycles. Each cycle of exploration was initiated not only by the conceptual growth of new questions that men asked about the sea but also by the development of new techniques of exploration. Nearly all these techniques can be characterized as means for extending the personality of the scientist into regions that he can never see. The scientific explorer of the earth beneath the oceans must rely on observations at a distance. He probes into the dark with long fingers of steel, or listens for sounds made far away, or studies other phenomena that reflect the invisible character of the buried rocks.

Among the new tools of geophysical exploration developed in recent years are echo sounding, underwater photography, bottom coring and dredging, seismic refraction and reflection methods, devices for measurement of heat flow from the interior of the earth through the sea floor, means for measurement of the acceleration of gravity, and continuous-recording magnetometers which can be towed from ship or plane. Some of these new methods and the results obtained will be discussed in the remaining part of this chapter.

12.2   Echo Sounding and Submarine Topography

In the 50 years before 1925, a great deal of time and effort was spent in making soundings of the ocean floor with lead and line. But the number of soundings was so small and the locations of the points of observation so uncertain that only the barest outlines of the shapes of the sea basins could be discerned. With the development of echo sounding—depth determination by accurate measurement of the time required for a sharp pulse of sound to travel from an observing ship down to the bottom and back again—the true shape of the sea bottom is being disclosed at a rate undreamed of 25 years ago. This development has been accompanied by a great improvement in means of navigation in waters within 200 miles of shore, so that it is now possible to make topographic maps of the border areas of the oceans which approach in accuracy topographic maps of land areas. There has been much less improvement in navigational methods far from land, but even here the speed with which echo soundings can be taken has made it possible to construct maps of considerable areas that represent rather well the shape of the sea floor, even though the absolute location of the surveyed area is only approximate.

Although new discoveries about the topography of the sea floor are continually being made, some of the characteristic features are already clear. In the first place there is a relatively sharp boundary between the continental blocks and the ocean basins. This boundary zone is characterized by broad shallow shelves, probably cut by wave erosion during the glacial epoch, which break sharply at their outer margins into the continental slopes. These slopes, though rough in detail, are gentle over all, descending downward into the abyss at an angle of about 5°.

At many places throughout the world, steep and deep submarine canyons, often with rocky walls, are cut in the slopes and shelves.

Perhaps the most remarkable characteristic of the boundary zone is the very fact that it exists—that the continents are present as great islands of relatively light rock floating in the denser material of the sea floor and that there is a sharp boundary between these continental rafts and the abyss of the deep sea.

Beyond the boundary zone each deep-sea basin has a group of characteristic features. Here we shall confine ourselves to the Pacific Ocean. In its broadest aspects the Pacific can be divided geologically into two regions, a central basin and a surrounding marginal zone. The line of separation between the two is called the *andesite line* (Fig. 12.1). Its western limb extends south of and parallel to the Aleutian and Kurile Islands, thence east of Japan and the Marianas Islands, south through the Carolines, southeast to a point north of the Santa Cruz Islands, east of the Tonga Islands and south past the Kermadec Islands and New Zealand, probably to Antarctica. In the eastern Pacific the position of the eastern limb of the andesite line is not clearly delineated, but it undoubtedly lies east of the Galápagos Islands and perhaps west of Easter Island, thence southward toward Antarctica. North of the Galápagos Islands it approaches the continental platform of Central and North America. Within the andesite line the igneous rocks of islands are principally olivine basalt, and we may consider this region as the true Pacific basin. Outside the andesite line, the igneous rocks of islands are relatively high in silica and alumina. In the South Pacific approximately at 20° south latitude, the western and eastern segments of the andesite line approach within 3500 miles of each other. To the west lies the island-studded area with average depths of about 1600 fathoms which has sometimes been called the Melanesian subcontinent. To the east lies the equally shallow Easter Island rise. Rocks of andesite composition occur on Easter Island and on the islands of Melanesia.

The deep Pacific basin inside the andesite line is pimpled with sea mounts, many of which have a rough and irregular shape and are undoubtedly active or extinct volcanoes. In the North Pacific some of these sea mounts, with summit depths of 2000 to 6000 ft below present sea level, are nearly flat on top over distances of 2 to 20 miles (Fig. 12.2) as if their summits had been cut by a gigantic plane (Hess, 1946).[*] Fossil remains of clams, corals, sea urchins, and other animals which once lived in shallow water have been collected from some of these flat summits (Hamilton, 1953), and it is evident that the sea mounts were once islands which rose above the sea and were cut off by wave erosion. Their subsequent relative subsidence was caused either by a rise in sea

* Corresponding bibliographic references appear at the end of the chapter.

level or a drop in the sea floor. On some of these drowned islands, coral reefs built upward at the same rate as the foundation subsided, and these became coral atolls. On others, for reasons unknown, the coral either could not get started or failed to keep up with the relative subsidence,

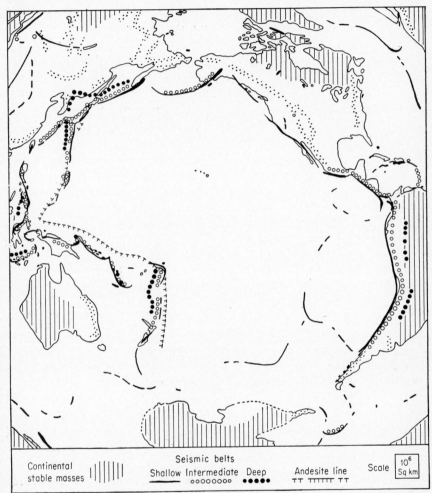

Continental stable masses ‖‖‖‖‖‖	Seismic belts			Andesite line TTT TTTTTT TT	Scale	10^6 Sq km
	Shallow ———	Intermediate ooooooo	Deep ●●●●			

Fig. 12.1 Approximate position of the andesite line separating the true Pacific basin from the marginal areas. (*After Gutenberg*, 1951.)

and these became flat-topped sea mounts. Sea mounts with flat summits have not yet been found in the South Pacific, but numerous atolls occur there, and the combination of evidence from seismic, magnetic, and topographic surveys on the Scripps Institution of Oceanography *Capricorn* Expedition of 1953 indicates that several thousand feet of coral limestones rest on foundations of volcanic rock and that there has been a relative subsidence of the old volcanoes by at least several thousand feet. Fossils collected from North Pacific sea mounts and from boreholes in Bikini (Ladd, Tracey, and Lill, 1948) and Eniwetok Atolls (Ladd, personal communication) show conclusively that the subsidence

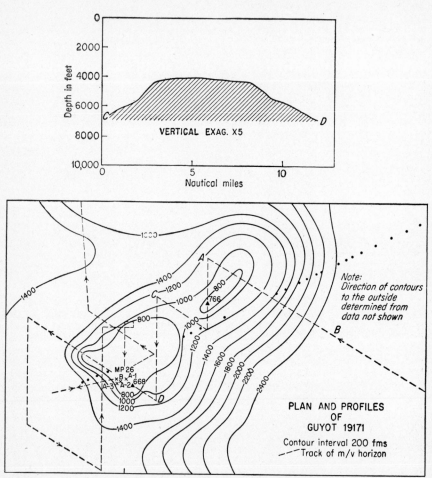

Fig. 12.2 Plan and profile of a flat-topped sea mount in the central Pacific. (*After Hamilton, 1953.*)

has taken place within the last 100 million years, about one-fortieth of geologic time.

One outstanding feature of the deep central basin of the Pacific is the relative absence of submerged mountain ranges which originated in folding or bending of the suboceanic rocks. For example, such island groups as the Cook, Society, and Marquesas Islands appear to rise as chains of volcanoes directly from the deep-sea floor rather than as peaks on a broad arch or swell (*Capricorn*, 1953). However, such a broad submerged structure is characteristic of the Hawaiian Islands and the Mid-Pacific Mountains in the North Pacific. In the South Pacific an uplifted fault block apparently underlies the atolls of the Tuamotus.

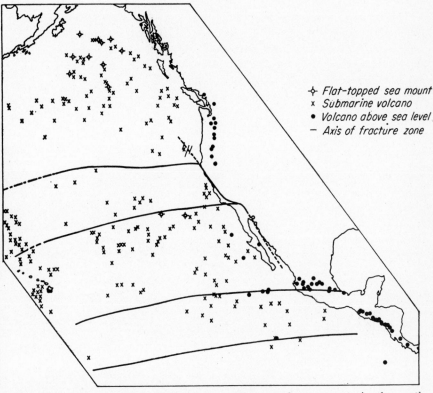

Fig. 12.3   Fracture zones, volcanoes, and flat-topped sea mounts in the northeastern Pacific.   (*From Menard*, 1953.)

Major zones of fracture are found.   Menard (1953) has recently shown that four straight and nearly parallel fractures at least 1500 miles long occur in the northeast Pacific (Fig. 12.3).   These originate on the west coast of North America and extend westward as zones of long and narrow ridges, troughs, and escarpments.   Each pair of fracture zones appears to bound a distinctive topographic province on the sea floor with characteristic average depth, degree of roughness, and shape of smaller topographic forms.   For example, between the Murray escarpment, which extends westward from Point Conception, and the Clarion fracture zone extending westward from the Revillagigedo Islands there is an unusually large number of sea mounts (estimated at more than 2000). Few, if any, of these are flat-topped. One may argue, by analogy with experiments on the fractures of variously shaped bodies under stress, that these quasi-parallel fracture zones are the result of a single planetary stress system. If they are, they do not correspond as far as we know to any stress system that has been proposed in the literature.

The characteristic topography of the so-called subcontinental areas outside the andesite line differs in many respects from that in the deep Pacific basin. For the most part these regions are a mile shallower than the central ocean area inside the andesite line, but they contain deep, flat-bottomed, relatively steep-sided isolated basins, such as the Fiji and Philippine basins. Elsewhere in the subcontinental areas, the topography is much rougher and more complex than within the andesite line.

A characteristic feature of the boundary zone along the andesite line is the existence of long, excessively deep, V-shaped trenches. Examples are the Aleutian, Japan, Marianas, Kermadec, and Tonga trenches. Each of these trenches is part of a deep reaching structure characterized by contemporary and extinct vulcanism, large gravity anomalies, and a very high seismic activity. A typical section across the Tonga trench from west to east may be used as an illustration (Fig. 12.4). We observe the following features (not all shown in the figure):

a. *Melanesian subcontinent* at a depth of 1000 to 1500 fathoms
b. *Volcanic ridge* rising to about 700 fathoms capped by volcanic islands and sea mounts
c. *Tofua trough* with a maximum depth of about 1000 fathoms
d. *Main island ridge* reaching up to 30 to 50 fathoms, from which the elevated limestone islands of the eastern Tonga Archipelago rise to heights of 100 to 600 ft
e. *Tonga trench*, extending to depths of more than 5000 fathoms
f. *East ridge*, rising about 200 fathoms above the
g. *Pacific basin* to the east, with an average depth of 3000 to 2500 fathoms

The very existence of this giant structure is a riddle. What implacable forces deep within the earth could have caused such a large-scale distortion of the sea floor? Did the trench form long ago and is it now gradually being filled up with sediments, or is it still being formed so that at some future time it may be even deeper than it is today? What has become of the material excavated from the trench? How can we explain its location, close to an island chain and along the boundary between the 3-mile-deep basin of the Pacific with its black and heavy rock floor and the shallower island-studded waters of the southwestern Pacific? Why is it so narrow, so long, and so straight?

Seismic surveys by R. W. Raitt indicate a thin oceanic type of crust beneath the sea floor on both sides of the trench. Beneath the trench the crust is significantly thicker than on the two sides, the Mohorovičić discontinuity lying at depths of at least 15 and perhaps 20 km. It seems evident from the narrow V-shaped profile, irregular rocky surface, thin veneer of sediments, frequency of earthquakes, and existence of large anomalies in the earth's gravitational field that active movements of the crust are taking place on a grand scale at the present time along the axis of the trench. Farther west along the line of volcanic islands, events of equal violence but of greatly different character are occurring.

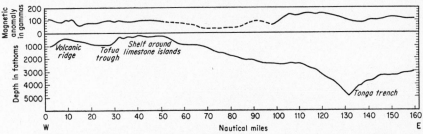

Fig. 12.4 Depth profile across the Tonga area. (*From Capricorn*, 1953.)

Along the trench every indication points to a squeezing together and downward bending of the earth's crust. In the volcanic region to the west, the rocks below the surface have melted and forced their way upward through the crust, perhaps because of relief of pressure at depth. One may reasonably inquire as to what has happened to the volume of rock which formerly occupied the space now filled with water in the trench. It is interesting to compare this volume with that of the material thrown out of the volcanoes. A rough computation, based on the thickness of volcanic sediments in the Tofua trough as found by the seismic refraction method, shows that these volumes are approximately equal. This does not imply that the material which was formerly in the trench has been turned into ash and cinders and vomited up on the sea floor by the volcanoes, but it may indicate that the material forced downward and perhaps westward from underneath the trench has filled at depth the space vacated by volcanic material thrown upon the sea floor.

One other computation is of interest: the heat per unit area and time released by this volcanic activity, supposing it has extended over 10 million years, is approximately equal to the average heat flow by conduction through the continents and through the sea floor. These two types of release of heat must be additive. Thus we have in this region much more energy flux through the earth's surface than over most of the earth.

12.3   Seismic Methods of Exploring the Crust and Mantle

It is not necessary to go to sea in order to explore the deep ocean. Gutenberg (1951), Wilson and Baykal (1948), Ewing and Press (1950), Stoneley (1948), and their collaborators have demonstrated the value, for determining suboceanic structures, of the study of earthquake records in which the vibrations have traversed paths underneath the ocean.

When an earthquake or other shock occurs in the earth, elastic waves proceed out in all directions from the point of origin and can be recorded by seismographs. Within the crust and mantle two types of waves exist —*compressional* or *P waves* in which the displacement is in the direction of propagation and *shear* or *S waves* in which the displacement is transverse to the direction of propagation. The velocities for the *P* and *S* waves are

$$V_P = \sqrt{\frac{k + 4\mu/3}{\rho}} \qquad V_S = \sqrt{\frac{\mu}{\rho}}$$

where k is the bulk modulus (the reciprocal of the compressibility), μ is the rigidity, and ρ is the density. The ratio of the two velocities is

$$\frac{V_P}{V_S} = \sqrt{\frac{2(1 - \sigma)}{1 - 2\sigma}}$$

where σ is Poisson's ratio. The velocities of both the *P* and *S* waves vary widely with the nature of the rocks through which they are traveling. Some typical values of V_P based on laboratory measurements are given in Table 12.2. Thus by measuring the travel times of compressional and shear waves from earthquakes (or large explosions) of known position to a receiving station, the elastic constants of the rocks through which the waves have passed and the geometrical configuration of the rocks can be determined; these in turn lead to a basic understanding of the geologic features. A summary of results from studies of nearby earthquakes and explosions in Europe, North America, and Africa concerning seismic velocity and thickness of the components of the earth's outer shell, called the crust, has been prepared by Bullard (1953). In most of these continental cases, velocities between 5.5 and 6.35 km/sec are found beneath a superficial layer of sedimentary rock. These are believed to represent a zone of plutonic "acid" igneous rock (called "granite" by the seismologists) at least 10 km thick. Beneath the "granite" there is evidence that a zone with velocities between 6.5 and 7.1 km/sec exists, but this is not found in all cases. At the bottom of the crust, the observed velocities increase sharply; this break is called the *Mohorovičić discontinuity* after its discoverer, and it occurs at depths under the continents of 27 to 47 km. As will be shown below, these inferences from seismic data on the structure and thickness of the crust under the continents are in marked contrast to the seismic results on the character of the crust under the oceans. The most convincing results under the oceans have been obtained from studies of the surface waves of earthquakes and by seismic refraction and reflection measurements on shipboard, using explosive sources.

Table 12.2 Velocities of Compressional Waves, Km/Sec

Material	At normal temperature and pressure	15 km below surface
Sand...................	0.2–2	
Alluvium..............	0.5–2	
Sea water.............	1.5	
Clay..................	1–2.8	
Sandstone.............	1.4–4.3	
Shale and slate........	2.3–4.7	
Limestone.............	1.7–6.4	
Gneiss and schist.......	3.1–5.4	
Granite...............	5.2–5.6	6.1
Basalt................	5.1–5.6	
Dunite...............	....	7.8

Although surface waves are more conspicuous features on most seismograms than the above-described body waves, their study has not received great emphasis, so that at present there are many unexplained or partially understood surface-wave arrivals. Elastic theory provides in general for two types of waves at the surface of a solid, commonly called *Love* and *Rayleigh* waves after their discoverers. Love waves are shear waves polarized horizontally. They depend for their existence on horizontal layering of some sort, and are always dispersive, *i.e.*, waves of different period travel with different phase and group velocities. Rayleigh waves are somewhat similar in particle motion to surface gravity waves in water, but the acting force is elastic rather than gravitational. They can exist at the free surface of a homogeneous semi-infinite solid, in which case they are nondispersive. But in the actual case of the layered earth, they too are dispersive, because the shorter wavelengths are confined largely to the upper layers of comparatively low velocity, while the longer wavelengths penetrate more deeply and are affected by the higher velocities of the deeper layers. For use in ocean studies, Ewing and Press (1950), employing relationships derived by Stoneley (1926), have computed group velocity of the first- and second-mode Rayleigh waves as a function of period and water depth for a two-layer system consisting of sea water (compressional wave velocity 1.52 km/sec) overlying a solid with a compressional wave velocity of about 8.0 km/sec and a Poisson's ratio of 0.25. They made similar computations for two cases of a three-layer system. In one case the intermediate layer had a compressional wave velocity of 5.5 km/sec, corresponding to typical velocities of the "granitic" rocks making up the top 10 km or so of the earth's crust under continents. In the other case, a velocity of 6.9 km/sec, typical of velocities observed in the crust under the oceans, was assumed. From these computations, they concluded that a "granitic" layer more than 5.5 km thick under the ocean along the path from an earthquake epicenter to the recording station could be detected if it were present. Examination of seismograph records from earthquakes having propagation paths under the Pacific and Atlantic Oceans showed, in general, no granitic layer under either ocean except possibly beneath the Easter Island rise in the southeast Pacific.

For any given period the velocity of the shorter-period Rayleigh waves depends critically on the depth of the overlying liquid layer. Because the sediments behave as if they were part of this layer, it is possible to determine the approximate thickness of sediments by comparing the computed depth of the liquid layer with that observed from soundings. Sediment thicknesses between about 500 and 1000 m in both the Pacific and Atlantic were obtained in this way by Oliver, Ewing, and Press (1953).

For Love waves traveling in a system of two rock layers, the longer-period waves approach the shear velocity in the lower medium, the duration of the train is determined largely by the difference between the two shear velocities, and the distribution of periods depends upon the thickness of the upper layer. Thus an examination of the train of Love waves on a seismograph record makes possible a rough determination of the elastic properties and geometry of the crustal layers along the line of propagation. Results obtained from studies of Love-wave records by Oliver, Ewing, and Press are similar to those obtained with Rayleigh waves.

Seismic refraction and reflection studies on shipboard using explosives as a sound source give more precise and detailed data for determining the crustal structure than seismograph records of earthquakes. In this method two vessels are used, a shooting craft and a receiving ship. A series of explosive charges is fired at depths of 100 to 300 ft beneath the sea surface, at predetermined distances from the receiving ship. The travel times between source and receiver are measured. Such travel-time data rarely yield a unique picture of the surface substructure, but in most situations it is possible to set up a model of subsurface velocities consistent with the observed travel-time curves. This model may resemble the true structure to a greater or lesser degree, depending on the local conditions and on the control achieved in shooting operations. The model ordinarily adopted assumes the existence of rock layers of constant sound velocity superimposed one on another, with each deeper layer having an appreciably higher velocity than the one above it (Raitt, 1952).

Figure 12.5 illustrates a subsurface section consisting of three layers with a velocity c_0, c_1, and c_2 respectively. In seismic work at sea, the

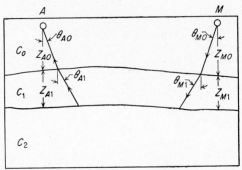

Fig. 12.5   Ray path of sound wave refracted through a rock layer beneath the sea floor. (*From Raitt*, 1952.)

upper layer is water. The receiving station is designated as A and the shot point as M. Sound rays are shown refracted through the third layer. The travel time T_{AM} from M to A is given by

$$T_{AM} = \frac{X_{AM}}{c_2} + \frac{Z_{A0} \cos \vartheta_{A0}}{c_0} + \frac{Z_{M0} \cos \vartheta_{M0}}{c_0} + \frac{Z_{A1} \cos \vartheta_{A1}}{c_1} + \frac{Z_{M1} \cos \vartheta_{M1}}{c_1}$$

where X_{AM} is the horizontal distance from shot to hydrophone and the Z's and ϑ's have the meaning shown in the figure. The term $(T_{AM} - X_{AM}/c_2)$ is called the *intercept time*. The four remaining terms are called *delay times* and are designated τ_{A0}, τ_{M0}, τ_{A1}, and τ_{M1}, respectively. In the typical deep Pacific Ocean τ_{A0} and τ_{M0}, called the *water delays*, are each of the order of 3 sec and are generally much larger than the delays pertaining to subsurface structure. Hence when the topography is irregular, the form of the travel-time plot is determined by bottom topography to a greater extent than by the underlying structure. These water delays are analogous to the "weathering" corrections of seismic surveying on land. The first step in the interpretation of the data is to subtract them from the observed travel times. After making this correction for water delay, the resultant travel-time data effectively represent the travel times that would have been observed if the shots and detectors had been placed on the sea bottom directly under the shot and detection positions. If the rock layers are flat or gently sloping, the velocity in the underlying rock layer is given approximately by $c_2 = 1/(dT'_{AM}/dX_{AM})$, where T'_{AM} is travel time corrected for water delay, and the thickness of the overlying rock layer underneath the receiving ship is given by

$$Z_{A1} = \frac{c_1 \tau_{A1}}{\sqrt{1 - (c_1/c_2)^2}}$$

Maximum ranges obtained by this technique depend on the background noise produced by the motion of the hydrophones through the water. In the region of the northeast Pacific tradewinds, Raitt has obtained maximum ranges in kilometers Δ given by $\Delta = 7W^{\frac{1}{2}}$ where W is weight of explosive in pounds.

Evidence from earthquakes suggests that the crust beneath the oceans is thinner than beneath continents and that granitic rocks are absent. Seismic refraction work at sea has confirmed the absence of granite and has shown quantitatively how remarkably thin the crust really is. Raitt (in *Capricorn*, 1953) has found in the Pacific that typical values of this thickness (defined as the distance between sea bottom and the Mohorovičić discontinuity) are 5 to 10 km, compared with a thickness of 30 to 40 km beneath continents. Above the discontinuity, a zone with an average sound velocity of 6.8 km/sec exists. Above this layer, there is often a zone of variable thickness around 1 km, with a velocity between 4.5 and 5.5 km/sec. Just beneath the sea floor there is usually a veneer of sediments 100 to 400 m thick. Velocities between 5.5 and 6.5 km/sec corresponding to the "granitic" zone on land are not obtained under the sea floor.

Over the Easter Island rise seismic velocities greater than 8 km/sec were not observed by Raitt; the maximum velocities at depths greater than about 7 km were 7.2 and 7.9 km/sec. Over the Melanesian subcontinent, two of Raitt's stations gave maximum velocities of 7.5 and 7.9 km/sec at depths greater than about 7 km, while two others (one in the Fiji basin where the water depth is more than 2000 fathoms, the other between Alexa Bank and Fiji) gave typical "Moho" velocities. Above 7 km, velocities and thicknesses in both subcontinental areas are essentially similar to those in the deep Pacific basin. The sea floor over the Easter Island rise and the Melanesian subcontinent is about 1000 fathoms shallower than in the deep Pacific. Thus if these areas are in isostatic equilibrium, there must be significant differences in density distribution below 7 km between the subcontinental and the oceanic areas.

12.4   Heat Flow from beneath the Sea Floor

In measuring the heat flow through the sea floor two quantities are determined, the temperature gradient in the bottom sediments and the thermal conductivity of the sediments.

A first attempt to measure temperature gradients in the sea bottom was made on the Swedish *Albatross* Expedition in 1947–1948. E. C. Bullard and A. E. Maxwell designed a gradient recorder at the Scripps Institution in 1949. Further development was carried out by J. D. Isaacs, J. M. Snodgrass, and Maxwell, and the instrument was first used successfully on the Scripps Institution–Navy Electronics Laboratory *Mid-Pacific* Expedition in 1950 (Revelle and Maxwell, 1952). Improved models were later used by Maxwell in the Pacific and by Bullard in the Atlantic.

The instrument (Fig. 12.6) measures the difference in temperature between two points in the bottom sediments, one about 2 and the other

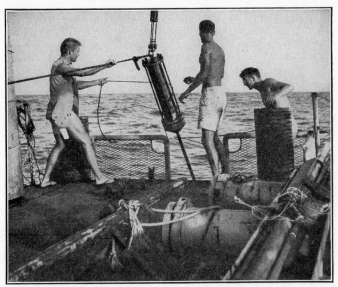

Fig. 12.6 Probe for measuring temperature gradients in deep-sea sediments being lowered from the research vessel *Spencer F. Baird.*

8 ft beneath the sea bottom. It consists of a hollow steel spear 10 ft long and 1.64 in. in outside diameter in which thermistors have been placed near each end. The spear is attached at its upper end to a water- and pressure-tight chamber, within which there is a battery-powered self-balancing null-type potentiometric recorder. From a 30-min continuous record of the temperature difference between the two thermistors, it is possible to deduce the undisturbed temperature gradient in the sediments. A core is obtained at the same station, and samples of the sediments are carefully preserved for laboratory determination of thermal conductivity. The product of the conductivity and the temperature gradient gives the heat flux through the sea floor.

The results of these measurements over wide areas of the Pacific show that the amount of heat flowing through the sea floor averages close to 40 cal/(cm²)(yr), about the same as that coming from the land. It can easily be shown that this quantity of heat cannot be accounted for by cooling of the earth and probably not by chemical processes within the interior. It must result from the decay of radioactive elements contained in the rocks of the crust and mantle.

Table 12.3   Radioactive Heat Generation in Typical Rocks*

Kind of rock	Concentration, g/g			Heat production, 10^{-6} cal/(g)(yr)			
	$U \times 10^6$	$Th \times 10^6$	K	U	Th	K	Total
Granite..........	4	13	0.04	2.9	2.6	1.1	6.6
Basalt............	1	3	0.012	0.7	0.6	0.3	1.6
Dunite..........	0.014	?	0.0003	0.01	(0.01)	0.01	0.03
Stony meteorites....	.....	..	0.002	....	....	0.05	

* From Birch, 1951.

Under the continental platforms the presence of granitic rocks high in uranium and thorium furnishes an adequate source for the observed heat flow, but the seismic results for ocean areas show that granitic rocks are absent there, and even the layer of basaltic rocks is thin. If the source of heat is radioactive decay in the mantle, much heat must originate deep within the interior, but here we are faced with a paradox. If the radioactivity is distributed through too great a depth, the temperature near the base of the radioactive layer will rise above the melting point at that depth. The latter can be deduced from the Clausius-Clapeyron equation:

$$\frac{dT}{dZ} = \frac{gT\,(1 - \rho_1/\rho_2)}{L}$$

where T is the melting point in degrees absolute, L is the latent heat of fusion, and ρ_1 and ρ_2 are the densities of the liquid and the solid. At ordinary pressures $T = 1300°C$, $L = 4 \times 10^9$ ergs/g, and $1 - \rho_1/\rho_2 = 0.08$, which gives a melting point gradient of 3°C per km. At the pressures deep within the earth's interior, the melting-point gradient will be even less than this value.

On the other hand, if the radioactive layer is made too thin, the rocks beneath the ocean will have to be assumed to contain an amount of radioactive material that is difficult to reconcile with the observed sound velocities.

Table 12.4 Simplified Model of Pacific and Continental Structures
(Computed for isostatic balance, 35.2 km below sea level)

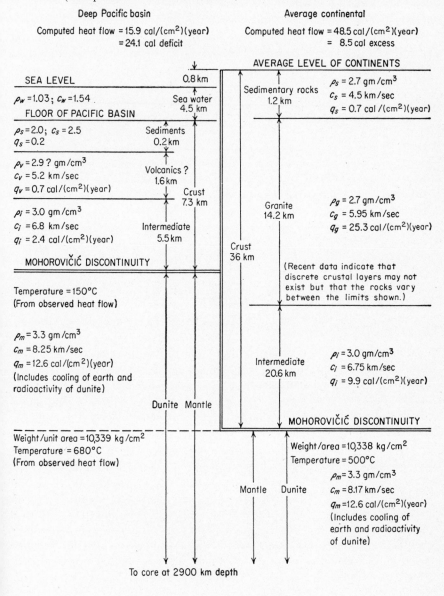

Deep Pacific basin

Computed heat flow = 15.9 cal/(cm²)(year)
= 24.1 cal deficit

Average continental

Computed heat flow = 48.5 cal/(cm²)(year)
= 8.5 cal excess

AVERAGE LEVEL OF CONTINENTS

SEA LEVEL   0.8 km

ρ_w = 1.03; c_w = 1.54
FLOOR OF PACIFIC BASIN

Sea water
4.5 km

Sedimentary rocks
1.2 km

ρ_s = 2.7 gm/cm³
c_s = 4.5 km/sec
q_s = 0.7 cal/(cm²)(year)

ρ_s = 2.0; c_s = 2.5
q_s = 0.2

Sediments
0.2 km

ρ_v = 2.9? gm/cm³
c_v = 5.2 km/sec
q_v = 0.7 cal/(cm²)(year)

Volcanics?
1.6 km

Crust
7.3 km

ρ_i = 3.0 gm/cm³
c_i = 6.8 km/sec
q_i = 2.4 cal/(cm²)(year)

Intermediate
5.5 km

Granite
14.2 km

ρ_g = 2.7 gm/cm³
c_g = 5.95 km/sec
q_g = 25.3 cal/(cm²)(year)

Crust
36 km

MOHOROVIČIĆ DISCONTINUITY

Temperature = 150°C
(From observed heat flow)

(Recent data indicate that
discrete crustal layers may not
exist but that the rocks vary
between the limits shown.)

ρ_m = 3.3 gm/cm³
c_m = 8.25 km/sec
q_m = 12.6 cal/(cm²)(year)
(Includes cooling of earth and
radioactivity of dunite)

Intermediate
20.6 km

ρ_i = 3.0 gm/cm³
c_i = 6.75 km/sec
q_i = 9.9 cal/(cm²)(year)

Dunite Mantle

MOHOROVIČIĆ DISCONTINUITY

Weight/unit area = 10,339 kg/cm²
Temperature = 680°C
(From observed heat flow)

Weight/area = 10,338 kg/cm²
Temperature = 500°C

ρ_m = 3.3 gm/cm³
c_m = 8.17 km/sec
q_m = 12.6 cal/(cm²)(year)
(Includes cooling of
earth and radioactivity
of dunite)

Mantle Dunite

To core at 2900 km depth

It can be shown that the melting point would be exceeded if the thickness of the radioactive material were greater than about 150 km. The heat generation needed to give a heat flow of 1.2×10^{-6} cal/(cm^2)(sec) would be 5.3×10^{-14} cal/(cm^3)(sec) for a 200-km layer and 9.2×10^{-14} for a 100-km layer after allowance has been made for original heat and for that from 7 km of basalt. These values are so much greater than the observed average of 0.4×10^{-14} cal/(cm^3)(sec) for ultrabasic rocks as to raise a real difficulty.

The preceding computations rest on the assumption that the heat flow is by molecular conduction. If convection plays a role, *i.e.*, if the rocks in the earth's mantle are slowly overturning, the observed heat flow can easily be accounted for. But other considerations, notably inhomogeneities deduced from seismic velocities in the upper 500 km of the mantle, argue powerfully against the possibility of convection.

Table 12.4 summarizes some of the possible inferences from data given in previous pages concerning the constitution of the outer parts of the earth beneath the continents and the oceans. It will be seen that the assumed densities and thicknesses of "layers" allow for isostatic equilibrium between the continental masses and the crust and mantle beneath the sea but that the computed heat flow through the sea floor, based on the assumption that the mantle under the ocean is like that under the continents, is much too small.

12.5   Deep-sea Sediments

The sediments of the deep sea may have constituted by far the larger part of all sediments formed throughout geologic time. Thus the geochemical transformations of the earth's crust during the past 3 billion years cannot be adequately understood until we have a more complete knowledge of the deep-sea deposits.

These sediments are unique in one most important respect. They are rarely if ever uplifted to form sedimentary rocks on land. No example is known of sedimentary rocks above sea level which are unquestionably of deep-sea origin. We must conclude therefore that the processes of weathering, erosion, and sedimentation have brought about a loss of materials from the continents to the deep-sea floor. The total amount of material thus lost from the continents could be computed if we knew the average rate of sedimentation on the sea floor throughout geologic time, or on the other hand, if we knew the total amount of material which had been weathered and the portion retained on the continents as sedimentary rocks or reincorporated in igneous rocks.

The relative amounts of deep-sea sediments and of continental sediments may be estimated by comparing the average chemical composition of continental sedimentary rocks with that of the igneous rocks from which they are derived. For example, the sedimentary rocks contain nearly three times as much calcium as the source material. Unless the average composition of igneous rocks has changed during geologic time, this must mean that for every gram of continental sedimentary rock nearly 3 g of igneous rock has been used up and that the mass of sediments transported to the deep sea is at least twice as great as the mass of continental sediments. From this and similar geochemical computations, Kuenen (1950) concluded that the total mass of deep-sea sediments deposited throughout the geologic past is about six times the total mass of sediments remaining on the continents and that the thickness of the deep-sea deposits should be of the order of 3 km.

At the present time, the preponderant type of deposition on the deep-sea floor is of sediments high in calcium, namely, globigerina ooze and other calcareous oozes. If the deposition throughout the geologic past had been like that at the present time, it would be impossible to arrive at a geochemical balance, because both the deep-sea and continental sediments would be higher in calcium than the igneous rocks from which they are derived. Thus we arrive at another most important conclusion, namely, that the character of the deposition on the deep-sea floor has changed radically with time; throughout most of geologic history, deep-sea sediments must have been lower in calcium than the average igneous rocks, whereas the present deposits have an excess of calcium.

Except for calcium and magnesium, all the major elements are more abundant in igneous rocks than in continental sedimentary rocks; hence these elements must have become concentrated either in solution in the sea itself, as in the case of sodium, or in the deep-sea sediments. This concentration in the deep sea is particularly striking for manganese, phosphorus, titanium, and iron. The sedimentary rocks of the continents contain only 10 per cent as much manganese and 30 per cent as much iron, phosphorus, and titanium as igneous rocks. Analyses of deep-sea sediments suggest that many of the minor elements, e.g., nickel and cobalt, have likewise been concentrated on the sea floor.

In areas of little horizontal transport near the bottom, a core 10 m long penetrates a continuous sequence of sediments laid down over hundreds of thousands and perhaps millions of years. When such a core is examined (Arrhenius, 1952), marked stratification is observed—the different strata must reflect variations in conditions of deposition and hence must constitute a record of past oceanic climate. For example, in the "eupelagic" area of the eastern tropical Pacific, the topmost layer of the cores is usually considerably lower in calcium carbonate and in number of diatoms but contains more shells of certain warm-water species of Foraminifera than the material 10 to 25 cm below the surface. As we go downward in the core, we pass through a series of alternating layers. The fluctuations in calcium carbonate content become smaller in amplitude near the bottom of the core.

Similar alterations between layers of high and low calcium carbonate occur in the tropical Atlantic (Schott, 1935) but with the remarkable difference that in many cores the surface layer is higher in calcium carbonate than the layer 25 cm below the surface.

Both of these sequences are believed to reflect changes in oceanic circulation and in the character of the surface waters during the glacial and interglacial stages of the Pleistocene. The top layers in both cases may have been deposited since the last retreat of the glacial ice.

Arrhenius has correlated the layers of high calcium carbonate, high diatoms, and low warm-water foraminifera in the tropical Pacific with the Pleistocene glacial stages. He supposes that during epochs of maximum glaciation the trade winds were narrowed and intensified. The resulting stronger divergence in the wind system near the equator would bring about a corresponding divergence of the surface waters accompanied by marked upward motion of nutrient-rich deeper water. Organic productivity would thus be greatly increased, the rate of precipitation of calcium carbonate and silica in the shells of planktonic plants and animals would be accelerated, and the quantity of shell material settling through the water would be increased. At the same time the circulation of the deep cold waters of the ocean would speed up; correspondingly the rate at which calcium carbonate would be dissolved in these deep waters would increase. Arrhenius believes that in the Pacific the increased productivity would overbalance the increased rate of solution. Hence the glacial stages were periods of high calcium carbonate deposition. In the Atlantic the intensification of the trade winds and of the vertical water circulation in the equatorial zones was much less pronounced, while the acceleration of the deep-water circulation was greater. Hence glacial stages were times of relatively low calcium carbonate deposition.

This hypothesis differs radically from the explanation proposed by Schott (1935) and now widely held. Schott proposed that the surface waters of the tropics were cooled by as much as 10°C during the glacial stages, with the result that organic precipitation of calcium carbonate was greatly reduced. At the same time, because of the relative elevation of the continents, their contribution to the sea floor was perhaps increased. Hence the deposits laid down during glacial periods should be low in calcium carbonate, while those of interglacials or postglacials such as the present should have high calcium carbonate content.

Actually the hypotheses of Schott and Arrhenius are not necessarily contradictory. In some regions cooling of the surface waters may have had the predominant effect on tropical pelagic sediments during the glacial period; in others the increased organic productivity brought about by the intensified atmospheric and oceanic circulation may have been most important; elsewhere, the increased circulation of bottom water may have resulted in solution of calcium carbonate before it could be buried, thereby determining the character of the sediments.

Many attempts have been made to estimate the rate of deposition of deep-sea sediments. The finding of fossil shark's teeth in dredge hauls led earlier workers to suppose that these deposits were laid down at an almost infinitesimally slow rate, less than 0.1 mm per 1000 yr. More recent workers have based their estimates on the occurrences of glacial and postglacial strata in cores. Assuming that 20,000 years have elapsed since the end of the ice age and finding an average thickness for the topmost postglacial layer of about 20 cm, they have concluded that the present rate of deposition is about 1 cm per 1000 yr. Similar results have been achieved by investigators who have used the decrease in radioactivity (which must come largely from the uranium-ionium-radium series) with depth in the cores as an index of the time since deposition of different layers. Both of these methods are subject to considerable uncertainty. The first essentially begs the questions of whether the different layers in the sediments can be correlated with Pleistocene glacial and interglacial stages and whether the oceanic circulation of the tropics synchronized with the retreats and advances of the ice in North America and northern Europe. The second method is questionable because absorption and diffusion of uranium and ionium in different constituents of the sediments may seriously distort the radioactive equilibrium. Moreover the rates of decay of uranium and ionium are too slow to give the precision needed for accurate dating of late Pleistocene and post-Pleistocene events. The successful use of radioactive carbon 14 as a means of dating carbon-containing materials from a few hundred to several tens of thousands of years old suggests its application to the problem of dating the upper layers of the sediments. Because of the amount of carbon required for the analysis, this method can be applied only to carbonate-rich calcareous ooze. Carbon 14 age determinations in cores of this material have been made by Arrhenius, Kjellberg, and Libby (1951) who conclude that the rate of deposition is about 10 cm per 1000 yr. This rate is undoubtedly at least ten times greater than that of the deep-sea deposits as a whole.

The thickness of the sediments has been one of the principal objects of the seismic refraction and reflection studies. We have already seen that geochemical considerations require a thickness of deep-sea sediments of the order of 1 to 3 km. Raitt's seismic refraction results indicate that the actual thickness of materials having a velocity less than about 4.5 km/sec is nearly everywhere less than 500 m. Velocities of 4.5 km/sec or more are unlikely to represent consolidated sediment, unless it be a crystalline limestone, and it has already been pointed out that during earlier geological time the percentage of lime in the deep-sea deposits must have been quite low. We are faced with another dilemma—either the geochemical calculations are wrong, or the lower layers of the sediments have somehow disappeared. At the present rate of deposition of about 1 cm per 1000 yr, the measured thickness of sediments would represent a total time of deposition of less than 50 million years. Allowing for compaction and for lower rates of deposition prior to the Pleistocene, the maximum thickness of sediments corresponds at most to a few hundred million years. We are thus almost forced to the conclusion that, if deposition of sediments was taking place in the deep Pacific prior to the late Mesozoic, these earlier deposits have disappeared or are not now detectable by seismic methods.

REFERENCES

Arrhenius, Gustaf, "Sediment Cores from the East Pacific," Reports of the Swedish Deep-sea Expedition, 1947–1948, Vol. 5, 1952, pp. 1–227.

Arrhenius, Gustaf, G. Kjellberg, and W. F. Libby, Age Determination of Pacific Chalk Ooze by Radiocarbon and Titanium Content, *Tellus*, 3(4): 222–229 (1951).

Birch, Francis, Recent Work on the Radioactivity of Potassium and Some Related Geophysical Problems, *J. Geophys. Research*, 56: 107–126 (1951).

Bullard, E. C., "The Interior of the Earth," Vol. 2, Chap. 3 of "The Solar System," edited by G. P. Kuiper, in press.

Capricorn, "Shipboard Report on the *Capricorn* Expedition," Scripps Institution of Oceanography Report, SIO Ref. 53-15, 1953.

Ewing, M., and F. Press, Crustal Structure and Surface Wave Dispersion, Part 1, *Bull. Seism. Soc. Am.*, 40, 4: 271–280 (1950).

Gutenberg, B. (ed.), "Internal Constitution of the Earth," 2d ed., Dover Publications, Inc., New York, 1951.

Hamilton, Edwin L., Upper Cretaceous, Tertiary and Recent Planktonic Foraminifera from Mid-Pacific Flat Topped Sea Mounts, *J. Paleontology*, 27: 204–237 (1953).

Hess, H. H., Drowned Ancient Islands of the Pacific Basin, *Am. J. Sci.*, 244: 772–791 (1946).

Kuenen, Ph. H., "Marine Geology," New York: John Wiley & Sons, Inc., Chapman & Hall, Ltd., London, 1950.

Ladd, H. S., J. I. Tracey, and G. G. Lill, Drilling on Bikini Atoll, Marshall Islands, *Science*, 107: 51–55 (1948).

Menard, H. W., Jr., "Deformation of the Northeastern Pacific Basin and the West Coast of North America," manuscript submitted for publication, 1953.

Oliver, Jack, Maurice Ewing, and Frank Press, "Crustal Structure and Surface Wave Dispersion Part IV, The Atlantic and Pacific Ocean Basins," Technical Report on Seismology No. 26, Columbia University, Lamont Geological Observatory, 1953.

Raitt, Russell W., "The 1950 Seismic Refraction Studies of Bikini and Kwajalein Atolls and Sylvania Guyot," Scripps Institution of Oceanography (Marine Physical Laboratory) Report, SIO Ref. 52-38, 1952.

Revelle, Roger, and Arthur E. Maxwell, Heat Flow through the Floor of the Eastern North Pacific Ocean, *Nature*, **170**: 199–200 (1952).

Schott, W., Die Foraminiferen in dem acquatorialen Teil des Atlantischen Ozeans, *Wiss. Ergebn. Deutsch. Atlant. Exp. Meteor.*, **3**, pt. 3, 1935.

Stoneley, R., The Effect of the Ocean on Rayleigh Waves, *Mon. Not. Roy. Astron. Soc., Geophys. Suppl.*, **1**: 349–356 (1926).

Stoneley, R., *Bull. Seism. Soc. Am.*, **38**: 263–274 (1948).

Wilson, J. T., and O. Baykal, Crustal Structure of the North Atlantic Basin as Determined from Rayleigh Wave Dispersion, *Bull. Seism. Soc. Am.*, **38**: 41–53 (1948).

13

Thunderstorms and Lightning Strokes

LEONARD B. LOEB

PROFESSOR OF PHYSICS
UNIVERSITY OF CALIFORNIA, BERKELEY

13.1 Introduction

The thunderstorm is a natural phenomenon which has awed and impressed man since the dawn of civilization. Although one important aspect of thunderstorms has been partially understood ever since Benjamin Franklin identified the lightning stroke as an electrical spark, the thunderstorm is still an awesome, obscure, and destructive phenomenon.

The thunderstorm cell, which develops from an atmospheric density imbalance, is in effect a gigantic electrostatic machine of enormous energy and power. The active lifetime of a thunderstorm cell is only about 2 hr, during which time it lowers to the ground its accumulated electrical charge in a series of catastrophic and terrifying flashes. During the early days of high-energy nuclear research attempts were actually made to use the enormous static potentials of thunderstorms for the acceleration of nuclear particles. More modern approaches to this problem are treated in Chap. 7.

On an average fair day a potential difference exists between the earth and the atmosphere. The earth is negative, and the atmosphere is increasingly positive at higher and higher levels, the field at the surface of the earth being about 1 volt/cm. Electrically charged ions created in the atmosphere by cosmic rays and radioactivity are moved by this field. The consequent electrical current amounts to roughly 1800 amp over the whole surface of the earth. Despite the flow of this atmospheric current, which tends to annihilate the vertical electrical field, the field remains constant, except for minor fluctuations, unless it is strongly

330

altered or even reversed by highly electrified thunderclouds. There is now much evidence that the earth's electric field is created and maintained by the action of thunderstorms and lightning strokes occurring over the surface of the earth. While the greater proportion of these storms occur in the equatorial regions, the earth is probably a sufficiently good conductor so that its surface charge density, and therefore its electrical field, is sensibly the same everywhere.

As a result of the postwar researches conducted by various government agencies, especially the Air Force, it is now possible to depict quite accurately the life history of the thunderstorm cell as it develops, reaches maturity, and declines.

13.2 The Thunderstorm Cell

The thunderstorm cell is created by any set of circumstances which lead to the heating and humidification of the air nearest the earth to such an extent that a strong convective updraft unit, called a *cell*, is formed. The updraft rapidly carries the moisture-laden air up to the levels of atmosphere where the temperature is well below freezing so that ice crystals can form. The conditions which produce such convective centers may be relatively local phenomena arising from high ground temperatures, as in summer thundershowers or intra-air-mass storms. Alternatively, the conditions may be associated with one of several air-mass movements, as in the case of frontal-storm systems. The cells connected with frontal storms usually are much more vigorous than the local cells, and many cells usually arise over wide areas. The convective action can also be produced by local heating of unusual origin, as in the case of the "fire storms" produced by incendiary bombardment of Hamburg, Tokyo, and other cities during World War II, or by volcanic eruptions.

Figure 13.1 is a schematic diagram of the beginning stage of thunderstorm-cell formation. At this stage precipitation is beginning to occur aloft, but no electrification has yet developed. Figure 13.2 shows the same thunderstorm cell half an hour later at the height of its activity. Note the heavy convection currents and high upward drafts, the entrainment of outside air, the heavy downdrafts caused by falling rain, and the ice and snow aloft. At this stage the storm is at the peak of its electrical activity, and its main lightning production is occurring. The dimensions of the cell are shown, and it is seen that an individual cell may be several miles in diameter.

It is important to note that no electrification will occur unless the convection carries surface air well above the freezing isotherm. It is now certain that effective electrification involves the presence of snow, ice, and hail in the upper levels of the cell, as well as that of water.

Updraft velocities have been measured in the range from 2 to 70 mph, or even higher.   While hail is not a necessary accompaniment of thunder-storms, it is often observed.   From the size of hailstones falling to the ground, we can estimate the maximum velocity of updrafts.   The largest hailstones authentically reported fell in Potter, Nebraska; these were 5.5 in. in average diameter and weighed about 1.5 lb.   These stones

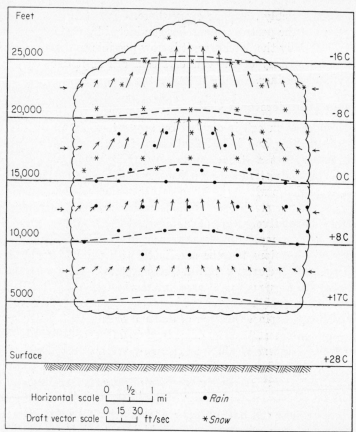

Fig. 13.1   Schematic diagram of the early stage of a thunderstorm cell, according to Byers and Braham in the Thunderstorm Project Report.   Note the dimensions and relation to temperature.   Note also the increasing wind velocities at the top.

have a terminal velocity of fall of 260 mph, so that updraft velocities of this order must have existed in the storm which created them.   Hail-stones of 4.8 in. diameter fall at 120 mph.   The most common large hail-stones are 2 to 3 in. in diameter, indicating a vertical updraft of 60 to 90 mph, while stones of 0.5 in. diameter require updrafts of 20 mph. Half-inch hailstones falling from heavy clouds have typically traveled about 8.8 km in 14 min; their laminated structure shows that they have made between 8 and 16 trips from the lower levels of the cell to the upper levels and back before falling out.

After the cell has continued for some 20 min in its most active stage, it gradually loses energy. In the course of about an hour its electricity

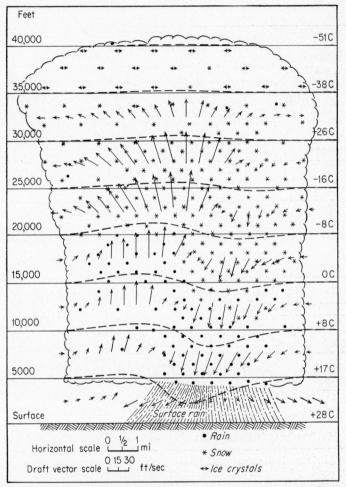

Fig. 13.2 Schematic diagram of the mature active stage of the thunderstorm cell, according to Byers and Braham of the Thunderstorm Project. Note the altitude reached extending to above the $-40°$ isotherm. Note the violent up and down drafts and the lateral entrainment of air. Note the association of down drafts with precipitation and the deflection of down drafts by the ground.

is discharged and it takes the form of the cloud shown in Fig. 13.3. Updrafts are greatly reduced, and rain falls out from almost the entire cloud base.

As a rule, the thunderstorm cell is not stationary in one position rela-

tive to the earth.   Usually considerable wind aloft will accompany the
conditions which cause thundershowers.   This wind displaces the cloud
and alters the convection pattern somewhat.

Figure 13.4 depicts the disposition of electrical charge in the thundercloud.   Some of the best data on this subject have been obtained by

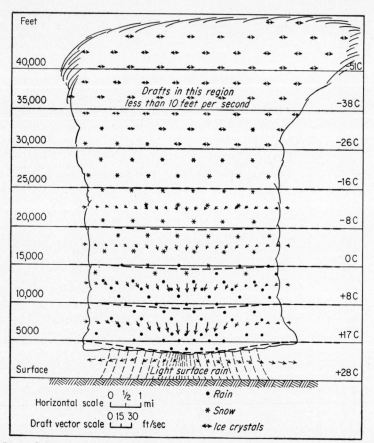

Fig. 13.3   Schematic diagram of the final stage of a thunderstorm cell as it is dissipating, according to Byers and Braham of the Thunderstorm Project.   Note that
rain is general and light, there are no updrafts, and lightning discharge has ceased.

Sir C. G. Simpson and F. J. Scrase using sounding balloons in England
and by Ross Gunn and his associates by means of airplane traverses
through thunderclouds.   More detailed information and confirmation of
results directly obtained have been gathered from networks of ground
stations which record the electrical fields produced by clouds and by the
lightning strokes.   The latter studies have been carried out by B. F. J.
Schonland and D. G. Malan in South Africa, E. J. Workman and R. W.

Holzer in Arizona, H. Norrinder in Sweden, Kuettner in Germany, and various observers in the Thunderstorm Project. Note in Fig. 13.4 that most of the positive charge is at the top of the storm cloud, where it is associated with the snow or frozen water. The main negative charge is in the section of the cloud cell where updrafts and downdrafts are most

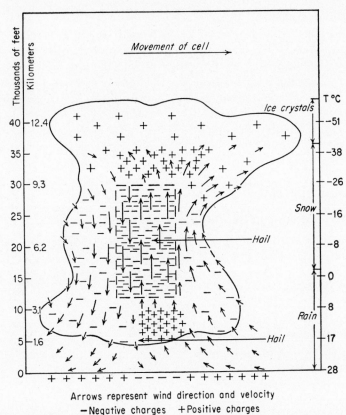

Arrows represent wind direction and velocity
—Negative charges +Positive charges

Fig. 13.4 Schematic drawing of approximate charge distribution in a very active cell in the mature stage, as reconstructed by the author. Note the up and down drafts, the concentration of positive charge above 10 km, and below it the large negatively charged vertical cell extending from 4 km to 9.3 km. The negative charge is associated with hydrometeors falling or rising. Note especially the dense accumulation of positive charge near the cloud base. Note the induced charges on the ground.

prominent. The negative charge is associated with most of the rain, and the majority of the rain falling from most thunderclouds is negatively charged. In most clouds studied there exists a low-lying accumulation of positive charge associated with large raindrops in the region of turbulence at the base of the cloud. This clump of positive charge probably plays an important role in many cloud-to-ground lightning strokes.

We see from Fig. 13.4 that the electrical charge in the thunderstorm cell is segregated in three cloud regions and is associated in all cases with snow, ice, or water droplets, collectively called *hydrometeors*. As we shall see later, the solid and liquid hydrometeors actually play the major role in the creation of the charge. However, even if they were otherwise generated, the electrical ions in a thundercloud would rapidly be picked up by the hydrometeors.

In the typical cloud there will be between 1 and 10 g of water per m^3, with an average of 4 g/m^3 distributed among a number of droplets ranging between 250 and 4×10^3. Ross Gunn has measured the electric charge of individual raindrops in aircraft flights. Drops of various sizes carried between 0.03 and 0.15 esu of charge. The electrostatic field at the surface of a typical drop ranges between 300 and 3000 volts/cm. The density of charge in a cloud thus can range between 38 esu/m^3 (250 drops, each with 0.15 esu) and 120 esu/m^3 (4000 drops, each with 0.03 esu). The larger value of charge density corresponds to some 240 coulombs in 6 km^3 of cloud, which is a figure that may be on the low side but is of the proper order of magnitude.

13.3 Mechanisms of Thunderstorm Electrification

While there is still some doubt about the charging mechanisms at work in thunderstorm clouds, I shall present the picture as we see it now. Within the last five years E. J. Workman and S. E. Reynolds have shown conclusively that when water of the degree of purity found in raindrops is freezing—*i.e.*, while ice and water are in contact—very high electrical potentials arise between the water phase and the ice phase. Thus, when very cold frozen particles descend into the moist regions, condensing and freezing the water vapor, or picking up raindrops and freezing them, a potential difference is generated between the liquid and solid phases. This also occurs when ice or snow particles descend below the freezing isotherm and melt. The sense of the potential difference depends upon the nature of the impurities dissolved in the water. If, as is usual, these impurities are such that the heavier solid particle is charged negatively and the liquid is positive, the blowing away of the liquid as the wet ice descends through the turbulent updrafts causes a positive mist to be carried upward while the falling ice or snow carries down the negative charge. The ice or snow ultimately melts in the descending drafts at lower levels and gives negatively charged rain. Experiments on the laboratory scale indicate that charging is produced in this way and that the amounts of charge produced are adequate to account for the main electrification occurring in thunderstorms. This is the only single process known that is capable of accomplishing the massive charging observed in thunderclouds.

It is quite possible that the positive charge observed on the large drops falling out of the small positive region at the base of the cloud arises from the Lenard process of spray electrification of water drops in the turbulent region at the base. Sir C. G. Simpson proposed this method of charging. It cannot be the mechanism which gives the main charge of the thundercloud, since it leads to electrification of the wrong polarity, the fine water spray being negative and the larger drops positive. In addition, it appears to be quantitatively inadequate. However, if spray electrification is active at the base of the cloud, it properly puts negative charge on the higher levels of the cell and yields the positively charged large raindrops which are observed to come from this region.

Once high electrostatic fields are established in the clouds, one further process of charging may act. This involves charging by ion movement and polarization of falling raindrops by the high field existing in the cell. This mechanism, which has been suggested by C. T. R. Wilson and others, yields the correct field polarity and may contribute some charge to the system. However, it clearly requires another process to create the fields which must exist before this process can act effectively.

Figure 13.4 shows that the positive charge extends up to very high altitudes. After the charge distribution of the cloud has been drastically altered by lightning strokes to ground, it is believed that a diffuse low-pressure discharge from the top of the cloud to the upper air may sometimes occur. This would have the result of projecting positive charge into the atmosphere at an altitude where the stratospheric winds can carry the charge to great distances from the cloud. Most of the charge that is lowered to the earth by strokes of lightning is carried in the main negatively charged cell some 3 km high. While it is impossible to know accurately the negative charge carried to the earth by thunderstorms, some estimates can be made. The resulting orders of magnitude are not out of line with the hypothesis that recharging by thunderstorm activity is responsible for maintaining the earth's electrostatic field substantially constant despite the atmospheric currents of electricity which act to discharge the earth.

It is clear from the mechanism of the Workman-Reynolds process of charging why thunderstorms require violent turbulence and occur only when precipitation begins to form well above the freezing isotherm.

13.4 Characteristics of Typical Thunderstorms and Lightning Discharges

The heights and diameters of thunderstorm cells and the characteristics of the storms themselves vary with the topography of the region of occurrence. Apart from differences caused by general meteorological features, storms of varying characteristics occur over deserts, mountains, lakes, and oceans.   The most important influence determining storm character appears to be that of land elevation.

The diameter of the cell which stores the major portion of the charge active in lightning strokes is generally below some 4 km.   This diameter is determined by the diameter of the most turbulent area carrying air upward.   In South African thunderstorms, which are not too different from those occurring in the Middle Western and Southern states, Schonland has found that the average height of the cloud base above ground is about 2 km.   The average length of the strokes to ground from such clouds ranged between 3 and 9 km.   The height from the cloud base to the top of the negative charge in the cell is closely correlated with the number of strokes that come from the cell.   The heights of weakly charged cloud cells giving two to four strokes to ground range between 4.4 and 8 km, while for cells giving 10 or more strokes to ground the height is around 9.3 km.   The number of successive strokes down the

Table 13.1

No. of strokes	Height, km	No. of strokes	Height, km
2	5.1	7 ⎫	
3	5.4	8 ⎬	8.9
4	6.3	9 ⎭	
5	7.1	10 ⎫	
6	7.6	11 ⎬	9.0
		12 ⎭	

same channel from the same cell increases progressively with the height of the cell, as shown in Table 13.1.   We see from Table 13.1 that the increment in height from one stroke to the next ranges from 0.3 to 1 km, with an average of 0.7 km.

According to Schonland, it takes 0.03 sec to drain the charge from 1 km of cell height in order to give the next stroke.   The first stroke to descend to earth leaves a conducting channel which is repeatedly followed by each of a series of succeeding strokes which lower higher and higher elements of cloud charge until the cell is discharged.   While many clouds are fully discharged only by 10 strokes or more—in fact as many as 40 have been observed—the average number of strokes is between three (for intra-air-mass storms) and six (for frontal storms), indicating that many thunderstorm cells are small.   During a storm, however, these cells recharge and in the course of time lead to new strokes.   R. E. Holzer has given data which bear on the recharging of storm cells of over 40 min life in desert thunderstorms.

In frontal storms the number of cloud-to-ground strokes is greater than the number of cloud-to-cloud strokes; the reverse is true in intra-air-mass storms.   After the cell of a frontal storm reaches maturity, the average number of flashes in each 10-min interval runs roughly 40, 80, 60, 40 to a total of 220; the maximum frequency of strokes occurs 50 min after the first stroke.   For an intra-air-mass storm the strokes run 30, 40, 30, 20, with a total of 120.   With six strokes per flash, or cell charge, in the frontal storm this means roughly 37 rechargings in 40 min; for the intra-air-mass storm with three strokes per flash a recharging also takes about a minute.   At an average of 20 coulombs per stroke (which estimate may be high) the charge generated by a cell during its active life of some 50 min may be as much as 2400 to 4400 coulombs.

The electrical process which lowers the charge to the ground follows a complicated sequence of events involving a mechanism called *leader strokes*.   The first ground stroke from a cloud is initiated by a very slowly moving process called the *pilot leader* which paves the way for a *stepped leader*.   The pilot leader is invisible at the distances involved, and its path wanders in such a way as to lead to the crooked and forked paths of the final channel such as that shown in Fig. 13.5.   The progress of the pilot leader is illuminated in steps when its channel is followed by the stepped leader.   Individual steps vary from 10 to 200 m in length.

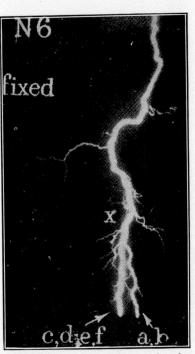

Fig. 13.5 A still photograph of a lightning stroke to ground (after Schonland) showing the crooked path and branching in the downward direction of propagation.

The intense illumination of the lightning discharge permits it to be photographed by means of a very high speed motion-picture camera.   A special-purpose camera often used in lightning studies was invented by C. V. Boys and has since been improved by others.   The original Boys camera had two lenses placed on arms in such a way that they could be rotated about an axis at radii of some 4 in.   The lenses were driven at a speed corresponding to a linear motion of about 500 in./sec, so that a measurable displacement of 0.0005 in. on the stationary film corresponded to 1 μsec of time.   Since two images of a stroke were produced by lenses moving in opposite directions, measurements of lateral displacement were possible.

Figure 13.6 shows a schematic diagram of a more recent embodiment of such a camera, as developed by D. J. Malan and R. D. Linton in Schonland's laboratory. The film strip E is 44 in. long and 35 mm wide. Cassettes external to the cylindrical camera shown in the figure permit the film to be changed after an exposure has occurred. The light enters at D and is reflected as shown by the fixed prism A. It reaches a Wollaston prism B which, together with lens C, is part of the rotating system driven by shaft F.

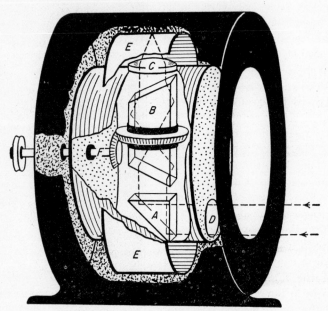

Fig. 13.6   Malan and Linton's modification of the Boys camera.

In later developments the radio signal produced by the first steps in a lightning-discharge sequence is used to trigger the camera shutter, so that the camera is merely pointed at the cloud and then photographs the strokes as they appear. Various other modifications have been made. Best of all are perhaps the various cameras which K. B. McEachron used to take photographs of strokes to the Empire State Building. These are triggered by the current flow up the lightning rod placed on the building. Still, slow-motion, and fast-motion pictures are taken and synchronized with current measurements on an oscilloscope. Considerable success in the measurement of long sparks was also achieved by T. E. Allibone and J. M. Meek, who used cameras with fixed lens and rapidly moving film.

Figures 13.7, 13.8a and 13.9 show examples of stepped leaders photographed by means of the Boys camera.

There are two types of stepped leaders. One of these is the α *leader*, in which a relatively weak discharge advances in uniform steps to the ground at a steady rate of about 2 × 10⁷ cm/sec. The more vigorous *β-type leaders* move at about 1.5 × 10⁸ cm/sec with much branching and large steps, whose initial rapid rate of advance gives way to the slower rate of the α leader. Such leaders are shown schematically in Figs. 13.10 and 13.11, following Schonland and Malan. In general, it takes between 2 and 20 msec for a stroke from the cell base at 4 km to advance to ground. The illuminating step advances over the 10 to 200 m of already ionized pilot-leader channel at a speed of around 5 × 10⁸ cm/sec.

When the ionized channel has reached within 10 m of the earth, it is met by an upward positive streamer which closes the gap and leads to the blinding flash of the return stroke. The only existing photograph of the upward positive streamer is shown in Fig. 13.12. The return stroke which follows the junction of the stepped leader with positive streamers coming from the ground is a very violent and exceedingly rapidly moving pulse of high luminosity that travels as a potential gradient up the ionized path left by the leader stroke. It reaches velocities as high as 10¹⁰ cm/sec but slows down to 3 × 10⁸ cm/sec as it approaches the cloud. This potential wave causes the brilliant illumination

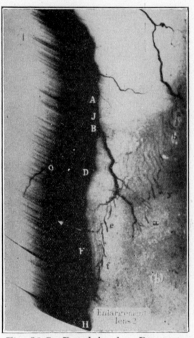

Fig. 13.7 Revolving-lens Boys-camera photograph of a stepped-leader stroke and return flash, by Schonland and Collens. This made history as the first published photograph showing the stepping process. Note the dark steps (film movement right to left). Note the faint channels behind the steps. Note the errant nature of the steps and branching. Note the brilliant (black) return stroke to the left and subsequent current flow to the left. The streaks are caused by points of persistent luminosity in the channel, as yet not understood. This stroke was an exceptionally vigorous one.

accompanied by the ionization which carries the heavy current flow that discharges the lower sections of the cell base. Such a *return stroke* appears to be common to most electrical sparks. After the return stroke, the channel may still carry current and remain luminous for a time of 0.2 to

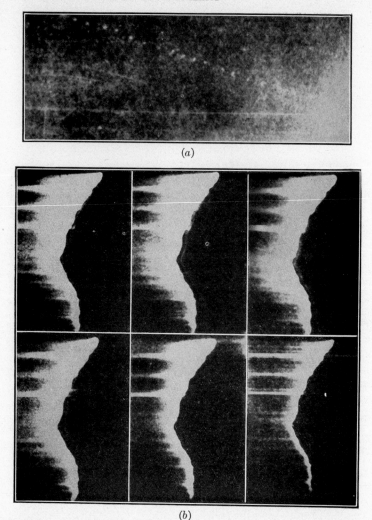

(a)

(b)

Fig. 13.8 A moving-film-camera picture of an upward-stepped positive leader stroke from the Empire State Building at the top, taken by McEachron. Lower traces are subsequent cloud-to-building strokes of the dart-leader return-stroke type. Film moves right to left at top for the steps and right to left for the return strokes of the flash initiated by the steps above, dart moving upward.

0.5 sec while it mops up remaining charge from the cell. The return stroke can be seen in Fig. 13.7; it is represented schematically in Fig. 13.13.

After the events which have been described, some time elapses until the potential at the cloud end of the channel rises to a point sufficient to reignite by a new leader process the now decayed path of ionization left

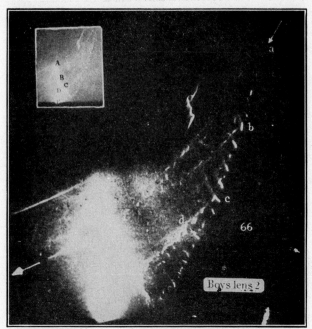

Fig. 13.9   Another cloud-to-ground stroke as observed by Schonland and Collens, showing stepping.   Motion of film rotating from right to left.   Note the branches beginning at steps b and c.

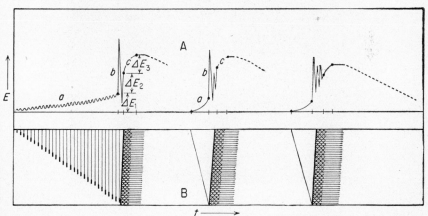

Fig. 13.10   Schonland and Malan's sketches of the α-type stepped leaders and subsequent strokes, as correlated with their oscillographic measurements of field changes.

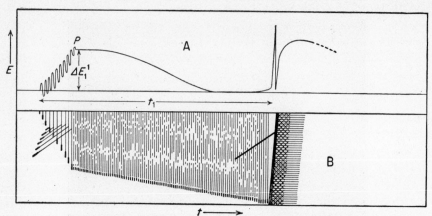

Fig. 13.11 Schonland and Malan's sketches of the β-type intense and branching stepped leaders, together with their oscillographic measurements of field changes.

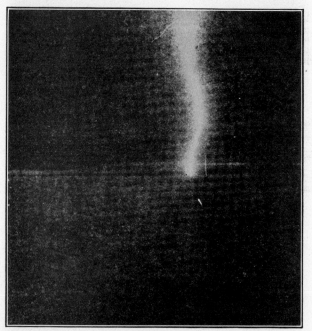

Fig. 13.12 Photograph of a stroke to the water about 100 ft from the camera on a New Jersey beach, as reproduced by K. B. McEachron. Note the three upward-moving positive streamers about 10 m long. One such met the stepped-leader channel, leading to the brilliant return stroke. The other streamers which failed to connect were photographed by the camera.

by the previous stroke. This second leader stroke over the preionized channel was originally termed a *dart leader* by Schonland and is now more often called simply the *leader*. It travels with speeds in the range from 10^8 to 10^9 cm/sec. Such strokes are shown in Fig. 13.8. Other repeated strokes photographed with the Boys camera are shown in Figs. 13.14 and 13.15. The scheme of such strokes is shown in the drawings of Fig. 13.16. We see that the time required for a leader to reach the

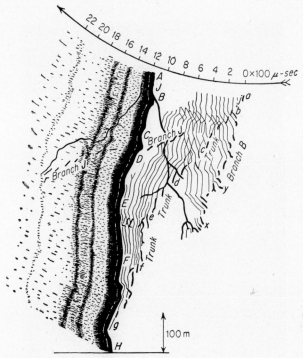

Fig. 13.13 An idealized sketch of Fig. 13.7, with time scale at the upper end, as given by Schonland. Here details are more clearly noted and the time scale helps study. The film effectively rotates from right to left about a point at the center of the arc along the time scale.

ground from a height of 6 km ranges from 1 to 3 msec, while separate strokes occur at various time intervals in the range from 10 to 90 msec, the average being 30 msec. This means that the collection of charge from 1 km up proceeds at about 3×10^6 cm/sec. The charge lowered to earth from the cloud by the first stepped leader may be about 5 coulombs for some 6 km of channel. The average charge per stroke is around 20 coulombs, but strokes carrying up to 160 coulombs have been observed by McEachron, and strokes carrying more than 200 coulombs may occur.

The current involved in the pilot leader and the stepped leader may amount to 50 to 600 amp; the return stroke builds a channel which carries currents as large as half a million amperes. The average current is probably in the range between 5000 and 30,000 amp. This peak current probably lasts only for 100 to 1000 μsec, though the duration of current flow may be much longer for the weaker currents.

When a heavy discharge has passed, its channel remains luminous for some 0.2 to 0.5 sec.

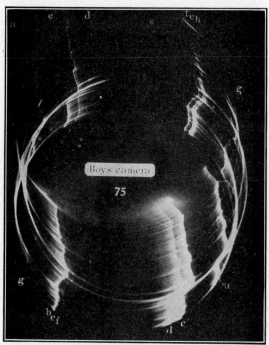

Fig. 13.14   A full-scale Boys-camera revolving-lens photograph of a primary stepped-leader stroke and subsequent dart-leader strokes, taken with two lenses by Schonland.

The diameter of the pilot leader is not known. The diameters of the stepped leaders photographed by Schonland and McEachron extend to as much as 10 m. This has been explained by the author as being caused by a transient radial expansion of the streamer in which the 5-coulomb charge of the leader is stored. The diameter of the highly conducting core of the leader that is reilluminated by the return stroke is probably only about 20 cm, in agreement with the diameter of fulgurites created by the melting of sand where lightning discharges strike beaches or deserts. The photographed diameter of the lightning channel is also some 20 cm. It is possible that the magnetic effects of the heavy current carried by the return stroke tend to constrict the ionized channel through which the current flows.

The electrical potentials of the charged cloud masses are not known. Schonland has estimated that the gradient in the stepped pilot-leader channel is about 1000 volts/cm; for 6 km of path this would make the negative potential relative to ground about 6×10^8 volts. The author believes that gradients required to maintain conductivity against attachment and recombination in pilot-leader channels must be more nearly

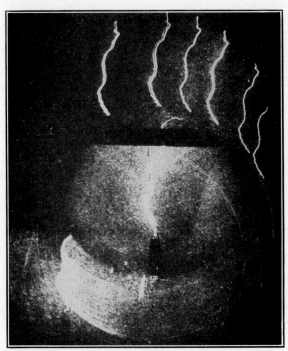

Fig. 13.15   A composite of photographs on several time scales of a stroke to the Empire State Building taken by McEachron. Center, the direct stroke to the building with fixed lens and film. Above, repeated strokes to the building with fast camera. Below, a slower sweep photograph of the stroke showing duration of luminous streaks. Motion from right to left in both the latter cases.

4000 volts/cm. The highly luminous conducting channels created in the stepping process have ion densities of around 10^{11} ion pairs per cm^3; over these channels gradients as low as 1000 volt/cm will serve to produce the currents observed. McEachron estimates the gradients in positive-streamer channels to be 3000 volts/cm. On these various estimates, the cloud potentials range from the 6.8×10^8 assumed by Schonland to as much as 2.4×10^9 volts.

The power developed in one of the heaviest lightning strokes amounts to 2.4×10^{11} kw. If this stroke lasted for a millisecond, the energy liberated would be 1.3×10^5 kwhr. Only about 1.6 per cent of the energy of the stroke would be required to ionize completely the gas in the column carrying the stroke. The rest of the energy is liberated as frictional heat in the movement of gaseous ions through the gas. During the 50-min life of a very active thunderstorm cell, 2.6×10^6 kwhr of electric energy is generated and dissipated by 200 flashes delivering 20 coulombs each.

The expenditure of such energy in the narrow channel might raise the temperature to 20,000°K in a millisecond. The temperatures have not

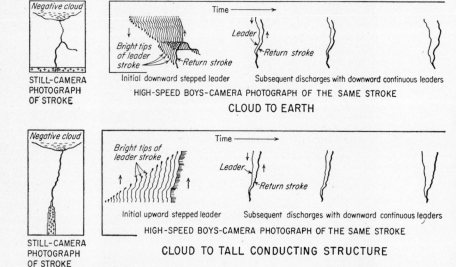

Fig. 13.16   Schematic drawings of cloud-to-ground and Empire-State-Building-to-cloud strokes as shown by McEachron. Left, still camera. Right, moving film. Lower, to building; upper, from charged negative cloud. Note that from the building the *positive* stepped leader moves to junction with the cloud and gives a bright flash. Subsequent discharges are by *dart* leader from the cloud and return flash.

yet been measured, and they may be either lower or higher than this estimated value.

However, certain consequences of the expenditure of energy in the channel are immediately observable. There is a brilliant luminosity which declines rapidly at first and then more slowly. Light may persist in the channel for as long as 0.2 sec, as shown by the luminous streaks in Figs. 13.14 and 13.15. The luminosity comes partly from excitation by the flow of electrical current and, after the stroke, by ion recombination and thermal ionization. Heating in the channel produces an adiabatic expansion which creates a shock wave. This shock wave is responsible for the characteristic sharp crack produced by a nearby lightning flash. After luminosity has died out in the channel, the remaining heat will cause the channel to expand to large dimensions; this ultimately produces rarefaction along the channel followed by collapse and damped oscillations in the air. The oscillating column of air is crooked, some meter or more in diameter and 3 to 6 km long. The atmospheric oscillations give rise to the intense low-frequency rumble we call thunder. The nature of these oscillations produced by lightning and large detonations was not well understood until recent studies connected with atomic explosions made it clear. The oscillation of such large air columns takes place at low frequency and resembles the oscillation of the air column entrapped by a large ocean breaker. The sound produced by thunder reaches an observer over a considerable period of time because of the great length of the oscillating column in which the sound is produced. This accounts for the characteristic rumbling sound of thunder. Considering the magnitude of the energy expended in an average lightning stroke (10^4 kwhr), the sound produced is not particularly impressive. The firing of a 16-in. gun liberates some 2000 kwhr of energy in a concentrated explosion which can be heard for about 30 miles, while thunder ordinarily cannot be heard at distances greater than 12 miles.

Except in the neighborhood of an approaching pilot leader, the electrical fields produced at the earth's surface by thunderstorm clouds are remarkably small. The fair-weather gradient of vertical electric field is 1 volt/cm with ground negative. Under thunderclouds the potential of the ground is usually positive, and the field ranges from 0 to about 50 volts/cm. If a pointed earthed conductor rises 10 m above the surrounding terrain at a gradient of 50 volts/cm, the potential between it and the air surrounding its tip is as much as 5×10^4 volts, which is sufficient to produce the corona which is known as St. Elmo's fire. The top of the Empire State Building is at a height of some 400 m and is thus raised to a potential of 2 million volts relative to the surrounding air. It is clear that any relatively high object near an advancing pilot-leader tip invites a lightning stroke.

All studies thus far made by traversing thunderclouds vertically by means of sounding balloons or horizontally in aircraft flights have failed to register any very high potential gradients. Fields of 300 volts/cm, or else a spark, have been observed with balloons and on the ground by Sir C. G. Simpson and S. J. Scrase. Similar findings have been made by Seville Chapman. Slightly higher fields have been reported by Ross Gunn, as observed on airplane flights through thunderstorms. He found that the fields were generally about ±500 volts/cm except when the airplane was traversing the section of the thundercloud containing the main charge. Here fields ranged up to ±1500 volts/cm, except once when

3400 volts/cm was recorded just before the plane was struck by lightning. Since a field of 30 kv/cm is needed to cause a spark in air at normal pressure, this situation needs to be clarified.

At the voltages and currents it involves, the lightning stroke can produce very destructive results. It can volatilize copper wire, at least up to No. 12 gauge (some 0.081 in.). A heavy stroke should be able to fuse an iron rod of $\frac{1}{4}$ in. diameter, although this seems to occur only rarely. The rate of change of current is so high that the inductance even of a straight conductor becomes important. Often the discharge

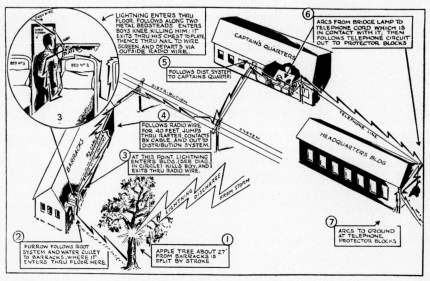

Fig. 13.17 Drawing by McEachron of a fatal and destructive lightning stroke at a CCC camp. It shows what happens when a stroke delivers some 20 or more coulombs of charge to a relatively nonconducting area through which passage to ground water is impeded.

will jump through the air across a bend in a metallic conductor. The magnetostrictive effects of the heavy current enable it to collapse a square copper tube 2×2 cm in cross section with walls 2 mm thick. The reason that more extensive destruction is not produced by heavy strokes probably arises from the circumstance that the current of the stroke is dissipated by a number of conducting paths at the ground end of the 20-cm channel carrying the stroke. When lightning strikes a tree, it tends to follow the channels carrying sap, and the steam generated by the resultant heating of the sap often shatters the tree. The behavior of lightning is most unpredictable when the heavily localized charge of the stroke is delivered to a poorly conducting region such as rock or dry earth. Under these circumstances, very complicated paths may be followed by the charge. See, for example, Fig. 13.17, which depicts the history of a stroke analyzed by K. B. McEachron.

13.5 Generation of Lightning Strokes

The detailed mechanism of the cloud-to-ground stroke discharging the main negative cell of a thundercloud is roughly as follows. The intense turbulence occurring in the throat of the cell will sometimes bring a considerable part of the low-lying positively charged region shown in Fig. 13.4 close to the negative base of the cell. This proximity of opposite charges can suddenly develop a fairly uniform field extending over hundreds of meters and of a value as great as 10,000 volts/cm. In electrical fields of this value, or even somewhat below, the surface-tension forces of the raindrops are overcome by electrical polarization and the droplet is drawn out into a spindle-shaped body with fine tips on either end. The upward tip is positively charged and the lower is negative, as observed by W. A. Macky. Both tips break into a fine spray, but the positive tip gives a point-streamer corona discharge in addition. No such discharge occurs at the negative tip, but the fine spray droplets ejected by the negative tip break into positive streamer corona produced by induction at their upper ends. This spray mechanism has been clearly delineated by W. N. English in our laboratory; it causes positive ions and positively charged fine mist to move upward into the negative cell base, leaving behind heavier particles and larger droplets which are negatively charged. This action is probably the basic mechanism by which the dispersed negative charge is drained from raindrops in the cloud. When the field is greater than 8 to 10 kv/cm, one of the streamers develops a very strong localized stress. This stress, progressing up toward the negative cell, leads to a lightning stroke between the area of positive charge and the negative-cell base. Macky has observed that water droplets not only break up and yield corona in uniform electric fields of the magnitude indicated, but also lead to a spark at such fields of about 10 kv/cm rather than at the 30 kv/cm required for sparks in dry air. Unfortunately, in the short scope of this chapter it is impossible to give the details of the mechanism by which the streamer process causes breakdown.

In the relatively short intracloud spark discharge whose genesis has been described, a considerable mass of negative charge at the base of the negative-charge column is suddenly transferred to the lower region occupied by positive charges. This neutralizes the positive charge and carries down excess negative charge by inductive inertia. Thus a very strong electrical field is suddenly created at the cloud base. The magnitude of the charge transfer and field distortions caused by the short intracloud spark varies over wide limits, being greater the more vigorous the cell and the higher the initial charges. Also, the more violent the intracloud stroke, the more conducting will be the intracloud spark channel and the greater the current fed into it from the negative cell base by the positive water-droplet streamers. Schonland has estimated that, on the average, the lowering of negative charge to the spark channel proceeds at a speed of some 3×10^6 cm/sec, draining off the negative charge from 900 m of cloud in 30 msec.

Once the stroke to the negative cell base has replaced the former positive cloud by a strong negative field, the fields are right for the advance of the negative electron-swarm streamer which is the negative counterpart of the upward positive streamer which initiated the spark to the negative cell base. This negative streamer, now called the pilot leader, advances earthward at a relatively low speed. The diameter of its channel is initially some 20 cm. The velocity of advance of its tip varies from about 10^7 cm/sec for very weak strokes to an occasional 2.5×10^8 cm/sec for the heaviest. The current involved in the pilot-leader–stepped-leader process ranges from 50 to perhaps 600 amp. The streamers create between 10^{13} and 10^{15} ion pairs per cm of advance. These ions are mainly created in the electron-swarm head of the pilot-leader streamer. Because of the flow of current in the 20-cm conducting channel, an excess of negative electrons over positive ions is created along the path. About 1.2×10^{-5} coulomb excess negative charge is distributed along each centimeter of path. This excess negative charge, created immediately behind the streamer tip, produces radial electric fields which cause the excess negative charge to expand over a region roughly 5 m in radius. Thus, immediately behind the advancing streamer tip, there exists an expanding channel of diffusing electron space charge which is *temporarily* luminous in some cases but not bright enough to be photographed. The actual conducting channel which carries most of the ion pairs, however, remains some 20 cm in diameter.

For some reason not yet clear, the progressive behavior of the pilot leader of any single stroke is remarkably consistent, while pilot leaders of different strokes differ widely in their behavior. The constancy of behavior in the stroke and variation between strokes are somehow connected with the fields at the tip of the negative-streamer pilot leader, with the rate of drainage of charge from the cloud, and with the dissipative processes which are active in the channel. These dissipative processes consist of recombination of electrons and ions, diffusion of electrons, and the attachment of electrons to molecules of oxygen to form negative ions. Under the influence of these agencies, the pilot-leader streamer slows down and comes to rest after a given distance of advance which is constant in a given stroke but varies widely from one stroke to another. For vigorous strokes Schonland has observed advances of some 200 m in 90 μsec, corresponding to speeds of 2.2×10^8 cm/sec. In other cases, the advance was 30 m in 30 μsec, or 10^8 cm/sec. Slower and shorter steps frequently occur but cannot be photographed. McEachron has observed in his studies at the Empire State Building positive pilot leaders advancing 10 m at speeds of 3×10^7 cm/sec or less. These observations were possible because McEachron's cameras were nearer to the strokes than were Schonland's.

The errant and interrupted advances of the actual pilot-leader streamers are not visible. Their presence has been inferred by what is next observed. As the pilot leader comes near the end of its step, it slows down. The potential gradient down the channel carrying the current flow decreases, and the current declines and disappears. Which of these is cause and which effect is not yet known. As this occurs the upper and older part of the channel has lost current carriers by dissipative effects and current flow, so that it has become less conducting. In consequence, assuming constant flow of current from the cloud to the region from which the leader started, the potential begins to build up next to the decaying plasma at the cloud end of the now stationary pilot-leader streamer. When the charge accumulation gradient to the inactive streamer channel has reached a certain value, a wave of ionization sweeps down the channel of the arrested pilot leader. The ionization density at the end of the pilot-leader channel has now decayed to about 10^8 electrons/cm over a 5-m radius. The ionizing wave of potential gradient travels at a speed of 5×10^8 cm/sec and increases the ionization density perhaps a thousandfold, to a value of 10^{11} ions/cm^3. The resulting channel of 5-m radius, which is between 30 and 200 m long in vigorous strokes, is the *luminous step* of the stepped-leader stroke as first observed by Schonland and his associates and later photographed by McEachron (Figs. 13.7 to 13.9).

After the conductivity of the channel has been revived, the negative pilot-leader streamer forges ahead once more for its next step of nearly the same length. Figures 13.10 and 13.11 illustrate schematically the advance of the α- and β-type stepped leaders, the black sections indicating the steplike regions as they flash up through the potential wave in the step process. Figure 13.16 shows the process as pictured by McEachron for positive and negative strokes.

Though the single steps are surprisingly uniform,* they do not all move earthward in the same straight line. There is a great deal of wandering and branching, as shown in Fig. 13.7. These actions are caused by local vagaries of the cloud fields, pockets of ionization, local changes of gas density in gusts, etc. Very vigorous stepped leaders proceeding by long

---

* The uniformity is surprising because it exists at all. Successive steps actually vary in length by factors of 2 or 3, but the average length and even more so the velocity in any given leader is rather close to the most probable value.

steps show prominent branching in the β strokes.   Branches dissipate the charge and slow the pilot leaders.   Branching always occurs in the direction of the stroke and leader advance.   Figure 13.5 shows how the characteristic branching indicates the direction of progress of the stroke. Only rarely do two branches of a single stroke strike the ground, since the return stroke occurring along the first branch to reach the ground hampers the advance of any other branch.

As the stepped leader approaches the earth, the gradient between its tip and the ground increases.   Most of the potential difference between the cloud and ground is represented by the 1- to 4-kv/cm gradient necessary to keep the current of 5 to 600 amp flowing down the channel.   At the tip of the streamer there exists a region perhaps a meter long in which the gradient is very high.   Between the tip and the earth there is an electrical field which, according to observation, may reach 3400 volts/ cm just before the stroke materializes, but does not appear to rise above this value.   Since the time scale is so short, the actual gradient between the tip of the leader and the earth just before the leader reaches the earth is not yet known.   Whatever the exact value of this gradient may be, it is clear that only a few centimeters of height—say 200 cm of a good earthed conductor—will at 3000 volts/cm give fields of nearly 1 million volts/cm at the tip of the conductor.   Such fields will produce a positive corona streamer that advances upward to meet the negative step channel.   It is generally believed that such phenomena occur in ways that vary widely with the nature of the terrain.   They have not often been observed, although Fig. 13.12 shows a beautiful picture of such upward leaders in a stroke occurring to the water only 100 ft from the camera.

Once junction between the leader tip and positive streamer has been achieved, all the accumulated potential difference appears across a short region of highly conducting plasma.   The wave of ionizing potential gradient which constitutes the return stroke travels up the channel at speeds in the neighborhood of 10^{10} cm/sec, leaving behind a channel 20 cm in diameter which is practically fully ionized.   The return wave slows somewhat and dissipates as it advances up the channel, especially when it reaches a branch which it reilluminates.   When the original wave has slowed sufficiently, a new pulse of potential starts and proceeds further up the channel.   When the cloud is finally reached and the negative base of the cell is connected to the ground through the brilliantly luminous, highly conducting channel of completely ionized gas, a heavy current of magnitude up to 10^5 amp flows until the lowest kilometer of the cloud base is discharged.   The discharge process and the return stroke are shown in Fig. 13.7 and depicted schematically in Fig. 13.13.

The return stroke thus follows and illuminates the relatively highly conducting inner channel of the pilot leader, some 20 cm in diameter, increasing its carrier density from 10^{11} to about 10^{19} electrons/cm³. It does not reionize the *larger channel* of 5 m radius that was initially illuminated by the electron space charge of the stepped leader. At the time of occurrence of the return stroke, the charge density in this large diffuse channel is too low to permit its reillumination. Its initial ionization density of 10^{11} electrons/cm³ has decayed to 10^7 electrons/cm³, or even less, by the time that the return stroke starts. The return stroke thus follows the region of 20 cm diameter in which the current flow of the streamer has kept ionization active, the electron density being in excess of 10^{11} electrons/cm³.

After the cloud base has been discharged by the first stroke, the initially heavy current in the channel declines because of diminished potential gradient, lowered electron supply, and decay of carriers. Meanwhile, the second section of the negative cloud cell has been stimulated by the field of the positive charge at the top of the first lightning-stroke channel. It begins to feed more charge to the top of the channel, which is by this time relatively nonconducting. When this process has produced fields of adequate magnitude over sufficient depth, a new wave of potential gradient, causing ionization by collision, sweeps down the old spark channel at a speed of around 5×10^8 cm/sec. This wave of ionization down the formerly ionized path is

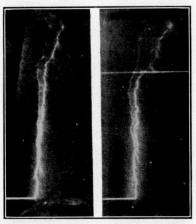

Fig. 13.18 Allibone and Meek's photographs of impulsive breakdown from positive point to negative plane in gaps about 1 m long. The point is on top. Film moves from right to left. In the photograph on the left, there is relatively low resistance in series with the gap. Note the downward streamer and upward return stroke. In the photograph on the right, there is a high resistance in series with the point. Note the stepping before the return stroke. The connection between current drain down the streamer channel and current supply to the point makes a significant analogy with the stepping in lightning strokes.

not stepped in its advance, but moves continuously. It is called the *dart leader* or *leader stroke* in contrast with the *initial stepped leader*. It is luminous for some 50 m behind the advancing wavefront and can be photographed. When the dart leader reaches the earth, a new return stroke follows, with high current as before. Figure 13.16 shows the process schematically, while Fig. 13.8 shows photographs of this process. Figure 13.18 shows positive streamers in impulsive sparks from a positive point to a negative plane 1 m distant. The trace on the left has been

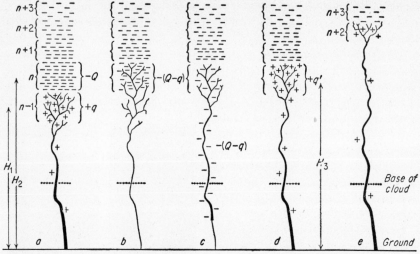

Fig. 13.19 A schematic drawing by Schonland showing how successive strokes down the same channel drain off successive sections of the negative cloud cell.

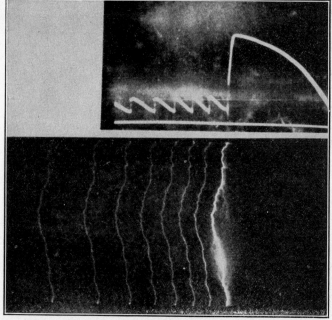

Fig. 13.20 Allibone and Meek's photographs of impulsive breakdown sparks from positive point to negative plane with point uppermost (slow motion from right to left). Here capacity and series resistance cause repeated sparks down the same channel at intervals of roughly 50 μsec. The oscillogram above shows the potential. Here again is the formal electrical analogue of the repeated lightning stroke.

stepped by the use of a high resistance. Observe the return stroke in both cases and the general resemblance between this phenomenon and the lightning stroke.

At intervals of some 30 msec, similar secondary discharges follow down the same channel, each with a dart leader as shown in Figs. 13.8 and 13.15. This process continues until the whole 6 km of cell height containing charge has been discharged. The successive discharge of higher and higher sections, as pictured by Schonland, is shown in Fig. 13.19. Successive impulsive sparks following an initial channel and simulating the behavior of lightning are shown in Fig. 13.20. Here, the charging of a capacitance through a resistance is responsible for the successive strokes.

During the life of a thunderstorm cell there will be several rechargings of the cloud at intervals of 1 to 10 min, depending upon its activity. Each such recharging leads to new strokes initiated by stepped leaders and dart leaders as explained above.

14

Transient Phenomena in Supersonic Flow*

WALKER BLEAKNEY
PROFESSOR OF PHYSICS
PRINCETON UNIVERSITY

Although the study of the mechanics of fluids has been going on for hundreds of years, there are many essentially simple observations that are not fully understood today. Transient behavior in physical systems is usually more difficult to predict theoretically than steady-state phenomena, especially when the fundamental differential equations describing the system are nonlinear as they are for the problems to be discussed here. Simple relations, such as Snell's laws for reflection and refraction of plane waves of light at the boundary between two mediums, have been known for three centuries, but the corresponding relations for pressure waves of finite amplitude in a compressible gas are still obscure. Fluid dynamics is full of difficult problems involving boundary layers, heat flow, skin friction, turbulence, and chemical kinetics. Each of these has both steady and transient aspects, but in this chapter the discussion will be confined to the more purely physical problem of shock waves and their interactions in gases.

14.1 Experimental Methods

Experimentally there are a number of ways of creating shock waves for the purpose of studying their characteristics. A sudden release of considerable energy in a small space, exemplified by a condensed spark or the detonation of an explosive, is a familiar way of generating a more or less spherical shock in the surrounding atmosphere. A missile in supersonic flight sets up a bow wave in the form of a shock propagating

* Much of the experimental work described in this chapter was supported by the Office of Naval Research. Reproduction, translation, publication, use, and disposal in whole or in part by or for the U.S. Government is permitted.

358

outward from the line of motion. Shocks are associated with many jets, nozzles, and all kinds of turbines and compressors where stream velocities exceed the speed of sound. Two of the most convenient sources of shock waves and other flow phenomena in gases for study in the laboratory are the wind tunnel and the shock tube. The tunnel is used chiefly for the investigation of steady phenomena, whereas the shock tube finds its greatest utility in the elucidation of transient behavior. Since this chapter is concerned primarily with transient effects and since most of the experimental observations were obtained from the shock tube, it will not be out of place to describe very briefly the principles of operation of this device. Should the reader desire more details an abundant literature[1,2] will supply his needs.

The shock tube in its usual form consists of a long straight tube of uniform cross section divided into two separate chambers by a thin transverse diaphragm. A pressure difference between the two chambers is produced by some suitable means. When the diaphragm bursts, a rush of gas into the chamber of lower pressure soon generates a plane shock wave which is propagated down the length of the tube. The mechanism of the development of a shock front will become apparent in the next section. If transparent windows are installed in the walls of the tube at some distance from the diaphragm, the passage of the shock front may be observed by optical means such as the flash picture of its shadow on a photographic plate. A more useful but more complicated procedure consists in placing the viewing section in one arm of an interferometer and noting the shifted position of the fringes when the disturbance appears. The fringe shift is then a direct measure of the change in density of the gas. A number of illustrations of this technique will be found in the figures to follow. Of course, the light flash must be sufficiently short to stop effectively the motion of the fast-moving shock. Exposures of the order of 1 μsec were used in the accompanying illustrations. Of course, many details of procedure and equipment necessary to the operation of the tube are omitted here, and only the barest principles necessary for what follows have been mentioned.

14.2   Characteristics of a Shock Front

When a plane progressive pressure wave or pulse of finite amplitude passes through a gas, its shape (*i.e.*, its profile of pressure vs. distance or time) changes as it proceeds along its course. Obviously, pressure, temperature, density, velocity, and other related quantities can be used as a variable to describe such a wave. Using the first, one observes that parts of the wave having different pressures travel with different velocities. There are two reasons for this behavior. First, the medium has been

[1] Corresponding numbered bibliographic references appear at the end of the chapter.

set in motion by that part of a wave preceding any given point, and the signals there will travel with the local speed of sound c plus the stream velocity u appropriate to the point. Second, the local speed of sound c will itself be changed with reference to the undisturbed value by the adiabatic change in pressure and hence in temperature that has been induced by the preceding part of the wave. Any increased pressure amplitude p_1 in Fig. 14.1a overtakes the smaller amplitudes ahead of it, and the front becomes progressively steeper, ending in a virtual discontinuity as in 14.1c. Similar arguments show that in a region of decreasing pressure the wave becomes less steep with time. This is all elementary and well known, but the direct experimental test of the phenomenon shown in Fig. 14.2 is new. In the interferogram of Fig. 14.2a, a plane

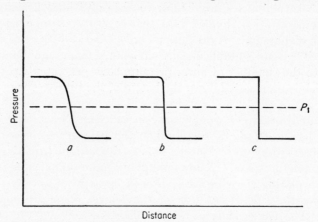

Fig. 14.1 Sketch of a pressure-distance profile of a compression pulse at three different times.

progressive wavefront of increasing density is proceeding toward the right. A short interval later it appears as in 14.2b, where the density change is more rapid; still later, the front has developed into an apparent discontinuity, as indicated in 14.2c. The wave is, of course, in rapid motion, the elapsed time from 14.2a to 14.2c amounting to about 1 msec.

From the standpoint of an observer riding with the wave, the only steady or stable compression of large amplitude that can exist in an ideal fluid is this discontinuous front which is called a *shock*. The differential equations describing the progressive wave are no longer valid across the front, and a set of difference equations, commonly referred to as the Rankine-Hugoniot equations, expressing the conservation of energy, momentum, and mass is required to relate the variables on the two sides of the shock.[3]

Up to now the shock front has been considered as a mathematical discontinuity, whereas there are ample reasons for believing that physically in a real gas the thickness of the front is finite.   The temperature gradient cannot become infinite, because the heat conductivity does not vanish; a stable profile is reached when these two effects come into proper balance.   The problem must be approached from the kinetic-theory point of view, but the solution is not yet entirely complete.   Detailed studies have indicated, however, that for a monatomic gas and for strong shocks the thickness, defined as the total change in pressure divided by the maximum pressure gradient, is certainly not more than a few mean free paths of an atom.[4]   The thickness increases as the shock strength

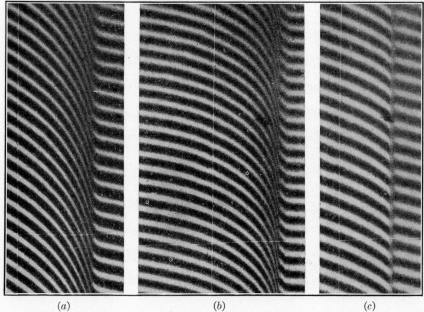

(a)   (b)   (c)

Fig. 14.2   Interferogram of a compression front (a) traveling toward the right. Later at (b) the front has become steeper, and at (c) a shock has developed.

decreases.   Put another way, the average number of collisions suffered by an atom during the passage of the front is about one for strong shocks and increases to a larger number for weak shocks.   Some experimental information on the thickness has been obtained by studying the reflectivity[5] of the layer for visible light; on the whole, these investigations confirm the general concepts of the theory.

When one turns to polyatomic gases or to such strong shocks that excitation of inner degrees of freedom is involved, the picture is somewhat changed.   Not only must collisions bring molecules into translational equilibrium with a new environment as they pass through the front, but also internal and rotational equilibrium must be established.

In many cases, the number of collisions required for the latter process is much larger than that required by the former.   A good example illustrating this effect is to be found in carbon dioxide, where only a few collisions are involved in the transfer of translational and rotational energy, while many thousands of collisions are necessary to establish complete equilibrium.   As the shock front passes, the apparent temperature jumps very rapidly above the final equilibrium value because the effective specific heat involves only translation and rotation.   Thereafter

Fig. 14.3 Shock front in CO_2 showing continuous change in density behind the front as a result of "relaxation" of the internal motions of the molecule.   This interferogram was taken in white light, permitting the identification of the fringes on the two sides of the discontinuity.

the temperature falls asymptotically toward its final state as the heat energy is more slowly absorbed in the vibrational states.   This process is pictured in Fig. 14.3 where the shock front is moving toward the right, the density given by the fringe shift showing a continuous rise as the temperature behind the front falls.   The pressure, as has been shown theoretically, undergoes little change except at the sharp front.   It is also worth noting that the final state of the gas is independent of the details of the transition process;[6] hence the Rankine-Hugoniot equations are still valid when applied to the initial and final states.   Superficially the appearance of the fringes in Fig. 14.3 is similar to that of the fringes in Fig. 14.2, but the underlying physical mechanisms are totally different.

Figure 14.3 represents a *steady* condition, while the profile of Fig. 14.2 varies with time. Similar "relaxation times" are associated with rotational degrees of freedom and dissociation of the molecules, some of which are shorter and some longer than in the particular example discussed here.

Having discussed briefly something of the nature of a shock front itself, we now inquire into the nature of its interaction with the boundaries of the homogeneous medium in which we assume it is propagated. It is convenient to divide the subject into three topics, the first dealing with reflection from a plane rigid wall, the second with the refraction at the boundary between two different gases, and the third with the manner in which shocks are diffracted around solid obstacles.

14.3   Reflection of Shocks from a Rigid Wall

Two parameters are sufficient to fix the initial conditions for a reflection problem. They may be taken as the angle of incidence α between

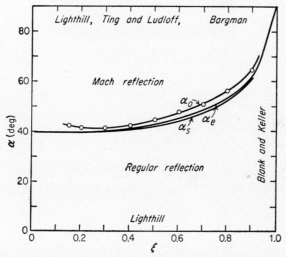

Fig. 14.4 Plot showing types of reflection in terms of initial conditions ξ, α. Below the curve α_s the flow along the wall relative to the shock intersection is supersonic. Above the curve α_e no solutions of the regular reflection problem exist. The boundary above which Mach reflection is observed is designated α_0. The regions where the various asymptotic solutions apply are indicated by the names around the boundary.

the normals to the shock and the wall, and the shock strength $\xi = p_1/p_2$, where p_1 and p_2 are the pressures ahead of and just behind the shock front. The permissible values of α run from 0 through 90° and those for ξ from 0 to 1. Any point in the $(\xi - \alpha)$ plane shown in Fig. 14.4 represents a set of possible initial conditions; the two general cases for the reflection configuration that result have been known for a long time and are commonly referred to as *regular* and *Mach* reflection. The regu-

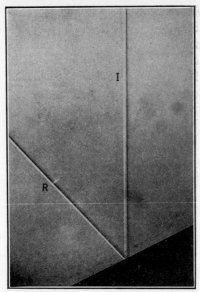

Fig. 14.5 Shadow photograph of regular reflection for an incident shock of pressure ratio $\xi = 0.94$.   Beyond the field of view the reflected shock is curved as a result of the influence of the corner where the interaction began.

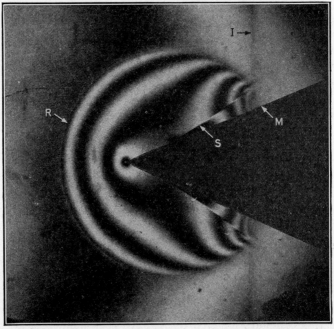

Fig. 14.6 Contour interferogram of the complete Mach reflection showing incident ve *I* moving toward the right, reflection *R*, Mach wave *M*, and slipstream *S* = 0.42)

ar reflection is a two-shock configuration, as illustrated in Fig. 14.5. The Mach reflection involves three shocks and a density discontinuity or slipstream, as illustrated in Fig. 14.6. The interferometric pictures are usually taken in one of two ways. In the first, the fringes in the undisturbed region are a system of parallel lines and the fringe shifts must be determined to measure the change in density when the disturbance comes along. In the second or *contour-fringe* method, the undisturbed region gives uniform illumination of light everywhere in the same

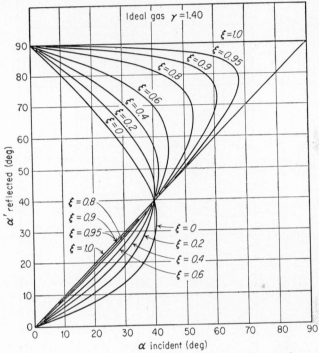

Fig. 14.7 Angle of reflection α' vs. angle of incidence α for shock strengths ξ in regular reflection.

phase and the fringes that appear in the disturbed region directly represent contours of constant fringe shift without further analysis. Figure 14.2 is an illustration of the first method and Fig. 14.6 of the second. Details of the technique may be found in the literature.[1]

As yet no complete solution has been given for either of these types of reflection, though "local" theories, meant to apply in the neighborhood of the intersection of the shocks, have been proposed. In the regular type of reflection the basic assumption is that after the passage of the two shocks the resulting gas velocity must be parallel to the wall. The corresponding assumption for Mach reflection is that the deflection of the flow, relative to the point of intersection, which is induced by the incident and reflected shocks shall be the same as that induced by the Mach wave and that the pressure must be continuous across the boundary between these two flows. It is an intriguing circumstance that experiment seems to substantiate the first solution but disagrees with

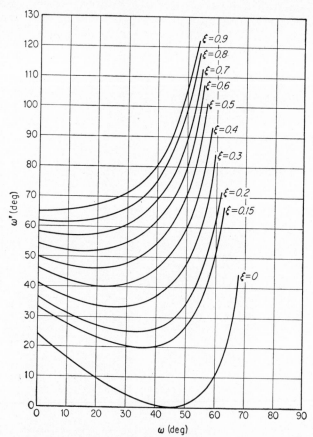

Fig. 14.8 Angle of reflection ω' vs. angle of incidence ω, each measured relative to the direction of motion of the shock intersection for different shock strengths in Mach reflection.

the second. Neither of these simple theories throws any light on the density field throughout the disturbed region nor gives any information on the rate of growth from the wall of the Mach shock.

The local theories give the angles and strengths of the other shocks as functions of the angle of incidence α and strength ξ of the incident shock. For finite shocks the angles of incidence and reflection are not in general equal, as one is accustomed to finding in dealing with light and sound waves. Instead, the relation for regular reflection is found to be that shown in Fig. 14.7, where it will be noted that for a permitted angle of incidence α there are in general two permitted angles of reflection α', the lower of which corresponds to the observations. In a similar way, Fig. 14.8 illustrates a family of solutions for the three-shock problem. Here

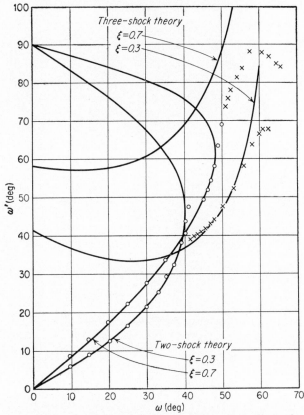

Fig. 14.9 Comparison of predicted and measured angles[7] shown by curves and points, respectively. Circles represent observed regular reflections, and crosses Mach reflections. Since some shocks are curved, the values refer to the angles of the tangents at the intersection.

the angles of incidence and reflection ω and ω' are measured relative to the intersection from the incoming flow, ω differing from α by a constant. Only one of two solutions is plotted here, the one closest to experimental observation. A sample of the comparison between these calculations and experiment is given in Fig. 14.9 where it will be seen that for strong shocks the agreement is not bad, while for weak shocks the three-shock results depart radically from the predicted values.

Space does not permit a full discussion of the reflection phenomenon, and the reader must refer to the literature[7] for more complete details. However, the present state of knowledge on the subject may be briefly summarized with the help of Fig. 14.4.   Some asymptotic solutions of

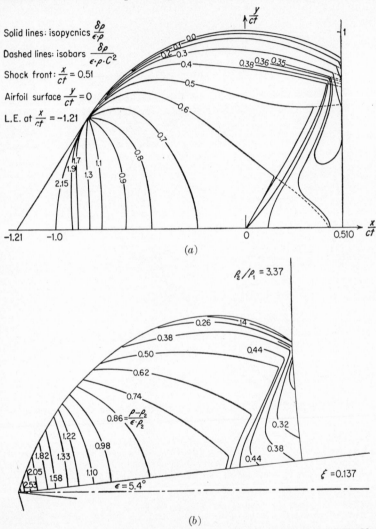

(a)

(b)

Fig. 14.10   (a) Predicted density contours for glancing incidence.[10]   (b) Observed density contours for nearly glancing incidence ($\alpha = 84.6°$).[13]

the problem have been found for limiting values of ξ and α, but in the general area of regular reflection below the lowest curve in the figure the local theory agrees rather well with experiment.   The curve labeled α_e, called the extreme angle, represents the boundary above which no solutions of the two-shock theory exist. Experimentally, two-shock configurations are apparently observed above this curve until the top curve, which represents the observed onset of Mach reflection, is reached. The local theory fails badly in the Mach region, and as yet there is no general solution here.

The complete asymptotic solution for weak shocks at nearly glancing incidence was given by Bargmann[8] and extended to strong shocks by Lighthill[9] and Ting and Ludloff.[10] The problem of regular reflection at nearly head-on incidence has been treated by Lighthill,[11] and the reflection of a sound pulse for all angles has been solved by Keller and Blank.[12] The areas where these solutions apply are indicated in Fig. 14.4. All

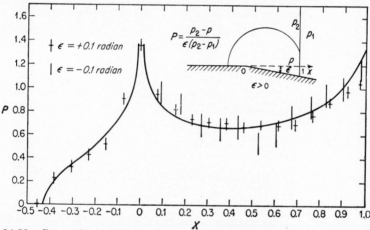

Fig. 14.11 Comparison of predicted and measured pressures on the wall at nearly glancing incidence[7] ($\xi = 0.5$).

these solutions have been compared with experiments performed under conditions approaching the limits imposed by the theory, and the agreement is satisfactory. One example[13] of this comparison is illustrated in Fig. 14.10a theoretical and b observed for a strong shock at nearly glancing incidence. Such discrepancies as appear can probably be attributed to the finite angle of the wedge necessary to produce measurable density contours. The pressure on the wall as computed and measured[7] is indicated in Fig. 14.11 for the nearly glancing case, and here also the agreement is good.

All the theoretical analyses have assumed a perfect inviscid and nonconducting fluid, and it is believed that this assumption is justified. However, more theoretical and experimental work must be done before the solution of the problem of the simple reflection of a shock can be said to be in a satisfactory state.

14.4   Refraction at a Gaseous Interface

Considering all the difficulties found in giving a rational explanation of the reflection of a shock from a rigid wall, it is not surprising that relatively less progress has been made in the elucidation of the refraction pattern at the boundary between two gases. The heading of this section is meant to apply to the complete interaction including incident, transmitted, and reflected waves. In spite of the complications, some useful theoretical and experimental work has been carried out, and at least in certain cases the physical pattern of waves is quite simple. Let us see what some of the boundary conditions are.

By analogy with sound and other waves and in accordance with observations on shocks under some conditions, one may begin by assuming a

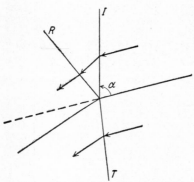

plane incident step shock I impinging at an arbitrary angle α on the plane boundary between two gases, giving rise to reflected and transmitted waves R and T which radiate from a common intersection with I on the boundary, as sketched in Fig. 14.12. If these waves are describable as functions only of angle as assumed here, a simple and logical boundary condition is that the total deflection of the flow relative to the intersection shall be the same on the two sides of the boundary and that the pressure remain continuous across the boundary. It will be noted that the boundary itself is deflected in

Fig. 14.12   Configuration of the refraction of a shock at the boundary between two gases. The arrows show streamlines of the flow relative to the intersection.

the process. The mathematical expressions for these conditions involving the characteristics of the waves have been set up by Taub[14] and Polachek and Seeger,[15] and some of the solutions have been investigated. There are five independent parameters altogether involved in the initial conditions, three of which are fixed by the choice of gases and may be taken as γ_1, γ_2, and a_1/a_2 where γ is the specific-heat ratio and a is the velocity of sound. The other two are given by the shock strength ξ and the angle of incidence α.

The algebraic equations that result from this analysis are too complicated to reproduce here. They have many families of solutions, and it becomes difficult to designate those which are physically realizable. The original assumptions can at best hold only for limited ranges of the parameters. It is useful, however, to review some of the principal features of this analysis and compare them with such experimental observations as are available. Under the specified conditions it is concluded that the transmitted wave is always a shock. The reflected wave may be either a shock or a rarefaction of the Prandtl-Meyer type (*i.e.*, pressure, for instance, is a function of angle but not of radius from the intersection), depending on circumstances. In many specific cases a critical transition angle of incidence is found on one side of which the reflection is a shock and on the other a rarefaction. At the critical angle one would therefore expect total transmission. It is also clear that certain a priori limitations on the angle of incidence exist for the picture we have assumed.

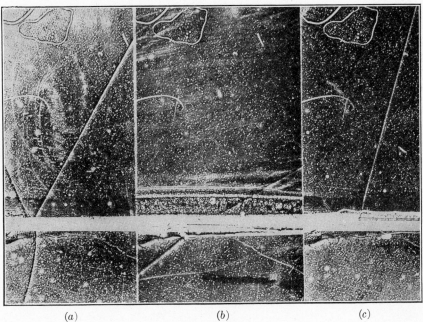

(a)   (b)   (c)

Fig. 14.13 Shadow pictures of the refraction of a shock going from air into methane. The two gases are separated by a soap film. In (a) the incident I, reflected R, and transmitted T shocks are evident. In (b) no reflection is visible, and it is presumed that it is a rarefaction which would not show in shadow. In (c) the angle of refraction has become imaginary, and no transmitted wave can be seen.

The component of the flow normal to the reflected wave on the incoming side cannot be subsonic, since this signal cannot travel slower than the local velocity of sound, but for some angles of incidence this condition is violated whatever the angle of reflection, and hence a reflection centered on the intersection cannot exist. A second limitation on the assumed configuration is that the angle of refraction shall not become imaginary, a situation analogous to total internal reflection of light. The physical interpretation is found in the case where the velocity of sound in the second medium is greater than the velocity of the intersection along the boundary.

According to Polachek and Seeger,[15] certain extreme angles are found even within the above restrictions beyond which solutions of what is thought to be the physically realizable type no longer exist.   The upshot of the matter is that in certain restricted ranges of the parameters a local theory predicting wave strengths and angles has been developed, and in analogy to the reflection on a rigid wall this might be called the theory of regular refraction.   The complete phenomenon is a transient one, and the influence of the corner must be included in its explanation.   The situation is obviously complicated at those angles of incidence where signals from the corner influence the reflected wave throughout its extent and something analogous to Mach reflection probably occurs.   It is even possible for the incident wave itself to be distorted when the signals in the second medium run faster than the intersection, since they may then come back into the first medium ahead of the incident shock.

Illustrations of some of these configurations are shown in Fig. 14.13.

14.5   Diffraction

The phenomena associated with the manner in which a shock wave envelops or gets around a solid object are here included in the term *diffraction*.   When a simple plane shock impinges on a solid object, a considerable perturbation of the flow field results with concomitant pressure-force distributions on the object.   Sometimes the whole disturbance is referred to as a *diffraction pattern*, even though various reflections and interferences play a role.   Here again only the simplest cases are amenable to reasonably complete theoretical treatment.

One of the simple cases can be handled by the methods already mentioned under Mach reflection at nearly glancing incidence, where the approximations linearize the equations so that the solution is valid for $\pm \epsilon$ where ϵ is the small angle of deflection of the wall.   The results of the analysis agree with observations made near these limiting conditions, an example of which was shown in Fig. 14.10.   Similar computations can be made by the methods of Friedlander[16] and Keller[17] for diffraction around corners of finite angle but for waves of weak or sonic amplitude. A partial solution for the flow around a corner of large angle given by Jones, Martin, and Thornhill[18] is applicable only to shocks so strong that the afterflow is supersonic with respect to the corner.   An interferometric density pattern of this case is given in Fig. 14.14.

Aside from these few cases, little can be predicted quantitatively about diffraction patterns or the pressure forces on various obstacles, the latter being of great practical importance to military and civil defense.   In spite of this discouraging view, it is of interest to investigate experi-

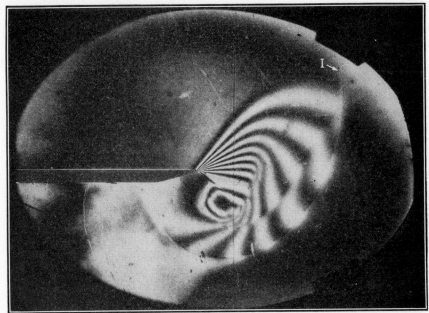

Fig. 14.14   Contour interferogram of the diffraction and resulting afterflow around a sharp corner when the incident shock is sufficiently strong to produce supersonic flow[19] ($\xi = 0.13$).

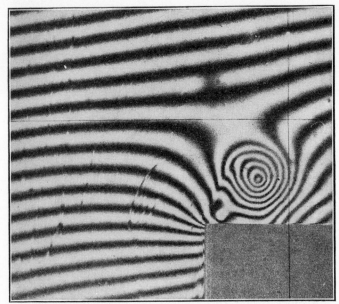

Fig. 14.15   Vortex formed at a corner when a shock (out of view) is propagated toward the right.   The vortex grows with time.

mentally the diffraction around simple two-dimensional forms to develop some intuitive feeling for what happens. Small-scale experiments performed in a shock tube[20] indicate that, in the process of getting around an isolated corner, a step shock in air sets up a strong vortex or eddy, as illustrated in Fig. 14.15. One of the simple characteristics of the pattern observed empirically is that the shape does not change with time. Only its size grows in the "pseudostationary" fashion (*i.e.*, the phenomenon is describable, for example, by two coordinates x/t and y/t). This is a great simplification in that a picture at one time is sufficient to

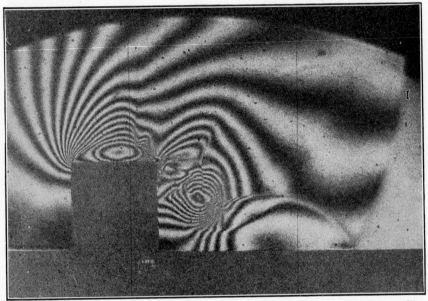

Fig. 14.16 Diffraction of a shock over a rectangular block. The shock traveling toward the right may be seen at the right edge of the picture, and its reflection from the horizontal plate after passing over the block is clearly visible.

predict the pattern at all other times. The word *isolated* was inserted above to indicate that besides the corner no other disturbing influence was present, and it is obvious that in a finite apparatus this condition can apply for a limited time only, after which the pseudostationary character disappears. It is not presumed that this description of the behavior is precisely correct for a real gas, but the experiments demonstrate at least that pseudostationary flow is a good approximation.

The vortices are regions of low pressure and have a marked influence on the forces exerted on the solid object. Figure 14.16 shows the diffraction of a shock over a two-dimensional rectangular block resting on a flat plate, and Fig. 14.17 gives the average force over the top as a

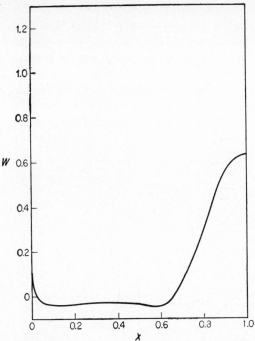

Fig. 14.17   Distribution of pressure W over the top of the block.   The ordinate is the overpressure in atmospheres $W = (p - p_0)/p_0$.   Note that negative values occur at some points ($\xi = 0.52$).

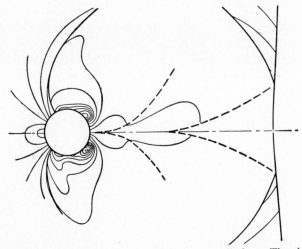

Fig. 14.18   Diffraction of a shock ($\xi = 0.55$) over a cylinder.   The shock front on the right has almost repaired itself after the obstruction.   Density contours taken from an interferogram are shown.   At this stage the pattern is symmetrical about a horizontal line through the center of the cylinder.

function of time.   The minimum near the front of the block is a direct result of the strong vortex formed behind the front corner.

As a final illustration of these effects, the density contour patterns of Figs. 14.18 and 14.19 show the transient behavior of a shock wave passing over a cylinder as the afterflow approaches a steady state, steady in the sense that only periodic disturbances remain.   Von Kármán[21] as early as 1912 discussed the behavior of this *vortex street* (as the series of alternating vortices are called) and gave an expression for the drag in

Fig. 14.19   Same configuration as the preceding figure after the shock has traveled a distance of 70 diameters.   Alternating vortexes are now peeling off above and below the center of the cylinder in a regular pattern.

terms of them.   Analysis of the shock-tube observations indicates good agreement with the predictions even though the theory was worked out only for incompressible flow.   The experiments indicate that the drag shoots up rapidly as the shock first impinges on the cylinder and settles down to an average force with a periodic component as the vortices start peeling off in a regular manner.   The resultant force perpendicular to the drag, *i.e.*, the lift, is zero in the early stages, but as the low-pressure eddies start alternating the lift oscillates with a frequency half that of the drag.

REFERENCES

1. Bleakney, W., D. K. Weimer, and C. H. Fletcher, *Rev. Sci. Instr.*, **20**: 807 (1949).
2. Lukasiewicz, J., "Shock Tube Theory and Applications," National Aeronautical Establishment of Canada, Report 15, 1952.
3. Courant, R., and K. D. Friedrichs, "Supersonic Flow and Shock Waves," Interscience Publishers, Inc., New York, 1948.

4. Mott-Smith, H. M., *Phys. Rev.*, **82**: 885 (1951).

5. Greene, E. F., G. R. Cowan, and D. F. Hornig, *J. Chem. Phys.*, **19**: 427 (1951).

6. Bethe, H. A., and E. Teller, Deviations from Thermal Equilibrium in Shock Waves, Ballistic Research Laboratory, Report X-117, Aberdeen, Maryland, 1945. Reissued, Engineering Research Institute, University of Michigan, 1951.

7. Bleakney, W., and A. H. Taub, *Revs. Mod. Phys.*, **21**: 584 (1949). Fletcher, C. H., A. H. Taub, and W. Bleakney, *Revs. Mod. Phys.*, **23**: 271 (1951). Smith, L. G., OSRD No. 6271, 1945.

8. Bargmann, V., OSRD No. 5171, 1945. Results summarized in Ref. 7.

9. Lighthill, M. J., *Proc. Roy. Soc. (London)*, **A198**: 454 (1949).

10. Ting, L., and N. F. Ludloff, *J. Aeronaut. Sci.*, **18**: 143 (1951).

11. Lighthill, M. J., *Proc. Roy. Soc. (London)*, **A200**: 554 (1950).

12. Keller, J. B., and A. Blank, *Communs. Pure and Appl. Math.*, **IV**: 75 (1951).

13. White, D. R., Proceedings of the Second Midwestern Conference on Fluid Dynamics, Ohio State University, 1952; *J. Aeronaut. Sci.*, **18**: 633 (1951).

14. Taub, A. H., *Phys. Rev.*, **72**: 51 (1947).

15. Polachek, H., and R. J. Seeger, *Phys. Rev.*, **84**: 922 (1951).

16. Friedlander, F. G., *Proc. Roy. Soc. (London)*, **A186**: 322, 344, 352, 356 (1946).

17. Keller, J. B., *J. Appl. Phys.*, **23**, 1267 (1952).

18. Jones, D. M., P. M. E. Martin, and C. K. Thornhill, *Proc. Roy. Soc. (London)*, **A209**: 238 (1951).

19. Griffith, W. C., and D. E. Brickl, *Phys. Rev.*, **89**: 451 (1953).

20. Bleakney, W., Proceedings of the Symposium on Earthquake and Blast, University of California, Los Angeles, June, 1952.

21. von Kármán, T., *Göttingen Nachrichten*, 509 (1911); von Kármán and Rubach, *Physik. Z.*, **13**: 49 (1912).

PART 3
Information and Its Communication

15

Electrons and Waves

SIMON RAMO

RAMO-WOOLDRIDGE CORPORATION
LOS ANGELES, CALIFORNIA

15.1 Introduction

It is now more than half a century since a stream of essentially free electrons was first produced, the influence of electromagnetic fields on the motion of electrons recognized, and the basic laws of this phenomenon established. Still, every year, the scope of the techniques collectively called "electronics" grows.

It is the purpose of this chapter to discuss some of the physical principles associated with phenomena in which free electrons interact with electromagnetic fields. We concern ourselves with four main categories of this topic: (1) the emission of free electrons and the formation of an electron stream; (2) the control of an electron stream once emitted, the ponderomotive forces exerted on the free electrons by the electromagnetic field, the interchange of kinetic energy between the electrons and the field, and the general relationship between the electron motion and associated electrical phenomena; (3) the absorption or termination of the electron stream upon its collision with some collecting structure; (4) the physical principles involved in guiding the electromagnetic energy to and from the immediate environment of the electron stream.

We are attempting to limit the present discussion to those classes of physical problems which owe their importance to the phenomena made possible when an essentially free stream of electrons is produced in a vacuum tube. During the last twenty years the subject of electronics defined in this way has probably received more attention than any other phase of physics discussed in this book. This has happened because each new discovery in the physics of electronics has made possible some immediate and valuable practical development in the field of communication, of control, or of measurement.

381

Since topics 1 and 3 are rather similar with respect to the physics which underlies them, only phase 1 is here given a substantial discussion. Subjects 2 and 4 are rather different from one another and from the other two. Thus we shall devote our discussion mainly to subjects 1, 2, and 4, with only a brief mention of 3.

15.2   The Emission of Free Electrons

The conduction electrons in a conducting solid are, as we shall see in Chap. 16, free to move upon the application of a suitable electric field. In a good metallic conductor the general drift of electrons so produced cannot be controlled in ways that will permit the amplification of feeble electrical signals. Such amplification has been accomplished by controlling the flow of electrons in materials called *semiconductors;* this forms the subject of the next chapter. At the present time the most important technique permitting the control of electron flow is that associated with the vacuum tube. Electrons emitted from the cathode of a vacuum tube are pulled by electrical fields out into an evacuated region where they can be controlled and directed by electrical fields produced by potentials applied to the metallic structures referred to as "elements" of the vacuum tube.

Hundreds of millions of electron tubes are now in use. In each of these there is a heated solid structure called the *cathode*, which is responsible for emitting the electron stream that the other elements control. Unfortunately, our present understanding of the physical phenomena which underlie the emission of electrons from the cathode of a vacuum tube is still superficial or entirely lacking. The whole field of practical electronics has developed so rapidly that we must usually accomplish engineering design by empirical studies rather than by reference to quantitative physical theories.

What applicable theory does exist is statistical in nature. The concept of temperature is adduced to describe the average energy state of the electrons, atoms, and molecules making up the substance of the cathode. Useful results can be obtained by regarding the electrons within the solid as being an "electron gas" with a distribution of individual velocities describable by the old kinetic theory of gases. Only a certain fraction of the electrons present in the solid will be sufficiently energetic to escape from the solid against the forces of attraction which tend to keep them within it.

The simple theory of the electron gas permits the theoretical calculation of certain effects which can be compared with experiment. For example, the density of electron-emission current as a function of temperature can be calculated reasonably well for certain pure metals, such as tungsten. Such calculations can be refined and made more accurate by including refinements dictated by the quantum theory.

Practical problems concerned with the thermionic emission of electrons concern themselves with emitting substances in which chemical impurities can have first-order effects on the emission. The type of cathode that is most widely used at the present time involves a metal, such as nickel, coated with an oxide that has empirically been chosen to give copious electron emission at a reasonably low temperature. The theory which underlies the use of such oxide coatings, or the effects on them produced by various impurities, is almost nonexistent.

The cathode which emits electrons is ordinarily in something like thermal equilibrium with the cloud of recently emitted electrons comprising the *space charge* near it. However, the space charge is subject to other forces which are not easily described in the equilibrium analysis. Electric fields acting to accelerate the electrons in the space charge away from the neighborhood of the cathode will make it difficult to apply an equilibrium theory.

If electrons which have been emitted from the cathode are caused by external fields to return to it with sufficient energy, they will produce the emission of "secondary" electrons which are—so to speak—"splashed" out of the cathode by their impact.

Because any stream of electrons is made up of individual entities, its instantaneous current density is subject to random fluctuation. Such fluctuation produces the disturbances called "noise" in electron-tube devices. We shall discuss this later.

Immediately after electrons have been emitted from a cathode, they are most susceptible to control forces, since they have only a low velocity. Events which occur in the vicinity of the element emitting the electrons are thus of great importance when we consider the control of electron streams.

Enough has been said to indicate the complexity of the problems which surround the creation of streams of free electrons within a vacuum tube. These problems involve the dependence of emission on the temperature of the cathode, on the chemical and physical composition of the cathode, including the important effects of impurities, on the influences affecting the space charge, on the secondary emission resulting from the return of electrons to the cathode, and on the statistical nature of the electron stream. At the high temperatures characteristic of electron-emitting cathodes, chemical and physical changes commonly take place within the substance of the cathode itself, involving migration or diffusion of atoms within the active layers of the cathode.

15.3 Returning Electrons

We now consider processes involving the bombardment of the electron-emitting cathode by returning electrons or by ions of the residual gas which inevitably remains in any vacuum tube. Electrons can collide with the molecules of the residual gas and ionize them; the positive ions thus produced are attracted to the cathode by the electric fields which are designed to accelerate away from the cathode the negative electrons that it emits. Bombardment of the cathode by positive ions produces additional heating and may also involve the destruction of the thin surface film or coating responsible for the efficient emission of electrons. Either positive ions or returning electrons which strike the cathode may give rise to the emission of secondary electrons.

In tubes intended to operate at very high frequencies the time required for a cycle of the radio frequency concerned may be comparable with the time required for electrons to travel between one electrode of the tube and another. In some types of h-f oscillators, a sufficient number of electrons return to the cathode after emission to maintain the temperature of the cathode at that necessary for electron emission without the expenditure of additional heater power. It is apparent that, under these circumstances, the statistical problem of predicting the density of electron emission from the cathode is very difficult to handle.

In practical problems there are so many parameters which affect electron emission that we have not yet been able to make a simple analysis of the problem from first principles. Present-day theories assume that the process of emission is a simple problem of statistical physics similar to the kinetic theory of gases. While results based on this assumption are successful in simple situations, it is clear that more sophisticated theories are required.

15.4 Control of Electrons Near the Cathode

The electrons emitted by the cathode are most susceptible to control just after their emission. A slow-moving electron, such as one which has just been emitted from a thermionic cathode, is readily caused to change its velocity under the influence of an applied electric field. An electron that is traveling rapidly, as it may be once it has moved well away from the cathode, is less susceptible to influence by an electric field. Amplification and the generation of sustained oscillations, which phenomena are most important in applied electronics, have their basis in the control by electromagnetic fields of free electron streams.

Figure 15.1 illustrates the thermionic triode first invented in 1907 by De Forest. The control grid, which is a porous structure interposed between the electron-emitting cathode and the plate which collects the electrons, controls by electrostatic fields the electron flow from cathode to plate. When the control grid is negative with respect to the cathode, the field into which emitted electrons emerge is a decelerating one which tends to push them back into the region of the cathode. Thus, only those electrons having greater energy than the amount necessary to over-

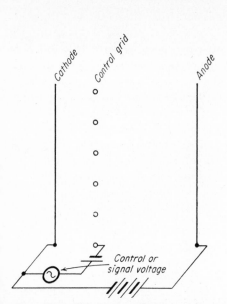

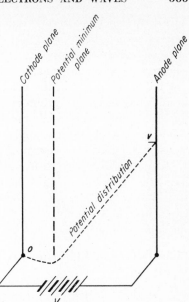

Fig. 15.1 Schematic diagram of a three-electrode vacuum tube.

Fig. 15.2 Potential distribution between cathode and anode of a vacuum tube.

come the decelerating field of the grid are able to pass through the grid to the plate. What the grid does, therefore, is to control, by varying the decelerating field it produces, the fraction of electrons emitted from the cathode that have enough energy to enable them to reach the plate. We see that the emission of electrons of different energy from the cathode is vital to the control action of the grid. If there were no differences in electron velocity, either in direction or in magnitude, then all electrons would either return to the cathode under the influence of the field of the grid or else would pass through the grid to the plate, or *anode*. Under such hypothetical circumstances the control of the electron stream would be an "on-off" sort of action.

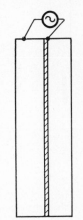

Fig. 15.3 Control of electron flow in a solid.

The spread of electron velocities which is inherent in the emission process not only makes continuous control of the plate possible, but also sets the limit to practical amplification. As we move the control grid closer and closer to the cathode, we finally reach the "potential minimum" region shown in Fig. 15.2. When the grid is in this region, the fraction of emitted electrons returned to the cathode and the fraction that go on to the plate will be determined by the amount of energy which the electrons receive upon emission from the cathode. Present-day vacuum-tube construction techniques have placed the control grid close enough to the cathode so that little further progress in the control of electron streams can be achieved by decreasing the cathode-grid spacing.

Further advances in the control of electron streams may conceivably involve an emission system such as that shown in Fig. 15.3, in which different kinds of material are maintained at different temperatures, with signal or control voltages applied between the boundaries of various portions of the matter as shown in the figure. The structure shown in Fig. 15.3 qualifies as a possible candidate for a form of "hot" transistor. This indicates, as it should, that the border line between the emission of electrons into a field-free space, and their subsequent control by applied electric fields, cannot differ much from the process of electron control within specially arranged solid substances.

15.5   Origin of Electron-stream Noise

One of the most important phenomena limiting the range of performance of electron devices is that of "noise." A stream of electrons is a parade of individual bundles of charge, each with its own velocity. The fact that an electron stream has this grainy structure is responsible for the generation of noise in its interaction with the electrodes by which it passes into circuits to which they are connected.

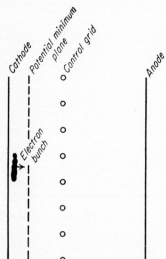

Consider, for example, a short period of time during which the cathode emits more electrons than the average number expected during that length of time. An instant later, when this more-numerous-than-average electron bunch has arrived at the potential minimum between the cathode and the control grid (Fig. 15.4), it will depress the electric field by virtue of its higher space charge, thus increasing the decelerating field acting upon electrons newly emitted from the cathode and

Fig. 15.4   Motion of an electron bunch through a vacuum tube.

thereby causing a decrease in electron emission. When the electrons travel away from the cathode fast enough, compared with the period of the electromagnetic waves being amplified, then any increase in emission from the cathode is followed "almost instantaneously" by a decrease produced by space-charge action which tends to cancel it. In the case of extremely high frequencies, when the time periods of interest are comparable with the time of flight of electrons from their point of emission to the region of the potential minimum, it is no longer true that the effect of space charge in depressing emission will compensate for the conditions which led to increased emission. If the unusually dense bunch of electrons emitted from the cathode takes as long to reach the potential minimum as a half cycle of the signal takes to occur, then the depression of electron emission which the dense bunch causes will produce a reinforcement of the noise.

The variations of electron velocity and of the rate of their emission, which produce noise in external circuits, depend not only upon the emission process but also upon the fashion in which the electrons are accelerated and focused into a beam. The example just quoted shows the effect of space-charge conditions on the noise. In the last analysis, when the noise arising from other effects has been reduced as far as possible, the randomness of the electron-emission process limits the degree of noise reduction that can be attained.

Here we are confronted by a dilemma: electrons are freed from the cathode by giving them sufficient thermal energy to escape the surface forces tending to hold them in the solid, while the variations in the energy possessed by individual electrons are greater, the higher the temperature of the cathode. We therefore desire to operate the cathode at as low a temperature as possible, but there is a minimum temperature at which the emission of electrons can be caused to occur.

15.6 Flow of Electron Streams

The electric and magnetic fields which control electron streams may be steady—as they are in an electron microscope—or may involve some combination of steady and alternating fields. When alternating fields are involved, they may change so slowly with respect to the time scale of electron motion that a steady-state description of the electron stream is a good approximation to the actual situation. In other cases, the fields vary so rapidly that a steady-state treatment of the problem is not even an adequate first approximation.

In attempting to describe quantitatively the formation and behavior of an electron stream, we may either concern ourselves with the paths of individual electrons or else regard the stream of electrons as a sort of continuously charged "fluid" whose behavior obeys the law of continuity. In the first approach to the problem we make use of the well-known laws of electrodynamics. In order to apply them we must have a knowledge of the electric and magnetic fields existing in the regions through which the electron moves. For certain simple field configurations it is possible to obtain analytical solutions of good accuracy, but often the geometry of a practical situation will be so complex that approximate techniques or model experiments must be resorted to.

The interactions with one another of the electrons making up the stream represent one of the most difficult things to treat in this analytical approach to the problem.   In order to know the electric and magnetic fields at a given point, we must know the density and the velocity distribution of electrons in the neighborhood of the point, since their charges and their motions will contribute to the total field at the point of interest.   Without a knowledge of the field distribution, we cannot determine where the electrons will be or how they will be moving. All in all, the detailed analytical approach to the motion of electron streams is so difficult that only a few of the simplest geometrical configurations of electrodes, such as parallel planes or concentric cylinders, lend themselves to this treatment.

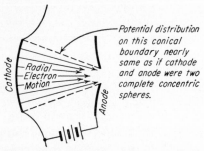

Fig. 15.5 Focusing of an electron stream by proper shaping of electrodes.

As an alternative technique, we can consider a stream of electrons as a charged fluid which obeys the law of continuity.   The important parameters in such a treatment of the problem are the density of charge, the velocity of flow, and the fields at each point.   When the electron stream is "turbulent"— *i.e.*, when the electrons at any given point have a variety of different velocities—the continuous-fluid approach is not very useful.   It is particularly useful for describing the behavior of electron beams that are essentially homogeneous.

Consider, for example, the situation shown in Fig. 15.5.   Here, following Pierce, we wish to describe the focusing of a stream of electrons emitted from a large cathode through a small hole in an anode.   The stream in question is made up of electrons moving as they would if they formed part of a radial stream flowing between concentric spheres.   If, everywhere on the conical surface which bounds the actual beam, we can produce boundary conditions which correspond to those which would obtain in the flow between concentric spheres, then electrons moving radially inward in the stream will move precisely as though they were taking part in a flow between concentric spheres.   Control of the boundary conditions is afforded by adjustment of the potential difference between cathode and anode and proper shaping of these structures.

15.7   Electron Optics

In many situations of practical importance it is possible to use the familiar techniques of geometrical optics to describe the behavior of electron beams.   This is particularly true of cases in which the electric and magnetic fields affecting the beam have axial symmetry, the axis corresponding to the general direction of motion of the electron stream. The general name *electron optics* has been given to this technique of describing the motion of electron streams.

An axially symmetric region of concentrated electric or magnetic field has the same effect on a beam of electrons passing through it as a lens has upon a beam of light. The concept of an *index of refraction* can be extended to the electrical situation, although it is complicated somewhat by the circumstance that the actual value of the index of refraction depends upon the velocity of the electrons in the stream.

The action of a simple electrostatic lens is shown in Fig. 15.6. The electrode structure is axially symmetric, and electrons move generally along the axis as they enter it from the left. The electric field within the electron lens has both axial and radial components, but it is also

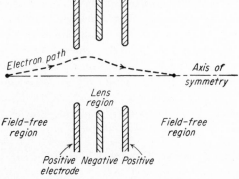

Fig. 15.6 Axially symmetric electrostatic electron lens.

axially symmetric. Any electron entering the lens with an axial component of velocity which tends to take it out of the beam will be decelerated in its axial motion and pushed inward radially as it approaches the negative electrode in the center of the lens. After it has passed the negative electrode, it is accelerated axially and subjected to an outwardly directed radial force as it approaches the second positive electrode. However, this outward acceleration will have a smaller effect on the electron's motion than did the inward acceleration produced by the negative electrode, since the electron is now moving more rapidly and thus spends a smaller time under the influence of the outwardly directed radial field. The net effect of all this is to reduce the axial divergence of the beam and to produce a focused image of the cathode from which the electron stream originated, or of a diaphragm interposed to limit the electron flow, at some point beyond the lens and on its axis of symmetry.

The analogy between the optics of electron streams and ordinary geometrical optics is quite close and complete. In particular, the familiar aberrations of optical systems have their counterparts in electron optics.

Spherical aberration is caused by the fact that lenses or mirrors with spherical surfaces will bring to a focus at a given point on the optical axis only those rays of light which make a small angle with the axis; rays moving at larger angles are brought back to the axis at a slightly different point. A similar property is exhibited by the electric or magnetic fields of electron lenses. The laws which govern their distributions produce fields which are not ideal for the focusing of off-axis rays of electrons. *Chromatic aberration* arises in the optical case because the index of refraction of a simple lens is different for light of different colors, *i.e.*, of different wavelength. The analogous effect occurs in electron optics, since the action of a given electron lens upon an electron passing through it will depend on the electron's energy. Thus, any spread in the velocity or energy of electrons in a beam will be reflected in slightly different final trajectories after passing through the lens.

The limits of optical magnification are ultimately set by the fact that we cannot resolve structures finer than the wavelength of the light that we use to view them, because of diffraction effects. A similar limiting resolving power characterizes electron-optical systems. However, since the wavelength of an electron moving even at relatively moderate speed (see Chap. 2) is much shorter than that of visible light, electron microscopes have been built which possess resolving powers greatly in excess of those attainable by the best optical microscopes.

15.8   Interaction between Electron Streams and Electromagnetic Fields

When we accelerate the electrons emitted from a cathode by attracting them toward a positively charged anode, we have imparted kinetic energy to the electrons at the expense of the voltage source which maintains a potential difference between cathode and anode. If nothing further happens, the kinetic energy possessed by the electrons in the stream will appear as heat or other radiation when the stream reaches the anode. However, if the electron stream moves through other electromagnetic fields on its way to the anode, the interaction between such fields and the electron stream can result in the transfer of energy to or from the stream.

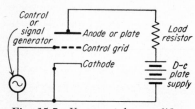

Fig. 15.7   Vacuum-tube amplifier.

The familiar triode amplifier is a simple case of this sort. As shown in Fig. 15.7, one source of electrical energy is used to give kinetic energy to the electron stream. This is usually a d-c source called the *plate supply*. Electrical fields produced by supplying small amounts of energy to a "grid" interposed between cathode and anode influence the electron stream in such a fashion that the so-called "load" resistor in the anode circuit receives far more a-c energy than was supplied to the grid to cause this action. The information represented by the varying signals applied to the grid is reasonably faithfully reproduced in the amplified signals appearing at the load. This is a simple example of many ways in which an electron stream can serve as the medium of energy inter-charge between sources and sinks of electromagnetic energy.

When interactions of this sort are treated from first principles, the physics entering the problem is essentially that of classical electro-dynamics. Occasionally, when the electron energies involved are high, we must include in our considerations the relativistic change in mass with velocity (Chap. 1). Despite the fact that the physics underlying the interaction between electron streams and electromagnetic fields is old and well understood, practical situations are often so complicated that a treatment of the problem, starting from first principles, is very difficult. For example, the behavior of a simple triode such as that shown in Fig. 15.7 becomes very complex when it is used at signal frequencies so high that the time required for one cycle of the signal is short compared to the transit time of electrons between cathode and anode.

15.9 Currents Induced by Electron Motion

The steady flow of an electron stream whose space distribution of charge density and electron velocity does not change with time offers a simple example of the flow of electrical current. The electric and mag-netic fields associated with the stream are steady and do not change with time. No current can flow in an external circuit that is connected to an electrode interacting with the stream unless the electrode concerned either emits or collects electrons. A difference of electrical potential may be set up between two electrodes between which no net current flows; this is the case, for example, when the control grid of a triode is biased nega-tively with respect to the cathode. No electrons are collected by the grid in such a case, and no current flows to the grid.

For changes in electrode potentials, and consequently in fields affecting the electron stream, which occur over times that are long in comparison with the time of flight of an individual electron in the stream, the steady-state conditions just described are an excellent approximation to the situation. The collection of charge by an electrode and the flow of cur-rent from that electrode can still be regarded as being identical.

Because of the effects of electrostatic induction, it is really the motion of charges in the vicinity of conductors which is responsible for the flow of current in external circuits containing such conductors. If two elec-trodes are connected through an ammeter as shown in Fig. 15.8 and we consider the motion of one electron through the space between the two

electrodes, then the action is as follows.   Before the charge leaves the
first plate, no current is flowing and the ammeter reads zero.   As the
charge moves away from the first plate, nearly all the lines of electric
force coming from the charge end on the first conductor because it is so
close.   As the charge moves away from the first conductor and toward
the second, the fraction of electric lines of force going to the second conductor will increase.   If the two conductors are identical and symmetrically oriented, then when the charge is midway between them an equal
number of lines of force will end on each electrode.   At this moment the
induced charge on each of the electrodes is equal to that on the other,
which means that half of the induced charge originally present on the
first electrode has moved around the circuit, through the ammeter, to

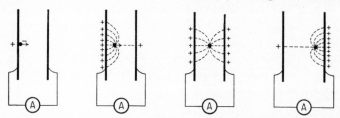

Fig. 15.8   Motion of a charge between conducting electrodes.

the other electrode.   If the moving charge should be stopped halfway
between the electrodes, the current between them will stop flowing.   It
will commence to flow again only when the charge moves once more; the
faster the motion of the charge, the higher is the current.   When the
charge reaches the second electrode and is collected there, it will neutralize the induced charge; all of it will have arrived at the second electrode
by the time the moving charge reaches it.

This simple example shows that the flow of current between electrodes
is caused by the motion of charges in their vicinity rather than by the
collection of charge.   Under steady conditions of electron-stream flow
this fact is obscured by the circumstance that as many electrons are
leaving one electrode per unit time as are approaching another, so that
the net current-flow phenomena can be described by attributing them
to the collection of charge.   When the fields or the conditions of electron-
stream flow are changing in times that are short compared with the
transit time of the electrons in the stream, an adequate description of
current flow can be made only in terms of the induction effects produced
by the motion of charges.

15.10   Energy Interchange for Finite Transit Times

To exemplify the remarks of the last section consider the circuit shown
in Fig. 15.9, in which the interelectrode spacing is such that electrons

have a large transit time between cathode and plate. Even when the cathode is at such a temperature that it emits electrons, few of them will reach the plate because there is no accelerating field, the plate being the cathode potential. Let us now apply to the grid, which we conceive of as an ideal very porous grid, a positive voltage pulse of short duration. If this pulse is sufficiently short so that the electrons it accelerates traverse only a part of the cathode-grid space before the pulse is finished, a finite "bunch" of electrons moving toward the plate will be produced in the region between cathode and grid. Even when the pulse is over and the cathode-grid voltage has dropped to zero, this electron bunch will continue to move through the grid and on to the plate, because there is no decelerating field to slow it down. After the conclusion of the pulse the cathode-grid voltage and the cathode-plate voltage are both zero.

Current flows, however, so long as the electrons are in motion. When the pulse is on, current flows between cathode and grid through the generator that produces the voltage pulse. After the pulse has finished and the voltage between cathode and grid is zero, current still flows between these two electrodes so long as the moving bunch of electrons is between the cathode and the grid. When the bunch of electrons passes through the porous grid, current begins to flow through the external circuit between grid and plate.

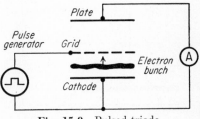

Fig. 15.9   Pulsed triode.

The moving electrons finally strike the plate and are collected, ending the current flow.

Note that the only source of energy input to the system is the pulse generator connected between grid and cathode. Energy is transferred into the tube only while this generator is active. Current flow, however, continues after the input of power has finished. No energy is transferred to or from the electron stream by current flow through the external circuits which connect the electrodes. Since the electrodes are all at the same potential after the end of the pulse, the field acting on the electrons is zero, so that their velocity and their kinetic energy remain unchanged during their flight to the plate.

In general, the instantaneous kinetic energy possessed by electrons traveling between electrodes in a tube is not simply related to the instantaneous potential difference between electrodes. In our example the kinetic energy of the moving electrons was determined not so much by the electrostatic field present at each instant, but rather by the history of the electrostatic field throughout the time of flight up to the instant in question. The energy of the electron stream was given it by the generator connected between cathode and grid, but this energy in the form of heat was delivered to the plate at a later time, despite the fact that the plate had remained at the cathode potential throughout.

In the case of a steady electron stream, the collection of electrons, current flow, and energy flow go hand in hand. In the more general case there are more complicated relations among these phenomena. We cannot add energy to a stream of electrons or abstract energy from it without the accompanying flow of current. However, it is possible to have current flow without energy transfer. The collection of electrons ends the current flow produced by the movement of the electrons that are collected. The period of heat production which corresponds to electron collection need not coincide in time with the period during which energy was transferred to the electron stream.

It is quite possible for electrons to be collected by a negatively biased electrode or for electrical energy to be abstracted from the kinetic energy of an electron stream without collection of electrons by the active electrode. Suppose that, in the triode of Fig. 15.9, a negative voltage is applied between grid and plate after the moving bunch of electrons has passed through the grid (Fig. 15.10). When the plate suddenly becomes negative relative to the grid, a decelerating field acts on the bunch of electrons to slow them down and remove some of their kinetic energy. This produces a flow of current in the external circuit between the grid and plate through the battery which maintains the potential difference between these electrodes; the current is in such a direction as to charge the battery. Thus the kinetic energy that is lost by the electron stream after the electrons slow down appears in a new form in the battery.

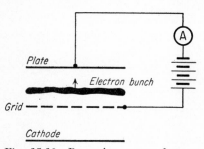

Fig. 15.10 Removing energy from a moving bunch of electrons.

If the retarding voltage between grid and plate is so chosen that the electron bunch is brought just to zero velocity as it is collected, no heat will be liberated at the plate. All the energy transferred to the stream by the pulse generator in the grid-cathode circuit is now absorbed by the battery in the grid-plate circuit. Thus we see how an a-c generator connected between two electrodes acting on an electron stream can supply energy to the stream even though no electrons ever depart from or land on the electrodes concerned. Collection of charges is a necessary part of energy transfer only for steady-state conditions or for fields which vary slowly compared with electron transit time.

15.11   Traveling Waves in Electron Streams

The newest class of electron tubes is based upon the interaction between traveling electromagnetic waves and electron streams which interact with them.   The electric and magnetic fields of a traveling electromagnetic wave will influence the motion of electrons comprising a stream moving along with the wave.   If the kinetic energy of electrons in the stream is increased by the action of the wave, then energy is being supplied to the electron stream at the expense of the energy of the electromagnetic wave.

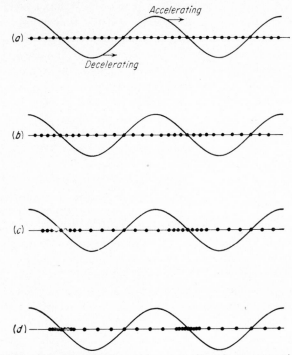

Fig. 15.11   Bunching of electrons by a traveling electromagnetic wave.

If the net effect of the interaction is to slow down this stream of electrons, energy will be transferred to the wave at the expense of the total kinetic energy of the stream.

We now know how to design and excite electrical structures that can produce traveling electromagnetic fields having phase and group velocities of various values.   Suppose that we send a stream of electrons down a tube through which is traveling an electromagnetic wave of about the same velocity.   At various points along the wave the electric field component will alternate in direction, first tending to accelerate the electrons in the stream and then, a half wavelength later, reversing and tending to decelerate them (Fig. 15.11).   Electrons that are moving along with an accelerating field will speed up with respect to their neighbors just ahead and begin to overtake them.   Similarly, those electrons which are moving with a region of decelerating field will slow down and move back toward their neighbors behind them.   The net effect is to develop bunches of electrons as shown in Fig. 15.11a, b, c, d, which represents the same electron stream at successively later instants of time.

Now suppose that the electromagnetic wave travels a little more slowly than the electron stream.   Then the bunches or regions of higher-than-average electron density in the beam will eventually move toward a region of decelerating field in the electromagnetic wave (Fig. 15.12).   By this time the regions of low electron density will find themselves in an accelerating field.   While this condition persists, the average effect produced will be to slow down the stream, since more electrons are being decelerated by the field than are being accelerated.   The kinetic energy lost by the electrons will be transferred to the electromagnetic field.

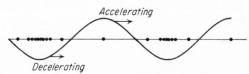

Fig. 15.12   Transfer of energy from bunched electron stream to electromagnetic wave.

This crude description of the interaction between the kinetic energy of electrons and the energy in a traveling electromagnetic wave can hardly be completely convincing.   However, electron devices based on the phenomenon just described—so-called *traveling-wave* tubes—have been built and work in the fashion described.   It has even been found that when two electron streams, one somewhat faster than the other, are near one another, electromagnetic waves, once properly set up, can grow, energy being transferred from the kinetic energy of the electrons into energy of the electromagnetic field.   The practical result of these techniques is that we can use physically large electron-tube structures to generate and amplify very short wavelengths.   The older electronic techniques were mainly based upon physical structures small compared with the wavelength corresponding to the a-c fields being handled; in the traveling-wave technique we deal directly with the waves as such, and the physical structures used can be several or many wavelengths in size.

15.12   Guided Electromagnetic Waves

Let us now turn to the present situation with respect to the guiding, propagating, and transmitting of electromagnetic energy in space and in matter.   Here we mean to include circuit theory, transmission lines, waveguides, resonant cavities, antennas, and the like.

In this entire field it is literally true that most of the advances have been simply logical deductions from concepts and physical laws which were well understood more than half a century ago.   Maxwell's celebrated equations of the electromagnetic field serve as the basis for all this work, and no new discoveries or concepts of a fundamental sort have been necessary to the enormous progress made during and since World War II.

Despite the lack of change in our fundamental ideas, there has been a considerable advance in the sophistication of our approach to practical engineering problems.   An example of this is afforded by the relationship between circuit theory and wave theory.   Until extremely high frequencies became important only a few years ago, it was customary to treat circuit theory and the theory of electromagnetic waves independently of one another.   It was not always understood that the simple lumped-circuit concepts such as resistance, inductance, and capacitance represented approximations that were valid only when the dimensions of a circuit were small in comparison with the wavelength of the signals handled by the circuit.   Larger systems were treated by the use of the concept of "distributed" circuit parameters.

Beginning with Maxwell's equations, which specify the relationship between electric and magnetic fields, we can either derive from them a lumped-constant circuit-theory approximation or else regard them as the practical differential equations to be solved subject to the boundary conditions of the problem at hand.   In general, a wide variety of waves satisfy Maxwell's equations as applied to any practical physical situation. A waveguide system can carry a variety of different classes of waves distinguished from one another by differences in phase velocity, in electromagnetic field distribution, and in attenuation.   Given the steady-state properties of a waveguide system, we can use the initial and final conditions to determine the distribution in energy among the various classes of waves possible in the waveguide system.

Thus we have advanced from the old situation, in which the following aspects of electricity and magnetism were taught and considered rather apart from one another:

   a. Static electric and magnetic fields and their effects on charged particles
   b. Circuit theory, including certain aspects of varying magnetic fields such as the relation between induced voltage and the rate of change of magnetic flux through a circuit
   c. Electromagnetic waves, typically plane waves characterized by a

plane front of constant phase, traveling with a phase velocity equal to that of light, the electric and magnetic fields lying in the plane of equal phase, being perpendicular to one another and to the direction of the advancing wavefront, their magnitudes being uniform over the front

Today it is customary to think more broadly in terms of first principles when we consider the interactions between electric and magnetic fields and the motion of electrons in such fields. Knowledge of the boundary conditions in any practical case will always, in principle, enable the situation to be described by appropriate solutions of Maxwell's equations in terms of waves. In especially simple situations, solutions in terms of plane waves or of simple lumped-constant approximations may be adequate. More often, especially at higher frequencies, the waves concerned in describing the phenomena will have a variety of complicated

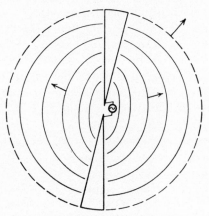

Fig. 15.13   Biconical dipole antenna.

distributions of electric and magnetic fields, a variety of phase velocities, and different attenuation. The net electric and magnetic vectors, obtained by combining the contributions of the individual waves, in general need not even be perpendicular to one another.

What has just been said can be illustrated by discussing briefly an example from antenna theory. Figure 15.13 shows a biconical antenna excited by a generator at its center. Spherical waves will travel outward along the boundaries of the cones until they reach the limiting sphere shown in the figure. At this point, some of the energy in the waves is reflected by the discontinuity, and some proceeds on into space. As one approximate description of the situation, we can think of the antenna as being a transmission line of a special kind guiding waves which encounter an "open circuit" at the end of the line and are reflected back. Alternatively, if the cones are sufficiently short compared with the wavelength, we can apply simple lumped-constant circuit concepts to the situation, regarding the two cones as having a capacitance which is important in connection with the electric field between them and an inductance which is important to the current path along the surface of the cones and the magnetic flux which links the circuit.

The simple transmission-line picture is inadequate if we limit it to a simple wave which travels down the cones from their vertices and is reflected at the end.   Actually, a series of more complex waves are initiated when the first wave reaches the end of the cones.   The proper combination of all these waves will yield the true distribution of electromagnetic field, the voltage and current at the source, the power transfer from the source to waves in space, and the distribution of fields at any specified point in space.   Detailed analysis shows that the reflected waves, all except the first-order or simplest one, attenuate rapidly as they travel back to the origin.   Their net effect can thus be represented by a lumped impedance at the end of the conical line.

Of course, Maxwell's equations must be used with due regard to the realities of any practical situation.   They tell us nothing about limitations which may be imposed by the fact that matter and electricity are ultimately granular in structure, that at any temperature higher than the absolute zero electrons, ions, and atoms are executing rapid random motions whose mean energy depends upon the temperature.   They ignore the fact that the dielectric strength of practical insulators is finite, and this ultimately limits electric fields, and so on.

In connection with the emission and absorption of electrons, classical physics is inadequate as a basis for explaining the phenomena that occur. We have already touched upon the electron-emission process.   When electrons strike the collector, secondary electrons, X rays, heat, and light are produced.   The properties of the bombarded surface enter very importantly into these phenomena, not all of which are adequately understood in detail.   Despite all this, it is a remarkable circumstance that so much of the recent engineering advance in the field of electronics has as its basis the straightforward application of the electromagnetic theory developed by Maxwell in 1878 and experimentally verified by Hertz a decade later.

16

Semiconductor Electronics

JOHN BARDEEN

PROFESSOR OF PHYSICS AND OF ELECTRICAL ENGINEERING
UNIVERSITY OF ILLINOIS

16.1 Introduction[1]

Semiconductors are becoming increasingly important in electronics. Diodes made from selenium and copper oxide and more recently from germanium and silicon are used in large numbers as power rectifiers, detectors, modulators, and in many other applications. Transistors are now beginning to come on the market, and it should not be long before they are a commonplace article of commerce. In 1950, a new member of the transistor family, the junction transistor, was announced. The remarkable properties of this device, particularly its ability to operate with very small power input, its high gain per stage, and its stability with relatively low noise, have attracted wide attention.

Evidence for current interest in transistors is that, in November, 1952, the Institute of Radio Engineers devoted the entire issue of its *Proceedings* to a series of 48 papers covering all aspects of transistors from basic physics and properties of the materials to circuit applications. Included is a long article on the physics of transistors by William Shockley[2] which gives an excellent and relatively nonmathematical account of the subject.

I plan first to review some of the basic properties of semiconductors and then discuss applications to photoconductive devices, diodes, and transistors.

16.2 Types of Semiconductors[3,4]

Semiconductors are intermediate in conductivity between metals and insulators. The term is generally restricted to electronic conductors whose conductivity depends markedly on impurities and on temperature.

[1] Corresponding numbered bibliographic references appear at the end of the chapter.

400

Electrons in a semiconductor can transport electricity in two different ways distinguished by the sign of the carrier and denoted by the terms *excess* and *defect*, *n* and *p type*, or *conduction by electrons* and *conduction by holes*. Excess or conduction electrons are in states which do not form part of the normal chemical bonds. They are free to move through the crystal, and each carries the negative charge of an electron. A hole corresponds to an electron missing from the chemical bonds; this defect in the normal electron distribution corresponds to a net positive charge equal in magnitude to the charge of an electron. Holes are also free to move through the crystal and contribute to conduction. It can be shown by quantum theory that holes behave in almost all respects like particles with a positive charge and an effective mass of the same order of magnitude as the mass of the electron.

In the ideal valence crystal at the absolute zero of temperature, all the electrons are in the valence bonds and the valence bonds are completely occupied by electrons. The substance is an insulator; there is no possibility of electrical conduction. At higher temperatures, electrons may be excited thermally from the valence bonds into the conduction states where they are free to move. The places from which they came, the holes in the valence bonds, also contribute to the conductivity. Conduction of this sort, which comes from thermal excitation of the electrons, is called *intrinsic*, and the conductivity of most semiconductors at very high temperatures is due mainly to this cause. At ordinary temperatures, on the other hand, conductivity usually results from carriers, electrons or holes, which are introduced by impurities in the crystal. Impurity semiconductors are called *n* or *p* type depending on the sign of the carrier—*n* type for crystals which conduct mainly by excess electrons and *p* type for crystals which conduct mainly by holes.

There are two main classes of semiconductors: (1) valence crystals with bonding orbitals formed from atomic *s* and *p* electrons and (2) crystals with atoms with incomplete *d* shells, mostly oxides of transition metals. Examples of valence crystals are

n type: ZnO, PbO_2, SnO_2, CdS, $CdSe$, etc.

p type: CuO, Cu_2O, Se, CuI, etc.

Either *n* or *p*: Si, Ge, Te, PbS, $PbTe$, SiC, etc.

Intermetallic compounds: Mg_2Sn, $InSb$, Cs_3Sb, etc.

Examples of *d*-band semiconductors are

NiO, Fe_2O_3, Fe_3O_4, CuO, MnO, etc.

Some are *n* type, some *p* type, and some are either, depending on the nature of the impurities.

Some semiconductors, such as ZnO, PbO_2, and Cu_2O, owe their conductivities to deviations from exact stoichiometric composition. For example, ZnO with excess zinc is *n* type; Cu_2O with missing copper ions is p type. Other crystals, such as Ge and Si, are n type when impurity atoms of higher valency, such as P or Sb, substitute for Ge in the lattice and p type when atoms of lower valence, such as Al or Ga, replace some of the Ge atoms.

Germanium, like carbon, has a valence of four and has the same crystal structure as diamond. Each atom is surrounded by a tetrahedral arrangement of four others, with each of which it forms a valence bond. If an atom of antimony with a valence of five substitutes for germanium, the extra electron does not fit into the valence bonds. It is so weakly attached to the antimony atom that it is readily freed, leaving the impurity as a positive ion in the lattice. Such impurities, which are normally neutral and become positively ionized by release of electrons to the conduction band, are called *donors*. If an atom of gallium, with three valence electrons, substitutes for germanium, there is one electron missing from the valence bonds. The impurity can fill its bonds with its four neighbors by taking an electron from a normal germanium atom in the lattice, leaving a hole. The gallium then becomes a negative ion. Such an impurity is called an *acceptor*.

Intermetallic compounds, which occur at certain compositions in alloys, are characterized by a high melting point and an ordered structure. Many of these alloys, ordinarily metallic, become semiconductors at the compositions at which intermetallic compounds are formed.   Until quite recently, their properties have been studied more extensively in Russia and Europe than they have been in this country. An important group consists of alloys of third- and fifth-column elements, such as InSb, which have a diamondlike lattice. Other interesting compounds with a diamondlike structure, such as ZnS, are formed from second- and sixth-column elements.

Conduction electrons and holes in valence crystals move about with thermal velocities and are scattered only by imperfections or by thermal motion of the crystal lattice. The mean free path generally is large compared with the interatomic spacing. To understand this, the wave aspect of electrons is essential: a wave can be transmitted through a perfect periodic structure without attenuation.

The d-band semiconductors are less well understood. Conduction occurs when there are ions of different valency in equivalent lattice positions. For example, when Li^+ replaces Ni^{++} in NiO, another nickel ion is changed from Ni^{++} to Ni^{+++} in order to maintain charge balance. The trivalent position corresponds to a hole which can move from place to place by transfer of electrons from neighboring divalent ions. The conduction is, therefore, p type. An example of an n-type d-band semiconductor is Fe_2O_3 with added Ti. Here Ti^{++++} replaces Fe^{+++}, and another Fe^{+++} is changed to Fe^{++} to compensate the charge.   The Fe^{++}

ion has an excess electron which can be transferred from ion to ion. In semiconductors of this type, the mean free path of an electron generally is so short that it is perhaps better to think of conduction taking place by exchange of electrons between neighboring ions. Such semiconductors have important applications in electronics as thermistor (*thermally sensitive resistor*) materials, because they can be prepared so that they have a large temperature coefficient of resistance which can be controlled by composition.

In this chapter we shall be concerned mainly with valence-type crystals such as Ge and Si, which can be made either n- or p-type semiconductors, depending on the impurities present. It is these materials which are used in transistors.

16.3   Energy Bands

We shall make frequent use of the energy-band picture, illustrated in Fig. 16.1. As pointed out by Professor Seitz in Chap. 3, energy levels of electrons in crystals occur in quasi-continuous bands rather than being discrete, as they are in atoms. In semiconductors there is a valence band, perhaps several electron volts in width, occupied by electrons, then an energy gap in which there are no allowed levels in the ideal crystal, and then another continuous band of allowed levels, the conduction band.

Excess or conduction electrons have energies in the conduction band. The lowest energy E_c corresponds to an electron at rest; increasing energy corresponds to electrons moving with increasing velocities. Holes correspond to electrons missing from levels near the top of the valence band. The lowest energy of a hole corresponds to an electron missing from the level E_v at the top of the valence band, and increasing

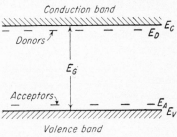

Fig.   16.1   Energy-level diagram for electrons in semiconductors.

energy for holes corresponds to electrons missing from electron states of decreasing energy. Of course, more energy must be expended to move an electron from a low-energy level than to move an electron from a level of higher energy. The energy gap E_G is the minimum energy required to transfer an electron from the valence band to the conduction band.

Donor levels E_D correspond to electrons localized on impurity atoms in the crystal. A donor atom normally is neutral when the level is occupied and a positive ion when it is unoccupied. The energy difference $E_c - E_D$ is the energy required to take an electron from a neutral donor and place it in the conduction band. The energy difference is so small in germanium that practically all donors are ionized by thermal agitation at room temperature.   Acceptor levels E_v lie a little above the valence band.   The acceptor atoms are normally neutral when the level is unoccupied and negative ions when it is occupied.   The energy required to take an electron from the valence band, creating a hole, and place it in an acceptor level is $E_A - E_v$.   This energy difference is so small in germanium that practically all acceptors are negative ions at room temperature.   In the subsequent discussion we shall assume for simplicity that all acceptors and donors are ionized.

In addition to donors and acceptors which have energy levels near the conduction and valence bands, respectively, there may be impurity levels in intermediate positions such that considerable energy is required to add or remove an electron.   An electron may stay in one of these levels for an appreciable time before it is released by thermal agitation.   Such levels are called *traps*.   Even when present in such small concentrations that they have little effect on the conductivity, they may be important because of their influence on the rate of recombination of electrons and holes, as we shall discuss later on.

16.4   Carrier Concentrations

The equilibrium concentrations of conduction electrons and holes are determined by the temperature and by the impurities present.   We shall use the following notation to denote the concentration of interest:

n = number of electrons in conduction band per cm^3

p = number of holes in valence band per cm^3

N_D^+ = number of donor ions per cm^3

N_A^- = number of acceptor ions per cm^3

The net charge density is

$$\rho = e(p - n + N_D^+ - N_A^-) \tag{16.1}$$

where e is the magnitude of the charge of an electron.   Except for limited regions in the neighborhood of rectifying junctions, semiconductors are electrically neutral and ρ is equal to zero.   Statistical considerations indicate that the product of the electron and hole concentrations at any temperature is a constant independent of the impurities and equal to the square of the intrinsic concentration n_i.

$$pn = \text{const.} = n_i^2 = AT^3 \exp\left(\frac{-E_G}{kT}\right) \tag{16.2}$$

The intrinsic concentration increases very rapidly with temperature. Equations (16.1) and (16.2) serve to determine p and n.

There are several limiting cases of interest, for all of which we assume $\rho = 0$:

Intrinsic:

$$p, n \gg N_D^+, N_A^-$$
$$p = n = n_i$$

n type:

$$n \gg p$$
$$n = N_D^+ - N_A^-$$

p type:

$$n \ll p$$
$$p = N_A^- - N_D^+$$

In an intrinsic semiconductor, the number of carriers created by thermal excitation from the valence band to the conduction band is large compared to the concentrations of donors and acceptors. In the opposite limiting case, the conductivity is predominantly n or p type, depending on whether the concentration of donors or acceptors is larger.

The intrinsic concentration n_i in germanium at room temperature is about 2.5×10^{13} per cm^3, which corresponds to about one carrier for 10^9 germanium atoms. In the n-type material normally used in diodes or transistors, n is of the order of 10 to 100 times larger than n_i and, from Eq. (16.2), p is then 0.1 or 0.01 of n_i and is less than 1 per cent of n. It should be noted that the concentrations of significant impurities of interest are of the order of 1 part in 10^7 or 10^8.

Electrons in this example are called the *majority* carriers, the holes the *minority* carriers. The conductivity type may be indicated by a subscript: n_n and p_n refer to the equilibrium concentration in n-type material, n_p and p_p to the concentrations in p-type material.

16.5 Lifetime of Minority Carriers

Under equilibrium conditions, electrons are continually being thermally excited from the valence band to the conduction band, creating electrons and holes, and at the same time electrons are dropping from the conduction band into levels from which electrons are missing, so that conduction electrons and holes are annihilated. This latter process is called *recombination* of electrons and holes. The rates of these processes can be expressed in terms of the *mean lifetime* τ_p of the minority carrier. A hole created thermally in n-type material will exist for an average time τ_p before annihilation by an electron from the conduction band. The average hole concentration p_n will be equal to the number of holes created per cm^3 per second g_{th} times the mean lifetime τ_p:

$$p_n = g_{th}\tau_p \tag{16.3}$$

The rate of generation can be expressed in terms of the concentration of the majority carrier by use of Eq. (16.2):

$$g_{th} = \frac{p_n}{\tau_p} = \frac{n_i^2}{n_n \tau_p} \tag{16.4}$$

Observed lifetimes in germanium single crystals depend on the perfection of the crystal and may be as long as several hundreds of microseconds. Recombination and thermal generation occur via traps which are located at impurities or crystal imperfections. An electron usually drops from the conduction band to a trap and then from the trap to the hole in the valence band, rather than directly from the conduction band to the hole.

16.6 Photoconductivity

The concentration of carriers may be increased above the thermal-equilibrium value by absorption of light, giving photoconductivity, or by current flow from an appropriate contact, as in a transistor. Electrical neutrality is maintained if the increase in electron concentration Δn is equal to the increase in hole concentration Δp:

$$\Delta n = \Delta p \tag{16.5}$$

An increase of this sort does not change the total number of electrons in both bands; only the distribution of the electrons among the energy levels is changed.

Electrons may be raised from the valence band to the conduction band by light, which can create conduction electrons and holes if the energy of the light quantum $h\nu$ is larger than the energy gap E_G. Under steady-state conditions, the increase in concentration is given by the product of the rate of generation by light g_L and the lifetime of the minority carrier. For n-type material,

$$\Delta p = g_L \tau_p \tag{16.6}$$

Except for large changes in concentration, τ_p is the same as that used in Eq. (16.3) in the discussion of the lifetime of carriers which are generated thermally. The lifetime can be estimated from the rate of decay of the added conductivity after carriers have been introduced by light or by transistor action.

16.7 Nature of Flow

Both diffusion and conduction are important in determining the flow of the carriers. We shall give a brief review of these concepts and later on show how they apply to phenomena involved in transistor action.

Electrons and holes move about with a random motion in which they are continually being scattered by crystal imperfections and by thermal vibrations of atoms about their equilibrium positions.   If there is a variation in density of carriers, this random motion gives a net diffusive flow from regions of high to regions of low concentration.   The net flow is proportional to the concentration gradient, and the constant of proportionality is the diffusion coefficient D.   For conduction electrons, the particle current density is

$$J_x = -D_n \frac{dn}{dx} \qquad (16.7)$$

and the electric current density is

$$I_x = eD_n \frac{dn}{dx} \qquad (16.8)$$

since each particle carries a charge $-e$.   There is a corresponding expression for the diffusion current of holes

$$I_p = eD_p \frac{dp}{dx} \qquad (16.9)$$

An important parameter which characterizes a semiconductor for transistor applications is the diffusion length.   This is the average net distance a minority carrier diffuses by thermal motion from the point of origin to the point of recombination.   It is equal to the square root of the product of the diffusion coefficient and the lifetime:

$$L = (D\tau_p)^{\frac{1}{2}} \qquad (16.10)$$

Values of L in germanium may be as much as several millimeters.

In an applied electric field E, a drift velocity v_d proportional to the field is superimposed on the random thermal motion.   The mobility μ is defined as the drift velocity in unit field and is usually expressed in units of $cm^2/volt$ sec.   The current densities for electrons and holes are

$$I_n = -env_d \qquad I_p = epv_d \qquad (16.11)$$

where

$$v_d = -\mu_n E \qquad v_d = \mu_p E \qquad (16.12)$$

Mobilities are always defined with a positive sign.   Many years ago, Einstein showed that there is a relationship between mobility and diffusion coefficients:

$$D = \frac{kT}{e}\mu \qquad (16.13)$$

where k is Boltzmann's constant and T the absolute temperature.   The current densities may also be expressed in terms of σ_n and σ_p, the conductivities for electrons and holes, respectively:

$$I_n = \sigma_n E \qquad I_p = \sigma_p E \qquad (16.14)$$

where

$$\sigma_n = neu_n \qquad \sigma_p = neu_p \qquad (16.15)$$

The total conductivity when both electrons and holes are present is

$$\sigma = \sigma_n + \sigma_p \qquad (16.16)$$

We shall discuss flow by conduction and diffusion in a number of the applications given in the following sections.

16.8 Applications of Photoconductivity

Before discussing diodes and transistors, we shall review briefly two recent applications of photoconductivity. One is to the *vidicon*,[5] a television pickup camera tube built by the Radio Corporation of America;

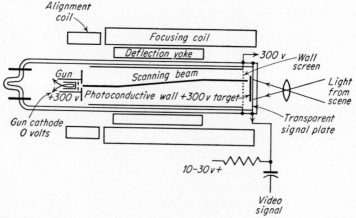

Fig. 16.2 Schematic diagram of vidicon television pickup tube. (*From P. K. Weimer, S. V. Forgue, and R. R. Goodrich, RCA Review, September, 1951.*)

the other is to *xerography*, a method for reproduction of images by light, especially useful for copying and duplicating, developed by the Haloid Company. Both make use of the unusual photoconducting properties of amorphous selenium. In both, a thin film of selenium, between 10 and 100 μ in thickness, is placed on a conducting backing. In the dark, the selenium is practically an insulator, so that an electrostatic charge placed on the outer surface will remain for an appreciable time. Exposure to light makes the film conducting so that the charge is neutralized by flow through the film. This flow takes place even though the light is absorbed only in a thin layer near the boundary of the film.

Figure 16.2 is a schematic diagram of a vidicon camera tube. The selenium layer has a transparent conducting backing. The opposite surface is scanned by an electron beam which maintains a charge on the surface. No current flows to the backing electrode while the beam scans

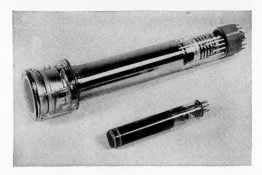

Fig. 16.3 Experimental 1-in.-diameter vidicon television pickup tube compared with standard orthicon in background.   *(From P. K. Weimer, S. V. Forgue, and R. R. Goodrich, RCA Review, September, 1951.)*

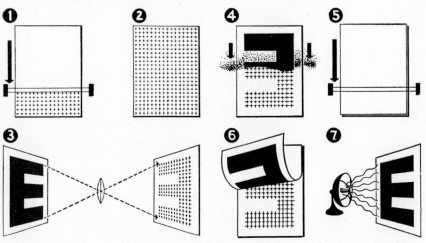

Fig. 16.4 The xerographic process.   (1) Plate with photoconductive surface layer is charged as it passes under the wires.   (2) Surface with positive charge.   (3) Exposed areas are discharged.   (4) A negatively charged powder adheres to positively charged image.   (5) A sheet of paper placed over surface receives positive charge.   (6) Powder is transferred to paper.   (7) Heat fuses powder to paper to form permanent print or master for duplication.   *(Courtesy of The Haloid Company, Rochester, N.Y.)*

a dark area, but a current will flow if the selenium film is made conducting by light.

The outstanding feature of the camera is the very small size possible. The sensitive area may be as small as 1 in. in diameter, as illustrated in Fig. 16.3.

The principle of xerography as invented by C. F. Carlson, a graduate in physics of the California Institute of Technology, is illustrated in Fig. 16.4.   A selenium film is placed on an aluminum backing.   The outer surface is given an electrostatic charge.   An image of the drawing or form to be reproduced is projected on this charged surface.   Areas exposed to light lose the charge.   Fine particles charged electrostatically to the opposite polarity stick to charged areas, making a reproduction of the original figure.   This may be transferred in various ways to make a single permanent copy or to make a master copy which can be used in a duplicating machine to run off a large number of copies.   The original plate may be recharged and used again.   Xerography is a simple and economical method for copying and duplicating forms.   Present plates are slower than those used in photography.   As illustrated in Fig. 16.4, they may be used for X rays as well as for visible light.

16.9   The Germanium Diode[6]

A metal "cat-whisker" contact to an n-type germanium block is a high-resistance rectifying contact; current passes much more readily when the metal wire is positive with respect to the germanium than when it is negative.   In the reverse or high-resistance direction, the current consists of electrons flowing from the metal into the conduction band of the germanium or of holes flowing in the semiconductor to the junction where they are filled by electrons from the metal.   Both of these currents are small; there is a potential barrier at the junction which makes it difficult for electrons to pass from the metal to the conduction band, and very few holes are normally present in the n-type germanium.

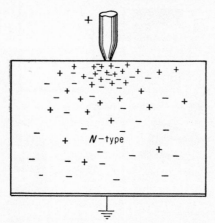

Fig. 16.5   Flow in forward direction from metal point contact to N-type germanium block.   Holes injected at contact increase conductivity in neighborhood of contact.

In the direction of easy flow, the current consists in part of electrons in the conduction band flowing to the junction and in part of holes, created at the junction, flowing into the block.   Under appropriate conditions, the latter current can be quite large and can constitute the majority of the current flow.   The space charge of the holes injected into the block is compensated by an equal increase in the concentration of conduction electrons.   The nature of the flow is illustrated in Fig. 16.5.   In the immediate vicinity of the contact there is a large increase in carrier concentration, perhaps by as much as a factor of 10 or more. Both holes and electrons tend to flow away from this region of high carrier concentration by diffusion.   The electric field is in such a direction as to aid the flow of holes and retard the flow of electrons.   The net result is that a large fraction of the current is carried by holes, even though the germanium normally conducts by excess electrons.   Holes introduced in this way tend to recombine with the electrons and so do not exist indefinitely in the germanium. The lifetime, as noted earlier, may be 10^{-4} sec or larger.

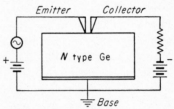

Fig. 16.6   Schematic diagram of point-contact transistor.

16.10   The Point-contact Transistor[7]

Injection of minority carriers is employed in a transistor in such a way as to obtain amplification of an input signal. Two point contacts are placed in close proximity on the upper surface of a small block of germanium which we shall take to be n type, although transistors may be made with p-type material as well.   A schematic diagram of a point-contact transistor is given in Fig. 16.6.   A large-area low-resistance contact is placed on the base of the block.   One of the point contacts, called the *emitter*, is biased with a d-c voltage in a positive or forward direction so as to inject holes into the block.   The second electrode, called the *collector*, is biased in the negative or high-resistance direction.   Current flowing to the collector produces an electric field in the germanium in a direction such as to attract the holes which come from the emitter.   They have no difficulty flowing to the collector junction where they are filled by electrons from the metal.   A large fraction of the emitter current thus flows in the collector circuit.   Since the emitter is biased in the forward direction, its impedance is low.   Biased in the reverse direction, the impedance of the collector is high and can be matched to a high-impedance load.   There is a large voltage amplification, since the signal current, introduced at low impedance at the emitter, flows into the high-impedance load.   It is found that there is some current amplification as well, although this does not follow from the picture we have presented so far.   Current amplification

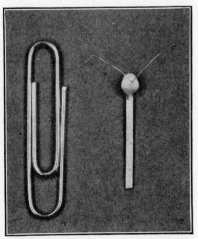

Fig. 16.7   M1689 point-contact transistor developed by Bell Telephone Laboratories.   (*From   J.   A.   Morton, Proc. IRE*, **40**: 1314.)

is associated with an electrical forming of the collector which is not yet completely understood. The over-all power gain is about 20 db.

Early point-contact transistors were not very stable, and the characteristics of units intended to be the same covered a very wide range. During the past few years, as a result of considerable effort, particularly by the group at Bell Telephone Laboratories under J. A. Morton,[8] much progress has been made toward reducing, but not eliminating, these difficulties. Transistors now being produced are more reliable than vacuum tubes, and the spread in characteristics of similar units is not greater. A current model is illustrated in Fig. 16.7. One of the main limitations is the large inherent noise, which is greater at low frequencies than at high. Response at high frequencies is limited by the time taken for the holes to flow from emitter to collector. The upper limit for most units now being made is about 10 Mc/sec, but reports have been made of laboratory units which operate at more than 100 Mc/sec. Special types have been designed for switching applications, for operation at high frequencies, and for general use in oscillator and amplifier circuits.

16.11   The Haynes-Shockley Mobility Experiment

Injection of minority carriers is shown very strikingly in an experiment devised by J. R. Haynes and W. Shockley.[9] As this experiment demonstrates flow of injected carriers both by diffusion and by an electric field, we shall discuss it in some detail. Figure 16.8 is a schematic diagram of the experiment. A rod of germanium (which we shall assume to be n type for the purpose of discussion) of small cross section has low-resistance contacts placed on the ends. An electric field acting along the rod can be produced by applying a battery voltage between these electrodes. A point contact, biased in the forward direction so that it acts as an emitter, is placed near one end of the rod. One or more point contacts, biased in the reverse direction, so that they act as collectors, are placed farther down the rod. The current flowing to the collector is shown on an oscilloscope.

An electronic circuit is used to send current to the emitter in the form of a sharp pulse, a fraction of a microsecond in duration. Holes injected into the rod flow down the rod under the influence of the electric field acting along its length. If the magnitude of the pulse is not too large, the concentration of injected holes will be small compared with the concentration of conduction electrons normally present in the n-type germanium, and the electric field will not be altered very much by the presence of the added holes. Holes could also be introduced photoelectrically by using a pulse of light of short duration. The drift velocity v_d of the pulse down the rod is given by the product of the hole mobility μ_p and the electric field. For a field of 100 volts/cm, the drift velocity is about 1.7×10^5 cm/sec, which is of the same order of magnitude as the velocity of sound. The pulse will appear at the collector point after a time

$$t = \frac{v_d}{l} = \frac{\mu_p E}{l} \qquad (16.17)$$

where l is the distance between the emitter and collector points. Holes flowing to the collector increase the collector current, and this increase gives a pulse on the oscilloscope. If two collector points are used, two pulses will be seen; the time between them is the time taken for the holes to flow from one point to the next. This experiment gives a direct and

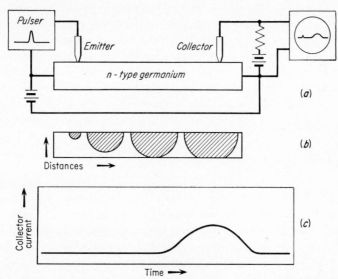

Fig. 16.8 Schematic diagram of Haynes-Shockley experiment for direct measurement of mobility of minority carriers. (*From W. Shockley, Proc. IRE*, **40**: 1289.)

precise method for measuring mobilities of injected carriers. The drift velocity is obtained directly from measurements of time and distance.

As a result of diffusion, the pulse spreads out and soon attains a Gaussian shape. The width of the pulse increases with the square root of the time. Thus, the pulse is broader at the second collector point than at the first, and from the increase in width the diffusion coefficient can be estimated. If at times t_1 and t_2 the pulse widths at half maximum intensity are w_1 and w_2, the diffusion coefficient is proportional to

$$\frac{w_1{}^2 - w_2{}^2}{t_1 - t_2}$$

Diffusion coefficients cannot be measured so accurately as mobilities.

Values obtained in this way check within experimental error with those obtained from mobilities and Einstein's relation.

16.12   *pn* Junctions

A *pn* junction is a boundary between a *p*-type and an *n*-type region, as illustrated in Fig. 16.9.   It forms a high-resistance rectifying junction. Best electrical characteristics are obtained if the junction is formed in a single crystal, in part of which there is an excess of acceptor impurities and in part of which there is an excess of donors.

The direction of easy flow is that in which the *p*-type side is positive and the *n*-type negative.   Holes, the majority carriers on the *p* side, then flow across to the *n* side, and electrons flow from the *n* side to the *p* side.   Carriers injected in this way increase the conductivity on each side of the junction.   A *pn* junction can act as an emitter in a transistor.

In the direction of high resistance, the current must consist of an excess of electrons flowing from the *p* side to the *n* side or of holes flowing from the *n* side to the *p* side.   As there are very few conduction electrons on the *p* side and very few holes on the *n* side, the current is small and it tends to saturate at a relatively constant value independent of voltage.

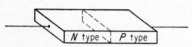

Fig. 16.9   Schematic diagram of *pn* junction.

If holes are introduced on the *n* side or electrons on the *p* side, either by light or by current flow, they may diffuse to the junction and contribute to the current.   To have a good chance of reaching the junction before recombination occurs, the minority carriers should be introduced within a diffusion length of the junction [see Eq. (16.10)].   The saturation current in the reverse direction consists of minority carriers which are created thermally in the vicinity of the junction and diffuse to the junction.

A *pn* junction can act as a collector in a transistor.   Since the currents, and therefore the electric fields, are very small, one must depend on diffusion to carry the minority carriers to the junction.   There is a marked difference in this regard between a *pn* junction and a point-contact collector.   In the latter, the flow of minority carriers is determined mainly by the electric field set up by the collector current.

A complete theory of the characteristics of *pn* junctions has been given by Shockley.[10]   This theory, developed before junctions with good characteristics were made in the laboratory, is now in excellent agreement with observation.   At the same time, Shockley also presented his theory of junction transistors, also in advance of experiment.   We shall not present the mathematical details of the theory here but shall discuss the physical picture involved.

Under equilibrium conditions, with no voltage applied, the electrostatic potential of the n side is positive with respect to the p side, as illustrated in Fig. 16.10.   The change in potential occurs in a narrow region, whose width is of the order of 10^{-4} cm, in which there are very few carriers of either sign.   It results from a double layer formed from uncompensated acceptors on the p side and uncompensated donors on the n side.   The tendency for electrons to flow from the p to the n side as a result of the potential difference is just compensated by a tendency to flow in the opposite direction as a result of the difference in concentration; the same

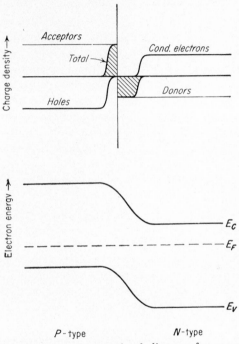

Fig. 16.10 Charge density and energy-level diagram for a *pn* junction with no applied voltage.

is true of holes.   The concentration of electrons or of holes of a given total energy E decreases with energy as $e^{-E/kT}$ and is independent of position.

The theory is particularly simple if it is assumed that the width of the uncompensated space-charge layer at the junction is small compared with the diffusion length.   This is a good approximation for junctions in germanium.

When a voltage is applied in the forward direction, the situation is modified, as shown in Fig. 16.11.   Most of the added drop in potential occurs across the space-charge layer.   We shall assume that the applied voltage V_a is positive when the p side is positive with respect to the n side. As a result of the applied voltage, the concentration of holes just to the right of the junction on the n side is increased by a factor $e^{eV_a/kT}$. The excess concentration drops to zero in a distance of the order of a diffusion length. There is a net flow of holes from left to right resulting from this concentration gradient. Similarly, there is a net current of electrons from right to left, and the total current is given by the sum of the electron and hole currents.

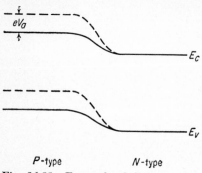

P-type   *N*-type

Fig. 16.11 Energy-level diagram for a pn junction with a voltage V_a applied in the forward direction.

It is at first surprising to note that the resistance of a pn junction, even at low applied voltages, is much larger than the value which would be obtained by dividing it along its length into segments, calculating the resistance of each segment from the local resistivity as determined by the local concentrations, and then adding these resistances in series. Mathematically, the resistance per unit area of cross section would on this scheme be given by

$$R = \int \frac{dx}{\sigma_n(x) + \sigma_p(x)} \quad \text{(incorrectly)} \quad (16.18)$$

where σ_n and σ_p are the local conductivities for electrons and holes, respectively. This calculation is wrong because electron and hole currents are conserved separately over distances of the order of the diffusion length. One should calculate the resistance for hole flow and the resistance for electron flow and then add the two in parallel. The main resistance for the flow of holes is on the n side where the hole concentration is small. The main resistance for the flow of electrons is on the p side where the electron concentration is small. One may, in fact, estimate the resistance at low applied voltages by calculating the resistance to flow of minority carriers in a distance equal to the diffusion length. For unit area, the resistance is then

$$R = \left(\frac{1}{R_p} + \frac{1}{R_n} \right)^{-1} = \left(\frac{\sigma_p}{L_p} + \frac{\sigma_n}{L_n} \right)^{-1} \quad (16.19)$$

where

$$\sigma_p = p_n e u_p \qquad \sigma_n = n_p e u_n \quad (16.20)$$

are the conductivities of the minority carriers and L_p and L_n the corresponding diffusion lengths. Equation (16.19) is, in fact, the correct expression as derived by Shockley for the low-voltage junction resistance in the limiting case where the diffusion length is large compared with the width of the space-charge layer.

The predominant carrier is that from the side which has the larger conductivity; the minority carrier in larger concentration is of the same sign. Thus, to make a good hole emitter, one should use a junction in which the conductivity of the p side is large compared with that of the n side.

A new phenomenon, and one which promises to have wide practical application, becomes important when the reverse voltage reaches a critical value. With increase in voltage, the electric field in the junction region increases; when it is sufficiently large, electrons are pulled directly from the valence band to the conduction band, creating electron-hole pairs which move rapidly apart under the influence of the field. Such a process was predicted on theoretical grounds many years ago by C. Zener, but it had not been observed directly until recently[11] in experiments on pn junctions at the Bell Telephone Laboratories. A rapid increase in carriers may also occur if the field is strong enough to accelerate conduction electrons or holes to sufficient energy to create additional electrons or holes by knocking electrons from the valence band to the conduction band. An avalanche is then formed. It shows up as an exceedingly rapid increase of current once a critical voltage in the reverse direction is reached. As illustrated schematically in Fig. 16.12, it appears as almost a right-angle bend in the current-voltage characteristic. The voltage at which the Zener current appears depends on the width of the space-charge

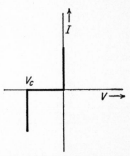

Fig. 16.12 Schematic diagram of current-voltage characteristic of Al-Si fused junction as seen on an oscilloscope. There is rapid increase of current in forward direction. In the reverse direction the current is small until a critical voltage V_c is attained there, when there is a sudden increase in current.

layer at the junction, which in turn depends on the distribution of donor and acceptor impurities in the region of the junction. It is likely that diodes exhibiting Zener current can be used in many applications which now employ gas tubes.

16.13 Junction Transistors[12]

Junction transistors not only are of great practical importance, but they are also of considerable scientific interest. The structure is sufficiently simple so that its characteristics are calculable. The theory was, in fact, worked out by Shockley[10] in advance of experiment. An npn transistor consists, as shown in Fig. 16.13, of a thin layer of p-type material interspersed between two n-type regions in a small single-crystal block of germanium.   Low-resistance electrodes on the ends make contact to the n regions, and a third electrode called the *base* makes contact to the p region.   The width of the latter, called the *base layer*, is shown on an exaggerated scale; actually its thickness is only a few thousandths of an inch.

When operated as a transistor, one junction (say the left) is biased in the forward direction so that it acts as an emitter: electrons are injected from the n region to the base layer.   The second junction, biased in the reverse direction, acts as a collector.   Electrons injected from the emitter flow across the p layer where they add to the collector current.   The electric field in the base layer is small; the flow is mainly by diffusion. The width of the layer is made small compared with the diffusion length for electrons in the layer, so that practically all (as much as 98 per cent)

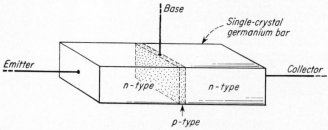

Fig. 16.13   An *NPN* junction transistor consists of a single crystal of germanium in which there is a thin p-type region between two n-type regions.   (*From J. A. Morton, Proc. IRE,* **40**: 1314.)

the injected electrons diffuse to the collector rather than recombining with holes in the base layer.

The emitter current depends on the voltage applied between emitter and base and is nearly independent of collector voltage.   This current flows to the collector, which has a very high impedance since it is biased in the reverse direction.   There is a close analogy with a vacuum tube; the emitter corresponds to the cathode, the collector to the plate, and the base to the grid.   As with a vacuum tube, the highest gain per stage is obtained if the signal to be amplified is applied to the base electrode. The load is connected between collector and emitter.   The signal current is then the small fraction of the emitter current which flows to the base, so that there is a large current amplification as well as a large voltage amplification.   The latter results from the large ratio between the impedance of the input and output circuits.   The over-all power gain may be as much as 50 db per stage.

Figures 16.14a and 16.14b illustrate the way a junction transistor operates.   Shown in a schematic way is the distribution in energy of electrons

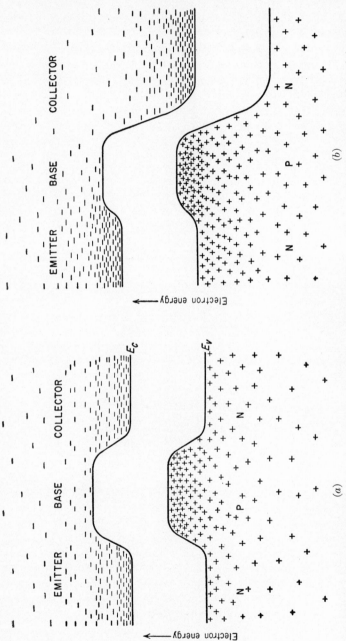

Fig. 16.14 Energy-level diagrams of junction transistor. (a) Equilibrium with no applied voltage; (b) biased for use as amplifier or oscillator. Actual decrease of carrier concentration with energy is much greater than illustrated in schematic diagram.

419

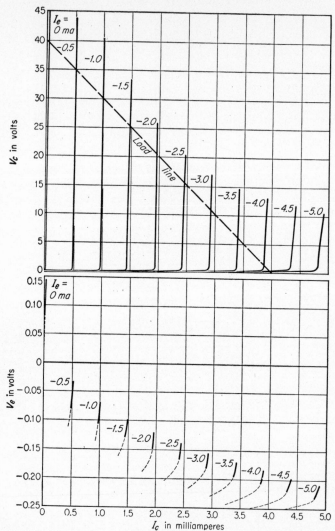

Fig. 16.15 Current-voltage characteristics of M1752 junction transistor. (*From J. A. Morton, Proc. IRE,* **40**: 1314.)

in the n regions and in the base layer.   Figure 16.14a is the equilibrium configuration.   The electrostatic potential of the p region is negative with respect to the n regions, giving a high potential energy for electrons, resulting in a small equilibrium concentration.

Figure 16.14b shows the changes in concentration which occur when the device is biased as a transistor, with the left junction in the forward direction and the right junction in the reverse direction.   The concentration of electrons in the base layer adjacent to the left junction is increased, and the concentration adjacent to the right junction is very small. Any electrons which pass over the potential barrier are drawn into the collector by the high field. The current across the base layer is produced by diffusion resulting from the large concentration gradient across the base layer. The magnitude of current flow is nearly independent of collector voltage. The main effect is an indirect one: an increase of collector voltage increases the width of the space-charge layer where the potential is changing rapidly, and this narrows the width of the barrier and increases the concentration gradient.

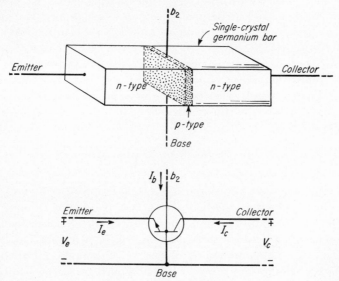

Fig. 16.16 Structure of transistor tetrode. (*From R. L. Wallace, L. G. Schimpf, and E. Dickten, Proc. IRE,* **40**: 1395.)

Current-voltage characteristics are illustrated in Fig. 16.15, which shows how the collector current varies with collector voltage for various values of the emitter current. The collector current saturates at a relatively constant value in the reverse direction. The emitter current adds almost directly to the collector current.

Junction transistors are stable, with relatively low noise, and should have an almost indefinite life. They are superior to vacuum tubes in at least one figure of merit, the gain-bandwidth product, which is a useful measure of amplifier performance. Since the characteristics are almost ideal, the efficiency under class A operation is very high—close to the theoretical limit of 50 per cent. The greatest advantage of the junction transistor is that it can be operated at very low voltages, less than 1 volt on the collector, and very low power input, less than 1 microwatt. As has been pointed out by R. L. Wallace, Jr., the latter is flea power in fact. He estimates that the energy required for a flea to jump once every 10 sec is no more than that required to run a junction-transistor oscillator which he built. A maximum power output of several watts has been achieved in especially designed units.

Major limitations of the *npn* transistor are relatively low-frequency response—useful gain is limited to the region below about 1 Mc/sec— and rapid change in characteristics with temperature. Response at high frequencies is limited by the relatively large capacitance of the collector junction and by the transit time for carriers flowing across the base layer. A major improvement in frequency response is obtained by adding a second electrode to the base region, as shown in Fig. 16.16. This fourth electrode is biased negatively, so that only a small part of the base region adjacent to the base electrode is positive with respect to the emitter. Since the emitter current is confined to this region, the base resistance is very small. Tetrodes of this type, made with a very thin base region to reduce the transit time, have been operated at frequencies above 100 Mc/sec.

16.14 Fused-junction Diodes and Transistors

Junction transistors described in the preceding section are made by introducing the appropriate impurities while the crystal is being grown from the melt. Another method, which may be applied to both diodes and transistors, is to fuse a metal containing donor or acceptors directly to the semiconductor, as illustrated in Fig. 16.17. Examples are indium on germanium[13] and aluminum on silicon.[14] Both metals are from group III and are, therefore, acceptors. When applied to *n*-type semiconductors, they form high-resistance rectifying junctions with characteristics similar to those of grown *pn* junctions. They are, in fact, a limiting form in which the conductivity of one side (toward the metal) is much higher than that of the other. When applied to *p*-type acceptors, they give a low-resistance ohmic contact. If donors are used, rectifying contact is made with *p*-type and ohmic with *n*-type material.

To form a fused junction, the contact is heated above the eutectic temperature of the alloy between the impurity metal and the semiconductor, so that a small region of the semiconductor dissolves to form the alloy. As the junction cools, there is some regrowth of the original crystal back into the melt. The regrown crystal contains a large excess of impurity. There also may be some diffusion of the impurity into the unmelted crystal, although the penetration is not great and is certainly insignificant in fused silicon junctions. The result in either case is to form a *pn* junction in which one side has very high conductivity. In a

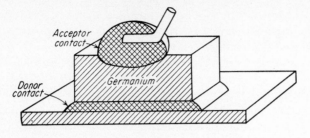

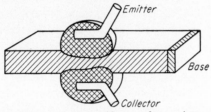

Fig. 16.17 Fused impurity contact rectifiers and transistors. (*From R. N. Hall, Proc. IRE, 40: 1512.*)

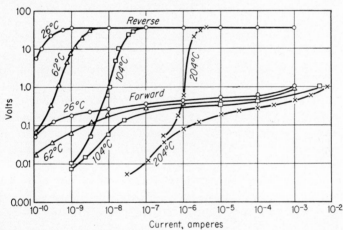

Fig. 16.18 Current-voltage characteristics of Al-Si diode at various ambient temperatures. (*From G. L. Pearson and B. Sawyer, Proc. IRE, 40: 1348.*)

rectifier made in this way, practically all the current is carried by the minority carrier of the semiconductor.

Fused junctions exhibit a Zener current when a critical voltage in the reverse direction is reached. The critical voltage is easy to control because it depends only on the conductivity of the semiconductor and is insensitive to the details of the fusion process.

Fused-junction germanium diodes, now an article of commerce, have importance as power rectifiers. Aluminum-silicon diodes rectify at

300°C, as illustrated in Fig. 16.18, a much higher temperature than is possible with germanium. Fused-junction germanium transistors of the *pnp* type have good characteristics and are now being produced on a commercial scale.

16.15   Unipolar Devices[15]

Prior to the invention of the point-contact transistor, attempts were made to make amplifying devices using semiconductors in which only one type of current carrier is important. One of these involved placing a grid structure in the space-charge layer of a diode so as to control the flow of current across the junction. This of course is in close analogy with a vacuum tube. Another made use of the "field effect," *i.e.*, the change in conductance produced by a transverse electric field. In one form of the latter, the semiconductor in the form of a thin film is made one plate of a condenser. The net charge on the film can be controlled by the voltage on the condenser. If the charge consists of adding or subtracting mobile carriers (electrons or holes), the conductivity of the film will vary with the voltage. In an experiment of Pearson and Shockley it was found that most of the charge introduced was an immobile surface charge and that only a fraction contributed to the change in conductance of the film. Neither of these ideas proved to be practical with the techniques available at the time.

With the improvement in semiconductor technology which attended the development of the transistor, devices making use of these basic principles may prove to be practical. Two devices suggested by Shockley are illustrated in Figs. 16.19 and 16.20. Since flow of only one type of carrier (electrons or holes) is involved, Shockley calls them *unipolar devices* to distinguish them from point-contact or junction transistors in which flow of both carriers is important.

The device shown in Fig. 16.19 is a modification of the one in which the conductance of a film is modified by a transverse electric field. The structure is similar to the junction tetrode, but the mode of operation is different. The device consists of a thin layer of *n*-type material sandwiched between two regions of *p* type. Electrodes attached to the *p* regions are biased negatively relative to the *n* region, so that the two *pn* boundaries are in the opposite directions. The charge which establishes the fields across these boundaries comes from changes in numbers of electrons and holes—there is no surface intervening where an immobile charge can reside. An increase in reverse bias voltage causes a decrease in the number of conduction electrons in the *n* layer. If the voltage is sufficiently large, the resistivity of the layer becomes large. According to Shockley's calculations, voltage amplification of an input signal is possible.

The second device is called an *analogue transistor* because of its close resemblance to a vacuum tube, as is evident from the schematic diagram in Fig. 16.20.   An intrinsic semiconductor of high resistivity replaces the vacuum.   The cathode is a cylindrical region of strongly n-type material located at the center of the device; the plate is a concentric cylinder, also

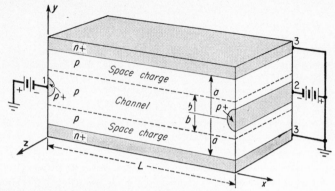

Fig. 16.19 Schematic diagram of unipolar "field effect" transistor.   (*From W. Shockley, Proc. IRE*, **40**: 1355.)

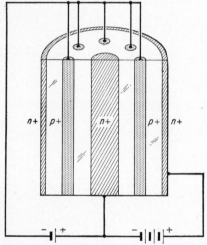

Fig. 16.20 Structure of analogue transistor. (*From W. Shockley, Proc. IRE*, **40**: 1289.)

of strongly n-type material.   When the plate is positive with respect to the cathode, a space-charge-limited current of conduction electrons flows. The magnitude of this current can be controlled by a voltage applied to the grid region, which consists of a number of cylindrical regions of p-type material.   The negative electrostatic potential of the p regions relative to the neighboring intrinsic regions tends to prevent conduction electrons flowing to the grid. Since the velocity of electrons in the solid is less than it would be in a vacuum, the dimensions of the device must be smaller for a given frequency response. Of course, it may be possible to use smaller dimensions in a rigid solid structure than in a vacuum tube. It remains to be seen whether such structures will prove to be practical.

REFERENCES

1. An excellent introduction to the subject of transistor electronics is W. Shockley, "Electrons and Holes in Semiconductors," D. Van Nostrand Company, Inc., New York, 1950.
2. Shockley, W., *Proc. IRE*, **40**: 1289 (1952).
3. Busch, G., *Z. angew. Math. u. Phys.*, **1**: 3 and 81 (1950).
4. Lark-Horovitz, K., Conductivity in Semiconductors, *Elec. Eng.*, **68**: 1047 (1949).
5. *RCA Rev.*, September, 1951.
6. The germanium point-contact diode was developed during the war. For an account of this work, see H. C. Torrey and C. A. Whitmer, "Crystal Rectifiers," McGraw-Hill Book Company, Inc., New York, 1948.
7. Bardeen, J., and W. H. Brattain, *Phys. Rev.*, **75**: 1208 (1949).
8. Morton, J. A., *Bell System Tech. J.*, **31**: 411 (1952).
9. Haynes, J. R., and W. Shockley, *Phys. Rev.*, **81**: 835 (1951).
10. Shockley, W., *Bell System Tech. J.*, **28**: 435 (1949).
11. McAfee, K. B., W. Shockley, and M. Sparks, Zener Currents in p-n Junctions, *Phys. Rev.*, **85**: 730 (1952).
12. Shockley, W., M. Sparks, and G. Teal, *Phys. Rev.*, **83**: 151 (1951); R. L. Wallace, Jr., and W. J. Pietenpol, *Proc. IRE*, **39**: 753 (1951).
13. Hall, R. N., and W. C. Dunlap, Jr., *Phys. Rev.*, **80**: 467 (1950); R. N. Hall, *Proc. IRE*, **40**: 1512 (1952).
14. Pearson, G. L., and P. W. Foy, *Phys. Rev.*, **87**: 190 (1952); Pearson, G. L., and B. Sawyer, *Proc. IRE*, **40**: 1348 (1952).

17

Communication Theory and
the Transmission of
Information

J. B. WIESNER

PROFESSOR OF ELECTRICAL ENGINEERING
MASSACHUSETTS INSTITUTE OF TECHNOLOGY

17.1 Introduction

The recent application of methods of statistical analysis to the problems of communication engineering and the concurrent definition of a measure of information have aroused widespread interest, not only among communication and electronic engineers occupied in allied fields of endeavor such as radar, guided-missile, or electronic-computer development, but also among such diverse groups as linguists and neurophysiologists.

The need to define the commodity processed by the communication engineer, and the desire to have a means whereby it could be given quantitative specification, had long been felt by workers in the field. In the course of the development of this theory, the field has progressed from an art in which the communication engineer was guided almost completely by his intuition, to a state where developments can follow in an orderly manner from basic understandings of the problem at hand.

By empirical means, the communication engineer learned to design communication circuits and how to take into account the two important variables: circuit bandwidth and the random fluctuations or noise which almost always appeared on a circuit. Experience showed that there was a definite relationship between the rate at which signaling could be accomplished on a given circuit and its bandwidth. Telephone circuits, which can handle more words per minute than a telegraph circuit, and therefore intuitively carry more information, also require more bandwidth for proper operation. A television system, having an even greater capacity

427

for transmitting messages, requires much more circuit bandwidth than is needed by the telephone.

If one attempted to cheat by using less bandwidth than was appropriate for the signal being transmitted, the information received was degraded: telegraph signals blurred together, telephone messages became less intelligible, and television pictures lost detail or became smeared. Obviously, the reduction of the circuit bandwidth was eliminating some of the information present in the original message.

The relationship between signaling speed and circuit bandwidth was first investigated by Hartley in 1928. In his paper entitled "Transmission of Information"[1] Hartley developed a quantitative measure of "information" which is similar to that presented later by Shannon for the so-called "noiseless case." In this work, Hartley investigated the limitation placed upon signaling rate by stored energy in the transmission system, i.e., bandwidth limitation on signaling.

By means of experience and experiment, the qualified engineer soon developed instincts, or at least acquired empirical data, which guided him in the design of equipment, and although the lack of precise understanding of the communication process may have offended the intellects of the more curious, the empirical methods were, for a long time, entirely adequate for coping with the problems that existed. Problems of implementation such as amplifier design, filter design, noise reduction, etc., were sufficiently great to occupy most of the attention of systems designers.

As soon as vacuum-tube amplifiers became available, it was shown that the existence of random electrical voltages due to thermal agitation of electrons in conductors, and the random emission of electrons in vacuum tubes, established a lower limit to useful electrical signals.[2,3] These random voltages had a definite mean-square value which could not be reduced, and as signal voltages approached the noise voltage in magnitude, the signals were corrupted. The larger the noise-to-signal ratio, the more the message was "spoiled." A message which had been contaminated by having a random noise added to it appeared to contain less information than it formerly did. A telephone message to which noise has been added is less intelligible than the original; as a circuit becomes noisy, it is more often necessary to request that words be repeated. Obviously, the noise has reduced the rate at which information can be sent over the circuit. As the noise increases, the intelligibility goes down, and so does the rate at which information is being sent, until a point is reached where no information is being conveyed and only noise is present at the output. In a similar way, the presence of random electrical fluctuations, or noise, appears to reduce the amount of information which can be sent on a television system. The presence

[1] Corresponding numbered bibliographic references appear at the end of the chapter.

of the noise reduces the number of light levels which can be discerned. The effect of a small amount of noise is to "wash out" or eliminate the fine light distinctions; as the noise voltage increases in magnitude, fewer and fewer distinct light levels remain. The picture becomes harder to watch. Eventually, when the noise becomes sufficiently large in comparison to the signal, no useful picture will remain. Here again, as the noise-to-signal ratio increases, the amount of useful "information" transmitted is reduced. The effect of noise in transmission systems can be reduced by increasing the signal power, although this obviously has practical limits. Also, it is sometimes possible to limit circuit attenuation so that the desired signal power never becomes as small as the noise power.

Here, then, was the riddle confronting the communication engineer of the 1940's. The amount of "information" which a circuit was capable of passing was clearly a function of the circuit bandwidth and the circuit signal-to-noise ratio, but how were the various factors quantitatively related?

During this period, another interesting and important discovery was made. Major Edwin H. Armstrong invented the wideband f-m system of transmission. This system had a very interesting property; the signal-to-noise ratio at the output of the system could be improved not only by increasing signal power but also by increasing the frequency deviation, or frequency swing. By using bandwidths which were wider than necessary to pass the basic intelligence carried by the signal, an improvement in signal-to-noise ratio was achieved. Was this a general property of communication systems? Was it generally possible to trade bandwidth for system power? And was the converse true? Could one use frequency bands narrower than the intelligence bandwidth would normally require and compensate for it by using more power?

As we shall see, these problems are related, and they are explained satisfactorily by the statistical communication theory, which provides a measure of "information" defined specifically for this application. It also provides a means for computing the information content of messages, the rate of transmission of information, and the capacity of a channel for transmitting information.

The fundamental understanding of the processes of communication made possible by the mathematical theory of communication is probably most noteworthy for the general perspective which it provides. It gives the communication engineer the ability to measure his accomplishment. It becomes possible to evaluate the efficiency of a system against a theoretically predicted standard of performance. In this regard, the theory serves much as the second law of thermodynamics does in the design of heat engines.

One of the most important contributions in the development of the new theory was made by Norbert Wiener[4] in connection with the development of predictors for antiaircraft gun-director control. In studying this problem, he found that it could best be handled by regarding the information provided by the radar as a statistically stationary random function of time. This work provided the basis for his now famous book "The Extrapolation, Interpolation, and Smoothing of Stationary Time Series." The statistical character of this problem led him to the realization that all communication problems are fundamentally statistical in nature and must be handled by statistical methods to be successful. In order to be transmitted by a communication system, a signal should never be a completely known function of time. If it were known a priori, its transmission could not convey any new information and, therefore, there would be no need to send it.

What can be known a priori about a message or signal is its statistical structure. It is possible to examine the field of potential signals and determine the probability distribution of amplitudes and the conditional probabilities in the voltage that represents the signal. Noise also can be described in statistical terms.

In this introduction, attention has been restricted to the transmission of messages by electrical means. The comments made regarding communication by electrical means obviously apply to all forms of communication. For example, written language makes use of a set of symbols, the letters of the alphabet, which are arranged in various combinations to convey meaning. In this case, not only the statistics of the individual letter need be studied, but the assembled groups of letters (i.e., words) also have statistical properties which must be examined if a complete understanding of the "information content" of a written message is to be obtained. Experience with written messages leads to the conclusion that not all symbols or letters contribute equally to the information which is transmitted. For example, if a teletype printer makes an error and prints a single wrong letter, it is generally possible to supply the missing information by referring to that part of the message which was transmitted correctly. Even if most vowels were omitted, the message could be reconstructed. (This is actually done in written Hebrew.) If, however, the teletype message happened to be a number, e.g., a coded message giving the location of a ship, one error could render the entire message incorrect. From this we see that some letters or, in the general case, some symbols carry less information than others. We shall see that this fact is related to the probability that a given symbol will occur if certain others have already been received. If the probability is high that the letter "h" will always follow the letter "t," then relatively little information is gained by its transmission. This is a simple example of a phenomenon called *redundancy*, which is found in many forms of communication. For example, speech communication is found to have much redundancy. Since the redundant information requires channel facility for its transmission, much effort has been expended in an attempt to design equipment which can remove the redundancy found in speech before it is transmitted. The Vocoder[5] is an example of a device designed for this purpose. This will be discussed in more detail in a later section.

Redundancy is not always undesirable. In a speech message it enables one to get the meaning of the message above noise or other obscuring effects. Redundancy is sometimes deliberately built into messages. The digits which are added to the words in a digital computing machine to make error correction possible illustrate this point.

Communication theory in its present form is due largely to Claude Shannon[6-8] who took the work of his predecessors, notably Hartley and Wiener, and provided a sound mathematical basis for it.

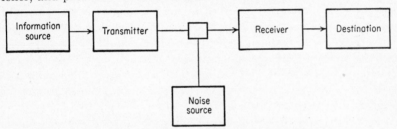

Fig. 17.1 Model of a communication system.

In the presentation of the theory, it is desirable to investigate successively three different models of the communication process, each of which illustrates important features of the theory. The three cases involve messages which can be represented as

    a. Discrete symbols without noise
    b. Discrete symbols in the presence of noise
    c. Continuous signals in the presence of noise

A communication system as defined by Shannon[7] will be of the type illustrated in Fig. 17.1 and will consist of the five parts which he defines as follows:

The information source, which produces the message to be transmitted to the destination. The messages obviously can be any of those previously discussed, *i.e.*, sequences of letters as in a teletype system, functions of time as produced by a telephone or radio system, or functions of both space and time as in the case of a television system.

A transmitter, which operates on the signal in some way in order to produce a signal suitable for transmission over the channel. Depending upon the form of the original message and the form of transmission, the transmitter may perform simple or complex coding operations on the original message.   Frequency modulation and pulse-code modulation are two examples of operations on the original message which are performed to obtain the signal to be transmitted.

The channel, which is defined as the medium used to convey the signal from the transmitter to the receiver.   It may be a pair of wires, an r-f circuit, etc.   During transmission, or at the receiver, noise may be added to the signal.   This is represented by the noise source shown in Fig. 17.1.

The receiver, which has the task of recovering the message from the signal as best it can.   This is usually accomplished by performing an operation which is the inverse of that carried out by the transmitter.

The destination, defined as the person or device (computer, recorder, etc.) for whom the message is intended.

17.2   Information Measure: The Discrete Noiseless Case

A discrete system may be defined as one in which the signals are represented by a finite number of individual symbols.   The alphabet is typical of a discrete set of symbols.   Electrical signals can be quantized in both amplitude and time and thus be represented by a discrete set of symbols. While many of the most important situations which are met in practice are really continuous, it is nonetheless valuable to begin with this case and generalize later.

17.2.1   *The Unit of Information.*   Since the manner in which the unit of information is to be defined is arbitrary, it is desirable that the definition, when made, result in a system of measurement which is intuitively satisfactory.   To achieve this result, the final choice should satisfy the following general requirements:

a. The amount of information corresponding to two independent units, *i.e.*, two symbols, or to the capacity of two independent channels should be equal to the sum of the amounts of information corresponding to the individual units.   Two pages of text should, on the average, contain twice as much information as one page.   Two telegraph circuits should have twice the capacity that one circuit has, etc.

b. Symbols having a high probability of occurrence should convey less information than those whose occurrence is less probable.   This requirement is associated with the observation that high-probability symbols can be predicted from the statistical knowledge stored at the receiver.

If the discrete source has available N symbols which can be recognized by the receiver, and if the ith symbol has a probability p_i of occurring, the measure of the information suggested by Shannon is given by

$$H = -\sum_{i=1}^{N} p_i \log p_i$$

If a message is formed by the transmission of two symbols in succession, N^2 combinations of the symbols are available for selection. It has been indicated that it is desirable to have the transmission of two symbols convey twice the information, on the average, that is transmitted by one symbol. The use of the log p_i accomplishes this. If the N symbols are equally likely,

$$p_i = \frac{1}{N}$$

and

$$H = \log_2 N$$

for a single symbol, while for two symbols

$$H = \log_2 N^2 = 2 \log_2 N$$

An understanding of the expression for H may be obtained by examining, in detail, the selection of one symbol from N equally likely choices.

If we define as the unit of information the simplest possible selection, *i.e.*, the selection between two equally likely choices, we see that the average information per symbol will in this case be

$$H = -\tfrac{1}{2} \log_2 \tfrac{1}{2} + \tfrac{1}{2} \log_2 \tfrac{1}{2} = 1$$

The $\log_2$ is chosen so that the elementary selection will contain just one unit of information. This unit has been named the *bit* of information (from *bi*nary digi*t*).

At this point, it is desirable to inject a word of caution. The unit of information is defined on the basis of the probability of occurrence of the symbols which are used to represent a given message, and as will be shown, this permits the information content of a message to be computed in terms of the smallest number of binary decisions which would be required to convey the message if it were properly represented. The information measure intentionally ignores the semantic information which may be present in the message. Much confusion can arise if this point is not understood.

17.2.2 *Selection from N Equally Likely Choices.* Further understanding of the information measure can be gained by considering the selection of a symbol from a group of N equally likely choices. In order to determine the amount of information corresponding to such a selection, this more complex choice should be reduced to a series of elementary selections. The number of elementary selections required to make the selection of a choice from the N possible selections is, by definition, the number of bits of information given by that selection.

For convenience we shall assume that N is a power of 2. Let the N symbols be arranged in a row, as shown in Fig. 17.2. The problem is to indicate one of the N symbols by using a succession of binary decisions. To do this the N objects are first divided into two equal groups, in this case into two groups of four symbols, as indicated. One binary decision will suffice to indicate the group containing the desired symbol. The indicated group can again be subdivided into equal groups and a second binary decision used to indicate the subgroup containing the desired symbol. This process can be continued until the desired symbol is uniquely specified. For the group of eight symbols shown in Fig. 17.2, three bits of information are a sufficient number to isolate the desired symbol from the others. Two subdivisions are required for $N = 4$, four for $N = 16$, and in general a number of subdivisions equal to $\log_2 N$ for an N-order selection. It can be shown that the expression is still correct when N is not a power of 2, provided H is now regarded as an average value over a large number of selections.

17.2.3 *Information Measure When the Choices Are Not Equally Likely.* In general, the selections will not be equally likely. It is still possible

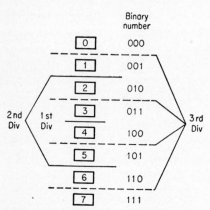

Binary number

000
001
010
011
100
101
110
111

2nd Div   1st Div   3rd Div

Fig. 17.2 Selection procedure for equally likely choices.

to carry out a process of selection similar to that which was followed in the previous section. The individual symbols are still assumed to be independent. Instead of dividing the group of symbols into subgroups containing equal numbers of symbols, an attempt is made to divide the symbols into groups having as nearly as possible equal probabilities, so that the selection of a group will still comprise a choice between equally likely possibilities. This procedure of selection is carried out until it is possible to separate any desired message from the remaining symbols. The selection will now, as before, be carried out by making a series of elementary selections. This procedure, developed by Fano,[9] is one method of coding symbols to permit more efficient transmission.

If the ensemble of messages is small, it may not always be possible to form groups having equal probability. If, however, the length of the message is increased indefinitely, it will be possible to form the subgroups with increasing accuracy, since the probability of any given message will tend toward zero. The following example will illustrate the procedure. The messages to be transmitted are formed by taking the symbols 0, 1, and 2, two at a time, with the following probabilities: $p(0) = 0.7$,

$p(1) = 0.2$, and $p(2) = 0.1$. The messages are first arranged in order of their probability, as shown in Fig. 17.3.   In this case, the first division is made between message 00 and the remainder of the group.   This results in groups having probabilities 0.49 and 0.51.   The selection of the first group (message 00) is made by the binary symbol 0.   If the desired message happens to be in the second group, this is indicated by the symbol 1.   The second group is again divided into groups having as nearly as possible like probabilities.   This division yields groups having probabilities 0.28 and 0.23.   Again choice is indicated by a binary digit. This process is continued until all the symbols are resolved.

Message	$P(i)$	Probabilities of groups obtained by successive division						Recoded message	$P(i) B_g(i)$
		Div. 1	Div. 2	Div. 3	Div. 4	Div. 5	Div. 6		
00	0.49	0.49						0	0.49
01	0.14	0.51		0.14				100	0.42
10	0.14		0.28	0.14				101	0.42
02	0.07		0.23		0.07			1100	0.28
20	0.07			0.14	0.07			1101	0.28
11	0.04			0.09	0.04			1110	0.16
12	0.02				0.05	0.02		11110	0.10
21	0.02				0.03		0.02	111110	0.12
22	0.01						0.01	111111	0.06

Fig. 17.3 Regrouping of messages by Fano technique to obtain efficient code.

The result of this procedure is very interesting.   The number of binary digits required to select one message from the group varies from message to message.   The messages with a high probability of occurrence require fewer digits for their selection than those which occur less frequently. If $p(i)$ is the probability of the ith message, we can see by examining Fig. 17.3 that the number of binary digits required to represent a symbol is an integer close to $\log p(i)$.   The approximation becomes better as N, the number of selections, increases indefinitely.   If $B_s(i)$ represents the number of binary digits required to select the ith message, then

$$p(i) \simeq 2^{-B_s(i)}$$

or

$$B_s(i) = -\log_2 p(i)$$

If the selection of messages from the group is repeated a large number of times so that the frequency of the ith message approaches $p(i)$, the

number of binary digits required, on the average, to select one message
will be the mathematical expectation of $B_s(i)$:

$$E(B_s) = - \sum_{i=1}^{s} p(i) B_s(i)$$

which, for an indefinitely large number of N-order selections, yields

$$H_N = - \sum_{i=1}^{N} p(i) \log_2 p(i)$$

the average amount of information per N-order selection, so that it is
shown that H is also the minimum number of elementary selections, on
the average, required to represent a symbol from the group.

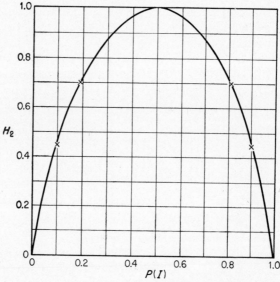

Fig. 17.4   Average amount of information per binary digit as function of $p(i)$.

The value of H_N is positive or zero for all values of $p(i)$.   If certain of
the probabilities are zero, the terms of H_N corresponding to these $p(i)$
will also be zero.   Note that if all but one of the $p(i)$ are equal to zero,
the remaining probability must be equal to unity, and H_N vanishes.
This result satisfies the intuitive requirements that the selection of a
symbol whose choice was certain should not convey any information.

When the N probabilities $p(i)$ are equal and each is equal to $1/N$, the
expression for H_N has its maximum value.   A proof of this statement is
given by Shannon.[7]   This is illustrated for the case of a binary selection
by the curve of Fig. 17.4, in which the average amount of information per

selection, H_2, is plotted as a function of the probability of one of the two choices. H_N has a maximum value equal to unity when $p(1) = p(0) = \frac{1}{2}$ and falls to zero when $p(1)$ equals zero or 1, *i.e.*, when one of the choices is certain.

Above we have considered the selection of a symbol from a group of N signals. Messages often consist of sequences of symbols rather than single symbols. The average amount of information conveyed by a sequence of n symbols will be given by

$$H_s = - \sum_{k=1}^{n} p(k) \log_2 p(k)$$

where $p(k)$ is the probability of the given sequence. If the sequence is made up of n selections from N symbols, the number of different sequences will be $S = N^n$. If the symbols are independent, as we have assumed, the average amount of information per sequence can be found from the amount of information per symbol, since

$$H_s = n H_N$$

17.2.4   *Source or Code Efficiency.* We have seen how to compute H_N, the average amount of information per selection given a sequence of N independent selections, and also that H_N represents the minimum number of binary selections required, on the average, to represent an Nth order selection having an arbitrary set of probabilities $p(i)$. H_N therefore represents the theoretical minimum number of binary choices necessary to communicate the message. Because of the similarity between the expression for H and thermodynamic entropy, Shannon has given the name *entropy* to the quantity H. H is a maximum when the N independent selections are equally likely, as previously pointed out, and has the value

$$H_0 = \log_2 N$$

The ratio H/H_0 is called the *source* or *code efficiency* η, and the quantity $(1 - \eta)$ is the redundancy. For the English language, which has 26 letters and a space symbol, values of 4.7 bits per letter for H_0 and 2.35 bits per letter for H have been estimated, so that η and $(1 - \eta)$ are both one-half. The figure of 50 per cent for the redundancy of English text can be arrived at by striking out letters at random from the text and seeing how well readers can restore the text. Shannon has employed more sophisticated methods for measuring η for English text. As mentioned previously, it is the existence of the redundancy in messages which makes possible recoding for more efficient transmission. In the noiseless discrete case, recoding, if ideally done, will allow messages to be transmitted at a rate $1/\eta$ greater than was originally possible with the same symbol rate.

The example given in Fig. 17.3 is an illustration of the improvement which can be achieved by recoding. For the original three symbols, H is given by

$$H = -(0.7 \log_2 0.7 + 0.2 \log_2 0.2 + 0.1 \log_2 0.1) = 1.157$$

and

$$\eta = \frac{H}{\log_2 3} = 0.73$$

while for the recoded groups

$$\eta = \frac{2H}{\Sigma p(i) B_g(i)} = \frac{2 \times 1.157}{2.33} = 0.993$$

17.2.5 *Nonindependent Symbols.* In the preceding sections, complete independence of the individual symbols has been assumed. In most messages, successive symbols are partially dependent on the preceding symbols. In simple cases, the dependence extends back only to the previous symbol; in more complicated cases, the dependence may extend back over a great many symbols.

It has been pointed out that the letters of the alphabet are not independent. On the contrary, when computing H for English text it is necessary to consider as many as eight letters to arrive at the value of 2.35 bits per letter for the entropy. The value 4.7 for H_0 is found by assuming that the letters are independent and equally probable.

Other kinds of messages show a similar dependence between neighboring symbols. A spot on a television screen with a high light intensity is much more likely to be followed by another spot of high intensity than by one whose intensity is low. In pictures, the structural dependence usually extends some distance away from the point being examined. At a given point in the picture, dependence can be found from frame to frame.

The fact that the successive symbols which comprise the message are not independent does not render the previous results completely wrong, but it does reduce them to the status of a first approximation. Since the statistical knowledge obtained from previous symbols changes the probability distribution of the symbols from what it would be if only the first-order probabilities were known, the amount of information, or the entropy, of the symbol is reduced.

Shannon has obtained an expression for H under these conditions which takes into account the correlation between a given symbol and its predecessors.

Let us consider the selection of the kth symbol of a sequence of n symbols, taking into account the statistical knowledge gained by the transmission of the previous j symbols. The knowledge of these symbols will reduce the uncertainty in the selection of the kth symbol. The conditional probability of the choice of k after a sequence of j symbols will be denoted by $p_j(k)$. H will then be given by the expression

$$H_n = -\sum_j p(j) \sum_k p_j(k) \log_2 p_j(k)$$

From this it follows that if $p_j(k_1) = 1$, that is, if the kth symbol always follows the jth sequence, the contribution of that term to the value of H_n will vanish even though $p(k_1)$ itself is small and would have a large entropy if independent.

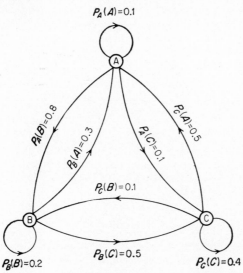

Fig. 17.5 Model of a source which generates a Markoff process.

In many important physical processes, the conditional probability of a symbol extends only to the previous symbol. Under these conditions a particularly simple model due to Shannon will serve to illustrate the behavior of the source. The source is represented as a device which can have n possible states. Figure 17.5 shows a source having three possible states. When the source is in any given state, as, for example, position A, there are three possible changes which it can undergo. It can go to B or to C, or it can return to state A. The conditional probabilities are given along the lines connecting the various states.

For example, if the source is in state A, there is a probability equal to 0.1 that it will return to the same state, a probability equal to 0.1 that it will go to state C, and a probability equal to 0.8 that it will go to state B.

Note that $p_j(k)$ need not equal $p_k(j)$.   A sequence formed in this way is known as a *Markoff process*.

17.3   The Discrete Source with a Noisy Channel

Previously, it was assumed that the communication channel was noise-less and therefore error-free.   In this section the effect of noise in the circuit will be considered.   The transmitted signals are perturbed in an irregular manner by the random fluctuations in the channel, so that it is not possible to reconstruct the message with certainty from the information supplied to the receiver by the channel.   In the process of transmission, some information is lost.   A measure of the amount of information that is lost has been developed by Shannon.   When the statistical character of both the messages and the noise is known, the loss of information due to the noise can be computed.   This loss of information or

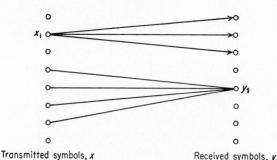

Transmitted symbols, *x*   Received symbols, *y*

Fig. 17.6   Illustration of the uncertainty introduced by the effect of noise in the channel.

the uncertainty which remains when the message has been received has been given the name *equivocation* by Shannon.   The equivocation is defined as the entropy of the input when the output is known.

Figure 17.6 illustrates the effect of noise on a communication system. The transmitter generates a set of symbols x_i which are recognized by the receiver.   In the absence of noise, there will be a unique correspondence between a given transmitted signal and the corresponding symbol in the receiver.   With noise present, however, the receiver will not be able to determine uniquely which symbol was sent.   In fact, for a given x symbol transmitted, there is the possibility of several different y symbols, and if a given y is received there will be uncertainty as to which x symbol was actually intended.   The effect of the noise on a discrete system can be defined by a set of conditional probabilities $p_i(j)$ called *transition probabilities;* these give the probability of receiving the jth symbol if the ith one has been transmitted.   If the channel is relatively noise-free, $p_i(i)$ will be approximately equal to unity and all the other transition probabilities from states x_j will be very small. If $p_i(j) = 1/N$, the output will be completely independent of the input.

17.3.1 *Measure of Equivocation.* In the presence of noise, the amount of information present in the output will still be

$$H_{out} = -\sum_{j=1}^{N} p(j) \log_2 p(j)$$

which may be rewritten as

$$H_{out} = -\sum_{j=1}^{N} \sum_{i=1}^{N} p(i)p_i(j) \log_2 \sum_{k=1}^{N} p(k)p_k(j)$$

since

$$p(j) = \sum_{i=1}^{N} p_i(j)p(i)$$

Part of H_{out} is due to noise. This can be seen by letting $p_i(j) = 1/N$, which ensures that the output is independent of the input. In this case the expression for H_{out} becomes equal to $-\log_2 N$. Since the output is independent of the source, all the output must represent error or equivocation. The error may be computed by repeating the same message continuously at the input and computing the amount of information at the output. For the ith symbol, this would be

$$H'_{out}(i) = -\sum_{j=1}^{N} p_i(j) \log_2 p_i(j)$$

This quantity, when averaged over all the input symbols, gives the average equivocation as

$$H'_{out} = -\sum_{i=1}^{N} \sum_{j=1}^{N} p(i)p_i(j) \log_2 p_i(j)$$

The equivocation is measured in "bits" per symbol or message.

The correctly received information is the difference between the total information at the output and the equivocation. This quantity is sometimes called the *intelligence* and is given by the expression

$$R_0 = H_{out} - H'_{out}$$

This analysis was based on the assumption that the individual symbols or messages were independent. When this is not the case, the meaning of the various probabilities can be altered in a manner similar to that done for nonindependence in the discrete noiseless case.

17.3.2   *Channel Capacity.*   In the noiseless case we saw that it was possible, with proper coding, to send information at the maximum rate corresponding to $H_0 = \log_2 N$ bits per symbol.   If the symbols occur at a definite rate, the number of symbols per second multiplied by H_0 would give the channel capacity.   When noise is present, the channel capacity is reduced from the noise-free value.   It is difficult to present a general expression for the channel capacity in the presence of noise.   However, in the special case in which the effect of the noise is the same on all input symbols, the channel capacity per symbol will be

$$C = \log_2 N - H'_{out}$$

17.3.3   *Coding against Noise.*   The channel capacity defined above establishes the upper limit to the amount of information which can be sent through a noisy channel.   This does not give any clue to the error rate that will result.   Shannon showed that, in theory, with the proper code the error can be made as small as desirable; if the rate of transmission is smaller than C, the theoretical limit for the equivocation is zero.

The manner in which this can be done is analogous to what people often do instinctively when they must communicate under poor conditions, as, for example, in the presence of a loud noise.   In this situation a code consisting of a restricted number of words, chosen because they sound very different, is used and all other words are ignored.   In coding symbols it is possible to employ the same technique.

If the symbols from a selection of N are ordered into sequences n symbols long, N^n possible sequences or messages will result.   Just as in spoken language, some pairs of sequences are more readily confused than others in electrical transmission.   If only those sequences are chosen which have a small probability of being confused with any of the others, the probability of error can be reduced.   Shannon has shown that, if the sequence length n is increased indefinitely, the probability of error can be made as small as desirable, and at the same time the number of sequences which must be omitted becomes a vanishingly small percentage of the total number.   This means that, if sufficiently long sequences or code groups are employed, information can be transmitted over a noisy channel at a rate not exceeding the channel capacity C and with an arbitrarily small error.

In practice it has so far been difficult to realize the advantages predicted theoretically.   One of the major difficulties encountered is that of providing adequate information-storage devices so that the groups of symbols can be stored, examined for statistical structure, and recoded.   A large amount of equipment is required if it is desired to exploit the existence of high-order statistical dependence.   Coding will be discussed in a subsequent section.

17.4   Transmission in the Presence of Noise: Continuous Signals

Here the signals are continuous in amplitude and are also continuous functions of time. Such signals, nonetheless, have properties which are best described in statistical terms.

17.4.1   *The Sampling Theorem.*   All continuous functions encountered in nature are band-limited (they require a finite time to occur). In this discussion the signal will be assumed to occupy a band extending from 0 to B cycles/sec. It can be shown that any band-limited signal of finite duration can be completely described by a finite number of discrete amplitude samples. If the signal occupies a bandwidth B and exists for a period T, it can be shown that the function is completely specified by $2BT$ samples forming a sequence of samples c_n which are spaced $1/2B$ sec apart. This can be seen by recognizing that the highest frequency component in the signal would have a frequency B, and therefore $2B$ Fourier terms (B cosine terms and B sine terms) would be required to describe fully a section of the signal 1 sec long. (The $2BT$ terms will be required only by those signals which fully occupy the band.) This is the reason why time-division transmission systems such as pulse-time, pulse-code, and pulse-width modulation systems sample at a rate at least twice as great as the highest frequency that the system is required to handle.

If samples are taken more frequently, no additional information is conveyed because the samples are no longer independent. The circuits which establish the finite bandwidth have sufficient energy storage, or memory, to maintain a high degree of correlation between sample points closer than $1/2B$ in time.

Each function of time T sec long can be represented by the n sample points c_n. It is therefore possible to consider each individual message as a point in an n-dimensional Euclidean space having coordinates c_1, $c_2, \ldots, c_n$, where $n = 2BT$. If the signal is a current dissipating its energy in a 1-ohm resistance, the total power into the resistance can be shown to be

$$P = \frac{1}{2BT} (c_1{}^2 + c_2{}^2 + \cdots + c_n{}^2)$$

so that the distance from the origin to the signal point is

$$r_0 = \sqrt{2BPT}$$

Since $r_0{}^2$ is proportional to the average power of the signal, all signals having a power p or less will lie within an n-dimensional sphere of radius r_0.

17.4.2   *Measure of Information for Continuous Signals.*   When the $2BT$ sample points are independent, the amount of information in a message can be computed by calculating the amount of information conveyed per sample point and then multiplying by $2BT$. For a signal with a continuous amplitude distribution, the amount of information per sample point is defined by

$$H = - \int_{-\infty}^{+\infty} p(\nu) \log_2 p(\nu) \, d\nu$$

where $p(\nu) \, d\nu$ is the probability of finding the signal in the amplitude range ν to $\nu + d\nu$. H still is interpreted as the uncertainty or entropy in the system.

17.4.3 *Channel Capacity for Continuous Signals in the Presence of Noise.* As in the discrete case, the effect of noise in the channel can be taken into account by finding the entropy of the output when messages are being sent by the transmitter and subtracting the entropy of the output when the message signal is held constant. The information in the output is given by

$$H_{out} = - \int_{-\infty}^{+\infty} p_0(\nu) \log_2 p_0(\nu) \, d\nu$$

where $p_0(\nu)$ is the density distribution of the output signal. The error or equivocation is found by keeping the input constant, finding the equivocation associated with each input signal, and averaging over all the input signals. By this means the error is found to be

$$H_{out}' = - \int_{-\infty}^{+\infty} p_n(\nu) \log_2 p_n(\nu) \, d\nu$$

where $p_n(\nu)$ is the density distribution of the noise.

The "intelligence" is given by

$$R_0 = H_{out} - H_{out}'$$

R_0 is the intelligence per sample; thus the system under these conditions can handle an amount of information equal to $2BR_0$ bits per second. It can be shown that the entropy of a continuous source is a maximum when its output has a normal-random or Gaussian distribution. The amplitude distribution of most fluctuation phenomena encountered in nature is also Gaussian. Under these conditions, if the noise is simply added to the signal and is independent of it, the capacity of a channel is

$$C = B \log_2 \left(\frac{S + N}{N} \right) \qquad \text{bits/sec}$$

where S is the average signal power and N is the average noise power.

When the channel noise perturbing the system does not have Gaussian statistical properties, it is not possible to get a simple expression for channel capacity.

17.5 Interpretation of the Channel-capacity Formula

The formula for channel capacity establishes a theoretical maximum for the amount of information which can be transmitted through a given channel. Previous considerations have established that this maximum rate can be achieved only when all the symbols produced by the transmitter have an equal probability of occurring and when successive symbols are completely independent. When the messages to be transmitted do not satisfy these conditions, it is desirable (although not always technically or economically reasonable) to recode the message so that the transmitted symbols or sequences more nearly satisfy these conditions.

With proper coding, a channel having bandwidth B and a signal-to-noise ratio S/N is capable of carrying information without error at a rate equal to C bits of information per second. Exceeding C will make it impossible to convey information without accompanying errors.

The expression for C shows quantitatively the nature of the relationship between bandwidth, signal-to-noise ratio, and system capacity, which experience has indicated must exist. Channel capacity is proportional to bandwidth, which means that by doubling the bandwidth the capacity is doubled. The capacity is proportional to the logarithm of S/N. In most communication systems, the noise power N is proportional to B, so that as the bandwidth is increased S/N becomes smaller. As a result, there is a limit to the capacity which can be obtained using a fixed input power.

The quantity $\log_2 [(S + N)/N]$ in the expression for the rate of information in a continuous system is analogous to the term $\log_2 N$ in the expression for channel capacity in the discrete case. This result may be interpreted to show that the total number of resolvable elements per measurement is equal to the signal power divided by the noise power. This is reasonable, since the noise represents the uncertainty in the measurement.

If the channel signal-to-noise ratio is kept constant while B_c, the channel bandwidth, increases, the channel capacity of an ideal system should increase proportionately. In an f-m system, C does increase with increasing channel bandwidth, but only logarithmically.

If the message bandwidth is held constant, increasing C will result in a better message signal-to-noise ratio. The improvement in message signal-to-noise ratio thus achieved in an f-m system is an example of an encoding process in which only the least ambiguous sequences are used. In the f-m system only one amplitude is employed, with the result that amplitude fluctuations cannot perturb the system. The effect of frequency perturbations is also reduced by using a wide frequency deviation.

17.5.1   *Geometric Interpretation of the Communication Process.*   The process of encoding can be illustrated by a simple geometric interpretation suggested by Shannon.[8]   We have seen that a message can be represented as a point in a $2B_M T_M$-dimensional space, where B_M is the message bandwidth and T_M the duration of the message.   The signal into which the message is to be coded can be represented as a point in a similar space.   If the channel bandwidth is B_c and the sequence of symbols representing the message is T_c sec long, the dimensionality of the signal space will be $2B_c T_c$.   To encode the message it is only necessary to map the message space onto the signal space, or onto that part of it which the coding procedure allows.   The mapping must be unambiguous; *i.e.*, no two distinct message points should be mapped onto a single point in signal space, or the message will not be recoverable.   In the course of transmission, noise is added to the message, and as a result the signal point is shifted slightly.   The noise may be regarded as a random point in the n-dimensional space, whose effect is to create a fuzzy sphere of uncertainty of radius $\sqrt{2B_c T_c N}$ about the message point. If the signals are restricted to an average power S, the set of allowed signal points will be contained in a sphere of radius $\sqrt{2B_c T_c (S + N)}$. Assuming that signal points lying within the same noise sphere cannot be distinguished, the greatest number of distinguishable signal points will be equal to the number of noise spheres which can be placed within the signal-plus-noise sphere.   This can be approximated by the relative volumes and is equal to

$$n' = \left(\frac{\sqrt{2B_c T_c (S + N)}}{\sqrt{2B_c T_c N}} \right)^{2B_c T_c}$$

Taking the base-2 logarithm of this number yields

$$\log_2 n' = B_c T_c \log_2 \left(1 + \frac{S}{N} \right)$$

which is, for unity time, the formula previously derived for the capacity of a channel.

This geometric representation can be used to describe ways in which coding may be carried out.   Shannon has pointed out that an approximation to an ideal code can be obtained if one selects points at random in the signal space and maps the messages onto them in an arbitrary fashion.   It will be recognized that the noise will still produce errors. The disturbance due to the noise can be minimized by employing a signal space of very high dimensionality, because the effect of this is to concentrate the probability of the noise sphere more sharply about its periphery.

Since the message bandwidth is generally fixed, the higher dimensionality can be achieved only by increasing the signal duration, *i.e.*, by encoding long sections of messages.

The statement that the surface of the noise sphere will become better defined as the dimensionality of the space increases can be made to appear reasonable for normal-random noise by the following argument. The mean power of the noise is determined by the mean-square value of the contributions corresponding to the individual dimensions. The actual position of a noise point will fluctuate about the mean value in a manner defined by the Gaussian statistics. As the number of random elements (*i.e.*, the number of dimensions contributing to the noise) increases, the relative value of the fluctuation will decrease.

Because of the random nature of the selection of the n signal points, the transmitted signal will ideally be cleared of all redundancy and have the character of a random "white" noise, *i.e.*, a noise whose energy is distributed uniformly over the entire signal band and for which the amplitude distributions are Gaussian.

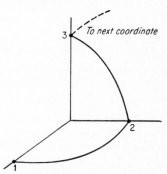

Fig. 17.7 Signal points distributed on a constant-power surface analogous to frequency modulation.

17.5.2 *Modulation as Mapping in Signal Space.* As indicated in the previous section, the modulation process may be regarded as the mapping of points from a message space to a signal space. The various modulation systems are distinguished by the manner in which the mapping is carried out and by the way in which the points in the signal space are employed. For example, in single-sideband amplitude modulation the signal and message spaces have the same dimensionality, and each point in the message space goes over to a corresponding point in signal space. In double-sideband amplitude modulation two symmetrical points in signal space correspond to one point in message space. In both of these systems all the points in the signal space are used, and the signal bandwidth is normally made just sufficiently large to pass the intelligence frequencies.

In frequency modulation the mapping is different. In transmitting, the signal power is held constant while the frequency of the signal is varied by the message. The restriction to one signal level limits the signal points to the surface of the n-dimensional sphere. This is illustrated for $n = 3$ by the path shown in Fig. 17.7. The mapping of the message line into the higher-dimensional space increases the effective length of the line and makes confusion by noise less likely.

Most systems in which coding of this type has been employed exhibit an effect known as the *threshold effect*. In a one-dimensional message space the effect of noise is generally to perturb the signal point to a neighboring point, but in mapping into a higher-dimensional signal space, neighboring message-space points may become remote. As the higher dimensionality defines the noise sphere more precisely, the net result is to lessen the effect of the noise upon the system to a definite critical magnitude, but when the critical value is reached, the system is dominated by the noise. This characteristic may be observed in f-m, pulse-width-modulation, and pulse-code-modulation systems.

It may sometimes be desirable to reduce the dimensionality of the signal space with regard to that of message space. This operation corresponds to using a narrower signal bandwidth than the corresponding message bandwidth, or to transmitting a message in a shorter time than was required to generate it. This process corresponds roughly to using one point in signal space to represent more than one point in the message space. The formula for channel capacity shows how channel signal-to-noise ratio must be adjusted to compensate for such a decrease in channel bandwidth or transmission time. Because of the logarithmic relationship between C and (S/N), large increases in (S/N) are required to compensate for modest decreases in the product BT.

It appears unprofitable to achieve appreciable bandwidth reduction by bartering signal power for bandwidth because of the large increase in signal power which would be required. An example cited by B. M. Oliver[10] will illustrate this point. A practical quantized channel requires a signal-to-noise ratio of about 20 db to ensure error-free operation. If the system is capable of sending 100 levels, a 60-db signal-to-noise ratio would be required in the channel. If the bandwidth were cut in two, 10,000 different levels would be required to represent all possible groupings of the signals taken two at a time. Under these conditions, a channel having a 100-db signal-to-noise ratio would be required for proper transmission.

17.5.3 *Pulse-code Modulation—An Efficient Modulation System.* We have seen that a continuous message may be represented by $2B_M T_M$ sample points, where the sample points represent amplitude values taken $1/2B_M$ sec apart. The transmitter has the job of conveying these values to the receiver through the noisy channel. In continuous-modulation systems, such as amplitude or frequency modulation, the signal amplitudes are represented as carrier-amplitude variations or as frequency displacements. Since noise and distortion make it impossible to transmit the exact amplitude of the sample, it is possible to limit the permissible amplitudes to a discrete set of levels, so that when a message is sampled the level nearest the true value is sent. When such a signal is received, the level nearest to the signal after it has been perturbed by noise is chosen as the proper value.   This process is called *quantizing the signal.* Since the permitted values of the quantized signal will differ by small amounts from the actual message, a *quantizing noise* will appear.   The magnitude of this noise will be determined by the number of quantization levels permitted and will be smaller when a large number of levels exist. Once the signal has been quantized, it may be relayed for any distance

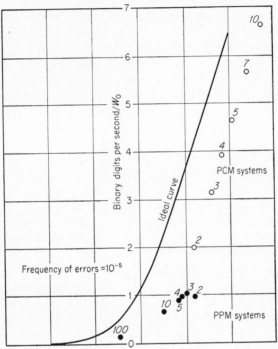

Fig. 17.8 Comparison of pulse-code and pulse-position modulation with ideal performance, for an error rate of 10^{-5}.

without further deterioration, provided only that the noise is never permitted to become great enough to prevent correct recognition of a specific level.   Instead of transmitting the discrete values of the amplitude, it would be possible to send numbers representing the values of the pulses. In electrical systems, on-off keying is especially convenient, since only the presence or absence of a signal need be determined by the receiver. To permit such operation the numbers representing the individual sample amplitudes can be represented in a binary code consisting of on-off pulses. The number of permissible levels and therefore the magnitude of the quantization noise is determined by the number of binary digits used to represent one sample; an l-digit binary number provides 2^l distinct levels.

The signal-to-noise ratio determined by the quantization noise will be $2^l/1$ in voltage. In decibels this will be $20l \log_{10} 2$. Each digit adds 6 db to the quantization signal-to-noise ratio.

The total number of on-off pulses required to transmit a message will be $2lB_M T_M$. Since the channel bandwidth must be increased to accommodate a higher pulse repetition rate, B_c will increase linearly with l. Note that as l (and therefore B_c) increases the number of binary digits that the system is capable of transmitting increases linearly, which means that bandwidth is exchanged for channel capacity in the manner required of an ideal system.

Unfortunately, a simple pulse-code modulation system will produce too many errors if operated at unity signal-to-noise ratio, and, consequently, systems are operated with about a 20-db safety margin, thus reducing the system efficiency. The performance of a typical pulse-code modulation system is shown by the curves of Fig. 17.8. The displacement between the ideal curve and that for the actual system is a measure of the safety margin discussed above.

The pulse-code system, like any other transmission system, will operate efficiently only if the messages which it is required to transmit are statistically matched to the transmitter. In this case the messages should have the properties of a band-limited white noise. When this is not so, recoding will be required to achieve higher channel efficiency.

17.6 Coding for Transmission

The discussion above has indicated that recoding of messages before transmission would lead to improved communication-system efficiency. The redundancy in a television signal has been estimated to be between 80 and 95 per cent. Such estimates take into account the long-term correlation which exists between picture frames, as well as the point-to-point and line-to-line correlation, and therefore a coding system to eliminate all the picture redundancy would be extremely complicated.

Speech signals also have a large amount of redundancy. The spoken language is an interesting example of an encoding process which permits communication under unfavorable conditions. A wide band of frequencies (300 to 5000 cycles/sec) is used to transmit a few speech symbols per second. A telephone circuit normally has a bandwidth of about 3500 cycles/sec and a signal-to-noise ratio of 1000 to 1 (30 db). The channel capacity of such a circuit is approximately 70,000 bits per second. Analysis of speech patterns made on the sound spectrograph leads to the conclusion that at most 200 bits of information are necessary to transmit the information in the speech message. The redundancy in speech is thus approximately 97 per cent. To remove this redundancy requires a coding system more elaborate than those which will be discussed here.

A device capable of removing much speech redundancy is the Vocoder, built and demonstrated by Dr. Homer Dudley[5] of the Bell Telephone Laboratories.

Two types of coding have been discussed above. Mapping of a message space onto a signal space was called coding. This process, in which a correspondence is established between points in the two spaces, is nonstatistical. The second process is one in which the message statistics are employed in order to match the source to the channel. In this coding process, an attempt is made to utilize the simplest code symbols or sequences for the most frequent messages, to make all symbols equally likely, and to remove all correlation from successive symbols. The objective is to make the average information rate H approach the theoretical channel capacity C while at the same time maintaining a small error rate. Only simple coding processes will be discussed in this chapter. A thorough discussion is contained in the paper "Efficient Coding" by B. M. Oliver.[10]

17.6.1 *Statistically Matched Codes.* It is always possible to map a sequence of binary digits into a sequence of selections from a group of arbitrary size, or vice versa, by a nonstatistical coding process which does not change the entropy of the message. For this reason it is customary to restrict the consideration of statistical coding to the binary case, with the understanding that after coding the resulting sequence may be transformed into a sequence representing selections from a different set.

When a binary system is used, a means must be provided for recognizing the beginning and ending of code groups. It would be possible to provide a special symbol to indicate the end of a code group, but this would be somewhat inefficient. A method of coding developed independently by Shannon and Fano makes the use of a space symbol unnecessary. The process is illustrated by the method of coding nonequiprobable symbols discussed in Sec. 17.2.3 and demonstrated by Fig. 17.3. We have already seen that, by dividing the symbols into equiprobable groups and indicating the choices by a 0 or 1, the smallest code symbols are assigned to the most probable message symbols. For large message sequences, the number of digits required by this code to indicate a message symbol approaches the theoretical minimum on the average. This process of coding has another interesting property. An examination of Fig. 17.3 will indicate that, when the sequences are ordered in this way, unique binary sequences are established for each message. No short binary sequence is contained in one of the longer ones. This method of ordering the symbols is known as the Shannon-Fano code. The end of a code group is indicated by the occurrence of a zero. The receiver can thus recognize the end of a code group without the transmission of a space symbol.

Some messages, such as television pictures, are characterized by frequent long sequences of the same symbol. When the message has this characteristic, a type of coding known as run-length coding may be employed. In this case the symbol is transmitted only once followed by a number specifying the length of the run. For efficient transmission, both the symbols and the numbers specifying the run length should be statistically matched to the channel.

17.6.2   n-Gramming. It is necessary to store and process large amounts of information in order to encode properly a message having correlation between symbols. If it is necessary to encode a group of n symbols from an N-symbol selection, N^n different codes will be required, and the equipment required to do this will become extremely complex. In addition, the encoding and decoding delay required by this process may be prohibitive. If n is kept small, much statistical information may be disregarded.

As a compromise, Oliver has proposed a code process which he calls n-gramming, in which the statistics of the preceding n symbols are employed to produce a reduced signal having more nearly independent symbols.

17.6.3   The Monogrammer. The simplest example of this type of code device is the monogrammer, which reorders the messages to provide more efficient transmission. The following example will illustrate this method. Suppose that a movable shaft can assume one of five positions and that the position information is to be encoded into a quantized pulse signal. The shaft positions, probability of each position's occurring, and the pulse height assigned without regard to the message statistics are shown in the accompanying table.

Position	Original pulse height	$p(i)$	Reordered pulse height
A	0	0.1	3
B	1	0.3	1
C	2	0.2	2
D	3	0.05	4
E	4	0.35	0

The system will be more efficient if the smallest pulse is assigned to the most likely position, requiring the least power to be used in transmission. Oliver suggests the device shown in Fig. 17.9 to accomplish the desired translation. The original signal is applied to the vertical deflecting plates of a cathode-ray tube. The resting position corresponds to the pulse of zero height; a pulse one unit high will deflect the spot to position A, two units high to B, etc. If an opaque mask with an adjustable transmission is placed in front of the tube, the transmission in front of each letter can be made proportional to the reordered pulse height so that the output of the photoelectric cell is proportional to the desired pulse height.

17.6.4   *The Digrammer.*   To take into account the effect of a previous pulse, the *digrammer*, also presented by Oliver and shown in Fig. 17.10,

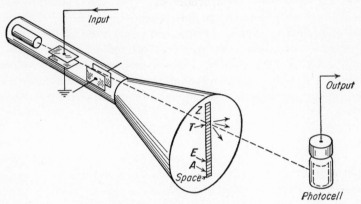

Fig. 17.9   The monogrammer.

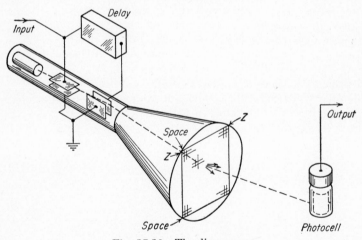

Fig. 17.10   The digrammer.

may be employed.   In this device, one pulse is delayed by a pulse interval and placed on the horizontal plates of the oscilloscope, while the following pulse is placed on the vertical plates, so that the beam is deflected vertically by the present symbol and horizontally by the previous symbol. The optical transmission of the mask at each point must now be proportional to the transition probability $p_i(j)$ of the jth symbol following

454   INFORMATION AND ITS COMMUNICATION

the ith.   The output of the digrammer can be recoded into binary digits if this is desirable.

Higher-order conditional probabilities can be taken into account employing more delay and groups of digrammers in cascade.

17.6.5   *More Elaborate Coding Systems.*   Many more elaborate coding schemes, including some making use of linear prediction and signal-gradient statistics, have been proposed.   The more elaborate systems will provide a better match to the transmission channel but are sufficiently complicated so that no practical application of them has been made to date.   However, the high cost of channel capacity for some messages, such as video signals, places a premium on the development of a practical system.   An increase in channel efficiency by a factor of 2 would provide an enormous saving on the transcontinental television relay.

REFERENCES

1. Hartley, R. V. L., *Bell System Tech. J.*, **7**: 535–563 (1928).
2. Nyquist, H., *Phys. Rev.*, **32**: 110 (1928).
3. Schottky, W., *Ann. phys.*, **57**: 541 (1918); **68**: 157 (1922).
4. Wiener, N., "The Extrapolation, Interpolation, and Smoothing of Stationary Time Series," John Wiley & Sons, Inc., New York, 1949.
5. Dudley, H., *J. Acoust. Soc. Amer.*, **11**: 169 (1939).
6. Shannon, C. E., *Bell System Tech. J.*, **27**: 379, 623 (1948).
7. Shannon, C. E., and W. Weaver, "The Mathematical Theory of Communication," University of Illinois Press, Urbana, 1949.
8. Shannon, C. E., *Proc. IRE*, **37**: 10 (1949).
9. Fano, R. M., Technical Reports 66, 149, Massachusetts Institute of Technology, The Research Laboratory of Electronics, 1949, 1950.
10. Oliver, B. M., *Bell System Tech. J.*, **31**: 724 (1952).

18

Computing Machines and the Processing of Information

LOUIS N. RIDENOUR

INTERNATIONAL TELEMETER CORPORATION
AND THE UNIVERSITY OF CALIFORNIA, LOS ANGELES

"Calculation is laborious and unremunerative"—Barlow

HISTORICAL INTRODUCTION

18.1   Meaning of the Term "High-speed Automatic Digital Computer"

In this chapter we shall be concerned with the design, construction, and use of high-speed automatic digital computers. It will therefore be useful to agree at the outset on the meaning of this term. The noun "computer" refers to a machine intended to perform part or all of the work of making a mathematical calculation; although, as we shall see, a machine capable of doing this is also able to do other useful things not always comprehended in the restricted meaning of "mathematical calculation." For the present purpose, it will be satisfactory to adopt the more limited definition.

A "digital" computer is one which works with numbers in their numerical form. The familiar desk adding machine can serve as an example of a digital computing machine. We distinguish digital machines because there exists a large and important class of computers that are not digital in nature. These nondigital computers are called *analogue* machines; the ordinary slide rule is perhaps the most familiar example. In an analogue computer, the numbers entering the problem are expressed in terms of the value of some physical quantity—in the case of the slide rule, the

455

factors entering a multiplication are expressed in terms of lengths respectively proportional to the logarithm of each factor. The input quantities are processed in accordance with the requirements of the problem—in the case of multiplication on a slide rule, they are set end to end—and the resulting physical quantity is measured to determine the result. To finish with our example of slide-rule multiplication, the length that is obtained by adding the input lengths (which are proportional to the logarithms of the factors) represents the logarithm of the product. This is measured on a logarithmic scale of length, and the result is available directly as the product of the two numbers which entered the calculation.

Many useful analogue computers have been designed and are in use, but we shall not speak about them here, since the capabilities and the promise of digital machines seem greater. Those who are interested in analogue machines will find references to works on them in the References at the end of this chapter.

What is an "automatic" digital computer? In the past, it has been the custom to use the word "automatic" to describe, for example, desk machines which can follow through the sequence of repeated additions (or subtractions) and shifts necessary to multiply (or divide) one number by another. This usage establishes the difference between such machines and other desk machines which are capable of performing only individual additions or subtractions. We shall use the word in a more restricted sense. In this chapter, an "automatic" machine is one that can perform a sequence of individual computational steps, each involving a pair of numbers. That is, we shall not regard as automatic a machine that can simply perform a multiplication by means of repeated additions and shifts; we shall reserve that term for a machine which is able to perform a series of additions, subtractions, multiplications, divisions, comparisons, and other operations, all in accordance with a program of instructions supplied to the machine at the outset of the calculation. One of the most important properties of the automatic machine is its ability to modify its own operations in the light of results it obtains in an extended calculation.

What is a "high-speed" automatic digital computer? During and immediately after World War II, several automatic digital computers were developed, principally at Bell Telephone Laboratories under S. B. Williams and at Harvard University under Howard Aiken. These interesting machines were vital to the development of the digital-computer art and were themselves very useful instruments which are, for the most part, still doing productive work. However, we shall not concern ourselves with them here, beyond making a few historical remarks. The reason for this seeming neglect is that relay machines, being limited in operating speed by the operating times of the electromechanical relays used in their construction, are many times slower than the newer electronic machines. The famous ENIAC, completed by the University of Pennsylvania under Army Ordnance contract in 1945, is the first high-speed digital computer ever built, under our definition of this term.

18.2 Desk Computers

Adding machines and desk calculators are of considerable antiquity. An excellent historical account of their development is to be found in the article "Calculating Machines" in the "Encyclopaedia Britannica." The first practical adding machine based on the use of number wheels was devised by Blaise Pascal in 1642, and a machine capable of multiplication by repeated additions accompanied by suitable shifts was designed by Leibnitz in 1671 and built in 1694. The first commercially successful machine was designed in 1820 by the Frenchman Charles Thomas; with minor modifications and improvements, this machine was being manufactured in Paris right up to the beginning of World War II.

18.3 The Work of Charles Babbage

Much of the modern development of the automatic digital computer was anticipated more than a century ago by the work of Charles Babbage, then Lucasian Professor of Mathematics at the University of Cambridge. From the second decade of the nineteenth century onward, Babbage had been interested in mechanical computing devices designed to lessen the labor of calculating extensive tables of functions, astronomical data, and the like. He proposed to the British government a design for a machine to calculate and print out tables automatically, by working with successive differences between the entries; this he called the *Difference Engine*. A government grant was made for the construction of this machine.

While he was working on the Difference Engine, about the year 1830, Babbage conceived the idea of another and much more powerful machine. This machine, which he called the *Analytical Engine*, was in all respects an automatic digital computer; it was to work with numbers in their numerical form, and it was to have the ability to perform long sequences of calculations, storing intermediate results as required during such a sequence. The nature of the sequence was to have been controlled primarily by a program of instructions prepared by the user of the machine, in just the same way as modern machines are controlled, and the machine was to have the ability to alter its program on the basis of the outcome of calculations performed earlier in the program.

Numbers and program instructions were to have been entered into the Analytical Engine by means of punched cards, which had been used as early as 1801 to control the weaving of complicated patterns in fabrics made on the Jacquard loom. Babbage thus anticipated by more than half a century the use of punched cards in computing machines; the idea was not seriously taken up again until the work of Herman Hollerith in 1886.   One of Babbage's most prized possessions was a portrait of Jacquard woven in cloth; it had the appearance of a fine etching, and it had been woven by a loom under the control of a deck of more than 25,000 punched cards.

Our knowledge of the plans for the Analytical Engine has been preserved for us in a very curious way.   Babbage lectured in Europe in 1842, and extensive notes on his lectures were taken by a General Menabrea, of the Italian army.   These notes were translated and greatly added to by Lady Lovelace, the daughter of the poet Byron; it is clear from her work that she had a deep understanding of the mathematical principles involved.   As an example of programming a problem for the Analytical Engine, Lady Lovelace made a program for the calculation of the Bernoulli numbers, which can be defined by the series

$$B_{2n-1} = \frac{2(2n)!}{(2^{2n} - 1)\pi^{2n}} \left(1 + \frac{1}{3^{2n}} + \frac{1}{5^{2n}} + \frac{1}{7^{2n}} + \cdots \right) \quad (18.1)$$

As an act of historical piety, the group working on the digital computer that was built for the University of Manchester by Messrs. Ferranti put on the machine, as one of its first problems, the computation of these numbers according to the program that Lady Lovelace had prepared for the Analytical Engine.

For various reasons, the Analytical Engine was never realized. Babbage was unsuccessful in getting government support for his work, perhaps partly because he had never completed the Difference Engine, in which he lost interest when he saw the greater vision.   He would have had to build the Analytical Engine as an entirely mechanical device, and the limitations of the mechanical engineering of his day were severe. In any event, he finished only parts of the machine.   His son continued the work after his death and built parts of what would now be called the arithmetic unit.   A committee of the British Association examined the machine after Babbage had died and reported:

Apart from the question of its saving labour in operations now possible, we think that the existence of an instrument of this kind would place within reach much which, if not actually impossible, has been too close to the limits of human endurance to be practically available.

This remark can be applied to present-day machines without the alteration of a single word.

Babbage himself had a remarkably prescient view of the use of the machine.   One of the important uses to which such machines can be put is that of calculating the Fourier series necessary to infer the structure of molecules from their X-ray diffraction patterns.   Compare what Babbage wrote in 1838:

The whole of chemistry, and with it crystallography, would become a branch of mathematical analysis, which, like astronomy, taking its constants from observation, would enable us to predict the character of any new compound, and possibly indicate the source from which its formation might be anticipated.

In many ways, Babbage's ideas seem to have been about a century before their time.

18.4 Punched-card Machines

As we have already noticed, the punched card was first used in connection with computing machines in 1886 by Herman Hollerith, an employee of the U.S. Census Bureau.   His early equipment, intended to facilitate the tabulation of census returns, has been continuously refined, improved, and extended to yield the fast, flexible, and reliable punched-card equipment commercially available today.

Although the IBM Card-programmed Calculator is nearly an automatic digital computer under the definition we are using, we shall not discuss punched-card equipment here.   Information on such equipment and its use is readily available from the two major U.S. manufacturers of such machines, the International Business Machines Corporation and Remington Rand, Incorporated.

18.5 Relay Computers

A good general account of the relay-type computing machines built in this country is to be found in Chap. 10 of reference 3, which also contains further references useful to those interested in more detail.   Here we content ourselves with listing a few of the leading properties of some of these machines.

Harvard Mark I Machine:
Begun 1939, finished 1944
Handles numbers of 23-digit length, with options of 12 and 46 digits
Operation times, approximately
Addition of two numbers	0.3 sec
Multiplication of two numbers	5.7 sec
Division	15.3 sec

Harvard Mark II Machine:
Begun 1945, completed 1947
Handles 10-digit numbers with floating decimal point
Operation times, approximately
Addition of two numbers	0.200 sec
Multiplication	0.700 sec

Bell Telephone Laboratories Model V:

Begun 1944; two machines built

Handles 7-digit numbers with floating decimal point

Operation times, approximately

Addition of two numbers	0.3 sec
Multiplication	1.0 sec
Division	2.2 sec
Square root	4.3 sec

18.6   The ENIAC

As already remarked, the ENIAC was the first of the modern high-speed digital computers. Completed in 1945, it was later transferred to the Ballistic Research Laboratories at Aberdeen Proving Ground, Maryland, where it is still in useful service, performing vast amounts of the détailed computation needed for the production of firing tables or for the elucidation of patterns of supersonic and hypersonic flow.

Being the first of its kind, the ENIAC is now regarded as being of obsolete and overconservative design. It uses some 18,000 vacuum tubes; yet its speed, memory capacity, and general performance are inferior to those of more recently designed machines having only two or three thousand tubes. It is one of these more modern computers that we shall investigate in detail, but the importance of the ENIAC as a pioneer achievement must compel admiration.

As compared with the relay machine just mentioned, the ENIAC operates in an entirely new regime of speed. The time it requires to add two numbers, each of 10 decimal digits, is 200 μsec; this is more than a thousand times faster than the same operation can be done by the relay machines mentioned in the last section.

COMPUTING MACHINES AND THEIR APPLICATION

18.7   The Parts of a Machine

18.7.1   *General Organization.*   In discussing the general organization of a computer, it is useful to keep in mind that the machine as a whole performs the same function as a human computer who uses a desk calculator, tables of functions, a work sheet on which has been laid out the plan for the calculation and on which intermediate results can be recorded, and—of course—his own mind for ordering and controlling the course of the calculation. To a substantial degree, the various parts of the machine can be identified with the various elements present when a man makes a calculation by hand. The most important parts of the machine are the arithmetic unit, the inner or high-speed storage or memory unit, the control unit, and the input-output equipment, as shown in Fig. 18.1. Their functions are as follows:

18.7.2 *Arithmetic Unit.* The arithmetic unit, or logical unit, is the part of the machine which, under instructions from the control, performs the individual arithmetic or logical operations required by the computation being conducted. Though it is electronic in nature, it is a close parallel to the desk calculating machine of our example.

18.7.3 *High-speed Storage Unit.* This part of a high-speed automatic digital computer is now, and has been for some years past, the least elegant and least satisfactory part of such machines. As we shall see, there are prospects for its early improvement through developments that in 1953 were just emerging from the laboratory stage. It is the function of the inner memory, or high-speed storage, to register numbers in a quasi-permanent way—both the numbers which originally entered the problem and intermediate results obtained in the course of the calculation—and to make them available to the arithmetic unit or to the output when so instructed by the control. Any number in the memory, which may contain several thousands of numbers, must be available on demand in a very few microseconds. The memory is ordinarily so arranged that it can store either numbers or *orders*, which are instructions to the machine that govern the course of the computation. The memory is analogous to the work sheet and tables of functions used in the computation performed by a man.

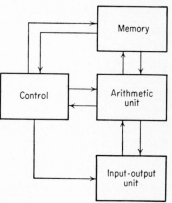

Fig. 18.1 Parts of a computing machine

18.7.4 *Control Unit.* This part of the machine is in charge of the whole computation. It keeps track of the progress of the work, determines at each step which individual operation should be performed next, and causes its execution. Its parallel in the case of the hand calculation is the brain of the human computer.

18.7.5 *Input and Output Equipment.* Input equipment is needed to enter into the machine the numerical data involved in the computation and the program of instructions for processing these data in accordance with the requirements of the problem. Output equipment enables the machine to communicate its results to its human operators. The input and output equipment is often so arranged that it can provide a large-capacity low-speed storage for numbers, orders, or intermediate results.

It may incorporate punched-card readers and punches, punched-tape equipment, electric typewriters and teletype page printers or special high-speed printers, reading and recording equipment using magnetic tape, a magnetic drum for intermediate-speed storage, or any combination of these media. All these input and output devices are primarily useful when the machine is used for scientific or engineering computation; other uses of digital computers, such as their application to large-scale clerical problems, demand more specialized input and output means. Very few such applications had been attempted by early 1953, and most of the input and output equipment in actual use was correspondingly of the simple type required to process numerical information.

18.8   General Design Considerations

18.8.1   *Representation of Numbers in the Machine.*   One of the most fundamental decisions that must be made in designing a high-speed digital computer concerns the manner in which numbers are to be represented within the machine. The familiar decimal system can, of course, be used—it was used in the ENIAC—but this is far from the most economical scheme. In the case of the decimal system, each element of a register which is to hold a number must be capable of reproducing 10 distinguishable states, corresponding to the digits 0, 1, 2, . . . , 9. This was accomplished in the ENIAC by using 10 bi-stable electronic circuits for each digit position in a register. These bi-stable circuits were the so-called "flip-flops" derived from the multivibrator invented in 1919 by Eccles and Jordan; each flip-flop has two stable states which can be referred to as "on" and "off," respectively. The 10 flip-flops used to represent a single digit were so arranged that only one of the 10 could be "on" at a given time; the digit value was indicated by the identity of the "on" flip-flop.

A more economical representation of numbers is afforded by the *binary-coded decimal* scheme. To understand this, let us remind ourselves of the properties of the binary number system. Binary numbers are based on the radix 2, just as the decimal system is based on the radix 10. When we move one place to the left in a binary number, the weight of the corresponding digit becomes greater by a factor 2, just as moving one place in the decimal system alters the weight of the digit by a factor 10. The first 10 digits are represented in the two systems as shown in the table on page 463.

In binary-coded decimal notation, a decimal number of several digits is represented by four times as many binary digits, each digit of the decimal number being separately represented by a four-digit binary number and the groups of four being gathered together as the binary-coded number. Thus we would represent the number 403682 in the following way:

4	0	3	6	8	2	Decimal number
0100	0000	0011	0110	1000	0010	Binary-coded
		010000000011011010000010				Collected

This scheme has the advantage of requiring only four flip-flops, instead of 10, for each decimal digit to be entered in a register. However, we can see that it is not the most economical system possible, for four binary digits can represent any number from 0 through 15, and we have arbitrarily chosen to use them to represent only the numbers 0 through 9.

Decimal system	Binary system	Explanation of meaning of binary notation
0	0	No 1
1	1	One 1
2	10	No 1 + one 2
3	11	One 1 + one 2
4	100	No 1 + no 2 + one $2^2 = 4$
5	101	One 1 + no 2 + one 4
6	110	No 1 + one 2 + one 4
7	111	One 1 + one 2 + one 4
8	1000	No 1 + no 2 + no 4 + one $2^3 = 8$
9	1001	One 1 + no 2 + no 4 + one 8

The use of straight binary representation of numbers is now preferred by most machine designers. In this system, the number 403682, used as an example in the last paragraph, can be written using 19 binary digits rather than the 24 needed in the binary-coded decimal representation. In fact,

$$403682 = 1100010100011100010$$

the verification of which is left as an exercise for the reader. In addition to the economy of the binary notation when on-off elements are used to represent digits, it has the further advantage that binary arithmetic is the arithmetic of logic, in a universe where a proposition is either true (one) or else false (zero). When the machine uses a binary representation of numbers, it can conduct both its nonarithmetical logical operations and its arithmetic calculations in the same formal terms.

Use of the binary system necessitates a conversion of numbers entering the machine from decimal to binary form and of numbers leaving the machine from binary to decimal; but the machine itself can perform this transformation most expeditiously, and this is no real disadvantage.

18.8.2 *Placement of the Decimal (or Binary) Point.* When a scheme for representing numbers in the machine has been chosen, it is necessary to decide whether the place values in the registers are to be fixed once for all, or whether the registers are to hold both the significant digits of a number and an exponent which indicates the placement of the decimal or binary point. The first scheme, which is referred to as *fixed-point* operation, can be realized with greater design simplicity, but numbers can, as a result of repeated operations, become of such a size that they begin to lose significant digits at one end or the other of a register; this demands that attention be given to this point in preparing a problem for the machine. *Floating-point* operation, which makes a smaller demand on the programmer, requires engineering complexities not met in the fixed-point scheme.

Both fixed- and floating-point machines have been built. On a fixed-point machine, floating-point operation can be programmed, but doing this requires spending ten to twenty times as much time on a given problem as is needed when the problem is done without using the floating-point program.

18.8.3 *"Serial" and "Parallel" Operation.* Another general machine characteristic which the designer must decide upon at the outset refers to the manner in which numbers are sent from one part of the machine to another. When a number is to be transmitted from one compartment of the memory to a register of the arithmetic unit, for example, it can be sent in either of two ways. The digits of the number may be transmitted sequentially over a single wire, the place of each digit being indicated by the time of its transmission in the sequence (*serial* operation), or else a separate wire may be used for the transmission of each digit, in which event all digits can be sent simultaneously (*parallel* operation). It is evident that parallel operation is, in principle, faster; but it also requires more equipment.

In a similar way, the arithmetic unit may be either serial or parallel, with similar consequences in terms of equipment requirements and operating speed.

Note that, in the serial machine, the time of arrival of a digit is important; for it is this which determines its place in the complete number being transmitted. In a parallel machine, the place value of a digit is already determined by the wire over which it is sent. Serial machines, in general, have their operations governed by a central clock whose timing of the various steps is relied upon to keep everything in its proper order. A machine so controlled is called a *synchronous* machine. A parallel machine, on the other hand, can be *asynchronous* in its operation; it needs no clock, since there is no unique significance to the time of arrival of any digit of a number being transferred or otherwise processed. In an asynchronous machine, the next operation can be begun as soon as the last preceding one is finished, without the necessity of waiting for the next tick of a clock. This affords another speed advantage to the parallel machine.

18.8.4 *Choice of the Order Code.* By all odds the most difficult decision confronting the machine designer is that of choosing the best set of orders to be understood and executed by the machine. The vocabulary of a machine—the set of orders that it can appreciate and act upon—is built into the machine at the time of its design and construction. As this vocabulary becomes larger, more and more complexity in the control unit is necessary to decode orders and act upon them; if the vocabulary is small, then the control can be simple. This is not a trivial point. An analysis of the elementary operations of arithmetic—addition, subtraction, multiplication, and division—shows that they are somewhat redundant and can be realized in terms of the elementary operations called "join" and "meet." Yet the formalism required by this reduction is so complicated that it is more sensible to instruct the machine in terms of the four familiar operations than it would be to program for the reduction of each arithmetical operation to its basic terms as expressed by the operations "join" and "meet."

How far can we go in the direction of building the machine to understand complicated arithmetical operations? Is it worth while, for example, to build the machine so that it will take a square root upon receiving a single instruction? The ENIAC has this ability. On a single order, the ENIAC will take the square root of a given number. Since the operation of extracting a square root is expressible in terms of the four elementary operations of arithmetic, a machine which does not understand a one-word instruction to take a square root can nevertheless extract such a root if it is provided with a sequence of orders designed to produce such a result by the application of operations which the machine does understand.

Here a balance must be struck between machine complexity occasioned by a complicated order code and program complexity necessitated by a simple order code. The balance chosen by most designers of modern machines involves a total number of about twenty to fifty orders that can be understood by the machine. All the complications of operation required by any problem must be dealt with using this small vocabulary; for there is no other way by which the programmer can communicate with the machine except through the use of the relatively small number of words that the machine has been built to understand.

18.9 A Typical Machine: The ORDVAC

To make the foregoing discussion more concrete, it may be of value to give a more detailed account of the properties of an actual machine. The machine that will be described is the so-called ORDVAC, built at the University of Illinois for the Ballistic Research Laboratories, Aberdeen Proving Ground. The ORDVAC is one of the family of machines whose logical design has been patterned after that of the machine built at the Institute for Advanced Study by von Neumann, Goldstine, Bigelow, and others. Though the ORDVAC owes much to the Institute machine, it is far from an exact copy; indeed, it was finished before the machine at the Institute was completed.

The ORDVAC is a parallel asynchronous machine. It deals with numbers in binary form; its registers are 40 digits in length. The first digit on the left is used to record the sign of a number; there are thus 39 binary digits to represent the magnitude of the number. This corresponds roughly to a register length of 11 decimal digits.

The machine has a fixed binary point, which stands between the sign digit and the most significant number digit. The machine thus handles numbers in the range between $+1$ and -1, and numbers of other magnitudes must be multiplied by an appropriate scale factor. This choice of number range has the advantage that the product of two numbers in the range will always remain in the range accommodated by the machine.

The memory of the ORDVAC has a capacity of 1024 numbers or orders, each of 40 binary digits. Other characteristics of the machine are summarized in Table 18.1.

Table 18.1   ORDVAC Characteristics

Adder carry time	9.5	μsec
Allowed carry time	13	μsec
Addition time	42	μsec
Multiplication time (all ones, positive multiplier)	1000	μsec
Multiplication time (all zeroes)	570	μsec
Division time	1000	μsec
Memory period	24	μsec
Time to load entire memory	38	min
Time to print contents of entire memory	38	min
Number of tubes	2718	
Machine d-c power	8.3 kw	
Machine a-c power	8.8 kw	
Total primary power (including power supplies and blowers)	35	kw
Kind of input	Five-hole Teletype tape	
Input system	Numbers to base 16	
Kind of output	Teletype page printer	
Number of digits assigned to an order	9	
Number of digits assigned to memory address	10	
Number of orders available	50	

Table 18.1 is taken from the paper by Meagher and Nash referred to in the References. Since its preparation, substantial improvements have been made both in the ORDVAC and in its sister machine, which was retained at the University of Illinois. Provision has been made on the ORDVAC for punched-card input and output; much faster input and output are now possible on the Illinois machine through the use of a high-

speed photoelectric tape reader for input and a high-speed tape punch for output. The full memory of the Illinois machine can now be loaded in less than a minute and punched out in less than 10 min. Times for arithmetic operations on the Illinois machine have been reduced about 30 per cent by the substitution of a logical adder for the Kirchhoff adder described below, and a magnetic drum has been added to the machine as a large-capacity memory of intermediate speed.

18.9.1 *Arithmetic Unit of the ORDVAC.* There are three main parts of the arithmetic unit: the registers, the adder, and the digit resolver. There are two shifting registers called, respectively, the *accumulator* and the *arithmetic register* and two nonshifting registers called the *number register* and the *order register*. Each nonshifting register consists of one row of 40 flip-flops, each capable of holding a binary digit. Information is communicated through them to the arithmetic unit and control from the memory. The number register holds addend, multiplicand, or divisor for arithmetic operations. The order register receives from the memory all orders which are to be handled by the control.

Each of the shifting registers consists of two rows of 40 flip-flops, one above the other. Since a nonshifting register can be made of half a shifting register, the physical appearance of the ORDVAC is that of a machine with three double registers.

A shifting register has two rows of gate tubes in addition to its two rows of flip-flops. These gate tubes furnish each stage of the register with two "up" gates and two "down" gates; the "up" gates transfer the digit standing in each stage of the lower row of flip-flops directly up to the corresponding flip-flop in the upper row, while one set of "down" gates transfers down one place to the right, the other down one place to the left. The bottom row of flip-flops holds the digits of a number while they are being sensed during an operation; the top row is used only as transient storage. A shift is accomplished by clearing the upper row, gating a number up to it from the lower row, clearing the lower row, and then gating the number back down to the lower row one place to the right or to the left, as may be desired. Note that information is not cleared from one location until its transfer to another has been accomplished. Since there are two "up" gates, of which only one is ever used in a shifting operation, an extra set of gates is available for other use.

Access to the memory is in parallel from the accumulator, and information from the input is entered serially into the accumulator, using the shifting properties of the register to put it in. The output is made in a similar serial fashion from the arithmetic register, it being possible for the memory to send numbers to this register.

The adder of the ORDVAC is a so-called Kirchhoff adder. The addend and the augend digits control gates from two constant-current sources

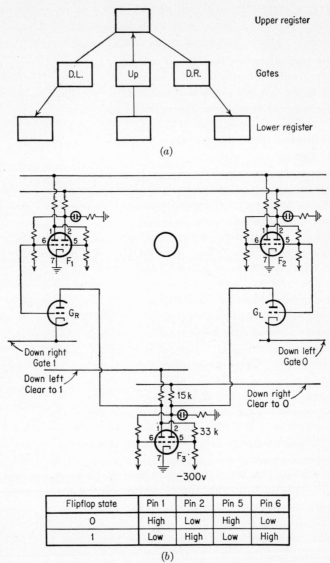

Flipflop state	Pin 1	Pin 2	Pin 5	Pin 6
0	High	Low	High	Low
1	Low	High	Low	High

(b)

Fig. 18.2 Shift register detail. (a) Schematic diagram. (b) Register circuit, showing two upper flip-flops, one lower flip-flop, and the "down" gating system.

which can send current through a summing resistor. The carry from the preceding stage controls the input voltage to the summing resistor. There are thus four possible voltages across the summing resistor, depending upon whether the sum at that particular stage is 0, 1, 2, or 3. If it is either of the latter two, a carry is propagated to the next stage.

Figure 18.3 shows the essential details of the adder. The summing resistor has a value of 10,300 ohms, and the constant-current sources are cathode followers each capable of supplying 4.85 ma. A carry from the preceding stage causes the input voltage to the 10,300-ohm resistor to drop from 210 volts to 160 volts. The four resulting voltages are thus separated by 50-volt steps, being 204, 154, 104, and 54 volts, respectively. The time required to propagate a carry through the 40 stages of the adder is 9.5 μsec.

The digit resolver converts the analogue adder voltages back into digital information. The addend and augend come into the adder from

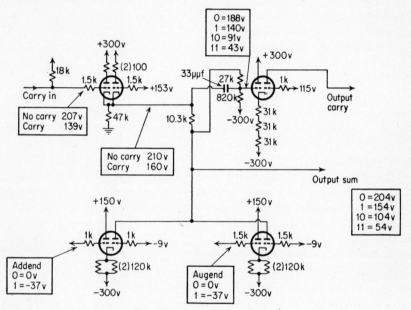

Fig. 18.3 Kirchhoff adder.

the accumulator and the number register, and the sum is returned to the accumulator after passing through the digit resolver. The digit resolver must distinguish those sums having the digit zero remaining in a stage from the sums having the digit 1. The former are the quantities 0 and 2 (having binary representations 00 and 10); the latter are 1 and 3 (having binary representations 01 and 11). The digit resolver thus furnishes -40 volts (corresponding to a zero) for the accumulator when the output of an adder stage is 54 or 154 volts, and furnishes 0 volts (corresponding to a 1) when the output is 104 or 204 volts.

18.9.2 *High-speed Storage.* The high-speed storage, or internal memory, of the ORDVAC is of the type originated by F. C. Williams, storing binary digits as patterns of charge ("dots" or "dashes") on the face of ordinary cathode-ray tubes. Three-inch cathode-ray tubes (3KP1) are used, each storing a pattern of $32 \times 32 = 1024$ digits; a bank of 40 tubes thus provides for the storage of 1024 complete numbers or orders.

Each tube can receive information from one digit of the accumulator and can transmit its stored information to the corresponding digit of the arithmetic, number, or order register. A slave cathode-ray tube controlled by a 40-position switch enables the contents of any of the memory tubes to be viewed.

Because of the spreading of charge due to the finite conductivity of the tube face, it is necessary to "regenerate" the stored information at frequent intervals. The digit held in a given position is sensed and rewritten. The regeneration proceeds from one storage position to another until the whole pattern has been regenerated; then the process repeats. Regeneration can be interrupted at the close of any 24-μsec cycle required to deal with a single storage position, if it is desired either to write into the memory or to read out of it. All the useful memory operations, including the clearing and gating of information, require about 16 μsec, but the period between cycles of memory operation has been set at 24 μsec for reasons of safety.

The position of the cathode-ray–tube beam corresponding to each of the 1024 memory addresses is set by specifying one of 32 steps of horizontal-deflection voltage and one of 32 steps of vertical-deflection voltage. These voltages are produced in an "address generator" which makes each one by adding the currents from five binary stages controlled by the digits of the address. Special care is taken to ensure that the deflection voltages are free from noise.

18.9.3 *Control.* Control in the ORDVAC is direct-coupled and asynchronous. No external timing device signals each operation to be performed; rather, each operation signals its own completion, and the next operation follows without delay. The speed of which the machine is capable is thus the highest of which its elementary circuits are capable, subject to some limitations imposed in the interests of safety. The safety circuits of the ORDVAC are designed to prevent the commencement of an operation before the preceding one has genuinely been completed, or the consultation of a control setting before it has been definitely established, etc. They do the following things:

a. They make the turnover requirements for the flip-flops in the control more stringent than the turnover requirements for the flip-flops being controlled. Thus, if the latter do not turn over, neither will the former, and the machine will stop. This guards against overlooking an improper response to a control signal.

b. They require that, when a control flip-flop is being turned over and sensed, the signal from it be used only after it has been positively turned. This guards against control by incomplete orders.

c. They require that before an operation in a sequence can occur the previous operation must not only have taken place but also have been turned off.

Corresponding to the logical safety measures is the care that has been taken in the design of the ORDVAC circuits to avoid inviting malfunction. All the flip-flops and other elementary circuits are direct-coupled, so that information is never stored momentarily in a capacitor but, instead, is always available as the setting of a flip-flop.

As we have already noted, the memory contains the only synchronous element in the machine: the clock which times the regeneration operation in the memory. One cycle of memory operation takes 24 μsec. When the control is carrying out operations which do not involve the memory, it works independently of this clock while the memory regenerates the information stored in each location. When an operation requires use of the memory, the control and the memory must be synchronized for one 24-μsec interval. To inaugurate the synchronization, the control furnishes a signal to the memory. Since this signal may come at any time during the 24-μsec operation cycle of the memory, the control must then wait until it is sent an "action-sense pulse" by the memory. When this pulse is received, the action cycle takes place: information is transferred to or from the memory, the necessary clearing and gating operations for such transfer being executed more or less directly by the memory pulses themselves.

The end of the action cycle is signaled by the next action-sense pulse from the memory, which arrives 24 μsec after the one which inaugurated the action cycle. On the arrival of this pulse, a "have-used-memory" signal goes to the control to indicate that the consultation of the memory has been completed. The memory resumes regenerating, and the control returns to its asynchronous operation. The synchronization of the control with the memory requires two flip-flops. One distinguishes between an action cycle and a regeneration cycle; the second distinguishes between the time before the action cycle, when the memory is still regenerating, and the later time when it has resumed regenerating but while the "have-used-memory" signal is on.

Much of the control is involved in setting up the proper clear and gate sequences for the registers. Everything that is accomplished in the arithmetic unit is a combination of sensing flip-flops, adding, clearing, and gating. Decisions as to which of these operations shall be performed are made on the basis of decoding certain combinations of binary digits, called orders, by means of logical circuits. The necessary number of orders for the machine is probably in the vicinity of 20 to 30, and this number of orders can be described by 15 flip-flops, 10 of them being used to specify the pertinent address. A decoding matrix involving five flip-flops would then be used to cause the correct one of 32 wires to be energized whenever the corresponding order is received. However, since numbers and orders may as well have the same length, and addresses require only 10 digits, the ORDVAC uses a scheme in which orders are entered in pairs, each order having 20 digits of which 10 specify an address and the other 10 define the operation to be performed. Actually, nine digits are used to specify an operation in the ORDVAC, which simplifies the control and permits the use of more orders. About 50 orders are actually used in programming, some of which were not foreseen when the control was designed. The decoding circuits involve a number of submatrices; a complete matrix is not used.

18.9.4 *Arithmetic.* The arithmetic used by the machine handles numbers in the range from -1 to $+1$, carrying negative numbers as

Table 18.2   Multiplication in the ORDVAC (1.101×0.101)

Operation	Multiplier digit	Accumulated product
1. Add multiplicand...........	1	1.101
2. Divide by 2................	..	1.1101
3. Divide by 2................	0	1.11101
4. Add multiplicand...........	1	1.10001
5. Divide by 2................	..	1.110001

complements relative to 2. Multiplication of two positive numbers without roundoff poses no problem; it is accomplished by repeated additions (when the multiplier digit is 1) and shifts (for every multiplier digit). If an operand x is negative, the machine holds the number $2 + x$, and if the sign digit of x is ignored, then multiplication by a positive y gives the result $xy + y$, so that subtraction of y will give the product. If x is the multiplier, there is no difficulty because y is available at the end of the multiplication and can be subtracted to give the product. But, if x is the multiplicand, y is lost during the process of shifting to inspect its digits. Hence it must be subtracted during the stepwise formation of the partial products.

The multiplication scheme used in the ORDVAC makes no distinction between positive and negative multiplicands. An algebraically correct division by 2 is made at every step, and the complete multiplicand with its sign is added if addition is required. A sample problem is given in Table 18.2.

The meaning of the calculation given in Table 18.2 is as follows: The multiplier 0.101 represents the number $\frac{1}{2} + \frac{1}{8}$, or $\frac{5}{8}$. The multiplicand is negative, as indicated by the digit 1 which stands to the left of the binary point. The digits of the multiplicand therefore are those of the number $2 + x$, where x is the negative number being represented. We then have

$$2 + x = 1 + \tfrac{1}{2} + \tfrac{1}{8} = 1\tfrac{3}{8}$$
$$x = -\tfrac{3}{8}$$

We are thus multiplying $\tfrac{5}{8}$ by $-\tfrac{3}{8}$, which will give the result $-\tfrac{15}{64}$. The machine representation of this number will be $2 + (-\tfrac{15}{64})$, or $1 + \tfrac{49}{64} = 1 + \tfrac{1}{2} + \tfrac{1}{4} + \tfrac{1}{64}$, or, in binary notation, 1.110001, the result obtained by the process detailed in Table 18.2. Note that, when a negative number is divided by 2 through a right shift of its digits, we must place a 1 to the left of the binary point in order to give the correct machine representation for $(-x)/2$; this also accords with the convention that negative numbers are distinguished by the digit 1 to the left of the binary point.

The problem posed by roundoff, which requires that the product be rounded to a sign and 39 places after the addition of 2^{-40}, has been solved by doing the roundoff before multiplication is begun. If there is no roundoff, the accumulator is cleared and the product xy is formed. If there is to be a roundoff, the accumulator is cleared, 2^{-1} is gated into it, and the quantity $xy + 2^{-40}$ is formed by the process just described. Since the accumulator holds only the sign and the first 39 digits of the product, it holds the rounded product.

This method of rounding off is fast, since there is no need to do an additional step at the end which involves waiting for carries in the adder, and it also provides the ability to gate the digit 2^{-1} into the accumulator for other orders. In connection with a shift, a digit can be placed anywhere in the accumulator by the use of this facility.

The algorithm for division is almost an inverse of the multiplication process.

18.9.5 *Power Supplies.* About 8.8 kw of a-c power is used to operate the heaters of the vacuum tubes of the ORDVAC. The d-c power consumption is as follows:

Voltage, volts	Current required, amp	Voltage, volts	Current required, amp
-2000	0.09	$+150$	3.8
-300	16.0	$+300$	5.2
$+100$	10.1	$+680$	0.4

A few odd voltages required by the machine are supplied by "bleeders" which bias vacuum-tube grids where the current drain is very low. The four voltages representing the bulk of the d-c power used by the machine are supplied by commercially built regulated rectifier units which can handle line-voltage changes and fast or slow load changes to ± 2 per cent.

18.9.6   *Performance.*   The ORDVAC has been a very successful machine.   A few weeks after its installation at the Ballistic Research Laboratories, it had an availability for use of over 90 per cent, and this excellent record has been sustained.   The similar Illinois machine has made an even better record of reliable performance.

18.10   Programming and Coding

The design of the control for a machine is intimately connected with the choice of the *order code*, or complete set of orders that the machine is to be able to understand.   A given order consists of two parts: first, an *instruction* which describes the arithmetical or logical operation to be performed, and then one or more *addresses* which refer to positions in the memory.

In a *one-address code*, there is only a single address included in each order.   This address may be, for example, that of an operand for the operation demanded by the instruction; it is implied that the next order to be followed by the machine will be found in the storage location next beyond that from which was taken the order being followed.   It is clear that two orders of the one-address type will be needed to call out the two operands required for a single addition or other arithmetic operation.   Despite the fact that programs are likely to be longer in a one-address code than they are in a multiple-address code, the programming flexibility of the one-address code has caused it to be the preferred type in many modern machines.

Multiple-address codes are used in some machines.   A *two-address code* can specify the location of two operands.   A *three-address code* can indicate the location of the two operands and simultaneously stipulate where the result of the operation shall be stored in the memory.   A *four-address code* can perform the functions of a three-address code and, in addition, specify the memory location from which is to be taken the next order to be performed.

The ORDVAC, whose properties we have already described in some detail, uses a one-address code.   Since the memory contains 1024 storage locations, 10 binary digits are necessary to specify an address.   Nine digits are used to specify the instruction, *i.e.*, the operation to be performed.   Since the register length in the ORDVAC is 40 digits, a single register (and therefore a single storage location) will hold two complete orders, with two digits to spare.   In the convention used, the digits 0 to 8 (or 20 to 28) describe an instruction, digit 9 (or 29) is not used, and the digits 10 to 19 (or 30 to 39) describe the address of the number involved in the left-hand (or right-hand) order, if the order deals with a number.   In the case of the shift orders and certain others, the address portion of the order is used for other purposes, such as specifying the number of places through which to shift.

A control counter keeps track of the address of the order pair last consulted; its reading is advanced by one each time an order pair is called out of the memory into the order register.   The left-hand order is executed first, then the right-hand order.   The control then calls out of the memory the order pair in the location one beyond the last, unless a control transfer has been specified in the program of orders.

The 50 orders available in the ORDVAC fall into the following classes:

A. *The Arithmetic Orders*
  1. The eight addition orders, which contain all possibilities represented by the following choices:

$$\left\{\begin{matrix} \text{Clear accumulator} \\ \text{or} \\ \text{Do not clear} \end{matrix}\right\} \quad \left\{\begin{matrix} \text{Add} \\ \text{or} \\ \text{Subtract} \end{matrix}\right\} \quad \left\{\begin{matrix} \text{Value with sign} \\ \text{or} \\ \text{Absolute value} \end{matrix}\right\}$$

  2. The three multiplication orders, which call for rounded multiplication, multiplication without roundoff, or multiplication followed by an addition to the product.
  3. The division order.

B. *The Eight So-called A Orders*
  These are identical with the addition orders except that the addend (subtrahend) comes from the arithmetic register rather than from the memory.

C. *The Shift Orders*
  1. Left shift which carries number digits from the left end of the accumulator successively into the right end of the arithmetic register, destroying the digits shifted off the left end of the arithmetic register and keeping the sign digit in the accumulator unchanged.   Or the same after clearing the accumulator.   Or the same after clearing the accumulator and inserting the number 2^{-1} in it.   Three orders.
  2. Right shift, as above.   Three orders.   Address part of shift orders used to specify number of shifts.
  3. *F* Orders.   Replace the contents $a_0 a_1 \cdots a_{39}$ of the accumulator and $p_0 p_1 \cdots p_{39}$ of the arithmetic register with $a_1 a_2 \cdots a_{39} p_1$ and $p_0 p_2 \cdots p_{39} p_{40}$, respectively, where p_{40} is the same as p_{39} was prior to the last order which used a right shift.   Or clear the accumulator and do the same.   Or clear the accumulator, insert 2^{-1} in it, and do the same. Three orders.
  4. *K* Orders.   Do the primary *F* order and transfer control to a specified memory location when the right-hand order has been executed.   Or the same after clearing the accumulator.   Or the same after clearing the accumulator and inserting 2^{-1} in it.   Three orders.

D. *The Input-Output Orders*
  1. Read one word from the tape into the accumulator.
  2. Print the contents of the arithmetic register on the teletype printer.

E. *The Store Orders*

1. Store the contents of the accumulator at a specified memory location.
2. Store the value zero (or $\frac{1}{2}$) at a specified location in the memory. Two orders.
3. Replace digits 2^{-10} through 2^{-19} (or 2^{-30} through 2^{-39}) of the number stored at a specified memory location by the corresponding digits held in the accumulator. Or the same after clearing the accumulator. Four orders.

F. *The Control Transfer Orders*

1. Unconditional transfer of control to the left-hand (or right-hand) order of the pair stored at a specified location, with (or without) clearing the accumulator. Four orders.
2. Conditional transfer of control to the left-hand (or right-hand) order of the pair stored at a specified location, accomplished only if the number in the accumulator is nonnegative. Two orders.
3. Stop the computer, with or without specifying the memory location which is to assume control when operation begins again. Two orders.

G. *The So-called R Order*

This clears the arithmetic register and adds into it the number stored at a specified location.

The 50 orders of the ORDVAC represent a larger vocabulary than many other machines have; the EDSAC machine at the University of Cambridge has, for example, only 18 orders in its code.

The conditional transfer orders are of the greatest importance in giving the machine flexibility of performance. They permit the programmer who is preparing a problem for the machine to demand the repetition of an iterative routine, for example, through as many steps as necessary to obtain the accuracy of result desired; and this can be accomplished without knowledge on the part of the programmer of the number of steps that may be needed.

Such an iterative routine, *e.g.*, one for finding the square root of a number, can be made up once for all and used over and over again as an element in a more complicated program for the machine. Such a "library" item is called a *subroutine*, and the establishment of a rich variety of useful subroutines is an important step in establishing a computing laboratory based on the use of modern high-speed computers. A subroutine need not involve an iteration, of course. Any computing step complicated enough to involve more than one order, of sufficiently frequent occurrence in problems to make it worth preserving, and of greater simplicity than a typical machine program deserves the name of subroutine. If the machine is equipped with a large-capacity memory of intermediate speed, such as a magnetic drum, subroutines can be stored quasi-permanently in that unit and called forth for use when they are needed. In a sense, the subroutines extend the vocabulary of the machine, enabling it to understand words more complicated than those comprehended in its basic order code.

An example of a simple program—in fact, a typical subroutine—may make clear some of the nature of programming. We shall take as an

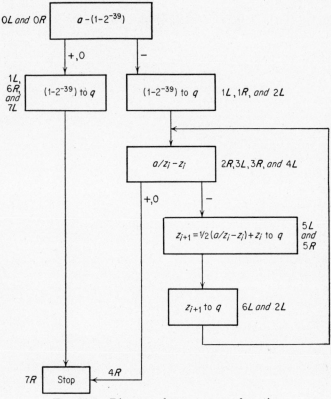

Fig. 18.4 Diagram of square-root subroutine.

example the extraction of the square root of a number a. This is accomplished by a succession of approximations given by the formula

$$z_{i+1} = \frac{1}{2}\left(z_i + \frac{a}{z_i}\right) \tag{18.2}$$

When this formula is used on the machine, it proves best to compute

$$z_{i+1} = z_i + \left(\frac{a}{z_i} - z_i\right)\frac{1}{2} \tag{18.3}$$

Then, if $0 \le a \le 1 - 2^{39}$, the sequence of numbers z_i obtained by setting $z_1 = 1 - 2^{39}$ and using formula (18.3) has the property that $z_i > z_{i+1} > a$ for values of i less than some value $i_0 > 1$. The quantity z_{i_0} is called the "machine square root" of a.

The above algorithm for finding the square root of a cannot be applied in the case $a = 1 - 2^{-39}$, since then $z_i = a$ (within the capacity of the registers of the machine) and $a + z_i = -1 + 2^{-39}$, which latter values would terminate the process. Therefore the program first tests for this improper value of a.

In addition to the orders, the following numbers must be stored in the memory:

Location	Contents
r	$1 - 2^{-39}$
p	a
q	z_i

The program, which is diagrammed in Fig. 18.4, then goes as follows:

Order Address		Order	Situation
0	L	Clear accumulator and add into it number at p	Accumulator has a
	R	Do not clear accumulator Subtract number at r	Accumulator has $a - (1 - 2^{-39})$
1	L	Conditional transfer; control to right-hand side of 6 if contents of accumulator nonnegative	
	R	Clear accumulator and add into it number at r	Accumulator has $z_1 = 1 - 2^{-39}$
2	L	Store the contents of the accumulator at location q	Location q has value of z_i
	R	Clear accumulator and add into it number at p	Accumulator has a
3	L	Divide number in accumulator by number at q	Arithmetic register has a/z_i
	R	Clear accumulator and add into it number in arithmetic register; transfer control to left-hand order in location 4	Accumulator has a/z_i
4	L	Do not clear accumulator Subtract number at q	Accumulator has $(a/z_i) - z_i$
	R	Transfer control to right-hand side of 7 if contents of accumulator are nonnegative	
5	L	Make one right shift	Accumulator has $(\frac{1}{2})[(a/z_i) - z_i]$
	R	Do not clear accumulator Add number at q	Accumulator has $z_{i+1} = (\frac{1}{2})[(a/z_i) - z_i] + z_i$
6	L	Transfer control to left-hand side of 2	
	R	Clear accumulator and add contents of location r	Accumulator has $1 - 2^{-39}$
7	L	Store contents of accumulator at location q	Location q holds $1 - 2^{-39} a$ in special case
	R	Stop computer	

18.11 Prospects for Future Development

The high-speed digital information machines of 1953 can be regarded only as the same crude approximations to the machines that we shall soon learn how to build as the motorcars of 1905 or the aircraft of 1911 were to the cheap, ubiquitous, and reliable high-performance vehicles that we have today. To see the development in its proper perspective, we must constantly bear in mind that the first automatic high-speed digital computer, as that term is understood in this chapter, is less than eight years old as these lines are written. There will be profound improvements in components and in the manner of using them, and another eight years of progress will bring great and largely unimaginable changes.

However, we can guess the direction that a few of these changes may take, and that is the business of this section. Curiously enough, the most important changes in components may be in the direction of liberating the design of information machines from the limitations imposed by the use of vacuum tubes. This is curious because it was precisely the use of tubes that made possible the operating speeds which divide the class of high-speed machines from the logically similar relay machines briefly considered in Sec. 18.5.

Used as a switch—as it is in computing machines—the vacuum tube is undeniably fast. A properly designed flip-flop circuit can turn from one of its stable states to the other in a time considerably shorter than a tenth of a microsecond. Despite this speed, which is a great advantage, the vacuum tube has drawbacks. It is complicated in its construction, and therefore it is expensive. Only through a miracle of mass production can the tube of today be made to sell for a dollar or so.

Worse than the first cost of the vacuum tube is the power required to operate it. About one watt is needed to heat the electron-emitting cathode of the tube, in order that it may work at all. Most tubes have such operating characteristics that another watt, or a substantial fraction of a watt, will be required in the cathode-to-screen-and-plate circuits of the tube in order to reach a satisfactory operating point on the tube characteristics.

There is no harm in expending power of this magnitude when the tube is being used in a power circuit: when it is operating a loudspeaker, for example, or doing the work necessary to change the deflection field in the yoke surrounding the neck of a television picture tube. These have been prominent fields of use for vacuum tubes. When a tube is used in a signal circuit, however, its responsibility is only to produce a signal which can be processed in other parts of the apparatus, usually by other tubes. The power level set by the requirements of the application is very low; it is necessary only for the signal to be kept strong enough not to be contaminated by the electrical "noise" present in all circuits. In absolute terms, the power level required is that of a millionth, or a few millionths, of a watt.

In a computer, the vast majority of the electronic circuits are concerned only with the processing of signals which are then to undergo further processing. There is no need for these signals to be carried at a power level above a few microwatts. Vacuum-tube circuits are therefore enormously wasteful of power in computer applications. In a simile due to Ralph Bown, of the Bell Telephone Laboratories, the use of a watt (required by a vacuum tube) to process a microwatt signal is as sensible as it would be to send a 12-car freight train, complete with locomotive, to bring back a pound of butter. Even in the case of the so-called "miniaturized" tubes, whose size and operating power have been substantially scaled down, we are sending a 10-ton truck to get our pound of butter.

The junction transistor, described in Chap. 16, will operate satisfactorily at total power levels in the microwatt range. It is thus admirably suited for use in signal circuits, such as those of a computing machine. Apart from its economy in operating power, the transistor promises other advantages. Its lifetime is surely long and may be indefinite; this is to be compared with a life of a few tens of thousands of hours for a vacuum tube. Its inherent simplicity is great, and it should therefore be cheap to manufacture, as compared with a vacuum tube. Its physical size is small, and this fact can be taken advantage of in design, since the transistor does not generate the large amounts of heat that are liberated by a vacuum tube.

In addition to the transistor, there is a whole family of nonlinear circuit elements based on the remarkable electrical properties of semiconducting materials. These include the diode rectifier, the welded-junction diode exhibiting the Zener-current phenomenon, the semiconductor tetrode, and so on. We appear to be at the threshold of a time when many of the switching and amplifying functions hitherto handled by vacuum tubes will be taken over by these new devices.

18.11.1 *New Storage Mediums.* It has already been remarked that the high-speed memory or storage element is the weakest part of present computers. The cost of high-speed storage is so great that practically no machine has as much as its designer would have wished, or its users may desire. Further, the time required for access to the memory is a major limitation on the over-all operating speed of most machines, since transfers into or out of the memory are required in almost every operation.

Most existing machines use "Williams-tube" memories, in which information is stored as binary symbols in each of a thousand or so spots on the face of a bank of cathode-ray tubes. Other schemes of electrostatic storage are also in use, but they differ from this only in detail.

Several valid objections to such forms of storage can be raised. For one thing, the stored information must be constantly refreshed to keep it from being lost; any power failure, or failure in a circuit important to the memory, will result in the loss of the stored information. Again, the necessity for regenerating the information stored in the memory diminishes the freedom, and therefore the expedition, of access to the memory. It is necessary to await the end of a regeneration cycle before consulting the memory, and the average time lost in this way is half the time spent

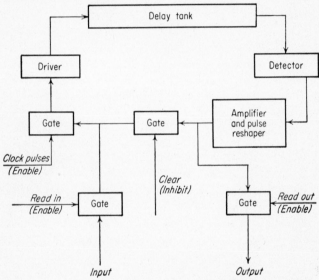

Fig. 18.5 Schematic diagram of acoustic-delay-line memory.

in completing a regeneration cycle, which in the aggregate can be quite formidable when all the steps of a complicated calculation are considered.

In fact, the disadvantages of the Williams-tube type of storage are so compelling that it is doubtful it would be used at all, given any acceptable alternative. Until very recently, there has been no acceptable alternative. The magnetic drum is more capacious, cheaper per item of stored information, and not subject to the difficulty that the stored information is lost in the event of a failure of power or of some pertinent circuit. However, the average access time is fixed by the mechanical motion of a relatively massive system and is correspondingly long. Several machines have been built which use the circulation of digits as ultrasonic pulses through mercury columns as a means of memory (cf. Fig. 18.5), but the necessity of awaiting the availability of the desired number is a major disadvantage.   If the column of stored numbers is long, then access time is correspondingly long, since the numbers are available only serially; if the column of numbers is short, then the cost of this form of storage is inordinately high.

There now appear to be alternative means of high-speed storage with lower cost, shorter access time, and better performance than either the Williams-tube electrostatic type of the ultrasonic delay-line type of memory.   The most promising at the present time appears to be an array of magnetic cores, whose state of magnetization can express a binary digit. Such cores can be very small as individual physical entities and, therefore, very cheap; the circuits that are necessary for their use are not outside the range of present technology.   It is likely that static magnetic-core memories will be used in the next generation of high-speed machines, because of their simplicity, cheapness, and short access time.

Other types of memory element are in the experimental stage.   One such is the ferroelectric memory, involving the use of dielectric materials having a permanent dipole moment which can be oriented by an applied field.   Just as the direction of magnetization in a magnetic material can be used to store a binary digit, so the direction of polarization in a ferro-electric medium can indicate the value of a stored binary digit.

18.11.2   *Real-time Operation.   Simulation.*   A major use of analogue computing machines has been their application to what is called *simulation, i.e.,* the reproduction of the operating environment to which some active element is subjected, with proper allowance for the behavior of the active element.   It may be desired to simulate the performance of a guided missile in flight.   To do this requires that the missile itself be subjected to the control signals appropriate to the past history of its flight and that the response of the missile to these signals be taken into account in calculating the future situation.   This sort of simulation is ordinarily accomplished by patching together a system which consists in part of the actual devices involved in the problem and in part of the computer that is used for the real-time simulation problem.

The meaning of the phrase "real time" in this connection should be obvious.   It is required that those parts of the system represented by the computer carry out their operations on the same time scale as the one appropriate to the other parts of the system, which are actually parts of the missile itself.   When proper attention is paid to securing a wide enough frequency response in an analogue computer, simulation of the complete flight performance of a supersonic guided missile can be accomplished.

Use of a digital machine for simulation has often been suggested and occasionally attempted.   However, such use is by no means so straight-forward as is the use of an analogue machine.   Since the digital machine works by processing numbers, it is necessary to turn physical quantities representing control forces, accelerations, and the like into numerical form before they are entered into the machine. The same remark applies to the digital-to-analogue conversion required at the output of the computer. In addition, some explicit model of the behavior of the system must be formulated, and explicit calculations must be carried through on the basis of this model. If the digital machine is not fast enough in its operation, these calculations will fall behind the events in real time which they are supposed to represent, and the attempt to use the digital machine for simulation will fail. Present estimates of the capabilities of digital machines for the real-time simulation of guided-missile performance indicate that the fastest existing digital machines are about an order of magnitude too slow to be used in this application.

This deficiency in speed is not so bad as it sounds, for not only are increases in speed quite possible in the light of current developments in computer components, but also no digital machine has recently been designed specifically for the purpose of performing real-time simulation problems. The so-called Whirlwind I at MIT was originally intended for this use, but before its completion it was diverted to other applications; as things turned out, it would have been a bit too slow to do simulation problems comfortably.

Just as important as the deficiency in speed which has so far prevented the use of digital machines in simulation is the deficiency in appropriate input and output equipment. When a complicated physical system is being modeled by the computer, it is of no particular help to be able to introduce numbers and orders, as such, into the machine nor to be able to print out numerical results. What is most helpful is to have available analogue types of input and output. It should be possible to vary the parameters entering the problem by adjusting manual controls, perhaps of the "joy-stick" type, and to view the results of the current calculations by means of an analogue type of display, perhaps in the form of a pattern on a cathode-ray tube. Very little attention has yet been paid to the devising of such input and output facilities for digital machines, largely because digital machines have been so useful in their current role as mathematical calculating devices. However, there are indications that this sort of extension of the usefulness of the digital machine will not be much longer in coming.

18.12   Digital Machines in Business and Industry

In the popular press, much has been made of the vast possibilities which digital information machines hold for use in business and industry. They are seen as being able to take over the vast bulk of clerical work, which is governed by rules that are sufficiently simple and unchanging to be presented to a machine as a program of orders.   It is also supposed that these machines will be able to serve as the quasi-intelligent automatic controllers of machines, thus relieving most factory workers of their jobs.   Concerning the social effects of such changes we shall have a word to say later.   Here we wish to consider the fitness of the digital machine of today for these roles which are being thrust upon it.

Just as a deficiency in input and output equipment is hampering the application of digital machines to the problems of real-time simulation, so also this same deficiency is slowing down the adoption of such machines by business and industry.   The control of production machinery is clearly a real-time problem, and the same factors which operate to limit the present applicability of digital machines in simulation affect the ability of such machines to serve as substitutes for men in machine control.   This is not an inherent limitation, be it noticed; it is simply a consequence of the direction that the development of digital machines has so far taken.

In their applications to clerical work, digital machines have made more promising beginnings.   Indeed, it is worth observing that one of the most competent of modern machines, the so-called UNIVAC of Remington Rand, evolved in response to the needs of the U.S. Census Bureau.   Just as, 70 years ago, punched-card machines were devised to meet the needs of the Census, so today the newest sort of clerical machinery is being demanded and supported by the Census Bureau.

Part of the reason that digital machines have been more immediately applicable to clerical work than to industrial control stems from the fact that clerical work is not done on any "real-time" schedule set by other physical apparatus, and part from the fact that the existing types of input and output equipment are more immediately adaptable to clerical problems.   They are not always perfectly adaptable to such problems, however.   Indeed, one of the major deficiencies of digital machinery in a clerical use arises because the speed with which data can be put into the machine and taken out of it is very slow in comparison with the speed of processing data within the machine.   This disparity is no disadvantage for most scientific problems, in which a great deal of operation within the machine is required for a few numbers entered into the machine by the input equipment and the output information is correspondingly small in comparison with the internal operations.

For many clerical problems, however, massive amounts of input and output data are involved, and the processing of these data is relatively simple.   Under such circumstances, the poor match between input and output speed as compared with internal processing speed becomes a real drawback.   Except for the development of a few types of high-speed page printers, very little attention has yet been paid to this problem. The input problem is especially severe and especially difficult.   What is wanted in many applications is a machine attachment which can read ordinary printing, and although such a device was in the laboratory stage in 1953, it was then still necessary to expend large amounts of human effort in instructing the machine as to its input data.

There seems little doubt that the problems specific to the use of digital machines for clerical work and for industrial control will soon be attacked and solved; they contain no real difficulties of principle. But, so long as the attention of machine designers is focused on the use of machines for engineering and scientific work, the match of such machines to the world of business and industry will be most imperfect.

Even the machines that we have today can do many things which are useful; the impression should not be given that they are worthless outside the range of scientific and engineering problems. An interesting example was afforded by the use, in November, 1952, of a UNIVAC machine to predict the results of the Presidential election on the basis of stored information concerning the relationship between early returns and complete results in the various states. About 10 o'clock, New York time, on the basis of fewer than 5 million votes, the machine had predicted pretty much the sort of Eisenhower landslide which actually occurred. Its human masters were not ready to believe a result so widely at variance with their own prejudices. They therefore suppressed the findings of the machine and diddled the past-history information that was supplied the UNIVAC to produce a result more nearly in accordance with their guesses.

At midnight in New York, on the basis of this distorted input information, the UNIVAC computed the odds on Stevenson as being about even. By that time, it was clear that the machine was wrong. Its operators made a handsome public explanation and apology, restored the right input information, and relayed to the listening public the strictly nonsurprising information which the machine then had to provide.

This example makes it clear that the UNIVAC, being possessed of no emotional bias, was capable of a prescience that its human masters could not match. It was further capable of drawing the correct conclusions in a complicated and incomplete situation. The fact that these conclusions were suppressed by the men managing the machine is incidental; for the purposes of our present discussion it is enough to notice that the machine was right.

In principle, digital information machines will be able to substitute for and surpass men in many routine tasks which are important in our society. They have not done so partly because they are new, partly because they are still somewhat expensive and unreliable, and partly because they have not been properly designed, in detail, for such a role. But there seems to be no doubt that they will be pushed into these tasks as their competence and their reliability improve, as they become more numerous, and as we learn how to design them for the greatest effectiveness in these practical jobs.

THE SOCIAL IMPLICATIONS OF
INFORMATION MACHINES

18.13   The "Second Industrial Revolution"

Professor Norbert Wiener, of MIT, refers to the present and the immediate future as the time of the Second Industrial Revolution.   By this he means to indicate that the application to practical affairs of information-processing machines derived from today's digital computers will have an enormous impact upon society—an impact possibly as great as the one experienced when the First Industrial Revolution was commenced by the introduction of practical power machines by James Watt and others.

Wiener's view of the Second Industrial Revolution seems to connote a major human dislocation, with vast technological unemployment being suffered by those who have been accustomed to earn their livings by using their central nervous systems in routine ways.   While he appears to regard the development and application of information machines as being inevitable, he also appears to hold the view that the resultant social and economic effects will inevitably be harmful, unless they are somehow consciously controlled to the good of men.

Since Professor Wiener is a thoughtful and intelligent man, we must take his views seriously.   He is not simply expressing another symptom of the common let's-stop-science-so-that-social-understanding-can-catch-up neurosis.   He has valid fears and doubts based on valid consideration of the problems involved.   There is no easy way of disposing of his objections to the human worth of the Second Industrial Revolution, but perhaps we can put them into a proper context by recalling comparable features of the earlier Industrial Revolution, which Wiener calls the First.   We shall do this in terms of what we may refer to as the natural history of machines.

18.14   The Natural History of Machines

The idea of a machine, and indeed even some of the machines that we use today, dates back many thousands of years.   Nobody now knows who contrived that wonderful device, the wheel; it was invented so long ago that we have no record of its beginning.   Ancient machines, except for a few wind-operated devices like sailing ships and windmills, were both powered and controlled by animals, usually horses and men in some combination.

For a good many of the primitive machines, a man provided not only the means of control but also the actuating power. The hand shovel is a machine in this class. It involves a practical application of the principle of the lever, but it requires a man both to dig with it and to tell it where to dig. Again, a wagon is drawn by horses controlled by a human driver. The wagon is the machine, the horses its power source, and the man the control mechanism charged with guiding the performance of the whole combination.

Quite recently in human history—about three centuries ago—the idea of the machine underwent a profound change. With the perfection of the steam engine by James Watt, the *self-powered* machine became practical. The mechanisms which had previously been worked by the labor of animals were now operated by a device which generated power. After the invention of power-generating devices having more flexibility than the steam engine, such as the electric motor and the internal-combustion engine, the range of self-powered machinery became very wide, even encompassing such small mechanisms as whisker clippers and cocktail shakers.

These last machines are frivolities in comparison with the power tools and great engines of transportation which are the most important of the self-powered machines. Self-powered machines had a revolutionary effect upon society, not always favorable in its short-range effects. Around 1810, the Luddites were smashing and burning machines, because they had upset people's lives.

What the Luddites and others feared can be stated, not unfairly, as follows. The introduction of self-powered machines displaced the horse as a prime mover and thereby greatly reduced the world population of horses. While only the mushroom growers were genuinely inconvenienced by the disappearance of the horse, so many men had been accustomed to spending their whole lives acting like horses that there was widespread concern lest vast and permanent unemployment might be produced by the introduction of self-powered machines. On another level of understanding, Marx and others were of the opinion that the lot of the worker was bound to get steadily worse in a society where the means of production—the machines—were under the ownership and control of people other than the workers themselves.

By now, it is plain that neither of these worries had any real foundation. Most of the people who would, in a previous age, have lived by the use of their muscles have found a way to live by the use of their minds. This major achievement can be recorded to the credit of the American ideal of universal education. It has probably never been easier to get a job and make a living than it is today. The dangers inherent in the social misuse of machines, which worried Marx and his followers, seem to have been largely avoided through orderly social evolution. This evolution, while it has been the unplanned outcome of the interaction and often the conflict of various ideas, creeds, groups, and movements, seems somehow to have been quite successful in guiding social change along lines which are favorable to the great majority of people. Meanwhile, the vastly higher and ever-rising rate of productivity per human worker made possible by self-powered machines has sharply increased everyone's standard of living.

The latest and the final step in the development of the machine has been the emergence of the *self-controlling* machine. While some simpleminded control mechanisms are found on machines of the self-powered class—James Watt himself invented not only the steam engine but also the flyball governor for regulating its speed—it was formerly the custom to stop short of designing a machine able to control its own performance. Instead, a human operator was required to monitor the behavior of the machine and adjust its controls to produce the result desired.

This was done partly because control instrumentation is more subtle and complex than power machinery, but not altogether for that reason. A century and a half ago, the Jacquard loom was weaving intricate fabrics under the control of punched cards which were the ancestors of the IBM cards used in present-day business machinery. Rather, the design of the machine was completed with a man because control instrumentation was then expensive and relatively unreliable, while the work of human controllers was cheap by comparison.

Technology has made great strides in the last few decades, so that control instrumentation has become cheaper, more reliable, and capable of a vastly wider range of satisfactory performance. At the same time, human machine controllers have become increasingly more expensive; men are now less willing than ever before to become mindless attachments to incomplete machines. Altogether, it is rapidly becoming more satisfactory to build self-powered machines which also control themselves than it is to build self-powered machines which must be controlled by human operators.

To recapitulate: the development of the complete machine has taken place in three quite distinct steps. First, the principle of the lever was used to make a shovel, or the lever was combined with Archimedes' principle to make a boat which floated and could be rowed, or the wheel was used to make the wagon. Such a primitive machine needed both to be powered and to be controlled; these functions were performed by man, often assisted by his domestic beasts of burden. In the First Industrial Revolution, an engine was added to the primitive machine to make the self-powered machine. Today, in the Second, the self-powered machine is being provided with automatic control mechanisms to make what we can properly call the complete machine—self-powered and self-controlling.

With the addition of control equipment to the self-powered machine, we have perfected the machine. This is not to deny any possibility of advances and improvements in the parts of a machine: better metals and more cleverly contrived levers to improve the primitive machine, newer and more effective power sources such as atomic energy, and more subtle and effective control devices. Neither does it deny the possibility of creating entirely new machines for new purposes. No such development will change the *idea* of the machine as it was changed when power was first added to a primitive machine and later when automatic control began to be used. However its details may change, the self-powered and self-controlled machine is, in principle, complete.

18.15 Results of the Second Industrial Revolution

What effect on the lives of men can we expect from the widespread introduction of complete (and therefore automatic) machines which need no human controllers? Many of these machines will be adapted for performing routine clerical work, others for tasks of industrial control. Professor Wiener feels that severe social dislocations will attend the displacement of office workers and factory hands by the complete machines we are now beginning to build.

While we cannot know what will happen, it may be that the history of the First Industrial Revolution will be a faithful guide to the future of the Second. Just as men were earlier liberated from grinding physical labor by the development of the self-powered machine, so they will now be freed of degrading routine tasks of two major sorts. One such task is that of acting as surrogate for a missing part of a power machine—this is the job of most factory workers. The other is that of performing the routine information-processing required by our society—accounting, bookkeeping, filing, order taking, and the like. There seems no question that the number of jobs in these two categories will be diminished sharply in the near-term future.

This may produce some individual hardships and dislocations, though wise forethought may prevent them. But, if the experience of the First Industrial Revolution is any guide, the longer-range result of this new change will be to let men live and work at a higher and more rewarding level of performance. Education, properly conducted, will enable all men, except for a few misfits who would have been disadvantaged in any society, to make the change from routine clerical work or machine tending to the performance of a higher activity that is still inaccessible to the machines. Hours of work will probably continue to diminish; yet productivity per worker will continue to rise. Life, in human terms, will have been rendered richer and more rewarding by the completion of the machine.

Optimism being rather out of fashion, I must apologize for this suggestion. Still, it seems inescapable on the basis of what has already happened. The Second Industrial Revolution, like the First, may let men move on from degrading routine tasks to perform at a higher and more challenging level. Nearly all men may succeed in making this transition, and the mysterious agencies of social evolution may regulate the change to the common good. The machines may be pushing us not toward disaster, but rather toward ever greater individual achievement and satisfaction.

REFERENCES

1. Hartree, D. R., "Calculating Instruments and Machines," University of Illinois Press, Urbana, 1949.
2. Korn, G. A., and T. M. Korn, "Electronic Analog Computers," McGraw-Hill Book Company, Inc., New York, 1952.
3. Stifler, W. W. Jr., ed., "High-speed Computing Devices," McGraw-Hill Book Company, Inc., New York, 1950.
4. "Review of Electronic Digital Computers," Proceedings of the Joint Computer Conference, American Institute of Electrical Engineers, New York, 1952. See especially the paper "The ORDVAC" by R. E. Meagher and J. P. Nash, pp 37–42.
5. "Annals of the Computation Laboratory," Vol. 16, Proceedings of a Symposium on Large-scale Digital Calculating Machinery, Harvard University Press, Cambridge, 1948.
6. "Annals of the Computation Laboratory," Vol. 26, Proceedings of a Second Symposium on Large-scale Digital Calculating Machinery, Harvard University Press, Cambridge, 1951.
7. Wilkes, M. V., D. J. Wheeler, and S. Gill, "Programs for an Electronic Digital Computer," Addison-Wesley Press, Inc., Cambridge, 1951.

Name Index

Subject Index